DISCARD

Research in Mathematics Education

Edited by
Richard J. Shumway
Ohio State University

**National Council of
Teachers of Mathematics**

Library of Congress Cataloging in Publication Data:

Main entry under title:

Research in mathematics education.

Bibliography: p.
1. Mathematics—Study and teaching—Research.
I.   Shumway, Richard J.
QA11.R46   510'.7'1   80-4
ISBN 0-87353-163-9

Table of Contents

Preface

This volume represents our best effort to develop a definitive reference work on research in mathematics education—one that each mathematics educator, each doctoral student, and anyone interested in research in mathematics education might want on his or her own shelf.

It began when the Publications Committee of the National Council of Teachers of Mathematics developed the following rationale for a professional reference book on research in mathematics education:

> The Council's explicit support of research in mathematics education is long-standing. The past twenty years have witnessed a dramatic growth in the number of doctoral programs in mathematics education and increased federal and institutional support for research. The Council has established the *JRME,* the Research Advisory Committee, several conferences and research oriented publications, cooperative efforts with ERIC/SMEAC and increasingly popular research sections at its numerous meetings. In short, the climate for and interest in research in mathematics education seems healthier than ever before.
>
> At the same time, there exists no definitive reference work on research in mathematics education. Such a volume could be of invaluable assistance in in-service and graduate study programs. (Publications Committee proposal to the Board, April 1975)

In attempting to further define the scope and nature of a professional reference on research in mathematics education, we posed the following questions to mathematics educators and others interested in research in mathematics education:

> Suppose we were to create a reference on research in mathematics education which you would insist be on your shelf, the shelf of every doctoral student in mathematics education, and the shelf of every person responsible for research in mathematics education. What would you want such a reference to contain? What do you think such a reference need not contain?

Out of that background has come this work.

The reference is divided into two parts. Part 1, on the research *process,* focuses on problems of research methods and their relevance to research in mathematics education. Our hope is that Part 1 will introduce the beginner to some of the issues and problems in the research process, stimulate further reading and study, and also raise issues that are of fundamental concern to both the beginner and the experienced researcher.

Part 2, on research *problems,* deals with the identification of critical, productive problems for researchers in mathematics education. In general, the problems are categorized in a psychological framework. Such an arrangement appeared to offer a comfortable partitioning of the problems for the editorial board and authors; only hindsight can tell us whether or not it will prove fruitful for the reader.

Authors of Part 2 were asked to organize their chapters about this general outline: (a) *status* of the research, (b) *trends*—where people seem to be going with the research, (c) the big *issues* of research, and (d) some specific *hypotheses* that are important, timely, and promising.

In the spirit of David Hilbert's famous list of 23 problems delivered before the Second International Congress of Mathematics in 1900, authors were asked to identify problems in their areas which, in their view, might have the same potential for shaping the organizing of research in mathematics education that Hilbert's problems did for research in mathematics. This was a tremendous burden to place on the authors. We believe they have responded with herculean efforts, which will act as critical, organizing determinants for research in mathematics education for some time to come. The judgment as to whether we have achieved the 75-year foresight of a Hilbert can best be answered by readers' continued research efforts and the scholars in the field of mathematics education in the year 2055.

RICHARD J. SHUMWAY, *Editor*

The following persons served on the editorial board:

| Donald J. Dessart | John R. Kolb |
| Jeremy Kilpatrick | Richard L. Turner |

Richard J. Shumway

Of great help to the editorial board and authors were the reviewing and critiquing efforts of the following:

Jeffrey Barnett	John Dossey	Judith Pyclik
John Bernard	Herb Ginsburg	Tom Romberg
George Bright	Ken Henderson	James M. Sherrill
Jere Brophy	Jim Hiebert	Edward Silver
Ralph W. Cain	Carl Huberty	Larry K. Sowder
L. Ray Carry	David C. Johnson	Les Steffe
Raymond O. Collier, Jr.	Tom Kieren	Lee Stiff
Tom Cooney	Charles E. Lamb	Gary Talsma
Marjorie Cosman	James Lockwood	Grace Vos
F. Joe Crosswhite	Mary Mallet	Russell Yeany
Carleen DeRidder	Douglas B. McLeod	

PART ONE

The Research Process

1

Why Do Research?

Edward G. Begle
Stanford University

E. Glenadine Gibb
The University of Texas at Austin

R ESEARCHERS in mathematics education and teachers of mathematics have a common goal—improving the teaching and learning of mathematics. To attain this goal, both groups must engage in complex activities based on conceptual knowledge drawn from mathematics, the philosophies of mathematics and education, and the psychology of learning and human development. Just as research in industry, business, medicine, government, agriculture, and other fields of education is responsive to both theoretical and practical needs, research in mathematics education also must cover a broad spectrum—from the theoretical foundations of cognitive development and individual differences among individual learners of mathematics to the decision-making needs of the classroom, the school, and the teacher-education programs of the colleges and universities. This response to both theoretical and practical needs does not imply a dichotomy but rather a continuum of research in mathematics education in fulfillment of its responsibilities to the mathematics education community.

Hilgard (1964, p. 406) suggests a continuum as a helpful guide to avoid a dichotomy of thinking between so-called pure and applied research. He identifies six stages according to their relevance for learning and educational practice in the classroom. This continuum extends from pure research through technological research and development. (See Figure 1.)

Edward G. Begle's death came before the final revisions of this manuscript were made in preparation for publication. Every attempt has been made to preserve his thoughts and efforts in the preparation of this chapter through its final revisions.—E. G. Gibb

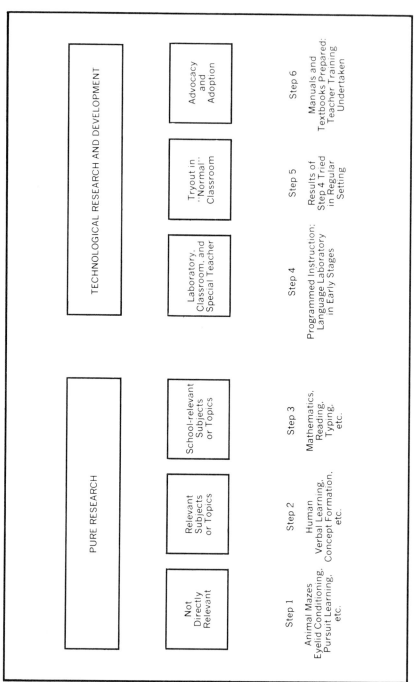

Figure 1. Steps in research on learning—pure research to technological development.

As can be inferred from Figure 1, research on learning in Step 1 is conducted without regard for its educational relevance. Although Step 2 is not concerned with educational practices, it is more relevant than Step 1. It deals with human subjects and with content nearer to that taught in the school. The nature of research in Step 3 is relevant in that the selected subjects are school students and the material is selected from school subject matter (e.g., mathematics, reading, sciences). Although it is closer to application in the classroom, it is not designed to show how mathematics should be taught. Research as identified in Step 4 might be described as research conducted in special laboratory situations with selected teachers. Whatever seems feasible from research in Step 4 must then be tried out in the more typical, normal classroom (Step 5), where the time for the new method or materials may be more limited and the students and teachers may lack the special motivation of those in Step 4. Thus, what has been found to advance the improvement of teaching and learning in Steps 4 and 5 is ready to be proposed for adoption in the classroom (Step 6).

Confusion may arise, however, between the efforts to seek scientific explanations with respect to human behavior in learning mathematics and the mindless fact gathering that often masquerades as research. The following letter written by Bernard K. Forscher (1963) to the editor of *Science* may emphasize the need to eliminate such masquerades and to guard against such confusion.

Chaos in the Brickyard

Once upon a time, among the activities and occupations of man there was an activity called scientific research and the performers of this activity were called scientists. In reality, however, these men were builders who constructed edifices, called explanations or laws, by assembling bricks, called facts. When the bricks were sound and were assembled properly, the edifice was useful and durable and brought pleasure, and sometimes reward, to the builder. If the bricks were faulty or if they were assembled badly, the edifice would crumble, and this kind of disaster could be very dangerous to innocent users of the edifice as well as to the builder who sometimes was destroyed by the collapse. Because the quality of the bricks was so important to the success of the edifice, and because bricks were so scarce, in those days the builders made their own bricks. The making of bricks was a difficult and expensive undertaking and the wise builder avoided waste by making only bricks of the shape and size necessary for the enterprise at hand. The builder was guided in this manufacture by a blueprint, called a theory or hypothesis.

It came to pass that builders realized that they were sorely hampered in their efforts by delays in obtaining bricks. Thus there arose a new skilled trade known as brickmaking, called junior scientist to give the artisan proper pride in his work. This new arrangement was very efficient and the construction of edifices proceeded with great vigor. Sometimes brickmakers became inspired and progressed to the status of builders. In spite of the separation of duties, bricks still were made with care and usually were produced only on order. Now and then an enterprising brickmaker was able to foresee a demand and would prepare a stock of bricks ahead of time, but, in general, brickmaking was done on a custom basis because it still was a difficult and expensive process.

And then it came to pass that a misunderstanding spread among the brickmakers (there are some who say that this misunderstanding developed as a result of careless training of a new generation of brickmakers). The brickmakers became obsessed with the making of bricks. When reminded that the ultimate goal was edifices, not bricks, they replied that, if enough bricks were available, the builders would be able to select what was necessary and still continue to construct edifices. The flaws in this argument were not readily apparent and so, with the help of the citizens who were waiting to use the edifices yet to be built, amazing things happened. The expense of brickmaking became a minor factor because large sums of money were made available; the time and effort involved in brickmaking was reduced by ingenious automatic machinery; the ranks of the brickmakers were swelled by augmented training programs and intensive recruitment. It even was suggested that the production of a suitable number of bricks was equivalent to building an edifice and therefore should entitle the industrious brickmaker to assume the title of builder and, with the title, the authority.

And so it happened that the land became flooded with bricks. It became necessary to organize more and more storage places, called journals, and more and more elaborate systems of bookkeeping to record the inventory. In all of this the brickmakers retained their pride and skill and the bricks were of the very best quality. But production was ahead of demand and bricks no longer were made to order. The size and shape was now dictated by changing trends in fashion. In order to compete successfully with other brickmakers, production emphasized those types of brick that were easy to make and only rarely did an adventuresome brickmaker attempt a difficult or unusual design. The influence of tradition in production methods and in types of product became a dominating factor.

Unfortunately, the builders were almost destroyed. It became difficult to find the proper bricks for a task because one had to hunt among so many. It became difficult to find a suitable plot for construction of an edifice because the ground was covered with loose bricks. It became difficult to complete a useful edifice because, as soon as the foundations were discernible, they were buried under an avalanche of random bricks. And, saddest of all, sometimes no effort was made even to maintain the distinction between a pile of bricks and a true edifice.

This letter may convince researchers of the need for perspective in building "edifices of knowledge" or making the "bricks" that are needed for those edifices. For those concerned about the quality of research, the letter may help instill an appreciation of the value of research studies and the discrimination necessary in seeking research-based support for practices and for selecting among alternatives in mathematics curricula. More specifically, research in mathematics education generates an improved knowledge of how the learning of mathematics takes place, which in turn provides a new vision of what is educationally possible, improvement in the teaching of mathematics, and direction for the development of mathematics curricula—the *why* of doing research.

WHAT IS RESEARCH?

Before considering the purposes for doing research, we should ask, "What is research?" The Committee on Educational Research of the National Academy of Education (Cronbach & Suppes, 1969) defines research as "disciplined or systematic inquiry concerning a certain event or events in an effort to further and/or verify knowledge." More specifically, according to the model proposed by Hilgard, research encompasses systematic investigation and experimentation based on hypotheses generated from previous studies, conjectures, and experience. Theories are built and revised in light of new knowledge that facilitates understanding the why, how, and what of mathematics education. Practical applications of those new or revised theories then should be made.

Some disciplined inquiries address larger issues of mathematics education. These inquiries often fall into the area of technological research and are usually more difficult to design because of the complexity of the issue. Other disciplined inquiries address rather narrow issues with carefully and precisely defined variables. These inquiries usually fall into the area of pure research. Criticism, openness, flexibility, and time provide a productive environment for research. Often the results of specific studies are less important than the conceptualizations they generate. These conceptualizations and theories are debated, and the factual conclusions are often reinterpreted or modified in light of new knowledge.

Some disciplined inquiries belong to the category of quantitative, empirical studies—for example, surveys and controlled experiments. Other disciplined inquiries belong to the category that includes logical analyses of writings of the past, philosophical treatments, and organized personal experiences—for example, historical studies, philosophical studies, and case studies. Philosophical statements, polemics, professional opinion, and other kinds of writing communicate viewpoint and information with respect to some aspect of mathematics education, but to the degree that they represent subjective opinion, they are not properly viewed as research. Nevertheless, the reporting of personal experience and wisdom by individuals provides an important motivation for reflection. Considered opinion—that is, opinion formulated through reflection on one's own ideas together with the ideas of others—provides the basis of much decision making in mathematics education. One might say that research is a means of turning opinion into knowl-edge. Of course, the most important characteristic of research is its quality. If research has high quality, then the knowledge produced may be con-sidered reliable. If a study produces reliable knowledge, then its implica-tions must be taken seriously. Many professionals feel that reliable knowl-edge produced through high-quality research is the only sound basis for significant changes in educational practice.

PURPOSES OF RESEARCH

What are the purposes of research in mathematics education? That is, why should we do research in mathematics education? Simply stated, there is a need to understand better how, where, and why people learn or do not learn mathematics. Operationally, the fulfilling of this need is most com-plex.

The complex experience of the teaching-learning interaction for the learner encompasses many determinants: the parameters of the learner, the content, the teacher, the mode of instruction. The learner's maturity, intellectual ability, learning style, attitudes, and emotional and social adjustment must be considered. Not only the analysis of the mathematics content to be learned but also the scope and sequence of the content and the expected rate for developing and processing mathematical under-standings and knowledge must be taken into account. Consideration must be given to the teachers' knowledge of mathematics, their art of teaching mathematics, their individual humanistic characteristics, and the roles they play in their students' learning experiences. Consideration also must be given to methods of teaching, the use of media, and the design of instruc-tional materials within the context of instruction.

The purposes of research in mathematics education, then, are to find out how and why something works and then to see what works in practice. Across the continuum of research, inspired both from school realities and theoretical intent, purposes for research may be reflected in a range of studies: (a) the cognitive styles, personality characteristics, and individual abilities of both learners and teachers as background for a general teaching-learning theory of mathematics; (b) the theoretical aspects of learning, teaching, and curriculum development; (c) the development of decision-making models that may be used in schools so that intelligent choices can be made among alternatives; (d) the evaluation of instructional procedures, programs, and materials for predicting their educational benefit; (e) the development of educational products such as curricula, achievement tests, and attitude scales; and (f) the development of improved "tools" for doing research in mathematics education.

As in other disciplines, the encompassing purpose of research is the advancement of our discipline. From the practice of farming grew the discipline of agriculture. From the practice of healing grew the discipline of medicine. From the practice of teaching mathematics grew the discipline of mathematics education. Research is the means used to further the discipline of mathematics education.

Unlike the field of mathematics, the field of mathematics education today resembles the state of agriculture in this country several generations ago. Although we draw from general theories of learning, we have no established general theory of learning mathematics to provide a basis for our discussions. We do have, however, many "bricks" of factual information. By exploiting what is already known and by carrying out the disciplined inquiries that these results tell us are needed, we could facilitate the construction of edifices of broad theoretical foundations for the teaching and learning of mathematics as well as curricula content and organization. Without such a foundation, we can only continue to spin our intellectual wheels.

As one must expect, theories are modified, altered, or even discarded on the basis of the continued seeking of new knowledge. A series of studies may lead to the development of a new concept or teaching strategy that is highly successful when first used. Subsequent studies, however, may reveal that the original research was incomplete or is less effective after the novelty has worn off.

These systematic inquiries are commonly classified as either basic or applied research. The Committee on Educational Research (CER) of the National Academy of Education (Cronbach & Suppes, 1969) uses the terms *conclusion-oriented inquiry* and *decision-oriented inquiry*. The conclusion-decision terminology seems to have gained preference over the basic-applied terminology in recent years by many educators, including mathematics educators. This preference may be due to a subtle change in the connotation of "basic" research in education, as suggested by Lehmann and Mehrens (1971): "Educators no longer feel it necessary to reduce all educational activities to psychological phenomena in order to 'add to scientific knowledge' " (p. 5).

The CER supports conclusion-oriented and decision-oriented terminology. A distinction between these two classifications lies in the organization of an inquiry and the constraints imposed. Although both may be commissioned, conclusion-oriented studies take direction from the investigators' commitments and hunches. The investigators formulate their own questions and are free to reframe these questions as they go along, taking advantage of each partial insight to redirect their inquiries. Decision-oriented studies are expected to provide information wanted by the decision makers, who provide the questions.

Whatever terminology might be used—basic and applied or conclusion-oriented and decision-oriented—each has a distinctive function (directly or indirectly) in our efforts to further our discipline for the improved teaching and learning of mathematics. The conclusion-oriented and decision-oriented terminology, however, seems more conducive to one's thinking of a continuum of research, but undoubtedly this is a matter of individual preference.

RESEARCHERS IN MATHEMATICS EDUCATION

Who are the researchers in mathematics education? Although individuals in the mathematics education community may assume different responsibilities for the advancement of mathematics education, each one can be regarded as a researcher during the time he or she is engaged in systematic inquiry into a well-defined problem in mathematics education.

What is learned in a given inquiry, however, is highly dependent on the competence of the investigator in devising procedures appropriate to the problem. No uniform standards exist for qualifying one to conduct research, but education and experience in accordance with one's professional aspirations are necessary. The methods, education, and experiences needed for successful research may never be defined completely; too many researchers, even those with similar general professional goals, do not fit a well-defined pattern.

Although competency in research is difficult to define, Walbesser and Eisenberg (1971) describe a program of four seminars designed to help graduate students in mathematics education attain competence in research. These seminars are designed as follows:

Seminar 1: To introduce the students to a behavioral approach to research on instruction. Thirty-eight hierarchically organized behaviors are to be acquired in this seminar.

Seminar 2: To define problems, including techniques for manipulating variables, obtaining measures for various variables, and holding variables constant.

Seminar 3: To analyze and replicate existing research. In this seminar students learn to replicate an experiment reported in the literature and to compare findings; to construct alternative explanations for a given set of findings; to distinguish between findings and conclusions; and to construct and conduct original research with two or three other individuals.

Seminar 4: To introduce computer-assisted instruction, computer-managed instruction, and problem-solving strategies. Two group-research projects and two individual projects are a part of fulfilling the requirements in this last seminar.

This exemplar provides colleges and universities with suggestions for planning programs of study in mathematics education. The attainment of the knowledge of research, both in its interpretation and in conducting inquiries, is a requirement of advanced-degree programs in mathematics education. As stated by Walbesser and Eisenberg (1971),

> the acknowledgement of an individual as a scholar in any discipline does . . . reside in his research contributions and not with a demonstration that a certain collection of course requirements has been satisfied. The initial demonstration that one has acquired the competencies of a scholar is the individual's dissertation. . . . The demonstration of a scholarly competence is not a matter of a single product, but is a continuing event. (p. 668)

Researchers should also possess certain personal qualities, such as creativity, curiosity, determination, objectivity, tolerance of frustration, logical reasoning, and the ability to make scholarly observations. Furthermore, teaching experience should not be overlooked as a contribution to research competency.

IMPACT OF RESEARCH

Understandably, the impact of research on practive lags behind its development; some have estimated that this gap may be fifty years or more. This delayed impact may be attributed to such factors as (a) time for creativity, development, and publication, (b) communication between the researchers and the users of research, and (c) the relevance of the research to the user.

Time

Many people, deeply embedded in today's educational crises, want quick results from research to give them direction regardless of the intent or purpose of the research. They become impatient to the extent that they feel that research in mathematics education has no relevance for the teacher of mathematics or for curriculum developments. A statement made by the National Research Council in 1969 and repeated by the Committee on Fundamental Research Relevant to Education (Kiesler & Turner, 1977) sheds light on this connection between research and the real world:

> Any basic science has an inner logic of its own, which for considerable periods of time, guides inquiry, defines problems, and discloses opportunities. This inner logic does not imply irrelevance to the practical world; it may however, imply patience in allowing the science to unravel its internal puzzles without demanding that relevance always be instant or direct. (p. 19)

A research study requires several years from conceptualization to completion, some time to write a report, and from two to six months (often much longer) for journal editors to review the report for possible publication. Furthermore, if the report is accepted for publication in a research journal (or is disseminated in some other manner), another lag of six months to two years or so can be expected before the general public has access to the knowledge. Even then, the research report can produce only new knowledge, which often must undergo public debate. An even longer period of time is required to develop a body of research to support any change in the mathematics curriculum or in the teaching of mathematics. A single study cannot be expected to support such action.

Communication

Teachers, who might be in a position to close the gap of time between inquiry and application, do not commonly read research findings that are published in journals. For many teachers who might have some understanding of research, there is little time to read professional research journals. Others who might read the reports find them too technical; this is often true because of space limitations in these publications.

As the Committee on Fundamental Research Relevant to Education (Kiesler & Turner, 1977) stated, the results of research and the practice of teaching are related in many more ways than as a dialogue between the researcher and the teacher. They suggest a third party to the dialogue, whose job it is to facilitate communication between the first two. These "disseminators" (e.g., popularizers, translators, journalists, reporters, professors of education) put the writings of researchers into a form that is useful to those who might benefit from it. As the committee members so carefully noted, this does not free us from the belief that the contribution of research is to tell teachers how to teach even though the purpose is actually to describe in general terms the possible linkages between research on one hand and the real world of teaching mathematics on the other. Certainly teachers think about what they read and how it relates to their work. Their attitude of reaching out for deeper understanding must be regarded as a commitment to act. Their seriousness feeds on the seriousness of others.

In a study by Reys and Yeager (1974) in which they interviewed 40 elementary teachers randomly selected from a group of 75, 87.5% responded that they seldom or never read research-flavored articles. Yet 97.5% reported that they always or frequently read general education journals. When asked why they avoided research articles, 80% gave either the lack of direct classroom application or a lack of time as their first or second choices. Also mentioned, however, were the inaccessibility of such articles, statistical jargon, stereotyped format, and an excess of charts, graphs, and tables. Thus, elementary school teachers of mathematics do not appear to be direct readers of research. To close this communication gap, it is natural to turn to the teacher educators, the school and state mathematics consultants, and the state and national organizations of teachers of mathematics. Several more years may pass before the results are reflected in teacher education programs if, indeed, the findings are ever used in preservice and in-service teacher education programs or in professional mathematics education meetings.

A similar lag can be expected on the part of developers of instructional materials. New findings must wait until the next set of instructional materials is designed. If research findings are likely to produce such a "different look" in the product as to cause rejection on the part of the consumer, who may not yet understand the change, the idea probably will be abandoned for fear that the product might be unmarketable. This lag is closely associated with another factor in the transmission of research to practice: relevance.

Relevance

Despite the lag from inquiry to practice, research has been put to use. Two topics have been selected as illustrations. Others may be found in Part II of this book. We first consider the topic of individualized instruction, which received new emphasis in the 1960s and 1970s. Certainly the idea is attractive, since we all know that no two students are alike. We also know that in the 1920s self-paced, continuous progress and systems approaches to individualized instruction had widespread popularity only virtually to disappear in the 1930s. Proponents argued again in the 1960s and 1970s that through individualized instruction students achieved more in mathematics and had more favorable attitudes toward the subject.

Although very little research testing has appeared in journals, Schoen (1977) identified over one hundred studies—mostly unpublished doctoral dissertations, the brickyard of mathematics education research—that compared self-paced instruction and traditional instruction. His careful analysis of the findings shows either that the idea of self-paced instruction is wrong or that we do not know how to go about it yet. The message to teachers is that perhaps we should forget about self-paced instruction until further research uncovers principles that can give better guidance as we move along the continuum to the classroom.

The second topic that we shall consider is ability grouping. The journals are full of articles either in favor of or opposed to ability grouping. The arguments on both sides are plausible and convincing but certainly perplexing to teachers and administrators who are seeking support for a decision that they must make.

Proponents claim that a teacher can more easily take into account the individual differences among students when the range of differences is small than when it is large. Consequently, teachers will be more effective and students will achieve more in homogeneous classes than in hetero-geneous classes.

Opponents claim that it can have unfortunate affective results because it causes low-ability students to be stigmatized and to develop a poor self-concept. Begle (1975) concluded after a review and analysis of some 70 empirical studies (bricks of knowledge in the brickyard) and 8 reviews on ability grouping for mathematics instruction that for both cognitive and affective measures ability grouping was better for the bright students and made no difference for the other students. Thus, he encouraged school systems to experiment with homogeneous grouping for students who are high in mathematical ability but to group the remaining students hetero-geneously. He also encouraged teachers to experiment with in-class group-ing, particularly the variation that uses regrouping at the beginning of each new topic.

Both of these topical studies demonstrate that we are likely to get results useful to classroom teachers not from single studies but rather from the cumulative results of many studies. Furthermore, they demonstrate the need for interconnected studies conducted by a number of investigators and for continuous review. However, when a single study produces signifi-cant findings, it is almost certainly the culmination of a number of re-lated investigations.

There are those who are committed to using the information from re-search to support change, and there are those who refuse to use it. Those who take the position that research has little to contribute to their profes-sional endeavors would undoubtedly appreciate the support that they might find for their actions if they would take the trouble to familiarize them-selves with research reports like those presented in Part II. When one is asked, "Why did you do what you did?" (and mathematics teachers in-creasingly are asked this question), research can provide a defensible rationale for the change. Some problems investigated by research seem unimportant to teachers, although the researchers expect the results of their investigations to be relevant to practice. More specifically, teachers often possess a "practice wisdom" that enables them to identify problems that are impeding their progress. When their problems and those identified by the researcher seem very different, the results of such studies seem of little importance to the practical world of teaching and learning mathematics.

Other Considerations

Even if we were to overcome such problems of time, communication, and relevance in our efforts to bring greater impact of research on the teaching and learning of mathematics, we might still be overlooking another factor. In a paper presented to the Third International Congress of Mathematical Education, Bauersfeld (1976) noted the small influence that outcomes of research have had on the reality of teaching and learning mathematics. He attributes this dilemma to the fact that "research has limped after the needs of school practice rather than hurrying on ahead" (p. 199). The recent indication of a change of direction from the curriculum and from the student to the teacher seems to him a more favored approach for bringing about greater impact of research on school practice. He proposes that

> the problems of a proper mathematical development and education of the individual student will not be adequately solved until careful analyses of the causes of individual differences are made, diagnostic aids for the teacher to identify differences are developed, corresponding preparation during the teacher's training is provided, and conclusions for school organization are drawn. (p. 209)

Thus, we must ask what direction research in mathematics education should take in the future if it is expected to have greater impact on the improvement of the teaching and learning of mathematics.

TOWARD THE FUTURE

Research in mathematics education has provided bricks for edifices of cognitive development, skill learning, concept and principle learning, problem solving, individual difference, attitudes, curriculum, instruction, teaching, and teacher education. Some edifices have been built—others are under construction. Furthermore, every mathematics educator (teacher and teacher of teachers of mathematics) can benefit from these edifices. For information regarding the status of the bricks and edifices, one is encouraged to read carefully the second part of this book. The benefits to be derived from this spectrum of efforts can be multiplied if, in the future, a few obstacles can be overcome that have in the past obstructed the fulfillment of the purposes for doing research in mathematics education.

New Directions

As Bauersfeld noted, the curriculum projects of the 1950s and the 1960s have not improved the teaching and learning of mathematics on a broad scale. Research has developed competing explanations for partial views of learning—for example, Piaget's genetic theory of epistemology, Gagné's hierarchical model, and the Gestalt theories—but generalizations from these partial theories are limited for the explanation and prediction of learning. Also, they are insufficient for the planning and realization of classroom practices. It is necessary to consider not only the student or the curriculum but also the general context of learning and the teacher's role in effecting learning. Thus, more sophisticated theories of the teaching-learning process in mathematics seem necessary.

An extension of the repertoire of research methods is needed. Researchers in mathematics education have been highly criticized for their restricted views of research techniques. As our repertoires of methods are reassessed, careful consideration should be given to other procedures, such as those used (a) in the *Soviet Studies in the Psychology of Learning and Teaching Mathematics* (School Mathematics Study Group, 1969–1975), (b) by Piaget, whose methods are familiar to both researchers and teachers, and (c) by Krutetskii (1976).

Whether we believe that research efforts in mathematics education should be directed more toward purposes of basic research or toward applied research, there is support for our position. Cronbach (1966) argues that

> educational improvements that really make an impact on the ignorance rate will not grow out of minor variations of teaching content and process. Effective educational designs, worth careful development and field trial, can emerge only from a deep understanding of learning and motivation. (p. 540)

Wittrock (1967) agrees. He states that

> educational psychology should invest most of its resources into its most important activity—basic research aimed at control and understanding of the problems and phenomena of instruction in schools. (p. 17)

Ebel (1967) argues what might seem to be the minority position:

> Let us also push, and rather more strongly, the kind of survey research that provides data crucial to the decisions that we must make. Let us not worship pure science and basic research unrealistically and irrationally. (p. 84)

If we are to advance the discipline of mathematics education, we must engage in systematic inquiries across a continuum such as that proposed by Hilgard (1964).

Perhaps of more substance, however, are the areas of research that can provide solid knowledge directed toward developing theories of teaching and learning for mathematics education with respect to the content of mathematics, mathematics as taught by the teacher, and the mathematics that is learned by the student. Certainly the subject matter varies in the teaching process as well as in the learning process. Insight into the individuality of teachers and students cannot support the *best* treatment. Instead the question should be, "What is optimal for which students and under what conditions?"

Cooperative Efforts

Research studies are often so narrow in focus that it has been difficult to compare one study with another. Commonly, one finds that several studies on a topic produce divergent findings. It is thus necessary to consider why these differences exist. Two investigators, even those observing identical data, may not draw the same conclusions. Thus, one cannot simply accept the report of the researcher at face value but must consider it in light of possible pitfalls. Since research is far from infallible, inquiring readers will be less frustrated if they expect it to provoke questions as well as supply answers.

If we are to have any substantial body of knowledge about mathematics education that we can build on, we need a series of interconnected studies by a number of investigators working together toward the solution of a common problem. Future research should be planned to include more coordination if we are to increase the efficiency of our research endeavors. Replications of the same design and an analysis and comparison of the conclusions related to the evidence can be expected to be part of such an effort. If different variables are to be controlled from investigation to investigation, the relatedness between the studies must be planned carefully.

In an effort to assure the relevance of problems, research teams should involve not only the researchers but also theorists, graduate students, and classroom teachers. This participation should produce insightful, conclusion-oriented research findings that are a viable source of information for the day-by-day decision making that confronts educators.

The Education of Teachers

There is a need to develop the research competencies and attitudes of teachers. Many classroom teachers have little or no direct contact with research that relates to their classroom practices. This may be due in part to their lack of familiarity with research. Although some teachers participate in varying types of research ranging from survey questionnaires to federal research projects, the majority tend to consider these forms of investigation something other than research. Thus, education with respect to research is highly desirable.

Through preservice and in-service programs, teachers can develop an appreciation for the necessity of research. They can be inspired to be involved in action research studies in their classrooms. Also, they can gain some insight into the complexities and difficulties involved in observing and measuring educational processes. An understanding of the problems faced by researchers can bring about a more realistic attitude in terms of expectations.

If research is to be used, however, teachers' knowledge should extend beyond exposure, even under the constraints of requirements in professional preparatory programs. College and university professors certainly need to make greater efforts to use research and make it relevant. Through the efforts of these mathematics educators, prospective teachers as well as those engaged in continuing education beyond the certification program can have direct experience in learning to make use of research. Such experiences, carefully designed, can result in a greater willingness among teachers to be involved in research and to make use of its findings. At least teachers might be expected to learn some "tools" with which to analyze the effects of the teaching-learning encounter in their classrooms.

Of interest to the mathematics education community is a study conducted by Short and Szabo (1974) in which a sample of 204 secondary teachers voluntarily completed a test on their knowledge of educational research. Subjects in this sample had major teaching areas in English, social science, science, and mathematics. Short and Szabo found that the teachers of mathematics were significantly more knowledgeable about educational research and held a more favorable attitude toward it than the English and social science teachers. An analysis of their findings led the investigators to recommend that teachers should be provided with opportunity, time, and incentive to use the knowledge that they have. (Remember that the subjects volunteered to take the test on which the findings were based.)

SOME CONCLUDING THOUGHTS

Although no one knows what the future has in store for mathematics education, reflection on the past provides assurance that changes will continue to take place. Throughout the history of civilization, virtually every age has provided new insight and new knowledge. Thus, greater and greater demands must be placed on researchers in mathematics education to push forward the frontiers of knowledge so that we can reach an understanding of the underlying nature of learning and teaching mathematics. In turn, these edifices must provide guiding principles for teachers and others responsible for making decisions with respect to the mathematics education of children, youth, and adults and for the continued improvement of the learning encounter in the mathematics classroom. Researchers in mathematics education, through their skill, intellectual commitment, and motivational commitment, are the architects for the edifices of understanding learning, the learner, and the teacher in the mathematical environment, relevant to the needs of today and the aspirations of tomorrow.

REFERENCES

Bauersfeld, H. Research related to the mathematical learning process. In B. Christiansen & H. G. Steiner (Eds.), *New trends in mathematics teaching* (Vol. 4). Paris: UNESCO, 1979.

Begle, E. G. *Ability grouping for mathematics instruction: A review of the empirical literature.* SMESG Working Paper No. 17, 1975. (ERIC No. ED 116 938)

Cronbach, L. J. The role of the university in improving education. *Phi Delta Kappan,* 1966, *47,* 539.

Cronbach, L. J., & Suppes, P. (Eds.). *Research for tomorrow's schools: Disciplined inquiry for education.* New York: Macmillan, 1969.

Ebel, R. L. Some limitations of basic research in education. *Phi Delta Kappan,* 1967, *49,* 17.

Forscher, B. K. Letter to the editor. *Science,* 1963, *142* (3590), 329.

Hilgard, E. R. A perspective on the relationship between learning theory and educational practices. In *Theories of learning and instruction* (Sixty-third Yearbook of the National Society for the Study of Education). Chicago: University of Chicago Press, 1964.

Johnson, M. C. *A review of research methods in education.* Chicago: Rand McNally, 1977.

Kiesler, S. B., & Turner, C. F. (Eds.). *Fundamental research and the process of education.* Final Report to the National Institute of Education by the National Academy of Sciences. Washington, D.C.: U.S. Government Printing Office, 1977.

Krutetskii, V. A. [*The psychology of mathematical abilities in schoolchildren*] (J. Teller, Trans., and J. Kilpatrick & I. Wirszup, Eds.). Chicago: University of Chicago Press, 1976.

Lehmann, I. J., & Mehrens, W. A. *Educational research—Readings in focus.* New York: Holt, Rinehart & Winston, 1971.

Reys, R. E., & Yeager, T. Elementary teachers and research in mathematics education. *School Science and Mathematics,* 1974, *74,* 431–436.

Schoen, H. L. Implications of research for instruction in self-paced mathematics classrooms. In F. J. Crosswhite & R. E. Reys (Eds.), *Organizing for mathematics instruction: 1977 Yearbook.* Reston, Va.: National Council of Teachers of Mathematics, 1977. See also *Arithmetic Teacher,* 1976, *23,* 90–96; and *Mathematics Teacher,* 1976, *69,* 352–357.

School Mathematics Study Group and Survey of Recent East European Mathematical Literature. *Soviet studies in the psychology of learning and teaching mathematics* (14 vols.). Chicago: University of Chicago, 1969–1975.

Short, B. G., & Szabo, M. Secondary school teachers' knowledge of and attitudes towards educational research. *Journal of Experimental Education,* 1974, *43,* 75–78.

Walbesser, H., & Eisenberg, T. What research competencies for the mathematics educator? *American Mathematical Monthly,* 1971, *78,* 667–673.

Wittrock, M. C. Focus on educational psychology. *Educational Psychologist,* 1967, *4,* 84.

2

Types of Research

David C. Johnson
Chelsea College, University of London

I N DISCUSSING types of research, one should first note that the most important step in the research process is defining the problem, that is, identifying an idea or need and specifying the hypotheses to be investigated (Stages 1 and 3 of Fox, 1969). All other matters—methodology, design, instrumentation, data-gathering procedures, data analysis, and quality of conclusions or decisions—are dictated by the concise conceptualization of the problem. Specifying the problem in a concise and well-defined form is the step that researchers generally find to be most difficult. For example, making a problem more specific might involve moving from the general question "Does the availability and use of calculators in school mathematics affect student achievement (the learning of skills and concepts)?" to a more detailed description of a question that is *researchable,* such as "Does using the calculator for arithmetic calculations when working with decimals in the introductory stages at Grade 5 to enable students to concentrate on the ideas of decimal placement and place value result in a better understanding of the concepts and processes?" The problem still requires more description, but at least some of the key components have been identified. Depending on one's interests, the original concern regarding calculators and student achievement might have been phrased in terms of curriculum development, for example, "Can one develop calculator-based lessons to teach the ideas of algorithms, applications of mathematics, and mathematical modeling effectively in Grade 8?"

Once defined and specified, the research question leads naturally to a consideration of what procedure or type of research would be most appropriate for collecting data that will provide at least a tentative answer to the question. For instance, an *experiment* that compares alternative approaches may offer the best means for gathering information relative to the first question (dealing with the improved learning of decimal concepts), whereas an *evaluation* (formative evaluation) study that assesses effectiveness against some predetermined criterion such as "mastery" might lend itself better to responding to the second question (dealing with curriculum development). If one had asked whether or not the availability of calculators results in different behavior in solving problems, the question might then lead to what is often described as a *case study* or *clinical research* or, more recently, the *teaching experiment*. In this type of study the researcher is interested in gathering a large amount of data from the careful observation of the behavior of a small number of subjects.

DESCRIPTION AND EXAMPLES

Most journal articles or books on research that address types of research generally include six or seven categories (e.g., see Johnson, 1966). This chapter, however, will be restricted to a consideration of five basic types. These are listed below with brief descriptions and examples.

Survey

Survey research also includes *status,* or *correlational,* studies. In survey research, data (information) is usually collected to ascertain the current status of selected variables. The research is generally undertaken to provide a descriptive picture of a situation without attempting to relate cause and effect. The major purpose is to establish norms and baseline data for consideration by researchers and practitioners in making their decisions, to help raise relevant questions, or to identify needed research.

Two classic studies in this area are the Committee of Seven reports (Washburne, 1930, pp. 641–670; 1939, pp. 299–324), which had a major influence on the grade placement of arithmetic topics in the 1930s and 1940s. Note the interesting debate between Washburne (1932) and Raths (1932a, 1932b, 1932c) in the *Educational Research Bulletin* (see also Washburne & Voas, 1932). A more recent example is the 1972–73 Mathematics Assessment of the National Assessment of Educational Progress (NAEP) (Carpenter, Coburn, Reys, & Wilson, 1978), which has provided valuable baseline data on selected age groups relative to general mathematical knowledge and the ability to apply mathematics.

Experiment

This type of research, sometimes referred to as *scientific experimentation,* is essentially the application of the method of laboratory experimentation in educational research. It involves the careful control of variables in an experimental situation to enable the researcher to associate mathematical probability with a result and to obtain an objective evaluation of the variables being studied. Many researchers advocate this type of research as having the greatest promise for establishing theory and ultimately finding definitive answers to the questions of how best to teach or learn selected content (e.g., see the positions taken by Kerlinger, 1977, and Jackson & Kiesler, 1977; see also an interesting response to the Kerlinger paper by Slavin, 1978).

In mathematics education, experimental research usually involves the contrasting of methods, materials, or strategies; the researcher uses a variety of measurements and applies the tools of inferential statistics for the analysis of the data. The key features of the experiment are the notion of hypothesis testing and the establishment of probable causality. The design and analysis of the experiment are the most critical components and, in general, represent both the strengths and weaknesses of the experimental research reported in the literature. To be an effective researcher in this area generally requires considerable study and training (e.g., see Walbesser & Eisenberg, 1971) and a strong foundation in experimental design. (The chapters by Hummel and White provide a more in-depth discussion of the many facets of design and analysis.)

There are many good examples of experimental research in the literature. One that stands out and illustrates careful attention to design, analysis, and interpretation is the classic experiment by Van Engen and Gibb (1956), which establishes the case for using successive subtraction as the strategy for teaching division.

Case Study

This type of study is sometimes referred to as *clinical research* or, more recently, as the *teaching experiment.* Johnson (1966) provides a brief but succinct description of this type of research:

> It involves the intensive study of individuals or situations. It may involve interrogation and observation of an individual to assess his characteristics and then relate these characteristics to certain performance patterns. In view of the complexity of human learning, it might be fruitful to investigate concept formation, problem solving, motivation, sources of difficulty or errors by this method. However, it is dangerous to state generalizations as if the findings applied to much wider groups, since the samples are usually limited. (p. 420)

One might note that viewed in this manner the case study can be thought of as a special form of the survey or status study.

The case study has recently come to include some aspects of instruction (to a small group or even an entire class) with follow-up interrogation or observation of selected individuals. The inclusion of an instructional component and the cooperation of the teacher and the researcher have led to the descriptor *teaching experiment.*

There are many good examples of case studies in the literature. Probably the best-known works are the research reports of Piaget in the area of number conservation (Piaget & Szeminska, 1952). In addition, the recent work by Krutetskii (1976), which uses the notion of an information-processing model, provides the basis for much of the current research classified as the teaching experiment (e.g., see Kantowski, 1977, and Kilpatrick & Wirszup, 1969a, 1969b, for examples of this type of research in investigations of the processes involved in mathematical problem solving).

Evaluation

Research of this type, unlike those types considered up to this point, is primarily concerned with changes that occur as a function of time. These studies include evaluations of curriculum (learning) as well as studies of the generalization of learning, commonly called "transfer of training." Often an evaluation study could have been designed as an experiment, but the constraints placed on the situation by the environment (e.g., a school setting) result in the selection of some criterion-based assessment or the collection of data on intact groups as the most viable alternative (see discussions of this point in the chapter by Hummel). In general, evaluation studies are classified as either *formative* or *summative*. In a somewhat simplistic sense the research is placed in one of these two categories according to its intended purpose. Formative evaluation is usually intended to provide developers with information for purposes of improving a product—modifying or adjusting the particular methods or materials employed—hence, the process is one of evaluation-feedback-modification-evaluation, and so on. An evaluation is considered to be summative when the information is to be used to test the efficiency of a total program in order to make a "go" versus "no go" decision. Of course, the distinction is seldom so clear-cut; hence, the dichotomy is not always useful.

Authors in the area of evaluation provide a number of models or technologies that might be employed by researchers. These models range from a somewhat "free wheeling" approach in which observation and common sense are used to make judgments or decisions at one extreme to an emphasis on the careful establishment of protocols and procedures with well-defined rules for making decisions (in which probabilities are sometimes used, as with the experiment) at the other extreme. The researcher who has a problem that lends itself to an evaluation study would do well to refer to the *Handbook on Formative and Summative Evaluation of Student Learning* (Bloom, Hastings, & Madaus, 1971).

An example of an evaluation study is the large-scale evaluation of the School Mathematics Study Group (SMSG) reported in the 32 volumes of the National Longitudinal Study of Mathematical Abilities (NLSMA). A special issue of *Investigations in Mathematics Education* (Osborne, 1975) is devoted entirely to a review and analysis of the NLSMA reports. Although NLSMA was not designed exclusively as an evaluation project, one major thrust of the data-gathering activity was oriented toward an evaluation of the effectiveness of the SMSG texts.

Philosophical or Historical Research

These two types of research do not always appear in listings of categories of research. They are unique in that they generally involve an investigation of information or data already in existence in order to bring out new facts or insights. There is a need for such research, since in building or formulating theory one often finds that a careful examination of current literature may lead to an amalgamation of two or three seemingly different positions that better explains or accounts for behavior previously observed in a number of research studies.

Other areas of research in this category include such diverse activities as the historical survey (e.g., one might trace curriculum change over time and relate this to sociological change) and the development of a hierarchy of skills and concepts based on an analysis of the logical development of mathematical ideas. Note that in the latter activity one can also apply selected statistical and data-gathering techniques to validate the proposed hierarchy; hence, this type of research is not always relegated to subjective assessments based on a search of the literature. Because of the wide range and diverse nature of research activity that can be classified in this category, it is difficult to select an exemplar. It is probably best to indicate that one can find numerous chapters in the yearbooks of the National Council of Teachers of Mathematics that emphasize applications of learning theory to instruction or some "logical" development of curriculum (e.g., see the Thirty-seventh Yearbook, *Mathematics Learning in Early Childhood,* 1975, or the 1976 Yearbook, *Measurement in School Mathematics).*

POTENTIAL CONTRIBUTIONS TO EDUCATIONAL PRACTICE

Much has been written regarding the relative potential of each of the five types of research for making a contribution to educational theory and practice. Such discussions often reflect a bias of the author as to what is important and tend to emphasize philosophical issues or theory as opposed to the practical concerns of the day-to-day activity in the mathematics classroom. Rather than take a position here, it is best to fall back on the opening remarks of this chapter—the researcher must decide what is important and pose a "real" question that is researchable. The type of research to be carried out is then selected on the basis of which type appears to represent the best means for obtaining data relevant to the question. For example, a question of the sequencing of materials *may* be answered best through a review of the historical development of mathematics and the application of task-analysis procedures for identifying prerequisite skills, whereas the question of an optimal teaching strategy—or dialogue "moves" —for teaching mathematical content (building a theory of instruction) *may* lend itself to an experiment. Value judgments should not be made on the relative importance of the different types of research; rather, their importance or value should be determined by the significance, practical or theoretical, of the problem and an indication on the part of the researcher that he or she has considered the alternatives available and can provide a rationale for the approach selected. Hence, although many consider the experiment to be the only effort that deserves the title of "research" and refer to the other types only as evaluation or status descriptions, this is not the position taken here.

As an interesting aside, survey or status studies have often had the greatest *observable* influence on educational practice (note earlier references to the Committee of Seven and the NAEP). This is not bad if such studies are done properly with input on goals and objectives (what is to be assessed) from those most knowledgeable about the place and role of mathematics in our society. Once content is determined, then the question of pedagogy, that is, how to teach something best, becomes a more practical concern. Yet, an overemphasis on content and pedagogy or strategies might well result in the production of a limited base of knowledge that is relevant, or generalizable, only to current practice. We need to know how children learn and what mental structures are developed at different stages (as from psychological studies) as well as how individuals might be expected to react to various stimuli in their environment (as from studies for developing theory).

INTEGRATING RESULTS OF RESEARCH

Before a more detailed look is taken at the research process, it is important to note that, as in most categorization schemes, there always seem to be some examples that do not fit. Rather than attempt to extend the list to include other types of research (e.g., descriptive, action, ex post facto, instrument development or test construction, etc.), it should suffice to note that most of these types generally reflect some, often slight, modification of the five basic types already described. There is, however, a somewhat recent movement toward developing well-defined statistical procedures for extracting knowledge from accumulated studies on a particular topic. This procedure or technique is called a *meta-analysis* (Glass, 1976) and uses the data from a large set of studies to arrive at generalizations. This is quite different both from a mere review of research results (where one is usually concerned only with "significant differences" that are reported in the literature) and from what is called a *secondary analysis* (see Cook, 1974, and Burstein, 1978), which involves a reanalysis of data for the purpose of answering the original research question with alternative statistical techniques or answering new questions with existing data. Secondary analysis requires only that the data from important studies be preserved and made available. Meta-analysis is used

> to refer to the statistical analysis of a large collection of analysis results from individual studies for the purposes of integrating the findings. It connotes a rigorous alternative to the casual, narrative discussions of research studies which typify our attempts to make sense of the rapidly expanding research literature. (Glass, 1976, p. 3)

The research base, that is, the research reported in the literature, is growing at an astounding rate, and in any single area the findings are limited (the term used by Glass is *fragile*). Studies tend to vary in almost confusing irregularity across contexts, subjects, and countless other factors. One need only peruse the literature on, say, class size or ability grouping to experience a feeling of frustration—what do all the results mean? The results defy making a simple summary. As Glass (1976) points out, "Their meaning can no more be grasped in our traditional narrative, discursive review than one can grasp the sense of 500 test scores without the aid of techniques for organizing, depicting, and interrelating data" (p. 4). Hence, there is a need for some formal procedure for analyzing the results. A description of the techniques of meta-analysis is beyond the scope of this chapter; however, the case for this type of research is quite obvious, and the reader is directed to a paper by Glass (1978), "Integrated Findings: The Meta-Analysis of Research," for a more comprehensive treatment of the topic.

SOME CLOSING REMARKS

Each of the foregoing discussions of the five basic types of research included a reference to an exemplar, or classic example; these examples were generally large-scale efforts. Past issues of the NCTM *Journal for Research in Mathematics Education* contain many other good examples of research that are of a less ambitious nature and more in line with typical practice. Four such examples, one for each of the first four types discussed here, are found in chapter 6, "Case Studies." Each of the studies in chapter 6 includes an extended abstract as well as a discussion of what decisions or "trade-offs" were necessary in order to actually conduct the research. These discussions of what actually took place were prepared by the authors of the original published reports.

Chapter 3 considers the steps in the research process as well as an indication of criteria for judging research reports. The reader may wish to read chapters 3 and 6 as a pair, since many of the points identified in the research process are highlighted in the case studies (note that the phrase *case study* as used in chapter 6 is quite different from its use in this chapter as a type of research).

Finally, chapters 4 and 5 provide the reader with background on experimental design. Those chapters contain somewhat technical discussions of the randomized-block design and common problems and errors in planning research and are included for the more serious researcher, or research trainee. They give a more comprehensive picture of "what research is all about."

REFERENCES

Bloom, B. S., Hastings, J. T., & Madaus, G. *Handbook on formative and summative evaluation of student learning.* New York: McGraw-Hill, 1971.

Burstein, L. Secondary analysis: An important resource for educational research and evaluation. *Educational Researcher,* 1978, 7(5), 9–12.

Carpenter, T., Coburn, T. G., Reys, R. E., & Wilson, J. W. *Results from the first mathematics assessment of the National Assessment of Educational Progress.* Reston, Va.: National Council of Teachers of Mathematics, 1978.

Cook, T.D. The potential and limitations of secondary evaluation. In M. S. Apple, M. S. Subkoviak, & J. R. Lufler (Eds.), *Educational evaluation analysis and responsibility.* Berkeley, Calif.: McCutchan, 1974.

Fox, D. J. *The research process in education.* New York: Holt, Rinehart & Winston, 1969.

Glass, G. V. Integrated findings: The meta-analysis of research. *Review of Research in Education,* 1978, 5, 351–379.

Glass, G. V. Primary, secondary, and meta-analysis of research. *Educational Researcher,* 1976, 5 (10), 3–8.

Jackson, P., & Kiesler, S. B. Fundamental research and education. *Educational Researcher,* 1977, 6(8). 13–18.

Johnson, D. A. A pattern for research in the mathematics classroom. *Mathematics Teacher,* 1966, 59, 418–425.

Kantowski, M. G. Processes involved in mathematical problem solving. *Journal for Research in Mathematics Education,* 1977, 8, 163–180.

Kerlinger, F. N. The influence of research on education practice. *Educational Researcher,* 1977, 6(8), 5–12.

Kilpatrick, J., & Wirszup, I. (Eds.). *Problem solving in arithmetic and algebra.* Soviet Studies in the Psychology of Learning and Teaching Mathematics (Vol. 3). Stanford, Calif.: School Mathematics Study Group, 1969. (a)

Kilpatrick, J., & Wirszup, I. (Eds.). *The structure of mathematical abilities.* Soviet Studies in the Psychology of Learning and Teaching Mathematics (Vol. 2). Stanford, Calif.: School Mathematics Study Group, 1969. (b)

Krutetskii, V. A. *The psychology of mathematical abilities in schoolchildren* (J. Kilpatrick & I. Wirszup, Eds.). Chicago: University of Chicago Press, 1976.

National Council of Teachers of Mathematics. *Mathematics learning in early childhood.* Thirty-seventh Yearbook. Reston, Va.: The Council, 1975.

National Council of Teachers of Mathematics. *Measurement in school mathematics.* 1976 Yearbook. Reston, Va.: The Council, 1976.

Osborne, A. R. (Ed.). Critical analyses of the NLSMA reports. Special issue. *Investigations in Mathematics Education,* 1975, *8*(3).

Piaget, J., & Szeminska, A. *The child's conception of number.* New York: Humanities Press, 1952.

Raths, L. E. The grade placement of addition and subtraction of fractions. *Educational Research Bulletin,* 1932, *11,* 29–38. (a)

Raths, L. E. The last word: A reply to Mr. Washburne's "rebuttal." *Educational Research Bulletin,* 1932, *11,* 409–410. (b)

Raths, L. E. Once again: A reply to Mr. Washburne's criticism. *Educational Research Bulletin,* 1932, *11,* 401–405. (c)

Slavin, R. E. Basic vs. applied research: A response. *Educational Researcher,* 1978, *7*(2), 15–17.

Van Engen, H., & Gibb, E. G. *General mental functions associated with division.* Cedar Falls, Iowa: Iowa State Teachers College, 1956.

Walbesser, H. H., & Eisenberg, T. What research competencies for the mathematics educator? *American Mathematical Monthly,* 1971, *78,* 667–673.

Washburne, C. W. The grade placement of arithmetic topics: A "Committee of Seven" investigation. In *Report of the Society's Committee on Arithmetic,* Twenty-ninth Yearbook of the National Society for the Study of Education. Bloomington, Ill.: Public School Publishing Co., 1930.

Washburne, C. W. Arithmetic grade-placement investigations of the Committee of Seven: A reply to Louis E. Raths. *Educational Research Bulletin,* 1932, *11,* 396–401.

Washburne, C. W. The work of the Committee of Seven on grade-placement in arithmetic. In *Child development and the curriculum,* Thirty-eighth Yearbook of the National Society for the Study of Education (part I). Bloomington, Ill.: Public School Publishing Co., 1939.

Washburne, C. W., & Voas, W. H. Rebuttal. *Educational Research Bulletin,* 1932, *11,* 405–409.

3

The Research Process

David C. Johnson
Chelsea College, University of London

BEFORE considering the various stages in the research process, one should reflect on the purposes of research identified in the chapter by Begle and Gibb. These purposes include (a) evaluating instructional procedures, programs, and materials to ascertain their educational benefits; (b) studying individual characteristics—such as cognitive styles, personality, and individual abilities—for the purposes of building theory; (c) improving decision-making models; (d) examining theory; (e) developing educational products; and (f) improving the tools of research. Within these broad areas, research in mathematics education can be categorized according to areas of study. This book includes the categories of cognitive development, skill learning, concept and principle learning, problem solving, individual differences, attitudes, curriculum, teaching, and teacher education.

THE RESEARCHER/SCHOLAR

The prerequisite for being an effective researcher either in the broad areas or within any of their subcategories is having a strong base of knowledge: a knowledge of the literature and experience. Hence one cannot really engage in research until one has become a scholar in a chosen area. This should be quite obvious, but it is important to make the point here; the first stage in the research process is to become familiar with the philosophical as well as the research literature in, say, concept learning or problem solving before selecting a problem and designing a study. Often a research student identifies an area of interest on the basis of reading one or two "interesting" articles. If this is not followed up with an in-depth,

29

comprehensive study of the area, there is a high probability that the research posed will contribute little, if anything at all, to the advancement of knowledge or the development of theory. Such work may well result only in some isolated information and have as its only benefit that it was a "good learning experience" enabling the "researcher" to apply certain techniques learned in graduate courses.

The importance of background knowledge is nicely illustrated both in Fox's (1969, p. 30) three-part listing of the 17 stages of the research process, given below, and in his flow diagram (pp. 26–29), which includes an indication of the outcomes and underlying dynamics for each stage.

Part One: Designing the Research Plan

Stage 1. The initiating idea or need and problem area

Stage 2. The initial review of the literature

Stage 3. Defining the specific research problem

Stage 4. Estimating the success potential of the contemplated research

Stage 5. The second review of the literature

Stage 6. Selecting the research approach

Stage 7. Stating the hypothesis of the research

Stage 8. Selecting the data-gathering methods and techniques

Stage 9. Selecting and developing data-gathering instruments

Stage 10. Designing the data-analysis plan

Stage 11. Designing the data-gathering plan

Stage 12. Identifying the population and invited sample

Stage 13. Pilot studies of the data-gathering approach, method and instruments, and the data-analysis plan

Part Two: Implementing the Research Plan

Stage 14. Implementing the data-gathering plan

Stage 15. Implementing the data-analysis plan

Stage 16. Preparing the research reports

Part Three: Implementing the Results

Stage 17. Dissemination of findings and agitation for action

Note that the first five stages greatly emphasize the need for a thorough knowledge of the problem area. Gathering this knowledge can take weeks, months, or, in some cases, years (and hence the importance for doctoral candidates in mathematics education to establish an area of interest and begin independent study early in their program). If one reads through the chapters of this book, it becomes quite clear that the author/researcher has spent considerable time in becoming familiar with the literature and has selected those articles and reports that provide the basis for further or needed research in order to give a more complete picture of the phenomena under investigation.

Although the first five stages are listed in numerical order, seldom does the researcher complete one stage before going on to the next. There is a continual flow back and forth from stage to stage, and in fact the culmination of the first five stages is the final statement for Stage 3, "defining the specific research problem." It is quite likely that this statement of the problem will go through many alterations or refinements. The critical nature of these early stages is illustrated in the case study reports in chapter 6 of this book (particularly the reports by Nelson and Thornton & LeBlanc).

Theory-related Issues

Inadequate preparation leads to perhaps the most significant shortcoming of much of contemporary research: the lack of adherence to any type of theoretical or conceptual framework to direct the research efforts and to provide a basis for interpreting the results of experimentation. For example, consider research in problem solving. (This discussion and the problem-solving example were contributed by Frank K. Lester, author of a chapter in this book.) With few exceptions, the research in this area conducted by mathematics educators has been generally atheoretical in nature. Shulman and Elstein (1975, p. 12) contend that a substantial portion of the psychological research on problem solving has also been lacking in a theoretical basis.

This condition is understandable, since problem solving is such a complex process and since there is a demand for research that has almost immediate relevance for classroom practice. However, for several reasons mathematics education researchers should give serious attention to the theories of problem solving (or other areas) that are being developed. (The word *theory* is being used rather loosely here to include both developing theories as well as more sophisticated theories. The point is that consideration should be given to some underlying theoretical framework during the conceptualization, conduct, and analysis of a research problem.) First, a theory serves as a means to explain observed phenomena. Second, it enables the researcher to make predictions about as yet unobserved relationships. Third, and possibly most important, a theory structures the conduct of inquiry by guiding the researcher in the process of asking questions, formulating hypotheses, and determining what key variables and relationships to investigate. An example may best illustrate the potential value of having a theoretical orientation to problem-solving research.

The famous matchstick experiment of Gestaltist George Katona (1940) illustrates the usefulness of theory-guided research. Katona was interested in the effects of different methods of instruction on problem-solving performance. Briefly, he presented a configuration of 16 matches, arranged to form five squares, to three different groups of subjects. The task was to reduce the number of squares from five to four by moving only three matches. Each group was then taught a different method of solution. One group was taught a rote solution, another group a logical solution, and a third group an intuitive solution. Katona found that the logical and intuitive groups learned more quickly, had greater retention, and had a higher level of transfer than the rote group.

Simon (1975) has provided an information-processing explanation of Katona's results that is somewhat different from Katona's analysis, which illustrates the use of a theory (or theories) to explain observed phenomena. Simon contends that the rote solution requires learning six facts and that if any one of these facts is forgotten, the solution cannot be completed. Consequently, a little forgetting can cause failure and eliminate any chance for transfer to different but similar tasks. The logical and intuitive solutions, however, require the learning of only one idea, which is applicable to all forms of the matchstick problem. The logical and intuitive solutions are different in that the logical information is stated in terms of a characteristic of the solution, whereas information provided by the intuitive solution requires that an action be taken. Also, the logical solution has a cognitive flavor and refers to a state-space, whereas the intuitive solution has a perceptual flavor and refers to an operations-space.

Simon concludes that

> the students who learned the logical and intuitive solutions "understood" the problem at some level, while those who only learned the rote solution did not. But the experiment warns us also that "understanding" is not necessarily a unitary thing. It may have a cognitive flavor or a perceptual flavor; it may largely involve explaining why something works, or it may involve explaining how to make it work. (p. 9)

Because he had a carefully formulated theoretical basis at his disposal, he was able to make confident interpretations. Without this basis it would have been difficult, if not impossible, for him to provide a logical rationale for his explanations. He would, as is so common in educational research, have had to appeal exclusively to "intuition" and "common sense."

It may be that there is no relevant prevailing theory for a particular issue in mathematics education. Hence it may be necessary to develop new theories. Let it suffice to say that researchers in mathematics education should *first* investigate the adaptability of various psychological theories (or evaluation models or whatever) to the learning and teaching of mathematics, and in the event such adaptation is not feasible, move to the creation of a new theory.

Debate will probably continue on the need for, and value of, having a theoretical orientation to research in mathematics education. However, it is difficult to ignore the fact that although theories are usually eventually modified and sometimes even discarded, the research they generate and the knowledge about the nature of the educational processes they uncover will survive and become incorporated into new, more appropriate theories that will extend our ability to provide a rationale for decisions regarding the teaching and learning of mathematics.

SELECTING A RESEARCH PLAN

As I noted in my earlier chapter, "Types of Research," the researcher, after formulating a precise statement of the research question, must decide what type of research will best provide the information necessary for answering the question. Thus, in addition to acquiring a base of knowledge relative to the context of the proposed area of research, the researcher needs to be familiar with the many aspects of design and analysis—that is, the assumptions and conditions underlying each of the approaches or types of research. This includes a consideration of those special characteristics or critical components unique to each approach.

In deciding on an approach, one must often operate under a number of practical constraints imposed by the available setting or sample. This is not to suggest that such constraints should be used to justify sloppy research but merely acknowledges that this is a very real problem or concern. The researcher should first consider an optimal situation and in this context follow through with Fox's Stages 6–12: Select the research approach, state hypotheses, identify appropriate data-gathering methods and instruments, formulate plans for data gathering and data analysis, and decide on an appropriate population and sample. Then, as the situation warrants, trade-offs can be made to enable the researcher to operate under the conditions imposed by practicality. However, these trade-offs require careful deliberation and consideration to ensure that one does not progress to the point at which results become meaningless because of flaws in the design or the violation of basic assumptions underlying the type of research approach selected. (*Note:* A careful record of these decisions should be kept and appropriate comments and rationale included in the final research report, Stages 16 and 17.)

Two separate and independent dimensions can assist in selecting an approach or type of research. "The first dimension is a kind of time line reflecting whether we believe the answer to the research question is in the past, present, or future. The second dimension is an intent dimension reflecting what we intend to do with the completed research" (Fox, 1969,

p. 45). These dimensions taken together suggest a certain type of approach or type of research (see Table 1).

Table 1
Interaction of Time and Intent Dimensions to Consider
in Selecting the Research Approach

Dimension 2: Intent of Research	Dimension 1: Time in Which Interest Lies		
	Past: Historical	Present: Survey	Future: Experimental
Description	Simple Historical	Simple survey Case study	Single-group experiment
Comparison	Parallel Historical	Multiple-group survey Correlational survey	Multiple-group experiment
Evaluation	Historical and criterion measure	Single-group or multiple-group survey *and* criterion measure	Single-group experiment with criterion measure

Note: Reprinted by permission of the publisher from *The Research Process in Education,* by D. J. Fox (New York: Holt, Rinehart & Winston, 1969), table 1, p. 46. © 1969 by Holt, Rinehart & Winston, Inc.

Table 1 interfaces nicely with the discussion in the chapter "Types of Research," except that evaluation is an "intent" category in Fox's table with a number of alternative evaluation strategies listed across the time dimension. Thus evaluation can be thought of both in terms of intent and as a type of research.

Once the researcher has made the two decisions relative to time and intent, the matrix (time × intent) indicates the approach. Fox (1969) illustrates the utility of this way of selecting an approach with the following examples:

> We wish to generalize about what might happen if we instituted one of the new methods. In the time dimension of [Table 1] this puts us in the column concerned with the future which suggested, therefore, an experimental approach. Moreover, we were interested in learning how each method compared to two other methods. In the intent dimension, this put us in the row for comparative research. In [Table 1], the cell corresponding to the interaction between "future" and "comparison" suggests a multiple-group experiment. This research approach, a multiple-group comparative experiment is consistent with our desire to generalize about the implications of putting one of three methods into practice in the future.
>
> On the other hand, assume we had been interested in showing that the [X] method would guarantee a certain percentage of newly arrived non-English-

speaking Puerto Rican pupils [performing] at grade level within a year of their arrival. In time, we would have still been concerned with the future, but our intent now would be evaluative and this suggests a single-group experiment with a criterion measure or standard. (p. 47)

Assuming one has established time and intent, a number of critical components are still associated with each type of research. Many good references in the area of research design and evaluation provide a fairly comprehensive treatment of the various methodologies (e.g., Ebel, 1969, and Travers, 1973). However, a few of the important points will be mentioned here to illustrate some of the problems and complexities that must be faced.

The Survey

A number of articles and references deal with the role of the survey. Riedesel (1968b) and Romberg (1968) discuss the role of the survey in mathematics education research and note the critical aspects of the selection or development of instruments, the selection of the sampling unit, and the importance of analyzing subscales as opposed to some overall composite score or measure. Sieber (1968) points out the many problems associated with the design of questionnaires and the considerable criticism leveled at poorly designed questionnaires.

Sieber also notes that although many authors of research methodology texts devote considerable space (20 to 30 pages) to a discussion of survey research, the treatment is usually very limited relative to specific procedures and techniques. The researcher whose approach is the survey will probably have to consider a number of sources (references) in order to build a model appropriate for the given situation. A good starting point for one interested in survey research methodology is Herriott's (1969) paper and extensive bibliography in the *Encyclopedia of Educational Research.*

The Experiment

There is no lack of useful information on experimental design and analysis. The characteristics of this particular type of approach to research are described in detail in this book in the chapters by Hummel (who also includes an extensive bibliography) and White. The key features of the experiment include notions of randomization, control, replication, measurement (instrumentation), and data analysis. Hummel points out that randomization is what enables the researcher to attach a probability to the results and make the case for causality. The notions of hypothesis testing and the ability to eliminate alternative hypotheses through good experimental design differentiate the experiment from other approaches (although this does not always hold true, as will be pointed out in the discussion of evaluation research).

Probability and testing hypotheses. One question often asked by teachers and other consumers of research is, "What does it mean to say that a particular '*t* statistic' or '*F* statistic' has $p \leqq .05$, and why does the author of a research paper then go on to discuss 'significant differences' that result in the selection of treatment A as best?' I have found the following discussion helpful in providing some intuitive feeling for the presentations of data analysis given in reports of experimental research.

The experiment involves setting up a straw man in the statement of what is called the *null hypothesis*. The null hypothesis is generally in the form of a statement of equality of means (or no difference in the means) for the different treatment groups—say, treatments A and B:

$$H_o: \mu_A - \mu_B = 0$$

(The Greek letter μ is used to designate the "true" means for the population being sampled and is estimated with the sample means $\bar{x}_A$ and $\bar{x}_B$.) This null hypothesis gives rise to a distribution such that if we were to repeat the experiment a number of times, each time using a random sample of size n for each treatment, we would obtain a number of different values for $(\bar{x}_A - \bar{x}_B)$. Think of flipping a coin 10 times and subtracting the number of heads from the number of tails—and repeating this experiment many times. In addition, we can calculate values for measures of dispersion for each sample (this is called the variance) and combine these to obtain an estimate of the variance of $(\bar{x}_A - \bar{x}_B)$, designated as $s^2(\bar{x}_A - \bar{x}_B)$ or s^2. We now consider the distribution in terms of the variance, that is, the distribution of

$$\frac{\bar{x}_A - \bar{x}_B}{s},$$

which is called the *test statistic*. Note that under the assumption that the null hypothesis is true, the majority of the values of the test statistic will be around zero (the numerator tends to be around zero) with fewer and fewer cases associated with positive or negative differences as we move away from zero on the x-axis. The typical picture of this distribution is the bell-shaped, or *normal*, curve. Depending on the sample size selected, the distribution is more peaked (large samples) or flattened (small samples). Also, if we know the sample size, we can now actually go to a table that gives the area under the curve associated with different values of the test statistic (we can attach a probability to the event of obtaining a difference greater than, or less than, a given value).

Keeping this hypothetical setting in mind, the distribution under the null hypothesis, we proceed to conduct an experiment: selecting our random samples, applying the treatments, and obtaining estimates for μ_A and μ_B

($\bar{x}_A$ and $\bar{x}_B$) and the variance s^2. We then calculate the test statistic for our single experimental event and go to the table to ascertain the probability associated with obtaining such a value (the area under the curve associated with all points exceeding the observed value). If the result is unusual, that is, associated with a low probability, we then *reject the null hypothesis* of equality of means and replace it with an alternative stating that the means are different and the difference favors one of the treatments. Notice that the probability obtained for our experimental result is, in fact, the probability of rejecting the null hypothesis when it is, in fact, true (this is designated as α and is called a Type I error), and of course we want the probability associated with such an error to be small. The idea behind rejecting the null hypothesis is similar to the mathematical notion of *proof by contradiction,* where we assume something that we wish to show false and show that this assumption leads to a contradiction of known information. The idea can be illustrated by considering throwing a die, say, 10 times. If we start with the assumption that all outcomes are equally likely, $p(1) = p(2) = \ldots = p(6) = 1/6$, we can then associate a probability with any given experimental event. Let us say we do the experiment with a given die and obtain a 3 on six of the throws. Using the binomial distribution, we find that under our initial assumption the probability of obtaining six, seven, eight, nine, or ten 3s is .002. Since our actual experimental result is quite unusual, that is, such a result would be expected to occur about 2 times out of 1000, we reject our original assumption of equally likely events and conclude that the die is biased and that the most likely outcome for this particular type of die is a 3.

An understanding of how probability is associated with the experiment is crucial for interpreting results. One often finds the results reported in terms of some predefined *critical value* (e.g., the value of the test statistic associated with, say, a p of .05 or .01 is obtained from the table, and the researcher only then discusses results for which the value obtained from the experiment exceeds this critical value). I prefer the reporting of actual probabilities obtained for each experimental event (e.g., the p may be .08, or .02, or . . .), since this allows the reader to make judgments on the significance of the results. This is particularly important when the results give probabilities between .10 and .05. If the critical values have been predefined, such results may not be reported; yet the reader may feel the research question to be important enough to consider an event with, say, $p \leq .07$ as an unlikely occurrence warranting further discussion or study.

One further point needs discussion under hypothesis testing. This is the discussion of results without associated low probabilities, which, hence, do not lead to the rejection of the null hypothesis. Some authors tend to treat this result of "no significant differences" as proof of equality or "the same as." This is inaccurate and usually unwarranted, since under the initial assumptions one is really only trying to knock down the straw man, and the statistical procedure is established for this purpose. When results do not lead to a rejection of the null hypothesis, the researcher is then caught in a dilemma. Since something different was done to each experimental treatment group, it is reasonable to expect that results should be different; however, it may be that the sample size was too small or the instruments too insensitive to detect a small, but real, difference. This leads to a consideration of *power*. (If we let β be the probability associated with failure to reject a false null hypothesis for a given predetermined difference in the means, called a Type II error, then power is defined as $1 - \beta$.) It is only in a discussion of power that a researcher is able to make statements about the similarity of performance produced by the treatments. The reader is directed to the research methodology literature (e.g., Cohen, 1969) for a more complete discussion of this topic. Suffice it to say at this point that most experiments resulting in failure to reject should stop there and merely report that "differences were not statistically significant."

The Case Study

The case study is unique in its potential for generating hypotheses or useful *detailed* information about learning or the instructional process. The notion of gathering such information using a relatively small number of subjects has great practical appeal in that it avoids many of the practical difficulties encountered in other types of research; for example, the survey and evaluation usually involve gathering data for a large sample, whereas the experiment requires the random assignment of subjects to treatments. However, it needs to be pointed out that although access to subjects may be easier, there is an extremely important and often very time-consuming component in conducting this type of research: that of carefully developing the protocols or procedures to be followed. This step is critical for success in obtaining data that can be interpreted and used to answer the research question. The importance of extreme care in developing procedures and the prior consideration of the wide range of potential problems that might be encountered is nicely illustrated in Gordon and Jester (1973) and in the case study reported by Nelson in this book.

There is no substitute for careful, thorough planning. In addition, the case study inevitably requires many hours of data gathering—time spent by the researcher coding (quantifying or qualifying) direct observation of subjects or in viewing and coding behavior recorded on videotape or audiotape. The protocols referred to above include developing well-defined rules or schemes for both the administration of the tasks and the coding and interpretation of the data. In almost all cases, these procedures must first be tested in a *pilot study* (see later section).

Evaluation

> In many respects the systematic evaluation of curriculum is only beginning to emerge as a recognizable field of educational research. (p. 280)

This statement by Heath appears in the fourth edition of the *Encyclopedia of Educational Research* (see Ebel, 1969). Much has transpired in the last 10 years, and there is now a great deal of pertinent literature, particularly regarding criterion-based assessment and notions of mastery learning. In addition, the formal technologies of evaluation research are continuing to evolve, and the reader is directed to such author/researchers as Michael Scriven, Robert Stake, Daniel Stufflebeam, Benjamin Bloom, Blaine Worthen, William Cooley, and James Popham. Also note the reference to the *Handbook on Formative and Summative Evaluation* by Bloom, Hastings, and Madaus (1971) in chapter 2.

Recent work in curriculum theory includes an emphasis on the development of evaluation schemes or models and applications of inferential statistics (hypothesis testing). Begle and Wilson (1970) in the Sixty-ninth Yearbook of the National Society for the Study of Education describe the achievement model used in the National Longitudinal Study of Mathematical Abilities (NLSMA): a study conducted by the School Mathematics Study Group (SMSG). In particular, the model was designed to enable the research team to classify content along levels of behavior. Wilson (1971) extends the model to include detailed descriptions, with numerous examples for each of the cells in the matrix. This illustrates a critical component of evaluation research—careful attention to outcomes to be assessed—which then considerably simplifies the task of interpreting results.

In addition to determining the outcomes to be assessed (the evaluation model), the researcher must select *appropriate* instruments (see Begle & Wilson, 1970, pp. 390–392) and decide on the techniques of data gathering and data analysis to be employed. In regard to this last point, one might note that the NLSMA study made use of regression analysis techniques to test for differences between groups. To test the effectiveness of alternative methods or materials, the experiment often represents the best approach; however, the constraints are such that one is forced to use intact groups (without randomization) and the statistical procedures for data analysis must be selected accordingly (e.g., see the paper on computing and mathematical problem solving by Johnson & Harding, 1979). Although such an approach may be appropriate, the researcher should note that this may result in a weaker set of assumptions and, hence, reduce the chances of finding significant results. On the other hand, if one is primarily interested in checking to see whether a particular experience or set of experiences produces superior achievement or performance at some specified level within a given period of time (criterion-based assessment), this most certainly lends itself to some sort of comparison using pretest and posttest data.

As is recommended for status studies, the researcher is also advised to consider analyzing subscales, or even items, from the assessment instrument as opposed to some overall composite score. It may well be that the data will suggest certain modifications or improvements in the materials (a formative evaluation model) or indicate that certain sections of one curriculum should be used for some part of the curriculum and sections from another used for the rest (a form of summative evaluation).

Philosophical or Historical Research

The reader interested in this type of research is directed to excellent discussions by Fox (1969, pp. 406–422) and Travers (1969, pp. 378–399). These authors use the terms *historical research* or *historical approach* to encompass most of what was described in chapter 2 as philosophical or historical research. Fox describes this as "past-oriented research which seeks to illuminate a question of current interest by an intensive study of material that already exists. . . the reinterpretation of events in the light of the increased amount of information available" (p. 406). He goes on to make this important point:

> This is critical to realize in planning research using this approach, for good historical research is not simply a massive searching party, but rather a thorough study of all available material by an expert in the discipline, leading to new insights and conclusions.
>
> The good historical researcher must be that rare person, expert enough to be able to encompass all of the known information and interrelate it and yet flexible enough to break the set of preexisting notions so that he can see a new relationship or explanation or finding, if it exists in the data. (p. 406)

A number of important considerations are central to this type of research approach. In particular, considerable emphasis is given to the *validity of inferences and reconstruction* (Travers, 1969, pp. 384–385) and the need for critical evaluation of written documents: authenticity, evaluating the expertise and intent of the original authors, and internal consistency of information (Travers, 1969, pp. 385–388; Fox, 1969, pp. 414–416). Fox lists nine major steps in the research process for this type of approach (p. 416) —a modification of his original 17 stages quoted early in this chapter.

THE PILOT STUDY

Although the necessity for a preliminary trial of the proposed research seems clear, it is also obvious from reading the research reported in the literature that many studies omit this step (Fox's Stage 13). One need only note discussions of limitations or read the reviews in *Investigations in Mathematics Education* to see that many of the studies could have been considerably improved if the design, materials, instruments, or other components had been subjected to some preliminary field testing.

Travers (1969) discusses the rationale for including a pilot study in the research process:

> The selection of a problem for study is not usually undertaken in a single step, for it is commonly necessary to run a preliminary study before the decision is finally made. The need for such a preliminary study does not arise when the problem requires the conduct of a research closely similar to one that has already been done, for it is then known that the research can be undertaken. However, when the field of inquiry is relatively new and does not have available a set of well-developed techniques, a brief feasibility study must almost always be run. Such brief trial runs *demonstrate whether it is practical to undertake the research, whether the available techniques are sufficiently sensitive to measure differences that it is desired to measure, and whether one can obtain the necessary cooperation of others involved in the study* [italics added]. Negative results in only one of these directions may be sufficient to cause the researcher to change his problem. (p. 79)

Note is also made that the pilot study may employ a less sophisticated design and be used to provide valuable information for selecting a final design and data-analysis plan.

INSTRUMENTS

After a problem area has been identified, the selection of an instrument is probably the single most critical component in the design of research. If the instruments selected are not sensitive enough to detect differences or if they are inappropriate to the goals of the research, the research would be better left undone. In fact, the careful selection or design (development) of instruments will often save a study having other flaws.

Riedesel (1968a) makes the point that "rather than the most available test, it is suggested that the researcher carefully consider the goals of the research and then develop and/or analyze tests in light of these goals or objectives" (p. 165). A good illustration of the implementation of such a procedure is give in the Begle and Wilson (1970) discussion of the evaluation model developed for the NLSMA study. Riedesel (1968a) goes on to state that researchers should not

> limit the instruments used for measurement . . . to conventional paper-and-pencil tests. The statement, "I would like to conduct a study of that topic—but it would be impossible to get an answer with a regular test," is often heard. The reply should be, "Develop some kind of instrument appropriate to the study." For example, if the desired outcome of an experimental treatment on teachers

in an in-service education program is to develop their skill in teaching via a "guided discovery" approach, then the researcher needs to develop and use some device for measuring teacher behavior [employing] observations, TV tape recordings, etc. The measurement of the variable must be in keeping with the purpose of the study. (pp. 165–166)

Fox (1969) is even more critical of the problems encountered in selecting proper instrumentation:

This stage of instrument selection or development involves a commitment to the adequacy of the instrument. The author insists that his students understand that once a researcher decides to select an instrument (his own or someone else's) he is committed to that instrument and must be willing to defend it as adequate. Thus if the expected or desired research results are not obtained, he *cannot* blame the instrument. If he has insufficient faith in the instrument and concludes that there is no substantial instrument available for his research, then he should either abandon the project or consider altering the project to an instrument-development project. (p. 55)

Note that the inadequacy of the instrument is often cited in the limitations section of research reports; according to Fox (and me), such a rationalization is inappropriate. This also illustrates the importance of the pilot study.

Numerous good references exist in the area of measurement and measurement theory. See the *Encyclopedia of Educational Research* (Ebel, 1969) for discussions of such topics as achievement tests, measurement theory (including item analysis, reliability, and validity), scores and norms, and test use; each of these sections includes an extensive bibliography. In addition, there are references that identify and describe available tests as well as regional and national research teams who are working on the development of instruments needed for particular research areas or problems. (Note the activities of the various Working Groups associated with the Georgia Center for Teaching and Learning Mathematics at the University of Georgia at Athens, and the paper by Suydam, 1974.)

The design of a new instrument is not an easy task, and the researcher who needs such an instrument might well consider making this the initial thrust of the research. (For the Ph.D. student, this may well be the doctoral study.) The development should include a consideration of item analysis, reliability, and validity and will probably involve the application of a number of statistical techniques (e.g., discrimination or even factor analysis).

For a consideration of the problems associated with measurement and evaluation within a wide range of contexts from teacher effectiveness to course evaluation, as well as a consideration of some special techniques of analysis, the reader is directed to the collection of papers edited by Walberg (1974). This is a good sourcebook of methods, instruments, and examples.

THE RESEARCH REPORT

Parts 2 and 3 of the Fox (1969) model of the research process (Stages 14–17) deal with implementing the research plan and preparing the report. The implementation is generally straightforward except for those unforeseen events (e.g., illness, mix-ups in the administration of treatments or in gathering the data, availability of new, relevant information, etc.) and other changes that are needed on the basis of feedback obtained during the conduct of the study. These problems are illustrated in the case study discussions in chapter 6.

The preparation of the report should be an ongoing activity and, in fact, should have been initiated very early in the process. The researcher should write out the rationale for decisions as they are made while they are fresh (note the suggestion by Grouws in his case study in chapter 6 regarding the importance of keeping a log). The final report should serve two purposes: (a) to describe what was actually done, and (b) to present the results of the research in the context of the specific research problem. In addition, the researcher should attempt to relate these results to what is already known and identify new research that is suggested by the results. The suggestion for replication of good research goes without saying.

The many listings of criteria for judging research can be a good source of information providing direction for preparing the report as well as calling attention to key aspects of each of the stages in design and implementation. J. H. Fox (1958) presents a concise set of statements regarding the criteria of good research and elaborates on each of these with a brief paragraph:

1. The purpose of the research, or the problem involved, should be clearly defined and sharply delineated in terms as unambiguous as possible.
2. The research procedures used should be described in sufficient detail to permit another researcher to repeat the research.
3. The procedural design of the research should be carefully planned to yield results that are as objective as possible.
4. The researcher should report, with complete frankness, flaws in the procedural design and estimate their effect upon the findings.
5. Analysis of the data should be sufficiently adequate to reveal its significance: and the methods of analysis used should be appropriate.
6. Conclusions should be confined to those justified by the data of the research and limited to those for which the data provides an adequate basis. (p. 285)

A more detailed listing of criteria for judging research reports and proposals was prepared by the Research Advisory Committee of the National Council of Teachers of Mathematics (August 1976), and a slightly modified version of this report was published in the *Journal for Research in*

Mathematics Education (Coburn, 1978). I have found the papers by Coburn (1978) and Romberg (1969) and an instrument developed by Suydam (1972) to be particularly useful in a graduate course aimed at interpreting and evaluating research reports: The course goals include an emphasis on developing the skills necessary to be an intelligent consumer of research. The Suydam instrument (and one developed by Kohr for evaluating survey research [Suydam, 1972]) includes a scoring guide enabling one to quantify the results of the evaluations. This guide then provides a basis for group discussion and debate—that is, individuals verbalize and discuss their rationale for differences in scoring.

One final, somewhat mundane but useful suggestion to assist in the preparation of the research report, dissertation, or article is to obtain and follow a style manual. Two standard references in this area are *Form and Style in Thesis Writing* (Campbell, 1969) and the *Publication Manual of the American Psychological Association* (APA, 1974).

THE ERIC CLEARINGHOUSE FOR SCIENCE, MATHEMATICS AND ENVIRONMENTAL EDUCATION

The following material on ERIC was contributed by Marilyn N. Suydam, associate director of ERIC/SMEAC.

The Educational Resources Information Center (ERIC) is a national information system that is actually a network of clearinghouses, each contributing to the collection of materials for a particular educational area. The documents forming the ERIC collection come from a variety of sources, including federally funded research and development projects, school systems and other educational agencies, meetings and conferences, educational journals, and individuals. In the clearinghouses, the information is indexed and abstracted in preparation for listing in one of two ERIC reference publications, *Resources in Education* (RIE) and *Current Index to Journals in Education* (CIJE), both of which are available in most university libraries. Copies of the majority of the documents may be purchased from the ERIC Document Reproduction Service. Besides manual searches of RIE and CIJE, computer searches of the ERIC document base, using specified descriptors or key words, can be conducted through public and commercial agencies.

The center for mathematics education materials is the ERIC Clearinghouse for Science, Mathematics and Environmental Education (ERIC/SMEAC), currently located at Ohio State University. In addition to the documents in the ERIC system, several types of publications are available from ERIC/SMEAC:

1. Bibliographies, including categorized listings of research reports

2. Research reviews on such topics as problem solving

3. Interpretive summaries that attempt to provide an analysis of a body of research with extensive discussion of its meaning and applicability

4. Reports of conferences and working groups, including the reports from the Georgia Center and invited talks on mathematics education sponsored by the Special Interest Group for Research in Mathematics Education

A publication list is available from ERIC/SMEAC (1200 Chambers Rd., Columbus, OH 43212).

A FINAL NOTE

There is no substitute for careful planning. The many hours spent in the early stages of the research process will pay multifold dividends when one implements the plan and ultimately prepares the report. This is a lesson often learned the hard way by the new or inexperienced researcher.

REFERENCES

American Psychological Association. *Publication manual of the American Psychological Association* (2nd ed.). Washington, D.C.: Author, 1974.

Begle, E. G., & Wilson, J. W. Evaluation of mathematics programs. In E. G. Begle (Ed.), *Mathematics education,* Sixty-ninth Yearbook of the National Society for the Study of Education, pp. 367–404. Chicago: University of Chicago Press, 1970.

Campbell, W. G. *Form and style in thesis writing* (3rd ed.). Boston: Houghton Mifflin, 1969.

Coburn, T. G. Criteria for judging research reports and proposals. *Journal for Research in Mathematics Education,* 1978, *9,* 75–78.

Cohen, J. *Statistical power analysis for the behavioral sciences.* New York: Academic Press, 1969.

Ebel, R. L. (Ed.). *Encyclopedia of educational research* (4th ed.). American Educational Research Association project. New York: Macmillan, 1969.

Fox, D. J. *The research process in education.* New York: Holt, Rinehart & Winston, 1969.

Fox, J. H. Criteria of good research. *Phi Delta Kappan,* 1958, *39,* 284–286.

Gordon, I. J., & Jester, R. E. Techniques of observing teaching in early childhood and outcomes of particular procedures. In R. M. W. Travers (Ed.), *Second handbook of research on teaching.* American Educational Research Association project. Skokie, Ill.: Rand McNally, 1973.

Herriott, R. E. Survey research method. In R. L. Ebel (Ed.), *Encyclopedia of educational research* (4th ed.), pp. 1400–1410. American Educational Research Association project. New York: Macmillan, 1969.

Johnson, D. C., & Harding, R. D. University level computing and mathematical problem-solving ability. *Journal for Research in Mathematics Education,* 1979, *10,* 37–55.

Katona, G. *Organizing and memorizing.* New York: Columbia University Press, 1940.

Riedesel, C. A. Some comments on developing proper instrumentation for research studies in mathematics. *Arithmetic Teacher*, 1968, *15*, 165–168. (a)

Riedesel, C. A. Survey research in elementary school mathematics. *Arithmetic Teacher*, 1968, *15*, 260–263. (b)

Romberg, T. A. Survey research: Guidelines for status studies. *Arithmetic Teacher*, 1968, *15*, 639–641.

Romberg, T. A. Criteria for evaluating educational research. *Investigations in Mathematics Education*, 1969, *2*, x–xi.

Shulman, L. S., & Elstein, H. S. Studies of problem solving, judgment, and decision making: Implications for educational research. In F. N. Kerlinger (Ed.), *Review of research in education* (Vol. 3), pp. 3–42. Itasca, Ill.: Peacock Publishers, 1975.

Sieber, S. D. Survey research in education: The case of the misconstrued technique. *Phi Delta Kappan*, 1968, *49*, 273–276.

Simon, H. A. Learning with understanding. In H. A. Simon (Ed.), *Mathematics education report*. Columbus, Ohio: ERIC Information Analysis Center for Science, Mathematics, and Environmental Education, 1975.

Suydam, M. N. Instrument for evaluating experimental research reports. In *Annotated compilation of research on secondary school mathematics, 1930–1970* (Vol. 1). Final Report, USOE Grant No. OEG-3-71-0085. University Park, Pa.: Pennsylvania State University, 1972. (ERIC Document Reproduction Service No. ED 062 165)

Suydam, M. N. *Unpublished instruments for evaluation in mathematics education.* Columbus, Ohio: ERIC Information Analysis Center for Science, Mathematics, and Environmental Education, 1974.

Travers, R. M. W. *An introduction to educational research* (3rd ed.). New York: Macmillan, 1969.

Travers, R. M. W. (Ed.). *Second handbook of research on teaching.* American Educational Research Association project. Skokie, Ill.: Rand McNally, 1973.

Walberg, H. J. (Ed.). *Evaluating educational performance.* Berkeley, Calif.: McCutchan, 1974.

Wilson, J. W. Evaluation of learning in secondary school mathematics. In B. S. Bloom, J. T. Hastings, & G. Madaus (Eds.), *Handbook on formative and summative evaluation of student learning*, pp. 643–696. New York: McGraw-Hill, 1971.

4

Avoiding Errors
in Educational Research

Arthur L. White

Ohio State University

VALID results can come from research in education only if the researcher has a persistent commitment to the understanding of learning and to the improvement of education. This commitment needs to be expressed in careful thought and meticulous attention to detail throughout the research process. The behavioral sciences have many problems in identifying the relationships between and among variables because they are so many in number and so complex. These relationships are difficult to discover, understand, and explain even when our methods, procedures, measurements, sampling, and analyses are all free from error; when the research efforts are plagued with avoidable errors, the probability of reaching valid conclusions goes down appreciably.

There are many errors to be made. Some are more common than others, some are more serious than others, and some are more easily avoided than others. The following section includes descriptions of errors, discussion on how to avoid them, and references to resources where further information can be found.

Error: Failing to identify the population from which the sample will be drawn

---

Drawing valid inferences from the statistical treatment of data is highly dependent on the sampling procedures used. The degree to which a sample represents the population directly influences the validity of any statements about the relationships between variables for the population.

Before a plan for sampling can be prepared, it is necessary to clearly identify the intended population. A rule should be written for categorizing individuals or elements as belonging or not belonging to the population. The principles of random selection require that all elements of the population have equal probability of being selected. If all the elements of the population are not identifiable, it is difficult to assure equal probability of selection.

If a research question is to be dealt with by conducting a survey of the public secondary mathematics teachers in the United States, then a number of questions concerning the definition of this population should be resolved. For instance:

- What conditions must be met for a school to be considered "public"?
- What grade levels are considered to be secondary?
- What percentage of a teacher's load should be in mathematics for that teacher to be included?
- Should part-time teachers be included?

Differences in resolving these and many other such questions will result in considerably different populations.

In a description and discussion of research activities in education, the term *population* is sometimes interpreted to refer to the subjects or people from which information is obtained. A more general interpretation, however, can be very helpful in organizing, thinking through, and consequently improving the design of research. The population should be thought of as the universe of persons, activities, events, or items from which a selection is made and to which generalizations are to be made. As we decide on questions for a survey or items for a criterion measure, we are in fact picking a sample of questions or items to *represent* a population or universe of information. As we select treatment conditions for experimental research, we must decide what treatments will be used out of all the possible treatments. Unfortunately, much of the research in education does not include the attention and care to the identification, description, and definition of the universe from which subjects, criterion measures, and treatments are drawn; consequently, it is difficult to replicate the work or to determine adequately how the population of subjects, treatments, or criteria represented by the sample actually differs from, or compares to, others. At a conference at the University of Georgia in 1975, Richard Turner stated that attention to the taxonomies of the universes of subjects, treatments, and criteria would help in the understanding and more accurate explication of research efforts in mathematics education.

> *Error:*   Making the sample too large or too small

The question of how many subjects should be selected for the research project needs careful attention. The first concern in deciding on this number is the type of inferences to be drawn from the data. Basically, three levels of inferences are to be desired:

Level 1. Descriptive statistics from the sample used to make inferences about the corresponding descriptive parameters of a population (such as frequencies, means, and standard deviations)

Level 2. Measures of association—that is, correlation coefficients computed from a sample used to make inferences about the relationships among variables in the population

Level 3. Measures of cause-and-effect relationships from a controlled experimental study used to make inferences about cause and effect in the population

For the descriptive inferences, the larger the randomly selected sample the more representative the sample is of the intended population and the more confidence we can place in the sample statistics as estimators of the population characteristics. It may be more economical to determine what variability is acceptable and to calculate the sample size needed to achieve the desired precision. These procedures can be found in Hansen, Hurwitz, and Madow (1956, pp. 126–129).

For inferences involving such measures of association as correlation coefficients, the calculation of the optimal sample size is more critical. It is possible to obtain too large a sample. In making inferences concerning the relationship among variables, calculate the number of subjects needed to measure the variables at the desired confidence interval or precision for the variables. Since the significance of measures of association is a function of sample size, it is possible to get a statistically significant correlation between two variables when the strength of the relationship is too small to be useful. A correlation of .15 may be statistically insignificant with 50 observations on each variable but statistically significant at the .001 level when 500 pairs of observations are used to compute the statistic. In both situations the strength of the relationship, and consequently its usefulness, may be inconsequential.

Likewise, it is possible (and quite common) for researchers to make inferences about relationships among variables with data gathered from samples that are too small. Data from a sample of $n = 10$ allows a Pearson correlation coefficient to range from $+.63$ to $-.63$ and still be considered zero at the 95% confidence level. With a sample of $n = 30$, the 95% limits are $\pm.36$. These ranges emphasize the fluctuation, or instability, that occurs when inferences concerning relationships among variables and prediction equations are made from small samples.

The question, then, becomes "What sample size is optimum for these purposes?'' The researcher must first come to grips with the question "What degree of association between the two variables will have implications that are educationally interesting or significant?'' This question cannot be answered without a knowledge of the variables under consideration. Thought must be given to the potential application of the results. Information concerning applications comes from results of previous reports, pilot studies using the response measure, judgments from the field concerning educationally significant effect size, and the consequences of making Type I or Type II errors. Without the knowledge of previous and potential applications, there is no rational way to estimate the required or optimum sample size for a study. In addition to the degree of association, other things must be specified:

- Acceptable Type I error rate (α level)
- Acceptable power for the degree of association selected

The use of these factors for calculating the needed sample size can be found in Hays (1973, pp. 422–424) and in Cohen and Cohen (1975, pp. 54–55). These procedures will assist the researcher in selecting a sample size large enough to detect reasonably strong associations but small enough to avoid identifying trivial (or weak) associations as significant.

In controlled experimental design research the optimal sample size must be determined in terms of the smallest unit of the design (cell) for which statements of inference and generalizability are to be generated. The size of these units influences the generalizability of the analysis as well as the power of the statistical procedures used. The ability to detect group or cell differences is directly influenced by the number of units in each cell.

Computations for selecting the desired sample size for experimental studies are based on the same principle as for inferences involving measures of association. The experimenter must have some notion of the strength of effect that he or she wants to be sure to detect. A great deal of preliminary study, pilot research, and careful planning is necessary for the optimum application of statistical procedures.

To determine the optimal sample size for experimental designs, the procedures by Hays (1973) are appropriate. In addition, Timm (1975, pp. 145–146) and Cohen and Cohen (1975, pp. 144–155) provide information relevant to computing the power of a test that is directly applicable to determining the needed sample size. Also included in Timm are power tables (appendix, Table 5, pp. 596–603). Required are estimates of—

- effect size represented as differences between means of the cells for which inferences are to be made;
- acceptable Type I error rate (α level);
- acceptable power for detecting specified effect size;
- estimate of population variance.

> *Error:* Stating that no differences exist as a result of a *no significant difference* result on a statistical test

Only limited conclusions can be drawn from a statistical test resulting in *no significant difference.* It is reasonable to claim that under the conditions of the study one has found no evidence of difference, but this is by no means conclusive. There is no accompanying statement of probability of error as there is when a significant difference is detected. One approach to improve the interpretation of a study yielding a result of *no significant difference* is to report the power of the test. A statement of the probability of identifying differences of a predetermined size as significant can be included. The power of the test tells the reader what the chances were of detecting an educationally significant difference.

> *Error:* Using procedures that result in a biased sample

To many, *randomness* is not a familiar concept, and the processes for ensuring the random selection of a sample are even more foreign. If a researcher were to ask the principal or a teacher of a public school to randomly select students for a research study, they might well proceed by asking for a show of hands and then selecting the students needed "at random" from the volunteers. First of all, the students who raise their hands become a sample from a population different from the intended population. Selecting a sample from volunteers considerably limits the generalizability. Secondly, the "at random" selection was most likely a process of picking students whose hands were eagerly waving or who were known by the principal or teacher for their cooperation or for some other conscious or subconscious reason. Even though no apparent or known bias enters into the way a sample is drawn, it is not a randomly selected sample until the procedures are such that *every* member of the population has the same probability of being selected. In practice, even with the best procedures and the greatest care, events occur that introduce conditions rendering an absolutely random selection difficult to accomplish. The statistical inferences include statements of probability representing the levels of error that can be expected. All these probabilities are dependent on the independence and normality of the distribution obtained by the randomness of the selected sample. Biased sampling will require analyses plagued with patchwork procedures and compensations that cast doubt on the results. Because of the importance of randomization to the generalizability of results and to the validity of the statistical procedures, careful and persistent attention to this phase of the research process is crucial.

A variety of valid procedures for random selection are particularly applicable to survey research. All of them depend on the initial identification of the elements of the population. After identifying all elements of the population, list and number them. The ordering makes no difference, but it is necessary that all elements of the population appear on the list.

The random number table is the most common system used by researchers for random selection. A review of the procedures for using a random number table can be found in many basic statistics books that are currently available (Hopkins & Glass, 1978, pp. 186–187, 406–407; Minium, 1978, pp. 243–244, 547–548). These procedures assure that the selection of a sample is relatively free of bias and make it possible to generalize the findings to the population sampled with an accurate specification of the error.

> *Error:*   Basing the research findings on response from only
>   a portion of the elements sampled

It is not uncommon to hear the following comment in regard to a survey research study: "We should send out 300 questionnaires so we can be confident of getting at least 100 responses." If you obtain responses from only a portion of the sample (in this example, one-third of your randomly selected sample), then your results are no longer free of bias. The generalizations to be made are relevant only to the population represented by those who responded, and the probability of errors for any inferences is no longer known. Too often the results of a survey to which only a portion of the sample has responded are used to set policy and determine the educational program as though the results were a valid representation of the population sampled.

Time, money, and other resources should be used in getting the responses from all elements that are randomly selected from the population. A common practice in survey research is to sample the nonrespondents and make follow-up mailings and phone calls to determine how the nonrespondents differ from the respondents. A follow-up study of the nonrespondents is, at best, an inadequate substitute for a 95%–100% return. The researcher should draw a smaller sample and reduce the amount of information solicited, using resources to make more personal contact and to provide varied and attractive incentives for subjects to respond. Procedures and suggestions for improving survey response rates are provided by Berdie and Anderson (1975, pp. 255–257) and Berdie (1973, pp. 278–280).

> *Error:*   Failing to assign the subjects randomly to treatment
>   groups

In experimental research designs it is rarely possible to obtain a list of all the individuals in the intended population. Experimental research is generally designed to study relationships among variables. It is generally expected that the relationships discovered will have implication for a very broad population, often including individuals not yet born. Under these conditions it is obviously impossible to obtain a listing of *all* the elements of the population.

The individuals in the sample should be randomly assigned to the different treatment conditions. The probabilities for each individual in the sample being assigned to each treatment group should be equal. The unbiased assignment of the individuals to the treatment groups is critical.

A table of random numbers should be used. Obtain a list of the subjects selected and number them sequentially. If the task is to assign subjects randomly to three treatment groups, then assign the subject represented by the first random number to Group 1, the second random number to Group 2, and the third random number to Group 3. Repeat, assigning the fourth number to Group 1, the fifth to Group 2, the sixth to Group 3, and so on, until all the subjects have been assigned. If a number is drawn more than once, that subject should remain in the group to which he or she was originally assigned and another random number selected. For experiments with more than three treatment groups (or less than three), a similar procedure should be used.

> *Error:* Failing to provide in the sampling for different effects of the treatment for different groups of subjects

Many phenomena in education—in fact, most—are complex systems with more than one factor having a functional relationship with the outcome variables. Often an important correlate, a variable expected to influence the effectiveness of a treatment, may be appropriately used to structure the sampling procedure systematically. If the influence of a treatment is expected to differ depending on the subjects' ability in mathematics, it may be advantageous to block on ability. That is to say, the random assignment of elements to treatments would be done within different ability levels. The procedure would be to subdivide the population into strata of ability levels and randomly assign the elements to treatment conditions for each level of ability. This would help ensure that the characteristics of subjects for each ability were randomly assigned, with no systematic bias for any treatment level. Advantages go beyond the ability to generalize to more specific subpopulations and include advantages of increased power and the potential for finding interactive effects between the blocking or grouping variables and the treatment variables. A more elaborate discus-

sion of blocking is included in chapter 5. It should be emphasized that for
the purpose of making causal inferences for the treatment effects on the
groups resulting from blocking, the subjects must be randomly assigned *by*
levels of the blocking variable to the treatment conditions before the treatments begin. To accomplish this, it is necessary to collect data for classifying the subjects into blocks or strata prior to beginning the treatments. The
subjects in each of those blocks can then be assigned to treatment groups
in the manner described earlier.

It is not uncommon to read reports in the literature in which the subjects
were randomly assigned to treatments and then, after the treatment was
completed, a blocking variable was identified and the sample divided into
high, medium, and *low* for purposes of using a factorial analysis of variance
to analyze the data. This process is highly dependent on the distribution
of the subjects in the original sampling and rarely provides an equal number of subjects for each treatment at each blocking level. The dividing
scores for high, medium, and low are often determined as a function of the
resulting cell sizes rather than as a rational reflection of the nature of the
construct represented by the blocking variable. The meaning of high,
medium, and low will be relevant to the sample and may or may not be
representative of the high, medium, and low of the population.

Error: Treating a group's pretest score as though it were
comparable to the group's posttest score when the
composition of the group has changed

It is necessary to identify subjects who responded to *both* a pretest and a
posttest before making statistical comparisons. If changes are detected and
the composition of a group is not consistent from pretesting to posttesting,
then it cannot be determined if the changes are due to the treatment or to
the different characteristics of the subjects responding.

Error: Failing to use a criterion instrument having a sufficiently high reliability

---

A large portion of the "noise" in educational research comes as a result
of poor measures of the response variables. A test with low reliability, such
as .6, has a large portion of resulting unsystematic error variance. The
standard error of measurement will be approximately 80% of the standard
deviation of the measure with a reliability of .6. The measurement source
of error variance will inflate the error term used for statistical tests of sig-

nificance. For instance, if an IQ measure with a standard deviation of 15 and a reliability of .6 were used as a criterion measure, then an individual with an observed score of 100 would have a true score ranging as low as 76 and as high as 124 at the 95% level of confidence. A lack of precision seriously depreciates the power of a statistical test.

To improve these measures, researchers should pilot *all* instruments with a sample of subjects from the population of concern in the research. Samples should be large enough for homogeneity, discrimination contribution, and item difficulty to be studied. It is advisable to carry out the instrument development analyses on samples of at least 50–100 subjects so that procedures such as factor analysis can be used. When smaller samples are used, the clusters of items are seriously influenced by the idiosyncrasies of the sample subjects or subtests and may not reflect the nature of the criteria when used with the population under consideration.

Procedures for factor analysis, along with some discussion of the analysis options, are included in the Statistical Package for Social Sciences (SPSS) by Nie, Hull, Jenkins, Steinbrenner, and Bent (1975, pp. 468–514). For the development of most instruments, a factor-analysis solution with the following options is appropriate:

1. Use the multiple correlation coefficients squared on the diagonal as the communality estimates.

2. Use varimax, an orthogonal rotation, to achieve simple structure.

3. Choose the number of factors to be rotated by considering the following:

    a) number of factors not more than one-third of the number of variables

    b) factors to be rotated should have eigenvalues of 1 or more

    c) number of factors indicated by using the scree method described by Cattell (1966, pp. 206–211)

The researcher must combine the statistical guidelines, along with other a priori information concerning the items and the relative interpretability of the factors, to decide on the factor solution to be used. This process, when combined with good selection and development of criterion items, can result in the identification of one or more homogeneous groups of items and will contribute a great deal to the reliability and construct validity of the criterion measures.

Error: Reporting the reliability for an overall test but presenting the results in terms of subtest scores for which no reliability is reported

---

It should be remembered that the items making up the scores for which inferences and interpretations are made should have reliability information. If subtest scores are to be reported, then also report reliabilities for the subtests as well as for the overall scores.

In pilot studies where instruments are tried and subjected to item analysis, factor analysis, and other multivariate data reduction procedures (such as multiple regression and multidimensional scaling), data reduction techniques tend to result in much more relevant, precise, and stable measurement of response variables.

The selection and application of statistical procedures for the analysis of data require a number of decisions based on the sampling of subjects, the design of the study, and the nature of the response variables. The common errors in the statistical treatment of data in educational research generally fall into two major categories:

Category I. Design and analysis procedures that do not maximize the probability of detecting differences or relationships that exist (power)

Category II. Design and analysis procedures that do not preserve the validity of the probability statements concerning Type I errors

Let us deal first with those errors that fall in Category I.

ERRORS IN CATEGORY I

> *Error:* Selecting the sample size too small to result in a reasonable expectation of finding existing differences

As noted earlier, attention to sample size must be given before the data are collected.

> *Error:* Failing to use the interactive effects of variables in making predictions or looking for treatment effects

There are several remedies for this particular error. Five of the common remedies are discussed in the following sections.

Multiple Correlation Techniques

Multiple correlation techniques can be used to combine sets of variables as predictors of a response variable. Including the interrelationship of the predictors may result in more power in predicting the response variable and, consequently, the potential for accounting for more variance. Collections of computer programs are available for calculating multiple and stepwise multiple linear regression equations for the optimum prediction of criterion variables by a set of independent variables. Sources of computer programs for these purposes include the Statistical Package for the Social Sciences (SPSS) by Nie et al. (1975) and Biomedical Computer Programs (BMD), edited by Dixon (1973). Often a combination of two or more individual variables yields much more predictive information than any of the individual variables does separately, and therefore the prediction has a higher probability of being valid.

Blocking

Blocking using variables identified from previous research as being highly correlated with the response variables helps to identify variance that may not otherwise be distinguishable from error variance. The identification and separation of variance due to the blocking variable reduces the error variance of the inferential statistic and may improve the probability of identifying effects due to the treatment conditions. Blocking should be a priori and should be incorporated into the sampling procedure. Every effort should be made to have equal cell sizes, since the analyses are generally not seriously affected by violating assumptions of normality and equal variance when cell sizes are equal. Further elaboration of the effects of unequal cells can be found in Glass and Stanley (1970, pp. 368–376).

Analysis of Covariance

Analysis of covariance is another procedure that can be used to increase the power of a statistical test. A variable or variables correlated highly with the response variables can be used to reduce the variability in the transformed response variable. The relationship between a covariate and a response variable is used to identify a regression equation. From the regression equation the variability in the response variable, which can be predicted from a knowledge of the covariate, can be removed from the total variability. Analysis of covariance tends to reduce the unidentified or error variance resulting in more power for the calculation of the F-ratio test of significance. It is important that the covariate be identified prior to the study. As is the case for the usual statistical inference tests, the researcher should recognize the importance of random assignment to treatments when using analysis of covariance.

The following guidelines should be used in the analysis of covariance:

1. The correlation of the covariate and the response variable should be statistically and educationally significant.
2. The covariate should have a high reliability.

3. The covariate should be a variable that is measured prior to any portions of the treatments.

4. The conditions of homogeneity of regression should be met. The slopes of the regression lines describing the linear relationships of the criterion variable and the covariate from cell to cell must not be statistically different.

5. All follow-up procedures for significant interaction or post hoc comparisons should be made with the adjusted cell or adjusted marginal means.

The analysis of covariance is a transformation of the raw scores to a new set of scores adjusted for the effects of the covariate. Conceptually the new set of adjusted scores becomes the data for an analysis of variance. Therefore the means for the adjusted scores are the referents for any differences detected. The analysis of covariance is often used in an attempt to compensate for not having made a random assignment of subjects to groups. The analysis of covariance is, at best, inadequate to compensate for the lack of random assignment but is commonly used this way. At times there may be no other viable alternative for analysis, but the interpretations can be highly misleading and generalizations should not be made.

Repeated-Measures Analyses

Repeated measures and t tests for dependent groups are analysis procedures that allow for the identification of individual subject differences. The variability due to individual differences from one testing time to another can be identified and separated from the residual variance for computing the F ratio of analysis of variance. The resulting benefit may be an increase in the power of the statistical tests. Trend analysis techniques can also be applied to detect patterns of change over time. Trend analysis procedures are described by Winer (1971, pp. 296–300) and Glass, Willson, and Gottman (1975, pp. 1–19). When the observations are expected to be correlated over time, as they would be when the same individuals are repeatedly tested, repeated measures analysis procedures assist the researcher in capitalizing on this dependence. When the number of subjects in each cell is small, additional power can often be obtained by collecting response variable measures over time.

Multivariate Procedures

Multivariate procedures can be used to detect complex influences of treatments on a set of response variables. In studies where several response variables have been measured, it may be that no single variable shows a statistically or educationally significant effect but that a consistent trend involving a number of variables might be significant. Multivariate analysis of variance procedures specifically include the correlation of the response variables in testing for differences among groups. If there is a "hidden" interactive effect in the response variables that helps to discriminate subjects in one treatment group from subjects in another treatment group, multivariate methods will help in the detection and interpretation of the differences. Discussion of these procedures can be found in Tatsuoka (1970, pp. 1–38), and computer programs are available in the SPSS, BMD series (Dixon, 1973), Clyde (1969), and other computer program packages.

> *Error:* Failing to use a priori information effectively to formulate the hypotheses

For t tests, for univariate analysis of variance, and for correlation, a priori hypotheses should be made in studies when the researcher has a pretty good idea of what he or she expects to happen. More power can be obtained than from the nondirectional tests or the post hoc comparison tests.

In many research questions, the expectations for the results are that the response variables and the treatment variables are either positively related or not related at all. If any effects are expected to occur, they will be detected by higher scores for the experimental group. Under these conditions, when dealing with two groups, the researcher should make such a statement of the expected results before collecting the data and should use directional tests of significance. These directional tests are commonly referred to as one-tailed tests.

A priori information should also be used with correlational hypotheses. If the researcher can expect to obtain from a priori information either positive or zero correlations between variables, then a one-tailed test of significance can and should be used to increase the probability of detecting a statistically significant difference. The power of the test is increased, since all Type I errors will occur at one end of the distribution and increase the probability of rejecting the null hypothesis. Remember that the educational significance must also be considered. A directional test allows a researcher to claim statistical significance for coefficients that are smaller than the correlation coefficients claimed as significant with nondirectional tests. If the correlation coefficient is squared (r^2), this indicates the strength of the relationship and represents the proportion of the variability that can be predicted by knowing the scores for other variables. A good look at the r^2 statistic can be used to decide if a relationship is strong enough to be useful.

In experimental studies where more than two treatment levels are used, it may be appropriate to use a set of orthogonal comparisons for detecting the important differences. A discussion of a priori orthogonal comparisons can be found in Winer (1971, pp. 172–177).

ERRORS IN CATEGORY II

Now we are ready to consider the second category of errors—those resulting from design and analysis procedures that do not preserve the validity of the probability statements concerning Type I errors.

> *Error:* Failing to include in the level of significance used for interpreting correlation coefficients the proper corrections for having computed several correlations involving a common variable from the same sample

In correlation studies a major error comes from calculating a matrix of correlation coefficients and considering each coefficient separately as though it were independent of all the rest. Assuming independence is not valid when all the variables are collected from the same sample. Probably the most attractive way to help deal with this problem is to reduce the number of variables to the "really important ones." This task can be facilitated by reviewing previous research in the area as a guide to what variables have potential usefulness. An empirical approach can be taken by using variable-reduction techniques such as stepwise regression, cluster analysis, multidimensional scaling, principal components, or factor analysis. Other techniques, such as canonical correlation and classification analysis, can also be used. These procedures can be found in Tatsuoka (1971).

In situations where the number of variables is greater than two, the Type I error rate can be projected by imposing a more stringent critical value depending on the number of correlations considered. The correction for making k significance tests can be made as follows:

$$\text{Actual Type I error} = 1 - (1 - \alpha)^k$$

where α is the probability level needed to result in the desired actual Type I error rate and k is the number of significance tests made or, in the case of correlation coefficients, the number of correlation coefficients under consideration. For instance, if I have computed two correlation coefficients and desire an actual Type I error of .05, then I would need to use the tabled value in a correlation coefficient significance table of approximately $\alpha = .025$. Roughly, the alpha level needed to enter the significance table will be $1/k$ times the desired actual level.

> *Error:* Testing for differences in an experiment by using a series of univariate F tests when a multivariate test of significance is appropriate

In the analysis of experimental studies, the Type I error rate can be protected by combining response variables so that one significance test on the combined variables can be used instead of multiple significance tests.

A number of techniques can be used. Response variables can be combined by various linear combination techniques. A commonly employed technique for experimental studies is the multivariate analysis of variance, which results in a weighting for each response variable. The weights are used along with the original scores on each variable to compute a new variable. The new variable is a linear combination of the original variables. The weights are determined so that the resulting linear combination will give the maximum discrimination between treatment groups. When there are two treatment groups, the linear combination will be the multiple linear regression equation for predicting whether the subject was in the treatment group or not.

Multivariate analysis serves two major purposes: (a) It combines the response variables into one variate so that one test of statistical significance can be computed, therefore preserving the alpha level; and (b) it incorporates interactive effects among the variables that may be useful in detecting and interpreting group differences. The follow-up interpretive procedures include looking at the standardized weights of each variable in the discriminant function as well as looking at the correlation of the individual scores on each original variable with their discriminant function score (Tatsuoka, 1970, pp. 38-55).

Error: Looking for pairwise differences between groups by
      doing a series of *t* tests

In univariate or single-response variable analyses, the identification of the group differences should be by appropriate a priori or post hoc multiple comparison procedures. It is not appropriate to do pairwise comparisons between groups when more than two groups are involved without appropriate adjustments to protect Type I error. The more appropriate pairwise comparisons and procedures for these comparisons can be found in Glass and Stanley (1970, pp. 381-397).

Error: Repeating *F* tests using different grouping variables
      on the same sample

Another error in analysis that inflates the alpha error rate is the repeated use of the response variables using different grouping variables. For instance, if ability and sex are grouping variables to be included in an analysis for the effect of treatment conditions, it is inappropriate to do a two-way analysis of ability by treatment and then another two-way analysis of sex by treatment. The appropriate procedure would be a three-way analysis of ability by sex by treatment. In addition to preserving the Type I error, the factorial analysis of variance generally provides more power by partitioning variance due to ability, sex, and ability by sex interaction. The factorial analysis tends to reduce the error variance of the F ratio and may increase power.

The last three errors are related to experimental design, violation of assumptions, and research reporting.

> *Error:* Interpreting changes due to regression toward the mean as treatment effects

Studies that use a pretest score to block the sample into high and low and then use the same test as a posttest may produce results that are confounded by regression toward the mean. When a test is given to a group, individuals who score the highest and those who score the lowest will tend to score closer to the mean the next time they take the test simply because the high and low scores are influenced by chance. They are more likely to have been influenced by chance than those near the mean. For instance, if an experiment were conducted for the purpose of testing a safety program for reducing highway deaths, regression could become a confounding factor. If the states having the highest accident and death rates were chosen for the experimental group and the other states were used as the control group, the effects of regression would confound the results. Those states with the highest death rate for the previous year were undoubtedly highest partly because of chance; therefore the death rate for that state the following year would be expected to be lower even if no safety program were in effect.

To avoid regression toward the mean, be sure that extremes, high or low, are equally probable in treatment and control groups. Further discussion of the regression toward the mean effect can be found in Hopkins and Glass (1978, pp. 167–169).

> *Error:* Violating assumptions for the use of parametric statistics

The major concerns for violating those assumptions required for analysis of variance can be minimized by having equal cell sizes. Equal cell size is highly recommended even to the point of randomly discarding cases from cells that have more than the minimum found in any one cell. The resulting overall sample size and the number of cases for each cell must be considered when decisions are made to discard cases. Be reasonable.

The three assumptions that follow are frequently related to errors in educational research.

Homogeneity of variance. With unequal cell sizes, violations of homogeneity of variance have the following effects:

1. When the cells with larger *n* have the greater variance, the actual Type I error is less than the intended Type I error. Therefore the test is conservative, and some differences may not be detected.

2. When the cells with the larger *n* have the lesser variance, then the Type I error is inflated, and some detected differences may not be valid. The relationship of cell size to variance should be considered in interpretations.

Homogeneity of regression. The violation of the assumption of homogeneity of regression for analysis of covariance has serious consequences. Lack of homogeneity of regression means that the relationship between the covariate and the response variable is not consistent from one cell to the next, and hence the adjusted scores will not be valid. Without homogeneity of regression, analysis of covariance should be avoided. In research reports using analysis of covariance, the results of a test for homogeneity of regression should always be included.

Independence. The analysis of variance assumes that the error scores between subjects are independent. It is therefore inappropriate to analyze the individual observations of student scores from an intact class group as though they were independent observations. Students will be influenced by one another and by the teacher; therefore, it is not reasonable to assume independence. When intact classes are assigned to treatments, the sample unit is the class and therefore the unit of analysis should be the class. It is then necessary to have more than one class for each treatment level if estimates of error and statistical comparisons are to be made. When the class is the unit of analysis, the group means become the response variables and are the data points for the analysis.

Error: Omitting important information from the report

It is important to include enough information for your colleagues to interpret your work and draw appropriate conclusions without being overwhelmed with numbers. It is also important to include enough information for the study to be replicated. Mathematics educators should be encouraged to replicate their own studies as well as those of others. Confidence in research findings is greatly increased if similar results can be obtained by repeating the treatment conditions with new samples.

Special attention should be paid to the definition and documentation of both the experimental treatments and the control conditions. Too often the research reports an experimental effect but fails to define the treatment clearly or provide data to document what occurred in the treatment and control groups.

The following list includes information to be included in research reports. This information is needed for any further analysis of the research using procedures such as meta analysis, and it is important to any further interpretation and application of results.

1. Sample size matrix
2. Reliability estimates for all response variables including total and subscales
3. Raw or adjusted means and standard deviations for any group or subgroup for which inferences and generalizations are to be made
4. Values of the test statistics used to test the hypotheses
5. Results on tests for homogeneity of variance or covariance as appropriate.

In the field of education it is important for research to guide us toward better decision making for short-term and long-term progress. If we are to move forward, the research we design, conduct, and report must be as free of bias and imprecision as possible. Perhaps closer attention to the procedures discussed here will bring the field forward at a faster rate.

REFERENCES

Berdie, D. R. Questionnaire length and response rate. *Journal of Applied Psychology,* 1973, *58*(2), 278–280.

Berdie, D. R., & Anderson, J. F. Effects on response rates of formal and informal questionnaire follow-up techniques. *Journal of Applied Psychology,* 1975, *60*(2), 255–257.

Cattell, R. B. *Handbook of multivariate experimental psychology.* Chicago: Rand McNally, 1966.

Clyde, J. D. *MANOVA: Multivariate analysis of variance on large computers.* Miami, Fla.: Clyde Computing Service, 1969.

Cohen, J., & Cohen, P. *Applied multiple regression/correlation analysis for the behavioral sciences.* New York: Wiley, 1975.

Dixon, W. J. (Ed.). *BMD: Biomedical computer programs* (3rd ed.). Berkeley: University of California Press, 1973.

Glass, G. V, & Stanley, J. C. *Statistical methods in education and psychology.* Englewood Cliffs, N.J.: Prentice-Hall, 1970.

Glass, G. V, Willson, V. L., & Gottman, J. M. *Design and analysis of time-series experiments.* Boulder: Colorado Associated Press, 1975.

Hansen, M. H., Hurwitz, W. N., & Madow, W. G. *Sample survey methods and theory*, Vol. 1. New York: Wiley, 1956.

Hays, W. L. *Statistics for the social sciences* (2nd ed.). New York: Holt, Rinehart & Winston, 1973.

Hopkins, K. D., & Glass, G. V. *Basic statistics for the behavioral sciences.* Englewood Cliffs, N.J.: Prentice-Hall, 1978.

Minium, E. W. *Statistical reasoning in psychology and education* (2nd ed.). New York: Wiley, 1978.

Nie, N. H., Hull, C. H., Jenkins, J. G., Steinbrenner, K., & Bent, D. H. *Statistical package for the social sciences* (2nd ed.). New York: McGraw-Hill, 1975.

Tatsuoka, M. M. *Multivariate analysis: Techniques for educational and psycholgical research.* New York: Wiley, 1971.

Tatsuoka, M. M. *Selected topics in advanced statistics, an elementary approach, no. 6: Discriminant analysis, the study of group differences.* Champaign, Ill.: Institute of Personality and Ability Testing, 1970.

Timm, N. H. *Multivariate analysis with applications in education and psychology.* Monterey, Calif.: Brooks/Cole, 1975.

Winer, B. J. *Statistical principles in experimental design* (2nd ed.). New York: McGraw-Hill, 1971.

5

The Randomized Comparative Experiment and Its Relationship to Other Research Procedures

Thomas J. Hummel

University of Minnesota

A S EDUCATORS, we are primarily involved with design science (Simon, 1969; Glaser, 1976). A design science deals with the principles of constructing humanity's artifacts, entities that do not occur naturally in the environment. Bridges, school buildings, and curricula are designed, respectively, by engineers, architects, and educators. Unlike, say, biology—a state science concerned with the study of existing animals—education involves the creating of new things, new mathematics programs, for instance.

Educators use information from state sciences to understand better the potential of students and the boundary conditions within which they must work. Although educators must sometimes carry out state science research when certain data are not available, they are primarily concerned with the design function, without which curriculum could change only through an unplanned evolutionary process. We believe, of course, we can improve on evolution by actively trying to improve curriculum.

Curriculum will be used here to refer to a broad range of intentions to provide educational opportunities.

> Included can be opportunities to become aware of different modes of knowing (for example, empirical, symbolic, and aesthetic), as well as to derive concepts, generalizations, and structures. In addition to opportunities for various levels and kinds of cognitive activity, there can be chances for such aspects of affective development as valuing, feeling, and enjoying and for development in the psychomotor area. (Lewis & Miel, 1972, p. 27)

As defined by Lewis and Miel, the concept also includes research that yields information only indirectly related to immediate curriculum decisions. In reference to research in mathematics education, curriculum thus suggests all efforts to affect what is intended to happen in the instructional process.

It is natural that alternative curriculum designs compete with one another in order that the better one emerge. How should this competition be carried out? If all students were exactly alike, the process would be simple and there would be no need for experimental design in the Fisherian tradition. Two students could be assigned to separate curricula. Since the students would be identical, it would not matter which one took which curriculum, and we could simply observe which student learned the most. But since students vary, it is difficult to determine whether to credit success to individual differences or to program effectiveness unless we use experimental methods that take this variability into account.

There is, perhaps, a hierarchy in research methods with respect to a given discipline. Some methods and procedures are more related than others to the fundamental work in a field. In agriculture, for example, the design and analysis of experiments is fundamental, whereas work in factor analysis is of little consequence. To mathematics educators, techniques such as multiple correlation, canonical correlation, principle components analysis, factor analysis, and cluster analysis are important but perhaps not fundamental in the same way as the design and analysis of experiments. Factor analysis, for example, was developed originally to study the structure of intelligence. This technique does not have the same potential for improving mathematics performance as the design and analysis of experiments. Factor analysis might aid in designing an experiment by answering preliminary questions, but ultimately curriculum is designed to be effective. One way to obtain effective curriculum is to try out new designs that are thought to be better than the old ones.

In departments of education, relatively little is taught about the design of experiments, probably because so few good texts have been written on the subject. If the *analysis* part of design and analysis texts were removed, there would be little left. (For an exception, see Cox, 1958.) The lack of adequate texts is unfortunate; experimental design is a difficult art to master, whereas the analysis of a well-designed experiment proceeds in a fairly straightforward fashion. In fact, with the aid of modern computers and statistical program packages, analysis can become one of the easier steps in the research process.

Texts reviewing the analytical procedures commonly used in the statistical computing packages are also available. The *Handbook of Measurement and Assessment in the Behavioral Sciences* by Whitla (1968) contains useful surveys of univariate and multivariate analysis of variance procedures, analysis of covariance, factor analysis, and regression techniques. Because of the availability of this and other good survey volumes, this essay will deal mainly with the *design* of comparative experiments. Careful attention to the design of an experiment and the use of an analysis deriving directly from the design may help to reduce some of the abuses that frequently accompany the easy access to computers.

We shall review the basic principles of experimental design as described by R. A. Fisher (1926) and relate them to two qualities of a good experiment: high precision and a lack of confounding. Experiments will be compared to other forms of research, and one alternative to the standard approaches to experimentation will be included.

The point of view to be presented here with respect to the design and analysis of experiments is not usually developed in popular texts used in education, although it is sometimes mentioned (e.g., Campbell & Stanley, 1966). It can be labeled "the randomization theory of experimental inference" (Kempthorne, 1955). The origins of randomization theory lie in the work of R. A. Fisher (1926, 1935), considered to be the founder of the modern school of design and analysis of experiments. Its development is presented in Oscar Kempthorne's (1952) important text, *The Design and Analysis of Experiments,* and in his numerous papers on the subject.

EXPERIMENTAL DESIGN

In his classic book, *The Design of Experiments,* Fisher (1935) described the basis for inference in experiments where the experimental units are not identical. He accomplished this with the simple, yet powerful, example of the lady tasting tea. The lady, who claimed she could tell whether the milk or the tea had been placed in the cup first, was given four cups made each way, the order of tasting the eight cups being determined at random. If her claim was completely false, the probability of her correctly identifying the method of mixing would be 1/70. Using this example, Fisher made it clear that probability remarks about the outcome of an experiment derived from the random assignment of experimental units to treatments.

Since 1935, much has been written about statistics, considerably less about the design of experiments, and, by comparison, a meager amount about randomization. ("Randomization" means the physical act of randomly assigning experimental units to treatments. Although randomization, as it is used here, is an instance of random sampling from a finite population, "random sampling" does not necessarily imply randomization. If one selected a random sample of males and females and compared these groups on some variable, randomization would not be involved.) In many fields randomization is considered virtually a necessary condition for a valid experiment. Quite often, however, after randomization has been used in treatment assignment, it is ignored in the analysis and statistical inference that follows. In spite of the fact that experimenters know they do not have independently, identically distributed random variables from a normal distribution, they continue to follow texts (e.g., Winer, 1971; Kirk, 1968) that present methods of analysis requiring this stringent model for the data. Across almost three decades, Kempthorne's writing has asked experimenters to stop, to consider what they are doing, and to think about changing to more logically defensible methods of design and analysis. However, Kempthorne's work has not had the impact it should have, especially in educational research. Some researchers have been influenced by his arguments, but he has been involved in an uphill struggle, going against much of the mainstream of current statistical teaching.

In objecting to analyses that assume a normal distribution, Kempthorne has not been simply offering another plea for nonparametric statistics, a class of procedures that includes randomization tests. Parametric statistics are useful, have a place, and should be used. However, in considering the purposes for which data from randomized experiments are analyzed, it is argued that inferences should be based on randomization theory and that these inferences should follow from a randomization analysis (or at least an approximation to this type of analysis). Of course, randomization is only one aspect of a well-designed experiment.

In his 1926 paper, Fisher described his three principles of experimental design, *randomization, replication,* and *local control.* Randomization is commonly accepted as important in an experiment, but this was not always so (see Collier & Hummel, 1977, pp. 71–77). Intuitively, it seems fair to assign experimental units to treatment conditions by a random method. To demonstrate why this intuition is justified, let us take, for example, an experiment involving a treatment and a control group.

Prior to being treated, N experimental units (e.g., subjects) have basal responses $x_1, x_2, \ldots, x_N$. If the treatment were applied to all subjects, their responses would be $x_1 + \delta = y_1, x_2 + \delta = y_2, \ldots, x_N + \delta = y_N$. The difference between the means of the x's, μ_x, and the mean of the y's, μ_y, is $\mu_y - \mu_x = \delta$. If $\delta \neq 0$, there is a treatment effect, and if $\delta = 0$, there is not a treatment effect. Suppose the experimenter assigns n of the $2n = N$ subjects to each group. Assuming the subjects are assigned at random, the probability of a particular subject (in effect, basal response) being assigned to a particular group is $1/2$. The number of ways of assigning N subjects to two groups is $M = N!/n!n!$, and therefore the probability of any particular arrangement of subjects in groups is $1/M$. If $N = 10$, the probability of obtaining, say, $x_1, x_3, x_6, x_7, x_{10}$ in the treatment group is $1/252$. After treatment we would have $x_1 + \delta = y_1, x_3 + \delta = y_3, x_6 + \delta = y_6$, and so on, and for the control group x_2, x_4, x_5, x_8, x_9. The mean of these y's is $\overline{y}$ and it estimates μ_y, and $\overline{x}$ estimates μ_x. The difference in $\overline{y}$ and $\overline{x}$ is an estimate of the treatment effect, $\hat{\delta} = \overline{y} - \overline{x}$. If the treatment effect is, in fact, zero ($\delta = 0$), the expected (average) value $\hat{\delta}$ over the M possible randomizations (arrangements) is

$$E(\hat{\delta}) = E(\bar{y} - \bar{x}) = \frac{1}{M} \sum_{m=1}^{M} (\bar{y}_m - \bar{x}_m) = 0,$$

$\bar{y}_m$ and $\bar{x}_m$ being the treatment and control means for the mth arrangement, respectively. Assigning subjects at random, therefore, leads to no systematic advantage for either group.

As is common in statistics, we would like to have an estimate of the error of $\hat{\delta}$, that is, to know something about its precision. Fisher (1926) recommended that experimental error be estimated from the variability of experimental units (subjects here) that have been treated alike. In order to have more than one subject treated in a particular way, one must provide for *replication,* the second principle mention above. Returning to the previous example with $N = 10$, we find that the differences $x_2 - x_4, x_2 - x_5,$ ..., $x_8 - x_9$ and $y_1 - y_3, y_1 - y_6, \ldots, y_7 - y_{10}$ all reflect experimental error, that is, differences not attributable to the treatment. The true experimental error is the variability of the basal responses, $x_1, x_2, \ldots,$ x_N and is indexed by $\sigma^2 = \Sigma(x - \mu_x)^2/N$. However, in practice we can only estimate σ^2, the usual estimate being

$$\hat{\sigma}^2 = \frac{\Sigma(x - \bar{x})^2 - \Sigma(y - \bar{y})^2}{n - 2} .$$

It can be shown that the expected value of $\hat{\sigma}^2$ over the M arrangements is $\Sigma(\hat{\sigma}^2) = \frac{1}{M} \Sigma(\hat{\sigma}^2) = \sigma^2$. In Fisher's terms, $\hat{\sigma}^2$ is a valid estimate of error.

To this point we see that randomization leads to an unbiased estimate of the treatment effect. In the popular monograph by Campbell and Stanley (1966), randomization by itself eliminates all sources of "internal invalidity." Put another way, the appropriate use of randomization eliminates confounding. In addition, randomization along with replication provides for a valid estimate of experimental error; that is, the estimate is systematically neither too high nor too low.

Besides wanting experiments that are unconfounded and yield valid error estimates, we want experiments that are precise. When we are estimating the treatment effect, δ, the smaller the standard error of this estimate the better. Under randomization (and also normal theory) the standard error of $\hat{\sigma}$ is $(2\sigma^2/n)^{1/2}$, and we wish to reduce this value. Clearly, increasing the number of replications beyond that necessary to estimate error will result in decreasing the standard error. This, of course, yields an increase in precision.

Another approach to increasing precision is to decrease experimental error, σ^2, thereby decreasing the standard error of $\hat{\delta}$. Increasing precision by reducing the experimental error brings us to the third of Fisher's basic principles of experimental design, namely, *local control.* Achieving the proper degree of control is at the heart of the design process. Randomization and replication are perhaps more easily understood than local control and, in most situations, more easily achieved. This third principle of experimental design will be approached by considering the use of "blocks" or "levels" in an experiment.

Consider a group of n subjects who are all assigned the same treatment condition. Following the administration of the treatment condition, each subject is measured on the dependent variable. Looking at the n values of the dependent variable, we notice that each value is different, even though every subject was assigned the same treatment condition. For convenience, we shall think of the variability as arising simply from variability due to experimental units. Some of this variability in the dependent variable may be directly attributable to known characteristics of the subjects, that is, variables useful in predicting individual differences.

The study of individual differences has gone on for many years in psychology and other fields and is usually accomplished by comparing groups of subjects that have been defined in particular ways. A popular classification variable is sex, males and females being compared with respect to intelligence, reading ability, finger dexterity, and so on. The general question relevant to local control is, "Can we define subsets of subjects such that their responses on the dependent variable will have reduced variability within subsets?"

It is necessary to form "blocks" or "levels" of the subjects that are relatively homogeneous with respect to the criterion measure, thereby allowing the experimenter to partition and assign variability to the blocking variable and consequently reduce error variance. In order to predict which subgroups of the subjects would be homogeneous with respect to the criterion variable, the experimenter may need some knowledge of the subjects' personality, intellect, attitudes, and other characteristics related to the response (criterion) variable. If characteristics of the subjects are found to be related to the response variable and can be used as a basis for blocking, it would be beneficial to form such groups. Groups homogeneous with respect to characteristics related to the response variable would tend to be homogeneous with respect to the response variable itself. Organizing subjects into blocks to reduce error variance and thereby to increase precision is not, for some, the first or primary reason to consider individual differences. The need to assess the interaction between treatment and subject variables may be of equal or more concern, and this topic will be discussed later.

When considering blocking variables in an experiment, we note a natural interface between *state science* (the study of existing systems) and *design science* (the study of system creation). Ideally, the mathematics educator should be able to rely on personality and cognitive development theorists and others to help explain the relationship between mathematical performance and other characteristics of individuals. However, ideals are seldom attained, and the mathematics educator may be motivated to explore relationships between student characteristics and mathematics performance.

To study individual differences with an eye toward the eventual improvement of experiments, the experimenter may need to use data analysis techniques that go beyond those usually associated with experimental design (factor analysis would be an example). This point of view is not in conflict with one relegating factor analysis and other similar techniques to a secondary position, for this state science research is seen as dealing with "enabling objectives" in the sense that the profession or discipline will be better able to accomplish its paramount objectives through experimentation if these other studies are successfully carried out.

A concern with reducing the variability of subjects treated alike and the consequent attention to blocking is a point of interface between the development of mathematics curriculum and the study of individual differences. It is not the only connection, to be sure, but it is an important one. Later we shall return to some of the data analysis procedures associated with the study of individual differences.

To integrate the concept of local control with the ideas of randomization and replication, consider the development of a somewhat more complex model than the simple one introduced for the two-group experiment. As we noted earlier, it is the differences between the basal responses that are the errors in the experiment: $x_1 - x_2, x_1 - x_3, \ldots, x_1 - x_N, \ldots, x_{N-1} - x_N$.

However, suppose that prior to the experiment it is decided that subsets of the subjects, such as males and females, are identifiable as having substantially different average basal responses. In an experiment with $N = 12$ subjects, suppose that $x_1, \ldots, x_6$ are basal responses for females and $x_7, \ldots, x_{12}$ are basal responses for males and that

$$\sum_1^6 x/6 = \overline{x}_F < \sum_7^{12} x/6 = \overline{x}_M .$$

One can *restrict the randomization process* so that the females are randomly assigned to treatment conditions and then, in a separate randomization, males are assigned to these same treatment conditions. This effectively stratifies the population of basal responses into two levels. Originally as a result of randomization, 15 of the 66 experimental errors, $x_1 - x_2, \ldots, x_{11} - x_{12}$, would have been assigned to the treatment group and 15 to the control group. However, given that the basal responses are blocked by sex, 3 of the 15 errors for females ($x_1 - x_2, \ldots, x_5 - x_6$) will be assigned to treatment and 3 to control. Likewise, 3 each will be assigned to treatment and control out of the 15 errors in the male group ($x_7 - x_8, \ldots, x_{11} - x_{12}$).

Without blocking, 30 of 66 possible errors would be randomly assigned, whereas *with* blocking, 6 of 15 will be drawn for females and 6 of 15 for males. In a sense, 36 of the original 66 errors will not be defined after blocks are imposed, since they are differences between basal responses for females and males. It is clear that blocking results in less information being available for estimating the population error variance. Intuitively, this leads to a decrease in precision rather than an increase. However, if there is a substantial difference between block means, that is, if $\bar{x}_M - \bar{x}_F$ is large, the differences between basal responses within sexes will tend to be smaller than they would have been if blocks had not been used. Therefore error is reduced. Although a trade-off is inherent, the larger the difference between block means relative to within-block errors, the greater the increase in precision.

The goal of local control is achieved to the extent that one can reduce experimental error by blocking on relevant characteristics of the subjects. The experimental units (subjects) are grouped into homogeneous subsets so that differences between the subsets can be computed and accounted for in the analysis. This general paradigm of randomly assigning n subjects to each treatment *within* each block has been called the *generalized randomized block design* (Wilk, 1955). The reader should note that restricted randomization is the key feature of the design.

The *conceptual* population of responses from which the obtained experimental data are drawn can be described as follows: For the conceptual population we imagine that *all subjects* have *all treatments*. We shall not actually observe all these responses; rather, we shall see a sample of them chosen at random. If we define $i = 1, \ldots, I$ as the treatment index, $j = 1, \ldots, J$ as the block index, and $k = 1, \ldots, K$ as the index of the kth subject in the jth block, then we can define a set of real numbers, y_{ijk}, which comprise the conceptual population of responses under all treatment conditions. In contrast to the earlier example, we have eliminated the need for the x's, which denote basal response, by using the i subscript to refer to treatment conditions. With *dot* and *bar* notations to indicate the subscript averaged over, we use grand ($\bar{y}\ldots$), row ($\bar{y}_i\ldots$), column ($\bar{y}\cdot_j\cdot$), and cell ($\bar{y}_{ij}$) means to define the following quantities:

$\mu = \bar{y}\ldots$, the mean of all y_{ijk},

$\delta_i = \bar{y}_i\ldots - \bar{y}\ldots$, the ith treatment effect,

$\beta_j = \bar{y}\cdot_j\cdot - \bar{y}\ldots$, the jth block effect,

$\delta\beta_{ij} = \bar{y}_{ij}\cdot - \bar{y}_i\ldots - \bar{y}\cdot_j\cdot + \bar{y}\ldots$, the ijth interaction effect between treatment and blocks,

and

$e_{jk} = \bar{y}\cdot_{jk} - \bar{y}\cdot_j\cdot$, the unit error, obtained by taking the average for the kth subject in the jth block across all treatments and deviating it from the average block response, that is, the average across all treatments and across all subjects in the block. (This setup is based on Wilk, 1955.)

The interaction term defined in the model ($\delta\beta_{ij}$), often of interest to the experimenter, serves to increase precision in the same way as β_j, for this source will not be included in the experimental error. This setup leads to a linear model for the y_{ijk} s as follows:

$$y_{ijk} = \mu + \delta_i + \beta_j + \delta\beta_{ij} + e_{jk}$$

The generalized randomized block design lends itself to the study of treatment-by-attribute (block) interaction and is therefore an important extension of the randomized block design. As the randomized block design is frequently presented in texts, it is defined in a two-way crossed design employing a treatment variable and a blocking variable, with one observation per cell. In the usual analysis associated with the randomized block design, the treatment-by-block interaction is assumed to be zero, and the sum of squares associated with that effect is used in estimating the error variance. In some design and analysis texts (e.g., Kirk, 1968), it is not clear which design is appropriate for estimating treatment-by-block interaction effects. In educational research, questions are often raised concerning the interaction of individual difference variables and treatments. The generalized randomized block design explicitly allows for the assessment of treatment-by-block interaction and is therefore useful in efforts to assess attribute-by-treatment interaction.

The characteristics of the generalized randomized block design with respect to the reduction of error variance (local control) and the study of interaction make it a useful addition to the completely randomized design. There are, of course, other methods of controlling error variance. Two techniques, difference (or gain) scores and the analysis of covariance, have been suggested in the literature. Both techniques have been compared by Feldt (1958) to a two-way design with one blocking variable and $n > 1$ for the cell frequencies. Feldt made certain normal theory assumptions regarding the distribution of the criterion variable and assumed that the continuous concomitant variable was linearly related to the criterion measure. From the point of view of the randomization theory of experimental inference, the results are not strictly applicable. There is enough relevance in those results, however, to suggest that the use of difference scores be avoided. We shall therefore turn our attention to the analysis of covariance.

There are at least three problems with the analysis of covariance: (a) It avoids explicit consideration of the interaction between the treatment and the concomitant variable and does not provide a proper analysis in the presence of interaction. This is a distinct and general disadvantage. (b) Under randomization theory, covariance analysis results in biased estimates of treatment effects, although probably not seriously so (Cox, 1956). (c) The analysis of covariance is valid only given very stringent assumptions, notably that the errors specified in the linear model are distributed independently and identically according to a normal density around regression lines having a common slope. Although there are uses for the technique, its utility in the analysis of randomized experiments is limited.

When randomization can be employed, the generalized randomized block design has broader applicability than the difference score or covariance approach.

A general layout for the generalized randomized block design is presented in Table 1. As stated previously, the y_{ijk}s represent each subject's response under each treatment condition.

Table 1
Layout for the Generalized Randomized Block Design

| Treatments | Blocks | | | | Treatment Means |
	1	2	$\cdots j \cdots$	J	
1	y_{111} $\vdots$ y_{11K}	y_{121} $\vdots$ y_{12K}	$\cdots$	y_{1J1} $\vdots$ y_{1JK}	$\bar{y}_{1..}$
2	y_{211} $\vdots$ y_{21K}	y_{221} $\vdots$ y_{22K}	$\cdots$	y_{2J1} $\vdots$ y_{2JK}	$\bar{y}_{2..}$
i	$\vdots$	$\vdots$	y_{ijk}	$\vdots$	$\bar{y}_{i..}$
I	y_{I11} $\vdots$ y_{I1K}	y_{I21} $\vdots$ y_{I2K}	$\cdots$	y_{IJ1} $\vdots$ $\bar{y}_{IJK}$	$\bar{y}_{I..}$
Block Means	$\bar{y}_{.1.}$	$\bar{y}_{.2.}$	$\cdots \bar{y}_{.j.} \cdots$	$\bar{y}_{.J.}$	

In practice we almost never apply all treatments to all subjects (there being a concern for carry-over effects, fatigue, etc.). The most typical plan is to apply one treatment to each subject. Assuming this to be the case and assuming that the question of which subjects receive which treatments is determined at random within each block, what we actually observe is a random sample of the y_{ijk}, say,

$$y^*_{ijr} = \mu + \delta_i + \beta_j + \delta\beta_{ij} + e^*_{ijr},$$

where $r = 1, \ldots, R$ indexes the experimental unit receiving the ith treatment in the jth block and $e^*_{ijr} = y^*_{ijr} - \overline{y}^*_{ij}$. The value of R indicates the number of replications of each treatment in each block. An example of a 2×2 generalized randomized block design is presented in Table 2.

Table 2
Conceptual Population and One Possible Sample for a 2×2
Generalized Randomized Block with $N = 12$ †

Treatments	Blocks	
	1	2
1	→y_{111} →y_{112} y_{113} →y_{114} y_{115} y_{116}	y_{121} y_{122} →y_{123} y_{124} →y_{125} →y_{126}
2	y_{211} y_{212} →y_{213} y_{214} →y_{215} →y_{216}	→y_{221} →y_{222} y_{223} →y_{224} y_{225} y_{226}
1	$y_{111} = y^*_{111}$ $y_{112} = y^*_{112}$ $y_{114} = y^*_{113}$	$y_{123} = y^*_{121}$ $y_{125} = y^*_{122}$ $y_{126} = y^*_{123}$
2	$y_{213} = y^*_{211}$ $y_{215} = y^*_{212}$ $y_{216} = y^*_{213}$	$y_{221} = y^*_{221}$ $y_{222} = y^*_{222}$ $y_{224} = y^*_{223}$

†The → indicates which elements of the population have been randomly chosen and the * indicates the sample values.

In analyzing the observations collected in an experiment using the generalized randomized block design, we compute the sums of squares presented in Table 3. These sums of squares are used to compute mean squares, which, in turn, are used to estimate certain population variances. The expectations for the mean squares under randomization theory are given in Table 4.

Table 3
Analysis of Variance of a Generalized Randomized Block Design

Source	Degrees of Freedom	Sums of Squares	Mean Squares	V
Treatments	$I-1$	$SS_T = RJ \Sigma (\bar{y}^*_i.. - \bar{y}^*...)^2$	$MS_T = \dfrac{SS_T}{I-1}$	$V_T = \dfrac{MS_T}{MS_E}$
Blocks	$J-1$	$SS_B = RI \Sigma (\bar{y}^*._j. - \bar{y}^*...)^2$	$MS_B = \dfrac{SS_B}{J-1}$	
Interaction	$(I-1)(J-1)$	$SS_I = R \Sigma\Sigma (\bar{y}^*_{ij.} - \bar{y}^*_i.. - \bar{y}^*._j. + \bar{y}^*...)^2$	$MS_I = \dfrac{SS_I}{(I-1)(J-1)}$	$V_I = \dfrac{MS_I}{MS_E}$
Error	$IJ(R-1)$	$SS_E = \Sigma\Sigma (y^*_{ijk} - \bar{y}^*_{ij.})^2$	$MS_E = \dfrac{SS_E}{IJ(R-1)}$	
Total	$IJR-1$	$SS_G = \Sigma\Sigma (y^*_{ijk} - \bar{y}^*...)^2$	$MS_G = \dfrac{SS_G}{IJR-1}$	

Table 4
Expectations of Mean Squares Computed in the
Analysis of a Generalized Randomized Block Design

Source	Mean Square	Expectation of Mean Squares
Treatments	$\boldsymbol{MS_T}$	$\sigma_E^2 + \dfrac{JR\Sigma\delta i^2}{I-1}$
Blocks	$\boldsymbol{MS_B}$	$\dfrac{IR\Sigma\beta j^2}{J-1}$
Interaction	$\boldsymbol{MS_I}$	$\sigma_E^2 + \dfrac{R\Sigma\Sigma\delta\beta ij}{(I-1)(J-1)}$
Error	$\boldsymbol{MS_E}$	$\sigma_E^2 = \dfrac{\Sigma\Sigma ejk}{J(K-1)}$

Variance ratio statistics are formed by dividing the mean square for the effect of interest by the error term. For example, the treatment variance ratio is $V_T = MS_T/MS_E$. For tests of Treatment and Interaction effect, the Error Mean Square is the valid error term, since under the hypothesis of no effect the numerator and denominator of each ratio have the same expectation. As is apparent from the expectations in Table 4, there is no appropriate test for Blocks. Each assignment pattern that could randomly occur will result in the same block means. In the jth block, the mean of the observations is $\overline{y}._{j}. = \overline{y}^*._{j}.$, regardless of which units get which treatments. The sum of squares for blocks is not a random quantity in this setup; therefore, no hypothesis is tested.

To one familiar with the usual development of the analysis of variance for a two-way layout with fixed effects, it is clear that the two variance ratios just defined are computed in the same manner as they would be if one assumed a normal distribution for errors and computed F statistics. Ideally, however, the significance of the V statistics of Table 3 is not judged using the F distribution. Instead, these statistics are compared to the randomization distribution.

To obtain the randomization distribution, V statistics would be computed for each possible random arrangement and a distribution constructed. For the simple 2×2 generalized randomized block example with $N = 12$, presented in Table 2, there are 400 ways of assigning subjects to the treatments: $(6!/3!^2)$ $(6!/3!^2) = 400$. Following randomization and treatment application, the experimenter would rearrange the data into each of the remaining 399 possible patterns and compute the statistics for each pattern. The reason for permuting the responses and obtaining statistics for all arrangements is that if the null hypothesis were true, the variance ratios obtained would yield a complete enumeration of what would have happened had the other arrangements been selected. The 400 statistics would be used to construct a reference distribution for significance testing. The experimenter would rank the statistics for highest (1) to lowest (400) and observe the position of the ratio computed for the *actual* arrangement used in the experiment. The rank of the statistic obtained for the actual arrangement divided by the total number of statistics is that statistic's p value (the probability of observing a value of the statistic greater than or equal to that obtained). In this example, rankings of 1 through 20 would lead to p values less than or equal to .05. A test of significance using the "randomization distribution" of V is an exact randomization analysis of the experiment. The usual normal theory assumptions including independence and homogeneous variance are not required.

As stated earlier, by estimating the variability associated with β_j and $\delta\beta_{ij}$, we remove these sources of variation from error, thereby increasing precision. Disregarding the blocking variable and using a completely randomized design can increase the error and reduce the sensitivity of the experiment. However, when ignoring the blocking variable, randomization tests of significance still have a valid error term, although in general they would be less sensitive than if blocks were included in the analysis.

The generalized randomized block design is, indeed, a very general conceptualization. If the number of blocks equals one, the design reduces to the completely randomized design, whereas letting the number of units equal one in each block-treatment combination has the effect of reducing the design to the well-known randomized block design. By adding treatment variables, we expand into factorial experiments and, of course, increase the complexity of the experiment. Additional blocking variables can also be included. However, if blocking variables are added indiscriminately, the design can become exceedingly complex with no concomitant increase in precision. From the point of view of efficiency, the loss of degrees of freedom (and therefore the loss in precision) inherent in adding blocking variables should be offset by reduced error variance.

The extension of the design to more complex experiments is straightforward and will be illustrated only through an example. Suppose one has two treatment variables, A and B, and two blocking variables, C and D, each of the four having two levels. Four treatment combinations, A_1B_1, A_1B_2, A_2B_1, A_2B_2, and four blocking variable combinations, C_1D_1, C_1D_2, C_2D_1, C_2D_2, result in a 4×4 layout. Assuming that subjects are randomly assigned to treatments within each of the four blocks, one could represent the design as being composed of four separate 2×2 completely randomized factorial experiments, one carried out in each block. If one were to view the two blocking variables as being crossed, it would be reasonable to carry out an analysis of variance to assess the following effects:

$$A, B, AB, AC, AD, BC, BD, ABD, ACD, BCD, ABCD$$

An immediate extension of the generalized randomized block design is realized by allowing treatments to be a generic term for the treatment combinations arising from crossing treatment factors. A similar conceptualization applies to blocks. Although indiscriminately adding treatment and blocking variables can cause an experiment to become unmanageable, simplicity of design is not an unqualified virtue. As Fisher (1926) has stated,

> No aphorism is more frequently repeated in connection with field trials, than that we must ask Nature few questions, or, ideally, one question, at a time. The writer is convinced that this view is wholly mistaken. Nature, he suggests, will best respond to a logical and carefully thought out questionnaire; indeed, if we ask her a single question, she will often refuse to answer until some other topic has been discussed. (p. 511)

As in most endeavors, one must seek a balance among competing design criteria. As designs become more complex and sample sizes increase, a major drawback of randomization analysis reveals itself. Randomization tests often require massive amounts of computation. The closely related Fisher's Exact Test for 2×2 tables comes to mind and conjures up the burdensome amount of computation involved. The analysis for a generalized randomized block design has the potential for even more. In fact, for some problems, which would not be considered that large in the field of educational research, the randomization distribution could not be obtained unless, perhaps, one had an extremely fast computer and literally millions of years.

It is no wonder that statisticians in general have not worked more actively on randomization analysis. At the time when the analysis of experimental data developed most rapidly, computers did not exist to work on even the smallest of problems. Also, obtaining expectations of mean squares under randomization often requires a prohibitive amount of algebra. One cannot "assume the problem down to size" and dispatch it with clever analysis.

There are, however, some ways of reducing the excessive computation required to obtain randomization distributions. For example, the arrangements can be sampled by Monte Carlo methods and the p value of the V statistic estimated with a high degree of accuracy. As a second example, an algorithm could be defined that would rearrange the observations in such a way that each new arrangement would result in a V being larger than that obtained for the experiment. If one were working at the .05 level, .95 or more of the arrangements could be ignored. This would lead to exact results for a limited part of the complete randomization distribution.

Any method for making randomization analysis more practical will still lead to much more computation than is required for a simple comparison of the variance ratio to an F distribution, as would be made when the normal distribution is assumed. But sometimes (this generally means if the number of observations is large enough) one can compare V to an F distribution while still basing the inference on randomization theory. Collier (1965) has investigated the tail areas of randomization distributions where the cut-off points were normal theory critical values for tests at the .10, .05, .025, and .01 levels of significance. He found, for example, that with three groups of 12 observations, tests of significance at a nominal level of .05 had true significance levels mostly in the range .04–.06. As the sample size increases, one would find that the approximation provided by normal theory cut-off points would improve. (See Kempthorne, 1952, pp. 130–132, and Baker & Collier, 1966.) Using an F distribution as an approximation to the exact randomization distribution may cause us to feel that we have almost come full circle. If we are willing to allow this kind of approximation, why not accept the usual normal theory assumptions (e.g., homogeneous variance) as a reasonable approximation? Given the robustness of F tests under a variety of violations of these assumptions, we could then proceed in the manner described in most design and analysis textbooks. Why is one approximation to be preferred over another?

If the reasons for adopting randomization theory were totally obvious and compelling, a change in thinking among educational researchers would long since have occurred. My preference for randomization analysis is based on the following reasons:

1. One important advantage is that the proper analysis is derived directly from the design—how the experimenter actually assigned subjects to treatments (e.g., Kempthorne, 1955; Wilk, 1955).

2. Statistical inferences are restricted to those people actually sampled in the experiment. Undefined, unsampled, difficult-to-conceptualize populations are not involved. For example, in a completely randomized experiment with a single treatment and control condition, where n individuals have been assigned to each condition, the inference concerns the $2n = N$ individuals. Conceptually, we consider that the population consists of the N basal responses before treatment and the N responses that would have been obtained had all N units been treated. The question is whether or not the treatment has had an effect on these N units. After random assignment and treatment, the researcher observes the difference between the means for the n treated units and the n untreated units. A significance test helps us judge whether the difference is due solely to randomization—that is, whether, through luck (or misfortune), higher (or lower) basal responses were assigned to the treatment or whether some part of the observed difference is due to treatment effect. The only time the population would be any larger than that based on the N experimental units would be when the N units were randomly selected from some larger collection of N' units.

3. The assumptions usually made in the randomization analysis concerning an additive treatment effect and absence of subject treatment interaction are simple. They are also assumptions for normal theory analysis. However, normal theory goes beyond these relatively primitive assumptions to assumptions that are often unrealistic. For example, experiments involve discrete variables that often do not approximate the normal distribution. The results of Monte Carlo studies of the robustness of normal theory analysis of variance are only partially helpful because one never really knows from what distribution the "sample" was "drawn" and, therefore, for what population the data are representative. At best, Monte Carlo results define some loose boundaries in which the F distribution can probably be used, but, of course, it is never really clear if one is within these boundaries. With Monte Carlo investigations of the adequacy of normal theory approximation to the exact randomization analysis, the situation is clearer. The adequacy of the approximation is a function of the characteristics of the actual observations, or data on hand. The researcher can look at the responses and determine if they have characteristics similar to those values used in the Monte Carlo study. For example, if there are a number of ties in the data, this can affect the adequacy of the approximation (Collier, 1965), but the researcher can easily look at the data and determine the number of ties with no need to guess about a parent population. (For a good review of simulation and analytical studies of robustness, see Glass, Peckham, & Sanders, 1972.)

4. When sample sizes are small, limitations with respect to inference are clear because the smallest achievable p value might not represent a strong statement of significance. With two groups of four experimental units each, the smallest achievable two-tailed p value is .029 under randomization. Therefore, a test of significance at the .01 level would be impossible to carry out. Under normal theory, a test could be carried out at any level desired. Considering the sample size, however, the normal theory analysis would be heavily dependent on assumptions. It is difficult to imagine when one would know enough to assume normal theory and make a strong statement of significance based on so few observations. Suppose one had eight intact classrooms that could be randomly assigned to treatment conditions. If one wanted a two-tailed test and intended to observe the .05 level strictly, a randomization test would result in significance only if all four treatment classroom means were either higher or lower than those for the four control classrooms. Under normal theory, any p value could be obtained, and the sample distributions of treatment and control means could overlap and significance still be obtained.

5. The randomization approach clearly distinguishes between *randomized block* and *factorial* designs. In many texts the two-way, fixed-effects analysis of variance is described. Whether or not one of the dimensions represents a blocking variable is immaterial. This is not, of course, true in randomization analysis, since the randomization distributions and even identifying which tests make sense to compute depend on whether or not the randomization was restricted by introducing a blocking variable.

6. The emphasis on the derived model used in randomization analysis, a model derived from the way the experiment was carried out, has focused attention on commonly ignored or inadequately dealt-with aspects of experiments, such as treatment error, measurement error, treatment-by-subject interaction, and the difference between observational units and experimental units. For example, treatment error arises whenever it is not possible to reproduce the treatment exactly each time it is applied to experimental units. These and other considerations have been studied under randomization theory. The design and the analysis have both been scrutinized. Although these considerations have not been completely ignored in normal theory investigations, they have not been as carefully studied in such investigations as they have by those using the randomization approach.

Especially relevant in this respect is a series of technical reports on topics dealing with analysis of variance by Kempthorne, Zyskind, Wilk, and others, which were produced during the late 1950s and early 1960s at Iowa State's Statistical Laboratory under the sponsorship of the Aeronautical Research Laboratory and Wright Air Development Center, Wright-Patterson Air Force Base. Sidney Addelman (1970) has written a good, brief introduction to these topics using a mixture of normal theory and randomization considerations.

Since this list of reasons for preferring randomization analysis is not totally compelling, one must temper one's criticism of the use of normal theory analysis. My reaction to the differences, however, has been to form a strong preference for the randomization approach.

AN EXAMPLE IN MATHEMATICS EDUCATION

The following discussion of an experiment published in the *Journal for Research in Mathematics Education* is presented to help highlight some of the previously mentioned points about the design and analysis of randomized experiments. The paper, "Cognitive Style and Mathematics Learning: The Interaction of Field Independence and Instructional Treatment in Numeration Systems" by McLeod, Carpenter, McCormack, and Skvarcius (1978), is a good example of a thoughtfully planned and carefully executed randomized experiment. In describing alternative approaches to the design and analysis of this research, I am not implying that the authors' approach was incorrect. As with most problems, however, it is possible to view it from a variety of angles.

To present the reader with the salient features of the design, the following excerpts from the paper of McLeod et al. are included:

> The purpose of the study is to look for interactions between cognitive style and treatments that vary in dimensions related to discovery learning. More specifically, this study investigated the relationship of the field-independence dimension of cognitive style to instructional treatments based on two levels of guidance crossed with two levels of abstraction. . . .

> Participants . . . came from four sections of a mathematics course. . . . Within each section, subjects were randomly assigned to one of the four treatment groups. Complete data were obtained on 116 of the 120 participants. . . .

> Four parallel instructional treatments were prepared on the topic of the addition and subtraction of whole numbers in bases other than ten. The treatments varied only in level of guidance and level of abstraction: Minimum guidance with manipulative materials (Min-M), maximum guidance with manipulatives (Max-M), minimum guidance with only a symbolic presentation (Max-S), and maximum guidance with a symbolic presentation (Max-S). The manipulative materials used were multibase arithmetic blocks.

> Instructors from two of the classes conducted the treatments. Like the students, the two instructors were randomly assigned to treatment groups so that each instructor was assigned each treatment group twice. . . .

> Students were given 50 minutes to complete the treatment.

> Minimal guidance was provided for the Min-M and Min-S groups. . . . If students asked the instructor for help, they were referred back to the printed materials or asked to solve a simpler problem. . . . The materials for the Max-

M and Max-S groups presented the concepts in considerable detail.... If a student asked a question, the instructor answered it directly and completely.

Instruction for the groups using manipulative materials (Min-M and Max-M) relied heavily on multibase arithmetic blocks. Both groups were shown how the blocks could be used to represent numbers in base five. After this introduction, the Min-M group began working on problems with no further instruction. The Max-M group received more guidance through examples (presented by the printed materials and by the teacher) using pictures of blocks before they worked on problems independently....

The treatments for the symbolic groups (Min-S and Max-S) made no mention of physical materials. Since the treatments were conducted in different rooms, the students in the symbolic group did not see the blocks during instruction.

All subjects were given a pretest, two posttests, two retention tests, and a test designed to measure field-dependence-independence....

Immediately after the tests for retention, the students were assessed on the field-dependence-independence dimension of cognitive style. The measure... chosen ... was the Hidden Figures Test (HFT)....

Thirty subjects were randomly assigned to each treatment group, but incomplete data led to the four groups varying in size from 28 to 30.... Dummy coding was used to represent ... two levels of guidance ... two levels of abstraction, and the interaction of guidance and abstraction. The interactions with HFT were the appropriate product vectors.

The generalized randomized block design provides an alternative approach to the research question investigated by McLeod et al. In describing the application of this design, we shall assume that certain procedures in the study could be changed. The first change concerns the Hidden Figures Test (HFT), which would be administered prior to treatment application rather than afterward as was done in the study. This would allow it to be used as a blocking variable in the randomization process. Measuring this attribute beforehand also precludes the possibility of its being affected by the treatments. If the treatments differentially affected the attribute variable, then a treatment-by-attribute interaction might appear that would be ambiguous to interpret because of confounding.

The values that the $N = 120$ subjects had on the HFT would be viewed as fixed constants. This avoids a consideration of measurement error in the blocking variable. Inferences would concern the scores obtained by the 120 subjects. Whether or not the HFT is viewed as having a "true" component and an "error" component is immaterial. The 120 scores represent a set of true scores and a set of error scores; neither is random, and there is no implication that the inferences apply to a setup where measurement errors become random variables because of their being randomly sampled.

The fact that not all subjects in a block have the same HFT score would not be a problem, given the model to be employed. The block effect is defined in terms of the block and grand means of the subjects involved in the experiment.

In the design now to be developed, the blocking variable based on the HFT would have two levels, high and low. This variable would be used in restricting the randomization and will be referred to as H.

The authors point out that the subjects came from four sections of a mathematics course and that within each section, the subjects were randomly assigned to one of the four treatment groups. Therefore, Section (S) would be a second blocking variable used in restricting the randomization. A question to be raised concerns whether or not the mean HFT score for the high level of H is the same from section to section and likewise for the low level of H. This will be dealt with momentarily.

Two treatment variables in the study, maximum guidance versus minimum guidance, to be referred to as A_1 and A_2, respectively, and manipulative versus symbolic, to be referred to as B_1 and B_2, respectively, are crossed to form four treatment combinations. These treatment variables are of primary importance, but they are not the only treatment variables implicit in the study. As the authors point out, two instructors were randomly assigned to treatment groups to administer the AB conditions, and therefore Instructor (I) is an additional variable to be considered. The Physical Environment (P) and Time (T) when AB combinations were administered could also have an effect. Since A and B were administered to Groups (G), G becomes still another factor to be considered.

To understand why these additional factors, I, P, T, and G, are being introduced, consider a less complex experiment with only two treatment conditions, say A_1 and A_2. We might be concerned about confounding if A_1 were administered to the A_1 group by instructor X in Classroom 1 during the morning and A_2 were administered to the A_2 group by instructor Y in Classroom 2 during the afternoon. Attention to such concerns is certainly not novel; the issues are amply described in Campbell and Stanley's (1966) widely used monograph. In more complex designs, the same issues are present. If the A and B factors are confounded with I, P, T, and G in each block, then they will be confounded across blocks. The authors' description of how the experiment was executed seems to imply that the sources of confounding just discussed apply to their study. For example, it seems that instructors administered A and B combinations within each section. From the description of how the combinations were administered to groups, it appears unlikely that groups could have been treated at the same time and place. This means that certain effects involving A, B, I, P, T, and G must be confounded.

As we develop a design meant to deal with some of these sources of confounding, it may seem idealized and impractical; yet the new design could be implemented. Even if it were impractical for some settings, it could still have heuristic and instructive value.

One reason for choosing the investigation by McLeod et al. was its complexity. As a rich example allowing many issues to be raised, it is a good candidate for comparison with a more idealized approach.

The suggested alternative design, a generalized randomized block, would be composed of two blocking variables, Sections (S) and field independence (H), and two treatment variables, A and B. Two additional sources of variation to be considered are Units (subjects) (U), and Repetitions (R), which will be described shortly. Thirty-two subjects per section for a total of $N = 128$ would be required. We shall assume that the high and low levels of H have the same meaning in each section, that is, that the HFT mean of highs is the same (or very similar) in each section and likewise for the lows. The same design could be used if this condition could not be achieved, but the analysis would change to a form somewhat less than optimal for present purposes.

The design would completely confound I, P, and S. This means that an instructor would administer all AB combinations to a given section with all administrations carried out in the same physical environment. Confounding these sources of variation seems reasonable, since none of the three was considered in the analysis of McLeod et al., and it can be assumed that the effects associated with these variables are not of particular interest. The crossing of S and H would result in eight blocks with 16 subjects per block. The four treatment combinations, A_1B_1, A_1B_2, A_2B_1, and A_2B_2, would each be administered twice in each block, requiring eight separate time periods. Two subjects within each block would be randomly assigned to each time period. The two subjects to whom the treatment is administered together are a repetition. Each of the four treatment combinations will be randomly assigned to two time periods in each block.

In summary, the study would employ a generalized randomized block design with two completely crossed treatment factors at two levels each for four treatment combinations. The treatment combinations would be administered twice in each of the eight blocks that result when S and H are crossed. In each block, there would be two repetitions of each treatment combination with two subjects per repetition. Table 5 presents the proposed layout.

Introducing R as a factor would double the number of treatment administrations needed. Each instructor would be required to spend over 13 hours with the various treatment groups, whereas the original plan required slightly more than 6 1/2 hours. However, there would be advantages. With two repetitions for each treatment, variance due to treatment error (i.e., the inability to reproduce treatments) would be included in the variance component for R. Also, the possible confounding effects due to G and T would be randomized when repetitions were assigned to AB combinations within blocks. This would result in a "random confounding" directly analo-

Table 5
Layout for an Alternative Design for the McLeod et al. Study

R: repetitions / H: high, low / Sections (S):		Treatments (A × B)							
		A_1B_1		A_1B_2		A_2B_1		A_2B_2	
		1	2	1	2	1	2	1	2
I	h	*							
	l								
II	h							'	
	l								
III	h								
	l								
IV	h								
	l								

*2 subjects in each cell

gous to that occurring when subjects are assigned to treatments in a completely randomized design. The conceptual foundation of the randomization test takes these and other sources of variation, such as subjects, into account. In other words, given randomization and replication, a significant result would not be attributed to differences due to time, subject, and treatment error.

Now let us turn to the analysis. A "variance component" notation is used regardless of the fixed or random status of the effect. For example, variation associated with A and B and their interaction is symbolized as σ^2_A, σ^2_B, and σ^2_{AB}, respectively. The variance between repetitions nested within treatment and block combinations is σ^2_R, and σ^2_U is the variance of subjects (units) within Repetitions. Table 6 presents the analysis of variance.

The analysis does not provide a breakdown for S and its interaction with other factors. As pointed out, this blocking variable has been purposely confounded with other effects. Recall that no variance ratio would be computed for H because the block means are constant under randomization. To return to an issue mentioned earlier, this analysis of variance assumes that the levels of H have the same meaning from section to section. If this were not so, one would probably want to partition the degrees of freedom for S and its interactions and carry out an analysis of A, B, and H for each section separately. Clearly this could make the interpretation more complex. As implied previously, convenience was part of the motivation for the analysis of variance in Table 6.

Table 6
Expectations of the Mean Squares That
Would Be Computed in Analyzing the Experiment in Table 5

Source	DF	Expected Mean Square
H	1	$32\sigma^2_H$
S	3	$16\sigma^2_S$
$H \times S$	3	$8\sigma^2_{HS}$
A	1	$\sigma^2_E + 32\sigma^2_A$
B	1	$\sigma^2_E + 32\sigma^2_B$
AB	1	$\sigma^2_E + 16\sigma^2_{AB}$
AH	1	$\sigma^2_E + 16\sigma^2_{AH}$
BH	1	$\sigma^2_E + 16\sigma^2_{BH}$
ABH	1	$\sigma^2_E + 8\sigma^2_{ABH}$
AS	3	$\sigma^2_E + 8\sigma^2_{AS}$
BS	3	$\sigma^2_E + 8\sigma^2_{BS}$
ABS	3	$\sigma^2_E + 4\sigma^2_{ABS}$
AHS	3	$\sigma^2_E + 4\sigma^2_{AHS}$
BHS	3	$\sigma^2_E + 4\sigma^2_{BHS}$
$ABHS$	3	$\sigma^2_E + 2\sigma^2_{ABHS}$
$R(ABHS)$	32	σ^2_E

The first group of mean squares involving only H and S contains no error and no tests would be carried out. The second group contains the effects of interest. Since all members of the third group involve S, they are confounded with Instructor (I) and Physical environment (P).

Those interested in a detailed description of the analysis used in the original study should consult the publication. Not surprisingly, it is quite different from that developed here. The authors restrict their attention to A, B, and H and employ a multiple-regression approach requiring the usual normal theory assumptions.

As I commented at the outset of this example, the intention here is to offer an alternative view, not to denigrate the authors' work. Their approach was obviously workable, since they have completed the project. The approach presented here would clearly be more difficult, but it has controls for more variables that could confound the results. At the very least, the design provides a contrast that should evoke pertinent design questions.

The preceding section has introduced the generalized randomized block design but not in sufficient detail to allow one to use the design and analysis considerations presented without further study. By raising issues rather than presenting a simple example in enough detail to show "how to do it," I have intended to motivate readers to look at the references cited. Studying these sources will enable researchers to improve the experiments they design and the interpretation of the results they obtain. Even when a situation thwarts the use of a good experimental design, a thorough knowledge of design principles can still be of benefit. The researcher will be well aware of the limitations of the research, which is the first step to any attempt to soften the impact of a flaw in the design.

ALTERNATIVE PURPOSES FOR RESEARCH

Kempthorne (1975) has spoken of three types of statistical inference: *experimental, sampling,* and *observational.* The present essay focuses primarily on one type of experimental inference, that which proceeds directly from the random assignment of experimental units to treatment conditions. The following paragraphs attempt to relate experimental inference based on randomization to these other forms of inference.

Sampling Inference

First, let us consider sampling inference. The researcher has a completely defined, totally enumerated, and therefore finite population, such as all secondary school mathematics teachers in Minnesota. The researcher wishes to collect information on a randomly selected subset of the population and to infer characteristics of the total population. A proven random device is used in the selection process, and each element in the population has a known probability of being selected. This probability sampling, as it is called, comprises almost entirely what is referred to as *survey sampling.* (Useful texts on survey sampling have been written by Cochran, 1963, and Kish, 1965.) There are nonrandom, sometimes fortuitous, samples, just as there are experiments that do not randomly assign subjects to treatments. But as in randomized experiments, the physical act of random sampling leads directly to concretely justifiable probability statements that have a frequency base. Nonrandom surveys and experiments will be considered momentarily, but first let us describe some relationships of probability sampling and randomized experiments.

In the generalized randomized block design presented in Table 1, one variable represents blocks. If the population exceeds in size the number of individuals to be used in the experiment, a subset could be drawn. If there were only a single block ($J = 1$), a simple random sample could be drawn. When more than one block is included, the sampling could be carried on within the blocks, or strata. For various types of probability sampling, such as stratified random sampling and cluster sampling, one can think of analogues for generalized randomized block designs when a subset of the population must be selected for experimentation. In this process, blocks in experiments and strata in surveys are similar. Each depends on the researcher's prior knowledge of the elements or units to be dealt with and on educated guesses as to what choices will lead to an efficient design. Also, when mixed or random models are of interest, actual sampling techniques could be used to select levels of both treatments and blocks.

The presentation of the generalized randomized block design in the preceding section assumed that all available experimental units were used in the experiment. A major concern in the design and interpretation was the attribution of mean differences to treatment effect rather than to some source of confounding. At times one may wish to generalize the experimental results to some larger population that can, in fact, be sampled. This leads to a melding of the previously presented principles of experimental design with that of survey sampling. In its most general form, the generalized randomized block includes the provisions for sampling from a larger population.

Observational Inference

Second, let us consider observational inference. The researcher collects data according to some specified procedures in the belief that the data can suggest a model, or underlying structure, that can explain a part of the real world. Kempthorne (1975) describes the data analysis strategy as one of "model search." One has data on hand, or a sample of convenience, and on looking at it one decides it is likely that the parent distribution from which the data are "drawn" belongs to a certain family of distributions. Deciding which family is the appropriate one is no simple task. A good bet, however, is that if a researcher is in education, the family will turn out to be a class of distributions referred to as "normal." At this point, procedures referred to as goodness-of-fit techniques could be used to see if the normal distribution is a plausible parent distribution. The number of candidate distributions will be small, and the search will probably be stopped after the researcher answers the following question in the affirmative: "Can I assume this set of data to be like a sample that could have been drawn from a normal distribution?" The researcher can then proceed to estimate the mean and variance and to test a hypothesis about the mean of the population. This would be a relatively simple model search, its validity resting on the assumption that the normal distribution is appropriate. In education, other distributions are seldom considered.

One can also imagine a situation where one has a group of individuals, each measured on a set of independent variables and a dependent variable. Suppose the dependent variable defines performance on some task and the independent variables are thought to predict success on the task. The researcher, let us say, is interested in carrying out a stepwise regression analysis (Draper & Smith, 1966) to determine which subset of the independent variables provides the "best" prediction. When the computer program that performs the analysis terminates after a number of steps, the number of hypothesis tests carried out could well be in the hundreds.

The problem with observational inference in either example lies in the meaning of probability and how probability will be assessed. Clearly, there is no frequency interpretation based on an explicit random procedure. Even if a random procedure were employed, attempting to assess the probability of arriving at a particular model after going through all the steps required would most often be impossible. Even if the process were a single step, much would depend on the initial selection of the family for the parent distribution.

Surveys that have not used probability sampling, nonrandomized experiments, and analyses of randomized experiments employing normal theory assumptions all have a good deal in common with observational inference. For none of these does a frequency interpretation of probability result directly from the use of a proved random device for random selection or assignment. Thus, the normal theory analysis of variance and covariance, correlational and regression analysis, inferential forms of factor analysis (e.g., maximum likelihood factor analysis)—essentially any approach that assumes the data are from a specified but unsampled population—share similar inference problems. The inferences are only as sound as the conjectures made about the probability model.

Consider this example of a quasi experiment. Suppose a school system must decide which of two mathematics texts to purchase. One teacher has tried both texts, one in each of two algebra sections. Trying to ascertain if the text made a difference, the teacher plans an analysis of covariance of the end-of-year achievement test scores. The previous year's scores and group intelligence test scores are taken as covariates. An attempt is made to determine if (a) the end-of-year scores are drawn from a normal distribution, (b) the regression of end-of-year scores on previous year and intelligence scores are the same across the parent populations for the groups, and (c) the population residual variances are equal. If these attempts are successful, then an analysis of covariance is carried out. The goal of the analysis seems worthwhile enough: to assess group differences with the effect of intelligence and previous achievement statistically removed from the analysis. But given this complex, four-step procedure, we would be hard pressed to assign a meaningful probability or degree of confidence that this complex process would lead to a particular decision. If this is the best that can be done, then the results might be cautiously suggestive of the text effect, the probability remarks that are typically made serving primarily to increase that caution.

The fact is that it is sometimes difficult, if not impossible, to either sample populations of interest or employ random assignment. If any inferences are to be made, one must assume some probability model for the data unless one considers simply dealing with descriptive statistics. Refraining from inferential statements about population parameters can be a viable path to take but one that many educational researchers would not be willing to follow.

Inferential statements make the reporting of research seem somehow more sophisticated and serve a useful purpose in adding conservatism to the results. Thus, they help the reader more realistically anticipate what might be encountered in a similar situation. For example, the presentation of confidence intervals can have a sobering effect, revealing both the accuracy of the point estimate (or lack thereof) and what might be reasonable limits for a future outcome. For these purposes the usual statistical methods used by educational researchers have utility and merit. One can accept both their limitations and usefulness.

It seems, however, that the design of experiments is at times dominated by analysis of the model search variety. One can actually find phrases such as "analysis of variance designs," which do little to advance the idea that the analysis should follow from the design. Some texts go so far as to discuss the two-way analysis of variance without differentiating the completely randomized and the randomized block design. Other texts explicitly describe and recommend randomization but then ignore it in the analysis. The situation is similar to that of observational inference; one must assume the data are from a particular distribution that has not been (and cannot be) sampled. Randomization theory, however, requires a strong union between the design of an experiment and its analysis. It provides for an adequate basis for probability remarks. These two features give it a definite appeal.

Experimental inference, sampling inference, and observational inference, taken together, provide broad classifications covering many of the purposes for which data are analyzed. At times, however, one is not interested in inference, at least in the formal sense of making probability statements. Factor analysis provides a good example. For years, there were no formal inferential procedures in factor analysis; hypotheses, for example, were not tested. As mentioned earlier, methods to test hypotheses on factor models are available, but the standard methods that form the bulk of Harman's (1967) important book on factor analysis still enjoy broad use. One purpose of factor analysis and its close relative, principal components analysis, is data reduction, which transforms data composed of many correlated variables to a few uncorrelated variables. A simple set of explanatory variables is sought to account for the interrelationship among a larger set of variables.

In the context of using generalized randomized block designs in experiments, factor analysis may be useful. When one is aware of a number of important blocking variables but knows that including them all will make the design too complex and unmanageable, it may be feasible to use factor analysis to reduce the number of variables while still accounting for much of the variance in the original set. This idea, suggested by Robert Pruzek in a conversation (1978), seems to deserve further investigation.

Somewhat similar to factor analysis is the technique of cluster analysis. An important application of cluster analysis is to take N objects measured on p variables and to form subgroups of the objects such that variability within the groups is small relative to variability between the groups (Veldman, 1967). Here, again, is a technique that might be of some benefit in forming blocks when using the generalized randomized block design. Candidate blocking variables could be used in a cluster analysis, and subjects could be placed in homogeneous subgroups with respect to these variables. These subgroups would then become the blocks in the experimental design.

Noninferential techniques have a place. They can be integrated into experiments, enabling researchers to improve experimental designs and make stronger inferential statements.

CONCLUDING REMARKS

There are those who believe it is, at best, difficult to randomize in their particular setting. However, with persistence and creativity, many more experimental settings than one might suspect will permit random assignment. Certain researchers say that random assignment would not be allowed in their research setting, but after they rethink the design and reapproach those in control of the setting, they sometimes find that a randomized design can be used. These extra efforts are essential; quasi-experimental designs simply cannot take the place of randomized experiments. In this context one might consider carefully the comment of Campbell and Boruch (1975):

> It may be that Campbell and Stanley (1966) should feel guilty for having contributed to giving quasi-experimental designs a good name. There are program evaluations in which the authors say proudly, "We used a quasi-experimental design." If responsible, Campbell and Stanley should do penance, because in most social settings there are many equally or more plausible rival

hypotheses than the hypothesis that the puny treatment indeed produced an effect. (p. 202)

However, at times there may be no possible way to randomize no matter what is tried. In these instances, it may be that the setting, a school, say, has too many activities in progress to allow for arbitrary assignment and still maintain normal functioning. In other words, a randomized experiment would be too disruptive. In such an ongoing system, it might also be that the system cannot tolerate one treatment being highly effective and the other miserable, especially if miserable means a decrease in the system performance that has come to be expected and depended on. In such settings, one must question whether any experiment, randomized or otherwise, would be appropriate. There are more appropriate paradigms than experimental ones for ongoing systems that cannot tolerate a serious degradation of performance.

Highly interesting among the alternative approaches is what are called evolutionary operations (EVOP) (Box, 1957). EVOP involves strategies for making gradual changes in systems in such a way that, over time, performance is increased. EVOP incorporates the results from small-scale (laboratory) experiments but depends on them only to suggest directions for change, leaving the actual directions to be determined solely by feedback from the continually evolving system. This model for gradual change and feedback could well be more appropriate for some settings than controlled experimentation.

In summary, educational research could benefit from more emphasis on the design of experiments and less on (sometimes unrealistic) methods of analysis. Randomization is essential to a well-designed experiment. It can provide a probability model that allows a proper analysis to be derived from the design. When randomization is completely impossible, the researcher should consider more alternatives than a quasi experiment and its attendant "model search" problems. In particular, evolutionary operations deserve some attention. Other research techniques, which assess the current state of affairs rather than the changes in performance resulting from curriculum modification, have their uses also, but they are one step removed from the most central concerns of a design science such as mathematics education.

REFERENCES

Addelman, S. Variability of treatments and experimental units in the design and analysis of experiments. *Journal of the American Statistical Association,* 1970, *65,* 1095–1108.

Baker, F. B., & Collier, R. O., Jr. Some empirical results on variance ratios under permutation in the completely randomized design. *Journal of the American Statistical Association,* 1966, *61,* 813–820.

Box, G. E. P. Evolutionary operation: A method for increasing industrial productivity. *Applied Statistics,* 1957, *6,* 81–101.

Campbell, D. T., & Boruch, R. F. Making the case for randomized assignment to treatments by considering the alternatives: Six ways in which quasi-experimental evaluations in compensatory education tend to underestimate effects. In C. A. Bennett & A. Lumsdaine (Eds.), *Evaluation and experience: Some critical issues in assessing social programs.* New York: Academic Press, 1975.

Campbell, D. T., & Stanley, J. C. *Experimental and quasi-experimental designs for research.* Chicago: Rand McNally, 1966.

Cochran, W. G. *Sampling techniques.* New York: Wiley, 1963.

Collier, R. O., Jr. *Randomization procedures for the analysis of educational experiments.* Cooperative Research Project 2593, Department of Health, Education and Welfare. Minneapolis: University of Minnesota, 1965.

Collier, R. O., Jr., & Hummel, T. J. (Eds.). *Experimental design and interpretation.* Berkeley: McCutchan, 1977.

Cox, D. R. A note on weighted randomization. *Annals of Mathematical Statistics,* 1956, *27,* 1144–1150.

Cox, D. R. *Planning of experiments.* New York: Wiley, 1958.

Draper, N. R., & Smith, H. *Applied regression analysis.* New York: Wiley, 1966.

Feldt, L. S. A comparison of the precision of three experimental designs employing a concomitant variable. *Psychometrika,* 1958, *23,* 335–353.

Fisher, R. A. The arrangement of field experiments. *Journal of the Ministry of Agriculture,* 1926, *33,* 503–513.

Fisher, R. A. *The design of experiments.* Edinburgh: Oliver & Boyd, 1935.

Glaser, R. Components of a psychology of instruction: Toward a science of design. *Review of Educational Research,* 1976, *46,* 1–24.

Glass, G. V, Peckham, P. D., & Sanders, J. R. Consequences of failure to meet assumptions underlying the fixed effects analysis of variance and covariance. *Review of Educational Research,* 1972, *42,* 237–288.

Harman, H. H. *Modern factor analysis.* Chicago: University of Chicago Press, 1967.

Kempthorne, O. *The design and analysis of experiments.* New York: Wiley, 1952.

Kempthorne, O. The randomization theory of experimental inference. *Journal of the American Statistical Association,* 1955, *50,* 946–967.

Kempthorne, O. *Why randomize?* Paper presented at University of Minnesota School of Statistics Colloquium, Minneapolis, December 1975.

Kirk, R. E. *Experimental design: Procedures for the behavioral sciences.* Belmont, Calif.: Brooks/Cole, 1968.

Kish, L. *Survey sampling.* New York: Wiley, 1965.

Lewis, A. J., & Miel, A. *Supervision for improved instruction: New challenges, new responses,* pp. 23–54. Belmont, Calif.: Wadsworth, 1972.

McLeod, D. B., Carpenter, T. P., McCormack, R. L., & Skvarcius, R. Cognitive style and mathematics learning: The interaction of field independence and instructional treatment in numeration systems. *Journal for Research in Mathematics Education,* 1978, *9,* 163–174.

Pruzek, R. Personal communication, April 1978.

Simon, H. A. *The sciences of the artificial.* Cambridge, Mass.: M.I.T. Press, 1969.

Veldman, D. J. *Fortran programming for the behavioral sciences.* New York: Holt, Rinehart & Winston, 1967.

Whitla, D. K. (Ed.). *Handbook of measurement and assessment in behavioral sciences.* Reading, Mass.: Addison-Wesley, 1968.

Wilk, M. B. The randomization analysis of a generalized randomized block design. *Biometrika,* 1955, *42,* 70–79.

Winer, B. J. *Statistical principles in experimental design* (2nd ed.). New York: McGraw-Hill, 1971.

6

Case Studies

INTRODUCTION

David C. Johnson
University of London

THE four papers in this chapter were selected as case-study exemplars of the four basic types of research described in chapter 2: status (Grouws), clinical (Nelson), experiment (Vos), and evaluation (Thornton). The primary reason for including these case studies is to illustrate that "research in the making" involves many *activities and decisions* that usually do not appear in the final published reports (a phenomenon that is similar to the difference between mathematics and "mathematics in the making"). The research papers that provide the bases for the case studies have been published in research journals *(Journal for Research in Mathematics Education* or the *Alberta Journal of Educational Research).* Although authors were given considerable flexibility in style and in the manner in which they wished to describe and discuss what actually took place, an attempt was made to establish some consistency and to relate the material to previous chapters in this reference. In particular, the general directions to authors asked them to *consider the problems or difficulties encountered in—*

1. *the formulation of the research question* (explicating the specific problem and reducing it to a manageable form);
2. *designing the study* (the trade-offs made in selecting the variables to be manipulated or controlled);
3. *implementation;*
4. *interpreting results;*
5. *influencing the profession* (e.g., incorporating into theory or changing current practice).

96

For the most part, authors also referenced or followed in some fashion the Fox (1969) listing of the stages involved in the production of a research report (see chap. 3).

The authors have provided critical analyses of their studies and have indicated what actually occurred, what trade-offs were made, and how they attempted to resolve particular issues. The reader may wish to begin by reviewing the published research report before reading a particular discussion. However, each narrative includes an extended abstract or overview of the research report, and an attempt has been made to provide sufficient discussion to allow each section to stand by itself.

CASE STUDY 1:

Status or Survey Research

Factors Associated with Third- and Fourth-Grade Children's Performance in Solving Multiplication and Division Sentences (Grouws & Good, 1976)

Douglas A. Grouws

University of Missouri—Columbia

ABSTRACT

The focus was on the performance of third- and fourth-grade students in solving open multiplication and division sentences such as $5 \times \square = 45$, $\square \div 8 = 4$, and $56 \div 8 = \square$. This included an examination of the relationships among pupils' solving performance, certain mathematical characteristics of the sentences, and other factors associated with the students. The four mathematical factors studied were operation, symmetric property, placeholder position, and existence of a whole-number solution. The student factors were ability, grade level, and sex.

A pencil-and-paper type of inventory was developed. Twelve types of open sentences can be generated from the general equation $a \circ b = c$, where $\circ$ represents an operation, if two operations ($\times$ and $\div$), three placeholder positions (a, b, and c), and the symmetric property of equality ($a \circ b = c$ and $c = a \circ b$) are considered. For example, one type would be $a \times \square = c$, in which the operation is multiplication, the placeholder position is b, and the operation is on the left side of the equality sign. Whole numbers were systematically assigned to generate two open sentences of each type. Also, one sentence having no whole-number solution (e.g., $2 = 9 \div \square$) was generated for each of the eight open-sentence types for which this was possible. The 32 open sentences were then assigned to four inventory forms so that each form had eight items and the mathematical factors were balanced among forms. All third- and fourth-grade classes in each of the 29 elementary schools in a metropolitan school district were tested using the open-sentence inventory.

Student aptitude was measured by the Cognitive Abilities Test. For purposes of analysis, these scores were used to divide the sample into three ability levels. For each of the 32 inventory items, a school $\times$ grade $\times$

aptitude portion-correct mean was computed by dividing the number of correct responses to an item by the number of pupils using the test form in which the item appeared. School $\times$ grade $\times$ sex portion-correct means were similarly calculated.

The data for the open sentences having whole-number solutions were analyzed in two parts. The first analysis was a $2 \times 3 \times 2 \times 2 \times 3$ fixed-effects analysis of variance. The first two factors in the analysis were the status variables of grade and aptitude, and the last three factors were operation, symmetric property of equality, and placeholder position. In the second analysis, sex was substituted as a factor for the aptitude variable in the five-way ANOVA. The data for the open sentences having no whole-number solutions were analyzed through planned comparisons.

In both analyses of data from open sentences with whole-number solutions, all main effects were significant ($p < .01$). Fourth-grade students outperformed third-grade students; an "average" fourth-grade pupil could be expected to solve about 17 of the 24 items correctly, whereas the third-grade counterpart could solve about 13 of the 24 correctly. Girls did significantly better than boys, especially at the fourth-grade level. There was a significant difference in the aptitude factor, but this factor interacted with other factors on only one occasion. Sentences involving division were much more difficult than sentences involving multiplication, with portion-correct means of .49 and .71, respectively. Sentences with the operation on the left side of the equality sign were significantly easier than those with the operation on the right. The a placeholder position was much more difficult than either the b or the c placeholder positions. The most difficult type of open sentence was of the form $c = \square \div b$; the easiest was $\square \times b = c$.

The analysis of the no-solution sentences showed that third-grade pupils significantly outperformed fourth-grade pupils. Also, as in previous analyses, aptitude was a significant factor. No-solution division sentences were significantly easier than the no-solution multiplication sentences. Also, within the no-solution multiplication sentences, the sentences with placeholders in the a position were significantly easier than sentences with placeholders in the b position.

The results demonstrate that meaningful factors related to large differences in pupils' solving performance can be identified. These results have implications for planning instruction (e.g., sequencing) and developing curricular materials (e.g., grade placement).

DISCUSSION

The charge given for the preparation of this narrative was to illustrate the many activities and decisions that are a part of the research process. The purpose of the study was to determine whether certain mathematical and status factors are related to students' solving performance on basic kinds of open sentences and to gather baseline data about the ability to solve these specific types of open sentences. This study could logically be considered a specific part of several important areas of research.

Formulating the Research Question

The research falls under the broad umbrella of individual differences because of the attention given to the variables of ability and sex. The study can also be considered as research designed to identify structural components in learning tasks related to differences in learning rates. One long-term goal of such research is developing mathematical models of the learning process, and the emphasis, in this study, on mathematical factors such as operation and placeholder position ties it to this realm of research. The study is also related to evaluation and assessment because the data characterize current performance of students on an important mathematical topic.

It is important to note that one of the prime motivating forces for doing the research was to extend the results obtained by Weaver (1971, 1973) in the areas of addition and subtraction. Poor performance on particular kinds of multiplication and division sentences might be related, perhaps highly, to easily identifiable mathematical factors inherent in each of the sentences. If so, then the instructional and curricular implications would be important, and the need would be apparent for doing further experimental work to determine whether or not instruction that focused on the mathematical factors identified would improve pupils' solving performance.

The decision to do this research was a gradual process; it would be very difficult to identify a particular time or day when the final "go" decision was made. Interest increased during the review of the related literature because very little directly applicable research had been done. Suppes's work with computer-assisted instruction and response latencies as well as some older research on the relative difficulty of the basic facts were examined but contributed very little to the conceptualization and implementation of the research. Thus, the previously mentioned research by Weaver and my own clinical research on addition and subtraction sentences served as the guideposts. The arduous and often monotonous task of reviewing the literature was greatly diminished because Weaver's (1973) review could be used as a starting point, and thus the search could be restricted primarily to recent studies. The strategy of building on previous reviews of the literature is a good one because of its time-saving features, but the danger in relying heavily on someone else's review of the literature is that the review may not have been as meticulous as it should have been; thus, an important piece of information may be overlooked.

Many researchable questions are obviously associated with students' solving performance on open sentences. This study was molded into one of manageable size in several ways. First, the researcher's personal interest dictated that the study would involve whole-number multiplication and division rather than, say, the rational numbers or other operations. Second, the desire to compare results with the Weaver study influenced the decision to limit the study to the performance of elementary school pupils.

With these as the given parameters, the decision was made to gather information in three broad areas. First, gathering data related to pupils' solving performance with the mathematical factors previously mentioned should be a top priority. Second, baseline data concerning this performance would then automatically become available, and gathering this information at several grade levels would be highly desirable so that growth in students' solving performance over a specific time interval could be estimated. Third, since information concerning status variables might help explain some of the results from the first two procedures, sex and aptitude were selected as the status variables to be examined.

Designing the Study

In defining the scope, I gave considerable thought to two situations: (a) open sentences that did not have whole-number solutions, and (b) the relationship between open sentences and verbal problems serving as models of these sentences. Both situations were important, but a balance had to be struck between what was desirable and what could be comfortably managed. The verbal-problem dimension was clearly far too vast to be incorporated. The no-solution sentences were feasible and were incorporated quite early in the overall planning.

At this time I was also involved in a separate, large-scale naturalistic study of teacher effectiveness in mathematics and wanted to use a content instrument that measured a narrow band of content in considerable depth. Scores from such an instrument would supplement standardized achievement scores that were already available. The study of teacher effectiveness was being conducted in third- and fourth-grade classrooms, and thus an inventory focusing in depth on the ability to solve open multiplication and division sentences seemed highly appropriate. After considering some of the pros and cons (e. g., appropriateness of content vs. narrow or limited nature at this level), I decided that an inventory of open sentences would be one of the measures used in the effectiveness study, and the inventory would be constructed such that data concerning the previously mentioned research questions would be generated. This sequence of events is one of several situations that were not mentioned in the published report because of space limitations.

The decision to collect data by means of the effectiveness study thus determined the sample for the open-sentence research. This was deemed to be a positive situation, since the effectiveness study was to include every third- and fourth-grade classroom in a large metropolitan school district. The solving performance of 3002 pupils in 135 classrooms could therefore be assessed. Also, since this school district had administered an aptitude test, aptitude could easily be used as one of the status variables.

Along with the acquisition of the sample came a fixed testing date. The testing date was reasonably close at hand, providing the impetus necessary for the project to move along at a rapid rate. It would have been convenient to have had more time to reflect on certain decisions, but one might still have felt this way even if one had been able to push forward the testing date.

The development of the inventory went smoothly. Early in this developmental stage, the decision was made that the instrument should, whenever possible, parallel Weaver's (1973) instrument so that results of the two studies could be easily compared. In fact, Weaver provided the essential components of the inventory, and my work on his earlier project no doubt influenced the multiplication and division study in numerous ways.

Several facets of the inventory development might have been done differently by another researcher. For example, two items of each of the 12 types of open sentences and one no-solution item for each of the 8 types[1] were written. This resulted in a total of 32 items—more than most pupils could respond to in one sitting. Thus, the items were systematically divided among four test forms in a way that preserved a balance among the mathematical factors being considered. Such a balance was not hard to achieve with the solution type of sentences, but it was a bit arbitrary with regard to the no-solution sentences. Alternative strategies considered included expanding the testing time to two days and reducing to one the number of solution sentences of each type. The factor that influenced our decision was the data unit, which was to be the class mean at a minimum; thus, it was more important to have two number facts involved with each type of open sentence than to have every pupil respond to every item.

Number facts were assigned to the types of open sentences to ensure a somewhat rough balance with regard to fact difficulty among the different types. This was necessary because there were only two items for each type of open sentence. Nevertheless, some might have preferred that this be done randomly. There are a number of other options that could have been exercised in forming the inventory, but the researchers have no second thoughts about the decisions that were made. If time had been available, it would have been interesting (even desirable) to do some pilot testing of alternatives. However, the feeling was that even if the instrument were

---

1. Note that open sentences of the form $a \times b = \Box$, $\Box \div b = c$, $\Box = a \times b$, and $c = \Box \div b$ always have whole-number solutions when whole numbers are used as replacements for the constants.

constructed differently, the result would have been the same, assuming that the new instrument was developed through a carefully conceived and logical plan.

A number of considerations of physical format were involved in developing the instrument to measure pupils' performance. Special attention was given to whether to use open boxes (□) or shaded boxes (■) as placeholders and to the context of "numbers hiding under boxes" in the directions. The latter choice was used in spite of its lack of mathematical appeal because the researchers felt that it was easy to understand, tended to motivate pupils at this age, and because Weaver had used this scheme in his study. Some discussion also centered on how to instruct the pupils to indicate "no whole-number solutions." A large X was used for this purpose, but there was concern that it would be overused, especially when pupils considered it synonymous with "I don't know" (this factor might also have been studied in a pilot). Considerable discussion also centered on appropriate sample problems and whether the answers to the sample problems should be given. The answer to the last question ultimately was no, because the possibility of introducing a teaching influence was too great.

Implementing the Study

The instrument was administered by the classroom teachers, primarily because of the large number of classes involved. This offered the advantage of a natural setting for the pupils but also introduced the possibility of nonstandardized testing conditions. Testing directions were written for the teachers to help minimize this effect. The general feeling was that videotaped instructions would have been better, but this alternative was ruled out because of the time required to produce a tape and the lack of playback equipment in the schools.

Perhaps the largest shortcoming of the research was fully realized at this point when the collection of data was to begin. No provisions had been made for gathering interview data about how the pupils had solved sentences or about the nature of their errors. This problem was not recognized sooner mainly because the rush to finish other aspects of the research allowed little time to think about the many uses for interview data had the information been available. In retrospect it probably would not have been feasible to include such data. Inclusion of interviews would have required additional trained personnel (of which none were available) and time to develop, field test, and refine interview protocols. The only consolation was that interview data could be collected in future studies, and the appropriate framework for such interviews would then be much clearer with the data from this study at hand. Also, tentative hypotheses could be generated from an examination of incorrect responses to the sentences on the inventory and from their frequencies.

Few difficulties were encountered in collecting the data. There were a few instances where a greater than expected number of a single test form were distributed in a classroom, but the investigators did not observe any other anomalies.

Preparing the data for analysis was time-consuming. In some situations certain data were missing. Some aptitude scores were missing, and there were no inventory scores for some students. This situation was anticipated, given the sample size, and it had been decided a priori that all observations with missing data would be deleted. In fact, the sample size was such that it was decided that school means rather than classroom means could be used. Blocking in this fashion was felt to reduce any error contributed by unusual grouping practices or the results of poor teaching practices by a single teacher within a school. Of course, such a decision was only feasible because of the large sample, and replication in another setting could well require more stringent controls.

The data analysis proceeded as planned except that in order to keep cell sizes at manageable levels, sex and aptitude were analyzed with the other factors using separate ANOVAs. This involved a trade-off in that all possible relationships could not be analyzed. However, the trade-off was deemed appropriate, since the major effects were more readily identified and tested.

Interpreting the Results

The results from this study were clear and comparable to the results of Weaver's study of addition and subtraction sentences. Interpretation, however, was a difficult matter. Interpretation by its very nature is a personal undertaking, and what is overemphasized or slighted is often unique in the eyes of the beholder. The principal difficulty in interpretation centered on ascribing differences in difficulty to prior teaching and background as opposed to difficulties inherent in the different sentences. It is difficult to ascertain the exact amount of influence that each has exerted on pupil performance.

Another aspect of interpretation should be mentioned. The generalization of the baseline data reported for the low-ability group had to be tempered somewhat because the sample was from a school district that had comparatively few schools of low socioeconomic status. Hence, baseline estimates for low-ability pupils may tend to be in error on the high side.

POSTSCRIPT

The extent to which textbook authors will give more attention to instruction designed to improve performance on those sentences shown to cause difficulty is yet to be seen. The back-to-basics movement, however, suggests that the direct computation sentences on which performance is already relatively high will be the sentences that get increased attention.

Finally, the value of keeping a detailed log during the research process cannot be overemphasized. In addition to providing needed information when writing the report, it has a multitude of uses that are often overlooked or not anticipated at the time the research is conducted (e.g., replicating the research, extending the research, and writing reports such as this paper). I regret that I was not more conscientious in this regard.

REFERENCES

Grouws, D. A., & Good, T. L. Factors associated with third- and fourth-grade children's performance in solving multiplication and division sentences. *Journal for Research in Mathematics Education*, 1976, 7, 155–171.

Weaver, J. F. Some factors associated with pupils' performance levels on simple open addition and subtraction sentences. *Arithmetic Teacher*, 1971, 18, 513-519.

Weaver, J. F. The symmetric property of the equality relation and young children's ability to solve open addition and subtraction sentences. *Journal for Research in Mathematics Education*, 1973, 4, 45-56.

CASE STUDY 2:

Clinical Research

The Nature and Development of Problem-Solving Behavior in Early Childhood (Bana & Nelson, 1977; Bourgeois & Nelson, 1977; Nelson & Kieren, 1977; Nelson & Sawada, 1975)

L. Doyal Nelson
University of Alberta

ABSTRACT

The problem-solving behavior of children of ages 3 to 9 was the domain of the study discussed here. Several research tasks were areas of focus. First, it was necessary to identify, select, and refine criteria for specifying and constructing mathematical problems that could be used effectively to study the problem-solving behavior of such children. Problem situations were then selected and constructed. Next, children were engaged in interacting with the problem situations under carefully controlled clinical conditions. The behaviors manifested by the children as they were thus engaged were observed, recorded, coded, and categorized. Finally, the development of problem-solving behavior was traced over the age range.

A number of constraints were imposed on the domain to make the research tasks more specific. The first constraint was on the content. Each problem situation had a definite mathematical interpretation or was the embodiment of some basic mathematical idea and in that sense was content specific. The second constraint concerned the mode of interaction. Most research in mathematical problem solving had occurred at a highy verbal level with the problem situations presented verbally and the solution expressed symbolically. In this research it was required that solutions could always be expressed by physical manipulation or movement. Thus, each problem situation needed to be a concrete embodiment of some mathematical idea and its solution amenable to expression through the manipulation of different components of the embodiment. Such manipulative behaviors were the prime focus; the purpose was not to explain thinking nor necessarily to explain the processes involved in problem solving. This level of interpretation placed a third constraint on the research. The modest aim forced complete attention on the manipulative behaviors of the children as they solved the problems. A final constraint was in the age range of children to be studied. In Piagetian terms children in the range from 3 to 9 years would be in either the preoperational or the concrete-operational stage of development. If effective communication was to be established and maintained over the age range, the constraint of concrete embodiment mentioned above was essential.

The establishment of a set of criteria on which to base the development of problem situations to meet the requirements was accomplished over a periods of years. Figure 1 lists such a workable set, reprinted from the *Alberta Journal of Educational Research* (Nelson & Sawada, 1975). This

A. *The problem should be of significance mathematically.* It is for the potential of the situation as a vehicle for the development of mathematical ideas that we choose a particular problem situation or family of situations above all others.

B. *The situation in which the problem occurs should involve real objects or obvious simulations of real objects.* The main consideration here is that it be comprehensible to the child and easily related to his world of reality.

C. *The problem situation should capture the interest of the child either because of the nature of the materials, the situation itself, the transformations the child can impose on the materials, or because of some combination of these factors.*

D. *The problem should require the child to make moves or transformations or modifications with or in the materials.* It is difficult to overemphasize the role of action in early childhood learning. Most of the mathematical models we are interested in at this level are what might be called "action models."

E. *Wherever possible, problems should be chosen which offer opportunities for different levels of solution.* If the child can move immediately from the problem situation to an expression of its mathematical structure it is not a problem.

F. *Whatever situation is chosen as the particular vehicle for the problems, it should be possible to create other situations which have the same mathematical structure.* Another way of saying this is that the same problem should have many physical embodiments. It may not be possible for a child to generalize a solution to a certain kind of problem until the problem has come up in a variety of situations.

G. *Finally, the child should be convinced he can solve the problem and should know when he has a solution for it.* If the child is somehow required to react with or transform materials used in problem situations it is usually easy to determine whether the problem meets the criterion or not.

Figure 1. Criteria for creating good problems.

same set of criteria, slightly rephrased, can be found in the Thirty-seventh Yearbook of the National Council of Teachers of Mathematics (Nelson & Kirkpatrick, 1975). With the seven criteria as the basis for selection, a group of six problem-solving situations involving different mathematical ideas were chosen from a number of previously designed situations. A second concrete and equivalent embodiment was constructed for each of these six problem situations. The basic problem situations, but not their equivalents, are described by Nelson and Sawada (1975).

These 12 problem situations were presented according to a prearranged schedule to 15 children at each age level, 3 to 8. Each child in this sample of 90 children was presented with six problem situations, four of which were different and two of which were the equivalents of two of the first four. A year later as many children as available were brought back and asked to do six more problems. There were 74 children in this second group. The particular problem situations in both the cross-sectional and the longitudinal sampling were established by the sampling schedule mentioned above. In both samplings, children were seated, one at a time, at a low table with an interviewer to their right. The interviewer presented the problems one after another at one sitting, which lasted from 20 minutes to a little over an hour. Children's manipulative and verbal behaviors were recorded on one-half inch videotape. Two black-and-white cameras and a device to provide a split image were used in order that two views of the children could be recorded at once, if desired. All cross-sectional data were recorded on 54 one-hour tapes and the longitudinal data on 45 one-hour tapes.

In the cross-sectional sampling, each problem situation was presented to 10 children at each age level. Five children at each level did the equivalent problems. The taped section of each child performing a particular problem was separated out and analyzed. There were 60 taped sections for each problem and 30 for each equivalent for the cross-sectional aspect. These 60 taped sections were analyzed as a unit. Complete reports of such analyses are available for 6 of the 12 problems (Bourgeois, 1976; Little, 1976). Summaries are also reported for four of the problems in Nelson and Kieren (1977) and Bourgeois and Nelson (1977). Other analyses are in various stages of preparation.

No preconceived system was established for coding the taped data to written form. It was required that the form of the code would be determined solely by viewing the tapes. A unique code had to be developed for each separate problem, and samples of the codes are provided by Bourgeois (1976) and Little (1976). Transferring behavioral data from tape to written form proved to be an arduous task.

Once the data were coded, behaviors were described and categorized using only the information from the tapes. A sample of the findings from such an analysis can be found in the papers by Bourgeois and Nelson (1977) and Nelson and Kieren (1977).

DISCUSSION

Formulating the Research Question

Unlike most reported research no attempt was made to formulate hypotheses that could then be tested through familiar statistical procedures. The primary aim was to determine how young children, ages 3 to 9, would behave or respond when faced with specific mathematical problems centered on, or embodied in, specific physical apparatuses.

The physical situations were constructed so that it was always possible to do the related problem tasks by manipulating the elements of the situation. This did not, of course, prevent any child from giving a more sophisticated or at least a more symbolic solution. Indeed, the problems were largely constructed so that a range of solutions from highly manipulative to purely symbolic was possible. As subsequent data were gathered, it became increasingly apparent that the presence of the apparatus and the nature of the questions directed to the child tended to encourage a manipulative rather than a symbolic response.

To err in this direction was considered to be more desirable than to err in the other. Previous work had suggested that even 3-year-olds had considerable control over many mathematical processes that they could express through their manipulations but not at all in any symbolic form. Increasing the probability of a manipulative response rather than a verbal or more symbolic one increased the probability that the younger children would respond if they had any knowledge or understanding of the underlying mathematical process or idea. It was assumed that older children who could respond in a more symbolic form would do so. The actual recorded responses of the children cast considerable doubt on the validity of this assumption. Older children who were capable of making a symbolic response gave a manipulative response as often as not and would produce a symbolic one only when urged to do so, or they would give both.

One of the most difficult aspects at this stage was to formulate the set of criteria that would serve as guidelines for the construction of the problem situations and for the formulation of the associated problem tasks. The set of seven criteria mentioned in the abstract (see Figure 1) were developed out of a *study of the literature and many hours of careful clinical work with children.* Still, the criteria are very crude and, although they do provide guidance for constructing the physical apparatus and associated problem tasks, they need further refinement. It is clear that some problems are "better" than others in that some conform more closely to the guidelines than others. Unfortunately, the problems that seem better when measured against the guidelines do not produce problem-solving behaviors on the part of children distinguishable in quality from those behaviors produced by problems that do not so measure up.

This is certainly not the first attempt ever made to define what a problem is or to provide criteria for producing suitable problems. These attempts, for the most part, have had only limited success and application. The attempt here is no exception. However, crude as these guidelines are, they help in lending some specificity to the problem situations and in formulating the associated problem tasks.

With the guidelines thus established, it was possible to ask an appropriate research question: *What is the nature and development of problem-solving behavior of young children while solving problems constructed in accordance with the guidelines?*

I hasten to point out that the reader should not get the impression that the important research question arose after the guidelines were developed. In fact, the question had occurred in a number of different forms long before, but always in connection with specific clinical encounters with children. These encounters led to the expectation that one could tap the considerable mathematical understanding and problem-solving ability of very young children if one only had a better method. Previous attempts had failed because the means adopted always required the child to produce, to a greater or lesser extent, some kind of written or symbolic response. The symbol system of young children is simply not established well enough or extensive enough to permit them to make adequate responses in this form. Analyses of any such responses could only lead to grave distortions. The development of the guidelines was an attempt to express more precisely what kind of situations and what form of responses would be more appropriate for very young children. Any reservations expressed here about the application of the guidelines should be understood as an indication that there is still more work to be done in this area.

Design and Implementation

Creating the problem situations. Informal clinical work with children over several years had established the basic form of some of the problems used. For the most part, though, the problems were designed in their original form specifically to provide information on the research question posed in the previous section.

The problem called Cargo Groups (Bourgeois & Nelson, 1977) is an example of one that was developed and refined over a period of years. In one of its early uses it consisted of a tagboard base with a cutout of blue construction paper running across to represent a river. The ferryboat was a tagboard cutout, and the "cargo" was made up of a number of 2 cm × 2 cm cutout blocks. The protocols used to present the situation to the child and to describe the problem tasks also had undergone a number of refinements. The equivalent situation, which became known as Animal Groups (Bourgeois & Nelson, 1977), was designed specifically for this study.

The method used in creating the majority of the problems can best be described by illustrating the process for a specific problem. The example used will be the problem called Fold-Out Shapes. For a description of the apparatus, see Nelson and Kieren (1977). To specify the mathematical idea or process involved for all the problems, a team made up of the research director, an associate, and four graduate students shut themselves in a classroom for a predetermined period (usually about two or three hours a day for three or four days each week).

The mathematical content considered appropriate for young children was outlined on a blackboard, and appropriate related problem situations were suggested for each. Applying the guidelines in developing problem situations and tasks was a fundamental requirement. Outlining the content proved not too controversial or difficult a task, but it took some time for all members of the team to learn how to apply the criteria specified in the guidelines. Since the Cargo Group problem was already available, it served as a good model for the application of the guidelines and was constantly referred to in the early stages.

Several geometry topics were outlined under mathematical content, and one such topic involved the construction of three-dimensional solids from two-dimensional elements. In order for children to see the relationships of the elements to each other and how they came together to form a network that could then be folded to make a three-dimensional shape, it was necessary that the elements could be easily attached to each other and as easily taken apart. With the cube, for example, there are six squares, and it should be easy for children to see them as individual pieces but also easy to assemble them to form the cube. At the same time it should be just as easy for them to perceive the reverse situation. There are several commercial sets whose elements can be put together to form three-dimensional shapes, but one problem of design is that they cannot be easily assembled and disassembled.

A Technical Services branch at the University of Alberta routinely deals with problems of design such as this, and the first step was to approach them. Their initial suggestion was to use Plexiglas elements and embed magnets at intervals along the sides. This would certainly meet the requirements of easy assembly and disassembly, but the resulting apparatus would probably be too bulky for a 3-year-old to handle.

The group went back again to the closed classroom to try to resolve this difficulty and, as it happened, resolved it in one session. In discussing possible means of joining elements, someone mentioned the material Velcro, whose most familiar use in this part of the country is as a cloth zipper to close pockets on winter clothes. One side of the zipper consists of a mass of tiny loops woven into tape; the other side consists of a mass of tiny hooks also woven into tape. When the two sides are brought into contact, the hooks engage the loops and make a positive join. A slight tug will separate the two sides. The material was ideal for our purpose!

A four-foot-by-eight-foot sheet of one-eighth-inch Plexiglas was purchased, along with Velcro of several widths and colors. Six 10 cm × 10 cm squares were cut from the Plexiglas, and alternate sides of the Velcro were cemented to the edges of the squares. A similar procedure was used for triangles and pentagons using the constant 10-cm dimension. (The reader is left with the problem of how to attach Velcro to elements having an odd number of sides.) With 6 squares, 20 triangles, and 12 pentagons it is possible to construct all the Platonic solids, and a number of other solids may also be constructed by combining the various elements in different ways.

There were a few additional problems of design to be solved even after the prototypes had been constructed. A saw was first used to cut the Plexiglas, but a cutter can be obtained that scribes the plastic as a glass cutter scribes glass. The plastic then breaks into straight, neat lines just as glass would. Ordinary contact cement was found unsuitable for attaching the Velcro to the plastic. After trying a number of glues and cements without success, we found that a *premium grade* contact cement was available that firmly glued the Velcro to the Plexiglas. Different widths of Velcro were tried, but it was found that three-quarter-inch Velcro served best on the one-eighth-inch Plexiglas.

The reader may think that design problems such as the ones described are not the province of research workers in mathematics education and should be referred to design experts for solution. Very creative people are doubtless available to do this if they can be found, but finding them is certainly not easy. In addition, research workers must be prepared to pay high rates for such services, and budgets are, more often than not, too tight to provide the necessary funds. Conveying the notion of precisely what is needed to even highly qualified designers is often difficult and creates further difficulties. We were fortunate enough to find a carpenter who could translate our specifications, descriptions, and crude drawings into highly attractice and creative apparatuses. His skills were precisely what we needed.

Written protocols for presenting the apparatuses and for outlining the associated problem tasks *were developed through extensive work with young children in the laboratory and in schools.* In the early stages it was estimated that children might be able to deal with about eight different problem situations in one sitting. It turned out, however, that the session for some became overly long, and the number of problems for each sitting was reduced to six. In developing the protocols, we decided that in the actual research situation the child should sit at a low table in the laboratory beside an interviewer and the problems should be presented one after the other.

The laboratory setup and procedures were refined through a large number of pilot runs. Clinical procedures proved interesting to children and to their parents with the result that there were more volunteers than could be used at this stage. From the outset a decision was made to record children's responses on videotape and to use these tapes as the sole basis for subsequent analyses. A number of people on the research team had had considerable experience with recording children's behavior on tape and film and gave indispensable advice in this area. It was apparent that color sometimes influenced the way children responded, but since color videotape facilities were not available, a compromise had to be made. Children's responses were recorded on black-and-white videotape, and key sequences were filmed on 8-mm color film. We were never able to overcome the difficulty of coordinating the taped and filmed sequences and therefore abandoned the use of color film.

With the assistance of competent technical personnel, two video cameras were trained on the table at which the children worked, one giving a close-up view of the action and the other a wide-angle view. There was a split-image capability, so that images from both cameras could be recorded at once. Technicians were trained to operate the cameras and to catalog the recorded data. Two members of the research team did all the interviewing.

Aside from inevitable technical breakdowns (which in our study were very few) there were no difficulties with filming. Every part of the procedure had been carefully systematized through hours of work with children before the actual research data were collected. It was also a considerable and time-consuming task to *systematize the protocols* used to present the problems and problem tasks to the children. Unfortunately, in the cross-sectional data a rather serious procedural error was induced. The reader may have noted that we feared some information would be lost through children's not responding—either through unfamiliarity with the apparatus, uneasiness with the situation, or some other reason. It was decided that when a child would not respond, the interviewers could at their discretion make minor changes in the protocol. Early in the collection of the cross-sectional data it became clear that our fears were unfounded. Very few children failed to respond, but deviations from protocol occurred for those who did not at first respond. We did not want to tighten the protocols at this stage and did not have the resources or the time to start over. *Subsequent analyses of the data proved to be difficult wherever there were deviations from the established protocols; the only way to handle this situation was to describe in detail precisely what deviations had occurred. When the longitudinal data were collected, the established protocols were followed faithfully, thus making analyses much simpler. Researchers who attempt clinical studies are strongly advised to develop protocols that do not vary from subject to subject or vary as little as possible.*

Decisions now had to be made about the sample. It had been found that children could do six problems at one sitting. Between 10 and 20 children at each age level had to be tested to stay within the budget and at the same time to provide enough data for the analysis. The decision was made that each child should do four different problems and two equivalents. Since four different problems can be chosen in $_6C_4$, or 15, different ways, it was advantageous to require 15 subjects at each age level, making a total of 90 subjects. This group provided the cross-sectional data. Then, a year later, as many subjects as possible would be brought back. This time they would do four equivalent problems and two original problems according to the same sampling scheme. The reader will be able to write out the 15 different patterns or problem sets for the cross-sectional data and the 15 sets for the longitudinal data. Each of these problem sets would be randomly assigned to each subject.

Clearly, the scheme would permit a number of checks. The growth of children's problem-solving ability for a particular problem could be traced over the year. The effect of the order of presentation could be checked because in the cross-sectional sampling the problem was given before its equivalent, whereas in the longitudinal sampling the equivalent problem was presented before the original. The longitudinal data would serve as a reliability check on the cross-sectional data. For example, whatever could be said about how the 4-year-olds differed as a group from the 5-year-olds when looking at the cross-sectional data could be checked by looking at the difference between the 4-year-olds in the cross-sectional sampling and the same children at age 5 a year later. The check could not, of course, be perfect because in the longitudinal sampling not all the original children were available. In this study there were, in fact, 16 children lost between the first and the second samplings.

It was assumed that children could be chosen from a volunteer group to provide data for the purpose described. Although the characteristics of such a group were not expected to be completely representative, such a shortcoming was assumed to have minimal effect. Then, too, the difficulty of getting a random sample of 3- and 4-year-olds in any community is well known. All findings in the study would therefore have to be checked further by more rigorous means.

In May and June of 1974, 600 notices were distributed to parents of children in Grades 1, 2, and 3 in five elementary schools and two day-care centers in the vicinity of the University of Alberta. These notices invited parents to permit their children, ages 3 to 8 years, to participate in the collection of data in the summer of 1974 and 1975. Except for the 3-year-olds, sufficient numbers of children were volunteered by their parents to allow selection by a random process. There were not enough 3-year-olds to make up the sample of 15, and so a number of personal requests were made to obtain the required number. The allocation of sets of problems to children within each age group was randomized. These sets were numbered 1–15 according to their occurrence in the systematic table used to construct the sets. Parents of the children selected were contacted by telephone in the order in which their applications were received, and an appointment schedule was compiled. The first appointment for the cross-sectional sampling was for 24 June 1974, and the final interview was held on 23 July 1974. Similar procedures were used for the longitudinal sampling. The interviews for this phase were conducted from 3 July to 25 July 1975. An attempt was made to adhere to a schedule of three interviews in the morning and two in the afternoon. No 3-year-olds were interviewed in the afternoon. Seven adults were normally in the room during the interview: two camera operators, the interviewer, two assistants, the director or associate director of the project, and a parent of the child. Once they became involved in the problems, none of the children appeared to be unduly distracted by the rather formidable laboratory setup.

Analysis and Interpretation

Nearly 100 hours of taped material resulted from the cross-sectional and longitudinal samplings. The taped segment for each individual problem was separated out. In the cross-sectional sample there were 10 children at each level who did each of the original problems and 5 children who did the equivalents. If all children had been available for longitudinal sampling, 10 children would have done the problem equivalents and 5 would have done the original problems. The attrition rate has already been mentioned.

Separating out the taped sections for each problem involved a great deal of tape changing in addition to the viewing time required to get the children's responses into some kind of manageable form on paper. Each problem required its own coding system. After a number of taped sections for children at different levels were viewed, categories for solution strategies began to emerge. These categories formed the basis of the analyses, but individual behaviors had to be detailed within the categories. One of the most serious problems at this stage was to find coders who were able to go through the tedious process of analysis and still remain alert for significant periods of time. Tolerance levels ranged from only a few minutes to as much as 3 or 4 hours. The analyses for some of the problems have been completed, but others are still in progress. Funding authorities and referees have to be convinced that the expense of such open-ended analyses is necessary.

At this juncture a word should be said about the risks involved when no a priori scheme is adopted for analyzing data. First, there is no guarantee that any sensible and interpretable patterns will emerge from the data (here, videotapes of children's responses) after much effort has been expended to collect them. In fact, this led to problems with referees who could not accommodate themselves to such tentativeness. These problems in turn affected the funding agency, which, on the advice of one referee, made a drastic and crippling cut in the requested budget. Fortunately, the decision to analyze problem by problem made possible the completion of important parts of the study before the funds ran out. When there are departures from accepted methodologies—as certainly was true here—it would be a rare occurrence for an agency to assign a completely sympathetic referee.

Examples of data analyses and interpretations are given in Bourgeois and Nelson (1977) and in Nelson and Kieren (1977).

Influencing the Profession

It was not intended that any of the outcomes of this research would have immediate application in the classroom. However, certain phenomena have emerged that would ultimately have very important implications for classroom practice. For example, some specific ways were discovered in which children are distracted when involved in problem situations. Reports of distractibility of children are certainly not new. Indeed, Piagetian nonconservation is essentially the result of predictable distractions in children's behavior. We need to be able to predict, with approximately the same assurance we have when dealing with nonconservation, what specific factors will prove distracting to children when we provide physical apparatuses designed to help them learn mathematics. In the meantime, teachers who introduce manipulative physical material in an attempt to aid mathematical learning must accept that there may be some aspects of the material or situation that could actually hinder learning.

Another behavior became apparent that has had less attention from researchers. Children in the age range involved here exhibited a marked reluctance to make a prediction about an outcome when they were asked to do so. About half the children at each age level substituted a variety of behaviors when asked to predict. Do teachers observe the same reluctance in school, or was this an artifact of the particular methodology used here?

The nature of children's spontaneous verbal behavior was of interest here, even though verbalizations were not the focus. Younger children tended to monitor or describe their manipulations or actions when involved in the problem tasks. Older subjects' verbalizations usually involved questions about the apparatus or questions to clarify the nature of the task they were being asked to do. Such verbal behavior, although different in quality from the younger to older children, seemed to help children to specify to their own satisfaction what the problem really was. Often the children were not solving the intended problem at all. Do teachers give children opportunities to comment or ask questions when they are engaged in solving problems? Or, what means are provided to ensure that the child is, indeed, trying to solve the intended problem?

These are just a few examples of the kind of behaviors of importance in the classroom that were revealed in the data analysis of this research. It points up the advantages of careful but free observation of children's responses but at the same time stimulates a vast array of questions that must be answered if we are to understand fully the role of problem solving in mathematics learning.

Research Needed

When one adopts a classical statistical design, some compromises are almost certain, but there is an accepted and reliable methodology available. In the kind of research reported here, a specific methodology must be devised without a great body of supporting literature. Thus, one of the important outcomes was the development of methods for collecting and analyzing data. It is recognized that the methods were far from perfect, but as variations are tried and used, it is almost certain that some aspects of the method will be perfected. For example, what is the best way of transposing information from videotape to a form that can be more easily interpreted? Will a universally applicable coding scheme emerge? How does one compensate for information lost when a preordained coding scheme is used? Does the presence of cameras so change children's behavior that the information gathered has no application in a school situation? Do major changes in the way a question is formulated cause major changes in how a child will respond in certain situations? These are only a few of the methodological questions that can be resolved only through further research.

Although this research revealed important information on different aspects of problem-solving behavior and responses in young children, it provided no information about the interrelationships of these behaviors nor any means for predicting responses when various elements of the situation are manipulated. Further research with appropriate hypotheses is needed before such information becomes available.

The reporter and a colleague have done a series of systematic follow-ups on the role of distractors in mathematical learning as a result of the outcomes from this study. The results of a series of pilot studies have been reported (Bana & Nelson, 1977) as well as those of a main study (Bana & Nelson, 1978). This is only the beginning of the kind of research that is needed if we are to be able to predict precisely how children will be distracted in specific situations and what effect such distractors will have on children's ability to cope with problems that involve physical apparatuses or the interpretation of physical situations. In this connection, too, some children who were distracted by certain elements of a problem were still able to solve the problem. Others who were similarly distracted could not overcome the distractions. Why is this? In what way should distractors enter a learning situation? Should there be a conscious effort to eliminate them in the early learning stages, or is the quality of such learning different when these aspects are eliminated? Some survey information is necessary at this stage, but testing hypotheses can go forward on different aspects of the questions raised above. What about the reluctance on the part of some children to predict? Does this reluctance seriously impede their problem-solving competence? Can predictive ability be developed or encouraged by any means? The ability of children to see the relationship between a number and its factors was found in this study to be all but absent in even the older children. Is this ability desirable in children 8 and 9 years old, and if so, can the ability be developed to advantage?

In summary, readers must be aware of the strengths and the limitations of the kind of clinical research reported here. It is a highly effective means of standing back from a situation and viewing children's responses without the usual impediment of other methodologies. Its open-ended and relatively unconstrained procedures provide a fresh look that may lead to insights not possible with more rigorous methods. It can provide the direction for research using more systematic methodologies. It gives a comprehensive picture that may provide new dimensions for the study of how children learn mathematics.

However, in such a larger, global picture some details are obscured while others may show up in unwarranted bold relief. It may be that no amount of clinical work will clarify the obscurities of some details or account for the emphasis on others. For example, the global picture in this work revealed that the process of partition as a means of division is only vaguely understood by children in the age range studied. Why this is so must be discovered by other methods; our methods cannot do it. The question of whether children can learn to partition systematically can perhaps be resolved best by using a variety of instructional interventions under controlled conditions. Such research must be completed before reliable recommendations can be made to the teacher. Clinical methodology might not be the most suitable approach for such work.

REFERENCES

Bana, J. P., & Nelson, D. Some effects of distractions in nonverbal mathematical problems. *Alberta Journal of Educational Research,* 1977, *23,* 268–279.

Bana, J. P., & Nelson, D. Distractors in nonverbal mathematical problems. *Journal for Research in Mathematics Education,* 1978, *9,* 55–61.

Bourgeois, R. D. *Young children's behavior in division problems.* Unpublished doctoral dissertation, University of Alberta, 1976.

Bourgeois, R. D., & Nelson, D. Young children's behavior in solving division problems. *Alberta Journal of Educational Research,* 1977, *23,* 178–185.

Little, J. J. *A mathematical and cognitive analysis of children's behavior in spatial problems.* Unpublished doctoral dissertation, University of Alberta, 1976.

Nelson, L. D., & Kieren, T. E. Children's behavior in solving spatial problems. *Alberta Journal of Educational Research,* 1977, *23,* 22–29.

Nelson, L. D., & Kirkpatrick, J. Problem solving. In J. N. Payne (Ed.), *Mathematics learning in early childhood,* Thirty-seventh yearbook of the National Council of Teachers of Mathematics. Reston, Va.: The Council, 1975.

Nelson, L. D., & Sawada, D. Studying problem solving behavior in young children—Some methodological considerations. *Alberta Journal of Educational Research,* 1975, *21,* 28–38.

CASE STUDY 3:

Experiment

The Effects of Three Instructional Strategies on Problem-solving Behaviors in Secondary School Mathematics (Vos, 1976)

Kenneth E. Vos
College of St. Catherine

ABSTRACT

A number of behaviors or heuristics can be identified as important or useful for solving mathematical problems. This study compared three instructional strategies for promoting the selected behaviors of drawing a diagram, approximating and verifying a solution, constructing an algebraic equation, classifying data, and constructing a chart. The experimental setting was six mathematics classes (N = 133) across three grade levels (9, 10, 11) at a private high school in Iowa. The research design was a one-factor, randomized, complete block with mathematics classes as a blocking variable. Each of the instructional strategies involved working on a problem, but variations were made in the placement of, and emphasis on, an implied problem-solving behavior. One instructional strategy involved only exposure to problems; the other two strategies each involved an instructional phase. The results indicated that the subjects given instruction that emphasized specific behaviors were more likely to exhibit and make effective use of the problem-solving behaviors in new situations than subjects not given such instruction.

DISCUSSION

This narrative explains the trade-offs involved in conducting an experiment in a classroom environment. The choice of an experimental study rather than another type of research to investigate the problem resulted in a greater payoff but also increased the hazards. Before the study was conducted, the following pitfalls were considered: unrealistic demands within a classroom setting, uncontrolled variables that seem to increase in a geometric progression within experimental studies, and the possibility that the contribution to the profession could be minimal or negligible. Nevertheless, the advantages of conducting an experimental study were also considered: the possibility to generalize if a well-planned and well-designed study is conducted, and the interest of the researcher in the question "What if this was done; what would happen?" The "what if" question must motivate an experimental researcher, who looks to future events. Such motivation is in contrast to the survey, which asks what is being done, or the historical approach, which focuses on what has been done.

Successful research must be a process that results from a well-formed plan of action. My greatest satisfaction lies in the actual designing of the plan, discovering unique methods of evaluation, and applying new techniques to data analysis. The joy drops off rapidly once the research has started and is almost killed by the time the data must be analyzed.

Formulating the Research Idea

Contrary to popular belief, research problems are not found by a sudden flash of insight that clearly defines a specific researchable idea. Rather, formulating the research idea involves real detective work and a dose of tolerance for ambiguity.

The path I followed to arrive at an idea for problem-solving research was somewhat unique. During my secondary school teaching experience I had a dislike for verbal problems in algebra; therefore I usually skipped them, much to the joy of the students. Thus, I chose an area that was weak in one way but strong in others. My bias was negative; this may have been an advantage, since it was less likely to influence results and also helped me resist the eagerness to consider only one view.

A kernel of the research idea was obtained by reading both mathematical and psychological sources in the area of problem solving. Disagreement among the researchers in the problem-solving area was (and still is) almost unbelievable. An understanding of what is meant by problem solving ranges from performance on bent-nail puzzles to translating each word in a verbal problem into a mathematical statement.

The final formulation of the idea was generated by listening to mathematics educators discuss the importance of problem solving but become vague on how one actually teaches problem solving to secondary school students. After listening and reading, I found that my view of problem solving was obviously too narrow, since I had based my perceptions on textbook problems. The interest of students appears to be stifled by problems that involve only a complex algebraic solution, but possibly the motivation for solving problems would be increased if students were taught techniques that mathematics teachers apparently assume all students possess—making a diagram, taking a guess and checking it out, organizing the information in a chart, or looking for a pattern. These skills are usually acquired by mathematics teachers through experience in mathematics courses, but they are very seldom taught as specific skills for secondary school students.

To clarify my thoughts on problem solving, I continued my review of the literature. The review of the research literature in problem solving can result in at least three different reactions: limiting the concepts involved in problem solving, broadening the ideas about problem solving, or discouraging the researcher from even attempting another study in this chaotic area of research. A difficulty with a review of literature on problem solving is that problem solving has the well-earned reputation of being one of the most chaotic of all identifiable categories of human learning.

A few decisions were made to limit the review of literature: (a) the time period of most of the research reviewed was approximately the past 15 years; (b) the studies conducted by educational psychologists using all forms of cards, matchsticks, puzzles, and mazes were omitted (assumed not relevant for purposes of this investigation); and (c) studies on verbal problems or word problems were relegated to a secondary status in the review.

A major purpose of the review of literature was to determine a philosophical basis for defining what is a problem and what is the concept that is labeled "problem solving." The focus of this research was greatly sharpened by attempting to define what is a problem and what is problem solving. More and more the emphasis was placed on the actions of the learner in problem-solving situations. What did the learner do? Could the behavior be changed to be more effective in solving problems? Agreement among the references reviewed was minimal, but a thin thread of commonality appeared to be evident. A second emphasis in the review was to become acquainted with the current research found in certain experimental studies. This part of the review also identified those aspects of problem solving that had been shown to be obvious assumptions. These assumptions actually formed the foundation of the research. Current research was not reviewed as thoroughly as possible, because of the time lag between the review and the actual experiment. Also, for every study reviewed it seemed that 10 more studies had been conducted that were not reviewed, again because of time constraints or ignorance of the availability of the studies. The literature reviewed, however, seemed adequate for couching the proposed research in a theoretical framework (emphasizing heuristics or behaviors) and for justifying the need for the research.

Designing the Study

A pilot study should illuminate the majority of the problems with a research design or the test instruments. A pilot study was conducted in the school 4 months prior to the experiment. This pilot study focused primarily on two aspects—the validity of the learners' guides for instruction and the construction of the test instrument. Unfortunately, the pilot study was conducted with seniors in a secondary school, whereas the main study was designed for students in Grades 9–11. This grade difference resulted in some unwarranted assumptions. One such assumption was related to the students' ability to attend to a mathematics problem for a reasonable period of time. Seniors were more willing to try a problem for an extended period of time; students in the lower grades became discouraged more quickly and quit after only a short trial period. Because of the seniors' willingness to try in the pilot study, the individual experimental periods were extended, but in the main study this length of time was found to be unnecessary. A better selection of the sample for the pilot study would have been more advantageous. Seniors were chosen for two reasons: (a) the main study was to involve secondary students, and so the pilot study should involve secondary students; and (b) seniors would have graduated before the main study was conducted, and the same students therefore would not be involved in the main study.

The population selected for the main study was composed of students in Grades 9, 10, and 11. Only those students enrolled in algebra I and II, elementary algebra, math survey, and geometry courses were included. This selection eliminated a small number of students not enrolled in these particular mathematics courses. Selecting only the mathematics courses as sources for the population made it possible to conduct the experiment in a self-contained classroom setting. Thoughts were given to involving all students in the school in the experiment by conducting the study in homerooms or study rooms. The decision was made to remain in the mathematics classes, since this setting enabled the researcher to communicate all information to only two teachers who were familiar with mathematical terminology. A disadvantage that resulted from conducting the study in mathematics classes was the tendency by both the students and the teachers to discuss the problems after certain experimental instruction periods. Curiosity about a solution would obviously be greater in a natural mathematics setting than in a study room without a mathematics teacher as a monitor.

Secondary students were the focus for the main study. This focus was deliberate, since the results of the review of literature seemed to indicate that a large proportion of the studies on problem solving involved elementary grades or preservice elementary teachers. Very few studies had been done in secondary schools, possibly because of the difficulty in gaining access to classrooms or obtaining cooperation with administrators at this level of education. Cooperation was excellent in this study, but two aspects may have increased this cooperation—the setting was a private secondary school, and I had taught mathematics in this school a few years before the study was conducted.

The research design was a one-factor, randomized, complete block with mathematics classes as a blocking variable. The students in each class were randomly assigned to one of the three experimental treatments. Randomizing within classes resulted in unequal cell sizes with some cells quite small in number. Blocking was done because it was believed that the mathematics maturity of the student would be reflected in the results. This belief was supported in the results from the data. Blocking did cause unequal cell sizes, but more seriously, it caused very small cell sizes in a few classes. There were cell sizes with as few as two or three students. A compromise had to be made, since the size of the cells was not a result of the experiment but rather a drop in predicted total enrollment in that particular grade. Since the low cell sizes were not a result of the experiment, it was decided to keep the particular mathematics class in the study but to interpret the results with extreme caution.

The single greatest weakness of the study centered on the task of constructing and designing the tests. It was quickly determined that there were very few commercially available tests that would measure the important aspects in the study. Therefore, two tests were developed by the investigator —Problem-solving Approach Test and Problem-solving Test (Vos, 1973). Designing the Problem-solving Test was fairly simple; it consisted of seven written problems that asked for a free response from the student. Scoring was based on a dichotomous (correct-incorrect) method and a modification of a partial score developed by other researchers. Designing the Problem-solving Approach Test was much more difficult. The test was designed to obtain information about how a student would approach a problem; in other words, what are the student's plans of attack on a given problem? It was found that secondary school students are reluctant to commit themselves to a plan that does not immediately result in a solution. This test gave the student an opportunity to make a low-risk commitment because the solution to the problem was not demanded; only an approach was requested. The construction of the test resulted in an unfamiliar format of responses and a weighted response-scoring scheme (Vos, 1973). The scoring scheme is not widely used in test construction, and doubts about its validity and reliability are well-founded. Formulating this single test instrument consumed more time and energy than most of the other parts of the experiment, and still the instrument had weaknesses that were difficult to remove. One particular weakness of the test was the way the scoring key or criterion for success was determined. I have since refined this process and now consider the measure to be a reliable problem-solving instrument.

Written test measures were chosen for two reasons: (a) the total sample was over 100, and it was felt that oral test measures would be prohibitive; and (b) protocol scoring schemes were not fully developed at the time the study was conducted. These scoring schemes are just beginning to be developed for problem-solving research (e.g., see Kantowski, 1977). Written tests obviously have many disadvantages, but in this study the test measures were felt to be adequate for the particular hypotheses under consideration. Nevertheless, a crucial weakness was the importance that had to be given to the investigator-designed tests. Most of the data collection and analyses of the results were based on the data obtained from the two investigator-designed tests. Reliance on these special tests may have caused unwarranted interpretations of the results.

A carefully planned data-analysis program should be completed prior to a study. Ideally, this plan should be fully developed before the beginning of a study. Many research studies unfortunately do not show that prior planning was in effect. In my study a majority of the data-analysis plan was determined by the evaluation measures that were specifically designed for the study. Common measures of analysis such as means, standard deviations, and analysis of variance were used. In addition, when appropriate a Newman-Keuls method was employed to analyze the differences between pairs of means. An unweighted-means procedure was conducted for the ANOVA procedure, since the unequal cell sizes in the study were in no way related to the experimental treatments.

The bias of the researcher is usually evident in the analysis of the data. My biases regarding the method of analysis lean toward using a simple procedure but with an emphasis on what one might call "an honest method of applying the procedure." One aspect of this bias is my obsession about reporting the number of subjects, means, and standard deviations. In reading research reports, I would prefer to form my own opinion about the importance of the results by looking at the sample size and descriptive statistics and deciding if the mean difference is meaningful as well as statistically significant. Another bias that I hold is the manner of reporting the F statistic. I want to know the p value for every result of importance. In some studies one can make the case for setting a predetermined significance level of, say, .01 or .05, but for many experiments conducted in an educational setting this approach may be unrealistic and, in fact, overlook important implications or trends. A reporting of the p values should force the reader to determine the proper significance of the results by considering the nature of the study or the method of data collection. My report was planned to include a summary table of all p values for all the mathematics classes. It was anticipated that this table would be a valuable aid when attempting to interpret overall results. Basically I wanted to do two things in the data-analysis plan: (a) If there is any action in the experiment, it must show up in an obvious way in the reported means; and (b) if an ANOVA procedure is used, a reporting of the p values is valuable for a realistic interpretation of the results and for assistance in designing further research.

Implementation

All the planning and decision-making aspects of the research must have been completed at this stage of an experimental study. Ideally, this should be a decision-free part of the study. However, unexpected events do occur whenever the research involves people—for example, subjects may be absent or they may receive incorrect instructions. Nevertheless, the decisions made during such unexpected events must be within the context of the previously planned data-gathering method.

During the actual conducting of this experiment, I had the uneasy feeling of a total lack of control over the events that were occurring. It is true that the researcher has the least amount of freedom during the implementation of the study, but I did feel a degree of anxiety. The possible abortion of the study by an unseen danger was always on my mind. Two different teachers were responsible for distributing the instructional guidesheets. What if they mixed up the coded subjects over a period of time? A total of 20 different instructional guidesheets were scheduled in a specific sequence. What if the teachers mixed up the schedule? Within each mathematics class there were three different treatments. One treatment involved only the problem task, another treatment involved both an instructional problem task and the problem task, and a third treatment was a combination of the instructional problem task and the problem task. What if the subjects from the different treatments shared their ideas? Students at this school were accustomed to working together on mathematics problems. What if they wanted to do this during the experimental instructional period? Would the three different treatments remain distinct? The specific reason for choosing the instructional mode of guided individual instructional sheets was to control the teacher variable, but this decision could force more subject interaction as well. Through informal discussion with the two teachers, I learned that the subjects followed the guidelines of individual consideration of the problems most of the time and did not work in groups. Nevertheless, after the instructional guidesheets was returned to the teacher, the subjects sometimes wanted to discuss the problem with each other. This occurred most frequently with difficult or interesting problems. It was difficult to document when these discussions took place and in what detail they actually occurred. However, any such conversations could have contributed to contamination and tended to reduce treatment differences. The two teachers claimed that they did not discuss the problems at length in any context with the subjects. Thus, I assumed that the subjects within each specific treatment could be considered the same throughout the entire experiment.

During the 15-week experimental period, the school administration expressed some concern over the amount of time that posttesting would consume after the instructional period. The schedule had been approved earlier by the administration, but when the actual time for testing was calculated, some alarm was expressed. A compromise was reached that did not affect the measures given but instead lengthened the time intervals between the various measures. In addition, I agreed to administer most of the posttests, thereby giving the two teachers involved some released time. I do not believe that this adjustment in the time schedule had any effect on the results of the test measures. However, this situation illustrates one of those unforeseen problems for which decisions must be made quickly without much time to reflect on the consequences.

One common criticism of most experimental studies conducted in classrooms is the short period of time allotted for the treatments. Possibly this criticism could be valid for this study. There were 20 instructional periods of 20 minutes each, giving a total treatment time of 6 hours and 40 minutes. The treatment time was spread over 15 weeks, and so there were long time intervals between instructional treatment periods. Constraints of classroom time dictated these time intervals. A longer period of time, such as 30 weeks and possibly 60 instructional periods, would have been ideal but was not possible in this situation. Another constraint was the scarcity of effective problem tasks. I had to search the problem-solving literature extensively to find 40 problem tasks that were both suitable for the purpose of the study and appropriate for secondary school students. The scarcity of appropriate problem tasks remains a concern for researchers in problem solving.

The implementation stage is not the time to revise plans hastily, add new dimensions, or reject complete segments of the treatments because of faulty planning. This study followed very closely a timetable for a specific sequence of events. The data analysis and interpretations of the results were easier to accomplish by adhering to these plans.

Interpretation of Results

Analyzing the results should consist of merely putting into effect the plans that were decided before the experiment was conducted. However, the interpretation of what these results mean can be a source of difficulty to the researcher. It is easy to succumb to biases toward a certain treatment or a result of a specific posttest measure. The researcher must be cautious when interpreting the results.

In my study, I made the following decisions before the data were analyzed: (a) the results were to reflect an honest statement of what occurred; (b) the complete set of results from all the subjects would be reported; (c) the data would be analyzed thoroughly but not redone and redone in an attempt to "find something"; and (d) the data should reflect obvious group comparisons before a strong statement could be made concerning certain treatments. It was possible to adhere to all the decisions within the context of interpreting the results. The interpretation of the results was considered in a highly conservative mode. Caution was used in generalizing the results to other settings or to other populations of students.

One table (Table 5—Summary of p Values of All Classes) was referred to most frequently within the discussion of my study. I found it most valuable to have available the p values for all results rather than referring to only specific p-value limits. I believe a more flexible range of p values should be considered in an educational setting. A range of from .05 to .01 may be unrealistic for experiments conducted in classroom settings. In this study I anticipated that I might be able to identify possible trends. Hence, I was comfortable in making reference to p values as large as .20 when these were part of an overall pattern of "significance." Such flexibility of acceptance values for p may not be applicable to most research studies, but I believe it was warranted in this situation.

It was my desire (I now consider this a naive attitude) that my study would give such outstanding results that it would be the last word, or maybe one of the last words, on problem-solving behavior. Unfortunately, as with many classroom-based experiments, this did not occur. It was only a small beginning toward any type of definite statement concerning success in instruction for problem-solving skills. Nevertheless, it was possible to make the following statement on the basis of the evidence obtained: Subjects given instruction on specific behaviors were more likely to exhibit and make effective use of the problem-solving behaviors in new problem situations than subjects not given such instruction. This statement was made with considerable caution, since the limitations were such that generalizations to other populations might not be possible. I believe that the results definitely support this statement, but as mentioned before, a number of aspects of the study warrant careful consideration before further research is conducted in this area.

Future Plans

This experimental study in itself does not seem to have the strength to have an impact on current curriculum development or classroom instruction in mathematics. It is difficult to apply the principles of the three treatments directly in a structured textbook or in different modes for classroom discussion. I consider this study a search for more promising ideas in the field of instruction for the improvement of problem-solving skills. A study must fit in a framework of research in order to have any possible impact. Therefore, I have continued to develop research studies that are rooted in this beginning study. The revision of different test instruments for problem solving has been pursued since this study was conducted. Further work has been done with specific problem-solving behaviors, namely, constructing a chart or table, approximating and verifying, and drawing a diagram or picture. Some of these related research studies have shown promising results for possible instruction in problem-solving skills and increasing learners' success in solving problems.

After a study is completely finished, I enjoy looking back and asking, "What would I do if I did it again?" This is what I would do:

1. Review the Soviet literature on problem solving in greater depth. At the time of this research study, very little information was available about the Soviet problem-solving research, but it was evident that in a few months a fairly complete set of research studies would be translated and available in English. In retrospect, the results of the Soviet studies suggest a number of alternatives that might have been considered—for example, more teacher input (teaching experiment), a smaller sample size with more data collected on each subject, more protocol data analysis, and a follow-up study of certain successful problem-solving subjects.

2. Reduce the number of problem-solving behaviors taught from five to three. Instruction in constructing an algebraic equation was not necessary for most of the subjects. The behavior, classifying data, was too vague and therefore may not be effectively taught as a behavior for solving problems.

3. Redesign the pretest procedures to include a measure that would verify each subject's degree of skill in solving problems before the experiment was conducted. The STEP test was given in this study, and results indicate that this was not the best measure for addressing this issue (Vos, 1973).

4. Continue using an instructional guidesheet but increase the amount of written instruction on each sheet. In other words, do more instructing and leave less opportunity for the subject to flounder.

5. Most of the data-analysis plan would remain intact. A possible change would be a more accurate scoring scheme for the process score on the written Problem-solving Test. Since this study has been conducted, different schemes for process scoring have been developed that are advantageous for research in problem solving.

Obviously this study did not answer as many questions as it raised. As a result, I am continuing to investigate an important area of research within mathematics education—problem solving.

REFERENCES

Kantowski, M. G. Processes involved in mathematical problem solving. *Journal for Research in Mathematics Education*, 1977, *8*, 163-180.

Vos, K. E. *A comparison study of the effects of three instructional strategies on problem solving behaviors.* Unpublished doctoral dissertation, University of Minnesota, 1973.

Vos, K. E. The effects of three instructional strategies on problem-solving behaviors in secondary school mathematics. *Journal for Research in Mathematics Education*, 1976, *7*, 264-275.

CASE STUDY 4:

Evaluation

An Evaluation Model Applied to the Indiana University Mathematics-Methods Program (Thornton, 1977)

Carol A. Thornton
Illinois State University
John F. LeBlanc
Indiana University

ABSTRACT

Purpose

The purpose was to explore a technique for evaluating the effectiveness of a teacher education program in terms of teaching competencies and, in particular, to apply that technique to the Indiana University Mathematics-Methods Program.

Rationale

Program evaluation is one vital and crucial element that should accompany the development of teacher education programs but is often neglected. Elam (1971) has designated such assessment as one of the weakest yet most difficult areas of development. In reviewing the state of research related to teacher education, Peck and Tucker (1973) noted that although serious difficulties still exist, both the quality of design and the reporting of such research have improved in recent years. In particular, the use of observation instruments (category systems, rating scales) or some adaptation of the microteaching technique in research studies, such as those by Gage (1968), have helped educators to focus more clearly on, and to delineate more carefully, the components of teacher-pupil behavior in the interactive setting. Further, an increasing number of process-product studies have been noted. These investigations, which relate teaching (process) behaviors to measures of pupil outcome (product), have been extensively reviewed by Rosenshine and Furst (1973).

Studies such as those mentioned above, together with the work of Popham and his associates (1968), who have developed a teaching "performance test" that assesses teacher competency in terms of pupil achievement, provided the framework of the general evaluation model formulated for this study and applied to the Indiana University Mathematics-Methods Program assessment. The Popham paradigm provided the theoretical basis for the evaluation model. An adaptation of the microteaching concept similar to that made by Gage suggested the instructional setting, and the process-product literature summarized by Rosenshine and Furst helped identify appropriate and adequate criteria of teaching effectiveness.

Research Design and Procedure

The evaluation procedures involved a process-product design in combination with a modification of Popham's performance-test paradigm and Gage's adaptation of the microteaching concept. Such a combination makes possible an in-depth analysis of specific teaching behaviors as well as an assessment of pupil learning that can be related to the teaching. The underlying premise of this assessment technique is that the attainment of the program goals of teacher education is validated only in the demonstrated teaching competencies of its trainees.

More specifically, the general evaluation model included the following major constructs:

1. The identification of teacher variables (skills or strategies)—
   a. that research has shown to be consistently related to pupil cognitive or affective growth;
   b. that are related to the philosophy or content materials of the teacher education program.

2. The use of Popham's performance-test paradigm to place teachers from alternative programs in mini-teaching situations (specific to the content field) where the growth of the learner is the criterion of effectiveness.

3. The videotaping of the teaching sessions so that in-depth analyses of the teacher variables identified in (1) can be facilitated.

To explore the effectiveness of the evaluation model, the procedures outlined above were used to partially assess Indiana University's Mathematics-Methods Program (MMP), an innovative teacher education program in mathematics education that has had nationwide impact. The present study focused on the MMP program at Indiana University (1973-74 academic year), which was implemented in two pilot classes as a 12-hour, two-semester course and included regular field experiences in mathematics teaching.

The sample of preservice teachers consisted of 30 college students majoring in elementary education, 10 trainees randomly selected from the Mathematics-Methods Program and 10 randomly chosen from each of two contrasting programs providing mathematics preparation for prospective teachers at Indiana University—Contrast I, no school experiences; Contrast II, school experiences of a more general nature than those of the MMP group (i.e., not restricted to teaching mathematics to children). The sample of 120 third-grade pupils was randomly drawn from the total third-grade population of two schools near Indiana University.

The preservice teachers were placed in a mini–teaching situation where pupil learning was the criterion of effectiveness. Each preservice teacher was given a list of instructional objectives on which to base an introductory lesson on equivalent fractions for four third-grade pupils. Three of the variables identified by Rosenshine and Furst—the clarity of presentation (Clarity), the teacher's use of different types of questions (Questioning), and indirect means on the part of the teacher to encourage pupil involvement (Involvement)—were chosen as the bases for analyzing the teaching styles and strategies of the preservice elementary teachers. The mathematical knowledge of each preservice teacher relevant to the topic of the mini–teaching sessions was also assessed (Teacher Knowledge). In addition, the relationship between these four teacher variables and the mean adjusted pupil scores (Pupil Score) was investigated.

The teaching of each preservice teacher was videotaped and subsequently analyzed by trained observers for Clarity, Questioning, and Involvement behaviors. Mean adjusted pupil posttest scores were used to assess the pupil learning promoted by each preservice teacher.

Two major questions were asked: (a) Is there any difference in the performances of preservice teachers from the Mathematics-Methods Program and from the two alternative programs on the multivariate composite or in the univariate analyses on the following dependent measures: Clarity, Questioning, Involvement, Teacher Knowledge, Pupil Score? and (b) Is there any relationship between the mean adjusted achievement scores of pupils taught by the preservice teachers and the other four dependent variables?

Findings

The major findings of the study are the following:

1. There were significant differences between groups on the multivariate composite of the five dependent variables. The MMP group performed highest, and those from the Contrast I group performed lowest on all five variables.

2. On separate univariate tests, significant group differences were obtained for all variables except Teacher Knowledge. Post hoc analyses indicated that the MMP group performed significantly higher than the Contrast I group on all four variables ($p < .05$) and significantly higher than the Contrast II group on Clarity, Involvement, and Pupil Score

($p < .10$). Preservice teachers from the Contrast II group performed significantly better on the variable of Pupil Score than the Contrast I trainees ($p < .05$).

3. There were significant positive correlations between Pupil Score and each of the variables of Clarity, Questioning, and Involvement ($p < .01$).

Interpretations

Several conclusions may be stated:

1. The procedures used should be considered as a viable technique for evaluating segments of a teacher education program.

2. The three teacher variables of Clarity, Questioning, and Involvement are strong correlates of pupil achievement.

3. The Mathematics-Methods Program appears to have promoted competencies associated with the variables of Clarity, Questioning, Involvement, and Pupil Score more effectively than the other two programs.

4. There is an indication that regular, *planned* school experiences in conjunction with the mathematics preparation of preservice elementary teachers will have an impact on the ability of teachers to produce mathematical learning in children.

DISCUSSION

Formulating the Research Question

In this age of innovation and change, with its emphasis on new and better teacher education programs at both the preservice and the in-service levels, the question of evaluation, of program validation, is critical. This study emerged at a time when, perhaps as now, program assessment was one of the weakest elements in teacher education (Elam, 1971). The investigator had been actively involved in helping to develop an innovative teacher education program in mathematics for prospective elementary teachers. Some comparative evaluation efforts had been launched related to the content achievement of these teachers in the MMP program as well as their attitudes toward mathematics teaching. But the question of whether this program prepared teachers who might be more effective had not been researched. Thus, an early and easy decision in formulating the research question was that the effectiveness of the MMP in its teacher education efforts would be assessed. The crucial question, one that had to be answered in defining the specifics of the problem, was *how* to assess its effectiveness. The early search was for a general evaluation model that could be used in program assessments such as that envisioned for MMP.

It was clear at the outset and was continually endorsed by careful reading of the literature that "effectiveness" is an illusive and difficult variable to examine. In reducing a problem of this magnitude to manageable form, we saw that it was necessary to be thoroughly conversant with the literature as a basis for the critical analysis of its contributions and shortcomings in the area of assessing teacher education programs. Finding no appropriate evaluation model, we realized that it would be necessary to develop one as part of the study. An early thrust was to use the literature to define a solid theoretical framework for its design and to specify appropriate and adequate criteria of effectiveness.

Trends in research on the effectiveness of teachers, which examined both teacher behavior and the correlation of teacher behavior with pupil achievement or change in attitude, coupled with movements toward competency-based teacher education in which the distinction is clearly made between "knowing" and being able to *apply* what is "known" in teaching, led to looking closely at program effectiveness in terms of what it trains teachers to *do*. It became sensible to define teacher effectiveness as the production of desired changes in pupil achievement or attitude and to look at the effectiveness of a teacher education program in terms of its demonstrated teaching *competencies*, that is, in terms of its ability to promote effective teaching.

The general model, as it emerged, was obviously riding on a lengthy chain of arguments. An awareness of the delicacy and intricacy of the teaching-learning situation and of the complexity of the intervening variables produced several key questions. The major issue loomed large—*"Can the connection between a teacher education program and pupil achievement be made?"* Do program experiences really influence the way a person will interact with children in the classroom? Are these experiences a *primary* contributing factor to effective teaching? What other variables, extraneous to these program experiences or unique to the learning style and personality of either the preservice teacher or the pupils involved, affect success in producing a change in pupil achievement or attitude? It is essential, in research as complex as program evaluation, that early in the formulation researchers take a careful look at each argument in the chain and take a position concerning these arguments.

It was decided, even though the case was *not* a clean, simple, direct one, that investigations such as that envisioned should be carried out in order to gain insights into teaching, teacher effectiveness, and the effectiveness of a teacher education program. The emphasis was to be on noting trends, on gaining perspectives and insights with respect to the effectiveness of a teacher education program in promoting pupil learning through its trainees, rather than on seeking specific cause-and-effect relationships. It was decided to view the assessment of a teacher education program through the chain of events illustrated in Figure 1. The attainment of program goals was to be evaluated in terms of demonstrated teaching competencies.

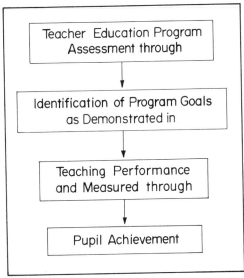

Figure 1

The next step was to formulate a general evaluation model that could then be applied to assessing the MMP. The work of Popham and his associates (1968) provided the theoretical basis for the model. In Popham's paradigm a teacher is given a set of instructional objectives, prepares and teaches a minilesson to a small group of students in an effort to meet those objectives, and is subsequently evaluated in terms of the amount of learner growth. Popham's procedures are based on the idea that a teacher education program is as good as the teachers it produces. Since his paradigm provides an assessment of teacher competency to meet prespecified objectives, the assessment simultaneously validates the program that set out to promote those teacher abilities.

Popham's model, however, concentrates only on *product*, or outcome, measures of teaching. Teacher educators also have a vested interest in *process*, or teaching, behaviors that are influenced by their program experiences and activities. There is further interest in the correlation of specific teaching (process) behaviors with pupil learning (product) behaviors in the classroom. Therefore, a slight modification of Popham's design was formulated that permitted the study of specific teacher variables as well. It was decided that ideally any teacher variables selected should be related to important program goals and be established in the literature as correlates of pupil achievement. The process-product litera-

ture summarized by Rosenshine and Furst (1973) identifies important
teacher variables that are high correlates of pupil learning and suggests
that certain techniques and strategies of the teacher, as well as pupil
achievement, can be used as criteria for measuring effective teaching.

To facilitate the analysis of such teacher variables and their relation
to pupil learning without distorting Popham's basic paradigm, the general
evaluation model was extended to include a videotaped recording of the
teaching performance test. Gage (1968) described this use of videotaping
as an adaptation of the microteaching concept. Microteaching, a mini–
teaching encounter scaled down in terms of class size (1–5 pupils) and
time (5–20 minutes), lessens the complexities of normal classroom teaching
and makes it possible to focus on specific teaching behaviors. Microteaching commonly involves a teach-reteach cycle in which feedback from
videotape is used to facilitate growth in teaching skills. When the
microteaching concept was adapted to teacher program evaluation,
however, the videotape feature was used only to record the teaching
sessions for subsequent analyses of specific teaching behaviors. The composition of the different component parts of the general evaluation model
is illustrated in Figure 2.

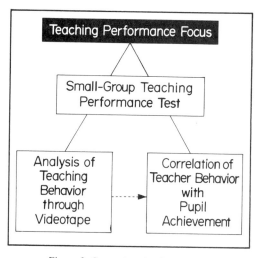

Figure 2. General evaluation model.

Formulating the research question involved coming to grips with the
complexity of evaluating teacher education programs and deciding that
the most crucial and potentially manageable aspect of assessment was that
which evaluated the attainment of program goals in terms of the teaching
effectiveness of its trainees. The formulation of the research question rested
on a chain of arguments that were at once subtle but reasonable. It involved admitting that such an assessment could, at best, result only in the

identification of trends and implications rather than in simple, direct inferences or causal relationships between a teacher education program and pupil achievement. It involved the commitment that this type of research was both important and necessary. It also involved a conscientious probe of the literature and common sense and imagination in the design of an evaluation model that was soundly based, adaptable to a number of programs, and practical to implement.

Designing the Study

The major thrust of the study lay in the application of the general evaluation model to the assessment of the Mathematics-Methods Program. The general design was, of course, structured by the evaluation model. Many specific decisions, however, had yet to be made. Selecting the criteria of teacher behaviors was perhaps the most difficult yet interesting task. In this study one did not need to look for variables. One had to be highly selective and occasionally had to decide how to control for unwanted variables! Teaching variables were selected primarily because they could be traced to important elements in the philosophy, stated objectives, or content materials of the MMP *and* because in the literature they were consistently related to pupil achievement. It was also important, however, to consider carefully whether it was possible to code behaviors specific to the variables during a mini-teaching session such as that suggested by Popham's performance test. When Clarity and Questioning were tentatively selected, for example, a second major question arose: *"Can these teaching behaviors be adequately measured?"* Other corollaries followed: *"Are there other variables that are more important to this particular research?"* and *"Would other variables be easier to observe, measure, and analyze?"*

The Clarity variable presented a matter of particular concern. Discussion and correspondence with Rosenshine underscored the importance of this variable yet highlighted the need for identifying specific low-inference indicators of "clarity." It was decided that the best method of dealing with the problem was to use the literature to aid in devising rating or category scales, to have the scales locally validated by experts in mathematics education and interaction analysis, and then to pilot their use.

Piloting each segment of the study proved most helpful in designing and redesigning specific aspects. It aided in the decision-making processes that involved the seemingly necessary trade-offs in educational research. The piloting process in general is helpful in laying out the design of any study. In this study it seemed particularly important to determine whether the chosen variables could be consistently identified and rated by observers, whether the lessons could be taught in the allotted time, whether children could grasp the chosen concept, and so forth. It was important that each part of the design and all possible outcomes be anticipated before the final design and implementation were effected. Such piloting and subsequent decision making seemed critical enough to use to advantage the time of all the individuals involved. In this investigation, as might well be true in any teaching study, the effects of the constraints were felt. But it was also realized that much could be learned even within the parameters in which it was necessary to work. Ideally, the following circumstances would have been better:

1. To have involved a larger number of preservice teachers, so that a broader generalization of results could be made. But additional numbers would have escalated the cost of the research and jeopardized control. The number selected for each group (10) was practical for the nature of the design and sufficient to perform the statistical analysis.

2. To have the preservice teachers teach two or three topics and to do so at more than one grade level, so that a broader base could be provided for making generalizations concerning teaching competence in mathematics. To have broadened the scope of the content, however, would have compounded the complexity of intervening variables and would have increased the cost and difficulty of control. The decision was that future replication studies using different topics and grade levels would provide more useful information to the mathematics education community.

3. To have dealt directly with in-service graduates of the program (a longitudinal study of sorts) rather than with preservice students currently in the program. But using in-service teachers would have introduced a vast array of intervening variables extremely difficult to account for or control, such as the intervening student-teaching experience or other course-and-field work. The replication of a simpler, short-term study might reveal trends and offer more valuable insights.

4. To have dealt with a broader range of important teaching variables, such as the variability of teaching techniques and strategies. These were omitted because of the time limitations of the videotaped sessions (two 30-minute sessions for each preservice teacher, half an hour on each of two consecutive days) and the investigator's desire to study thoroughly those teacher characteristics that were selected for analysis.

The "behind the scenes" and "before the fact" decisions such as those outlined above were crucial to the subsequent flow of the study. It seemed critical at the planning stage that every plausible difficulty or outcome be either actually or mentally piloted. Only in this way could problems be met, or simulated, and resolved. Some factors could not, of course, be controlled—personality differences and background experiences of the preservice teachers, differences in ability to work effectively within the time limits and other constraints of the videotaped sessions, differences in school field experiences over and above those provided as part of the current program activities, the meshing of learning styles of the school-children with individual teaching styles, and so on. The pilot studies and subsequent decision making focused on those variables that could be controlled to make the study as clean as possible.

Research Formulation and Specific Design: A Close Interface

It is apparent how the careful formulation of the research question and the narrowing of it to manageable size etch the framework of a study's design. Yet it is also true that one's ability to design a research study carefully and cleverly influences and at times even modifies the extent, the quality, and the nature of the specific questions that can be addressed. This aspect is a two-sided coin with a very narrow interface!

The present study is a case in point. One could not divorce the specifics of the MMP evaluation design from the formulation of the broader issue—needed assessment in teacher-education programs. In developing the general evaluation model, one had to keep in mind continually how such a model might be easily and practically implemented and to what extent it adequately and consistently assessed important segments of the overall program. At the same time, the specific need for MMP evaluation suggested important constructs for the general model. It became crucial to formulate the general questions in such a way that corresponding specifics could be—

- designed;
- observed;
- measured;
- analyzed.

An important consideration was to review repeatedly the chain of arguments to which the research questions were anchored. This review included a careful reflection of the interface between the theoretical issues and the basic design—between the research and the existing literature. Consideration was given to the implications of the possible outcomes and the potential impact on the relevant body of knowledge. Again, this review of all possible projected outcomes and the subsequent modifications prior to implementation were made to increase the likelihood of completing a study with significant results that would leave its mark on the mathematics education community.

Implementation

The actual implementation and the analysis of data, although time-consuming, were the easiest parts of the study. Piloting each of the major segments and dry runs of computer programs needed for the data analysis had debugged the procedures. Thus it largely became a matter of carrying out what had been carefully planned.

The greatest difficulty in the actual implementation lay in coordinating the schedules of college students, schoolchildren, and videotape operators. It is imperative, in a study such as this in which schools' teaching schedules are affected, that proper permissions and contacts be made *well in advance* and that schedules, planned to accommodate the school situation, be carefully kept. It also seemed important for the classroom teachers to feel that their children would gain from the research experience—that the time spent was worthwhile. Such rapport with teachers, established early, prompted all-out cooperation of the school personnel and ensured a smooth-flowing schedule. The preservice teachers, too, felt they benefited from the mini-teaching sessions. The option given them to view their own tapes afterwards was an added plus in this regard. One concern that needed some attention was to assure the instructors of the two control programs that the study was not designed to "do them in." They felt quite protective of their programs, as do most college instructors. Care was taken to provide the instructors with the rationale and purpose of the research. As a result they proved most cooperative.

Organization and the ability to anticipate and divert problems are key ingredients for successfully implementing a study such as this in which many people take part. A tedious task, but one that paid off, was the making of personal calls or delivering written reminders to each college student on the day preceding his or her videotaping session. Small things like thank-you notes to school personnel were deemed essential. The personal rapport paved by such consideration makes a valuable contribution to the efforts of other researchers in the area.

Interpretation of Results

This particular study presented more problems in interpreting results than might ordinarily occur. This difficulty, although anticipated because of the lengthy chain in the research design connecting the teacher education program to pupil achievement, required serious study and reflection. Of necessity, the study was not a simple one that yielded clear, direct interpretations. Instead, it was necessary to look for trends and valid implications. Whereas one had to be careful not to overstate the inferences in the data, it was also important not to minimize them. Reaching a happy medium was time-consuming—the result of long hours of analysis, consultation, discussion, writing, and rewriting.

Some decisions, made well in advance, were helpful in drawing conclusions from the data. No attempt at a total program assessment was ever made. The procedures outlined earlier dealt with only one phase of a program's evaluation—that which assessed the attainment of program goals in terms of the exhibited teaching competencies of its trainees. It was also recognized that the low-inference behaviors defining Clarity, Questioning, and Involvement, although drawn primarily from the literature, were themselves limiting. Had other (or additional) behavior choices been made, the results would probably have reflected these changes. Not only the choice of variables but also the operational definitions given them, as well as the coders' interpretations and consistency in scoring, were crucial to the interpretation and generalization of results.

Influencing the Profession

A study can influence current thinking or practice or make its impact in extending the research literature only if it is made visible to the mathematics education community. After completing the research, it was felt important to present it at research sections at regional and national NCTM meetings and to prepare a research article for the *Journal for Research in Mathematics Education.* Another means of disseminating the results has been to emphasize the practical implications at conferences and workshops and to cite the research, when appropriate, in expository articles. Common or suggested practices in mathematics education are made more credible when given firm support from research.

In reflecting on the research, one is tempted to ask, "What would be done differently if one were to do it again?" The answer to that question, from the point of view of the researchers involved, is, "Probably very few, if any, changes would be made." The content of the teaching sessions, equivalent fractions, was selected because it is a key topic in the elementary school mathematics program. Only a few objectives related to this topic were identified as points of focus for the videotaped teaching sessions. Perhaps the length of the study or the range of objectives might have been increased. But the negative factors in such a decision, greater burdens on the people involved and additional lack of control, have already been discussed. Clearly, there is a need for additional studies related both to the evaluation model and to other program goals of the MMP. Beyond the scope of this research there is a need for longitudinal studies on the influence of teacher-education programs on in-service teachers. Very little is known about what is effective in the central task of our profession—teacher preparation in mathematics.

REFERENCES

Elam, S. (Ed.). *Performance-based teacher education.* Washington, D.C.: American Association of Colleges for Teacher Education, 1971.

Gage, N. L. An analytical approach to research on instructional methods. *Phi Delta Kappan,* 1968, *49,* 601–606.

Peck, R. F., & Tucker, J. A. Research on teacher education. In R. M. Travers (Ed.), *Second handbook of research on teaching.* Chicago: Rand McNally, 1973.

Popham, W. J. The performance test: A new approach to the assessment of teaching proficiency. *Journal of Teacher Education*, 1968, *19*, 216–222.

Rosenshine, B., & Furst, N. F. The use of direct observation to study teaching. In R. M. Travers (Ed.), *Second handbook of research on teaching.* Chicago: Rand McNally, 1973.

Thornton, C. D. An evaluation of the mathematics-methods program involving the study of teaching characteristics and pupil achievement in mathematics. *Journal for Research in Mathematics Education*, 1977, *8*, 17–25.

EPILOGUE

David C. Johnson
University of London

These four case studies, although different in the sense that each deals with a different type of research, have a great deal in common. In particular, one should note that—

1. the problem dictated the design and type of research;
2. unless one has almost unlimited resources, one must usually reduce the specific problem to a manageable form and accept the fact that the results will only contribute to "the big picture" (it is difficult, if not impossible, to design a study that completely answers the question);
3. all the authors indicate that there is no substitute for careful planning and record keeping;
4. materials, instruments, and protocols (careful attention to the selection and design) are critical components for success;
5. interpretation must include a careful consideration of pitfalls, limitations, and alternative explanations.

Although such statements reflect common sense, it is the opinion of this author that a considerable amount of what is attempted under the guise of research lacks adequate attention to these ideas.

PART TWO

The Research Problems

7

Research in Cognitive Development

Thomas P. Carpenter
University of Wisconsin—Madison

T HE basic concern of research and theory in cognitive development is to describe the growth of children's basic concepts over time and to explain the processes by which these concepts are acquired and applied. Cognitive development can be characterized in a number of different ways. A useful distinction between two different conceptions of cognitive development has been proposed by Reese and Overton (1970). One is based on an organismic model and is represented by the works of Piaget and his followers. This model takes as its analogue the biological organism and is concerned with the development of complex cognitive systems. The other conception of cognitive development is based on a mechanistic model and is essentially an extension of behavioristic theories to explain development. The theories of Gagné (1968, 1977) regarding development are representative of this orientation. The mechanistic model is based on the machine and is concerned with the development of discrete, chainlike associations. From the mechanistic perspective, the only distinction between learning and development is the duration of time involved. Development deals with change in behavior over weeks, months, or years, whereas learning theory deals with changes in behavior over much shorter periods of time.

Even within the organismic framework, cognition is an elusive concept. However, although any attempt to characterize cognition in detail remains open to argument, certain fundamental premises of the organismic model

The project presented or reported herein was performed pursuant to a grant from the National Institute of Education, Department of Health, Education and Welfare (Center Contract No. OB-NIE-G-78-0217). However, the opinions expressed herein do not necessarily reflect the position or policy of the National Institute of Education and no official endorsement by the National Institute of Education should be inferred.

The reactions of a number of individuals to earlier drafts of this chapter contributed to the final version. The extensive comments of James Hiebert, Herbert Ginsburg, and Leslie Steffe were especially significant.

can be identified. The basic premise is that any intelligent behavior must be explained by reference to internal psychological mechanisms of some kind (e.g., groupings, transitive inference, logical grammars, etc.). There is far from universal agreement as to what internal mechanisms are most appropriate for explaining intelligent behavior, but the general organismic view is that they do not consist of a series of independent associations but instead are organized into well-integrated structural systems. Furthermore, it is generally recognized that these systems are not restricted to higher-order conscious behavior but operate on a wide range of mental functions, including such functions as perception and memory.

From the organismic perspective, the study of cognitive development is the study of the development of these cognitive systems. Whereas learning involves the application of intellectual structures to new events, development entails transformations in the cognitive structures themselves. The primary focus of developmental research is not to identify what specific knowledge a child possesses at a given point in time but to study how the child processes or operates on information. There is relatively little concern with finding out which addition facts are known by most second graders or identifying the age at which most children master the addition of two-digit addends; the focus is on concepts like conservation, transitivity, and seriation that involve the application of logical inference and seem to be closely linked to underlying cognitive structures. The interest in a concept like conservation is not simply that it is an important bit of factual knowledge, that is, that quantities remain invariant under certain transformations; rather, performance on conservation tasks is viewed as a measure of underlying cognitive structures that the child can apply to a wide variety of problems. In other words, a child's performance on a conservation task does not simply demonstrate a knowledge of an isolated fact about the physical world. It is indicative of the way that child processes information in a variety of problem situations. This is a central issue in cognitive development. Those who attach relatively little significance to concepts like conservation generally regard them as no more than bits of factual knowledge, whereas those who attribute a central role to such concepts regard them as measures of basic cognitive processes.

Mechanistic models do not recognize the integrated cognitive systems that are the essence of cognition within organismic models. Although internal mediating responses are acceptable, these are organized into chainlike associations rather than integrated into complex systems. Mechanistic models also are concerned more with product than with process.

As with cognition, the two types of models provide radically different conceptions of the nature of development. In organismic models the individual actively participates in the construction of knowledge. New information is not received passively. The subject actively assimilates it and interprets it in light of the existing cognitive structures. The mechanistic position is that knowledge is a copy of reality and that people are essentially reactive rather than active in acquiring knowledge.

Experience plays a key role in development in both types of models, but experience is characterized in different terms in each type of model. Within organismic models, experience traditionally has been regarded as a function of the sum of all an individual's experiences. The environment is considered to be something like a black box within which specific cause-and-effect factors are undifferentiable. Research based on organismic models traditionally has been observational and correlational rather than experimental, and until recently there has been little attempt to manipulate experimental variables. Note that this holistic view of experience is an integral part of a theory that hypothesizes the existence of an integrated cognitive system in which individual elements cannot be significantly altered without changing the structure of the entire system.

Mechanistic models focus more on the specific effects of training. In the last 10 to 15 years an increasing number of training studies have been based on traditional organismic variables. Indeed, even from an organismic perspective it is becoming accepted to attempt to identify specific mechanisms of development. Even Piaget and his associates have been conducting training studies in the past few years (Inhelder, Sinclair, & Bovet, 1974). Thus, organismic models do not preclude analyzing development or studying part processes, but the parts must ultimately be interpreted in the context of the whole of which they are a part.

The ultimate source of cognitive mechanisms is another point of disparity. Most mechanistic models hypothesize that behavior can be explained strictly on the basis of environmental determinants, and it is assumed that all internal mechanisms originate solely from experience. However, organismic models allow that some structure exists at birth and that others develop through maturation and the interaction of present structures and the environment.

Organismic models generally view development as proceeding through an irreversible, fixed sequence of qualitatively different stages, and the mechanistic model views development as being essentially continuous, reducible to quantitative change. Thus, for organismic models development results from change in the organism itself, and for mechanistic models development reduces to quantitative increments.

Organismic models tend to be teleological in that they are goal oriented in their characterization of cognitive development. A child, for example, is inexorably developing toward a stage of formal operations. Mechanistic models do not rely on teleological causes to explain development. Organismic models also tend to be more species specific; their proponents maintain that to understand human behavior it is necessary to study the cognitive development of people, whereas proponents of mechanistic models are more likely to generalize from research with simpler organisms.

Many of the significant issues in cognitive development reduce to differences over which type of model of cognitive development is more appropriate. Issues involving the stage concept, the effect of training, and the significance of conservation all revolve around the question of which type of model of cognitive development has been adopted. Experimental paradigms have been proposed (Watson, 1968), and a wide range of studies (Beilin, 1971) have been conducted that attempt to resolve the conflicting theories that result from adopting one or the other of these two models. In general, these studies have done little to resolve the basic issues or establish the validity of either model.

Reese and Overton (1970) propose that these models represent two independent world views that are based on different sets of assumptions and are essentially irreconcilable. In essence, this means that it is futile to attempt to synthesize an organismic approach like Piaget's with a behavioristic, mechanistic approach. In fact, the central question is not which model is valid or accurate. To quote Reese and Overton (1970), "It is not being asserted [in a model] that the real world is thus and so, only that the real world behaves as if it were thus and so" (p. 120). Thus, the relevant question is pragmatic. Which model is more fruitful for adequately explaining and predicting behavior? Since any model limits the domain of problems that are susceptible to investigation, the choice of a model essentially involves a value judgment as to which problems are most significant to solve.

Since neither model appears to be sufficient to account for the whole range of human behavior, several eclectic theories have emerged. For example, White (1965) maintains that at about the age of 5 to 7 years a qualitative change occurs in children's behavior. A mechanistic, associative model best accounts for early behavior, but a cognitive model is most appropriate after this transition. Kohlberg (1968) and Uznadze (1966) also attempt to integrate the two models to explain simple and more complex behavior.

Many of the lower-level skills in mathematics, like learning addition facts, are readily reduced to associations and lend themselves to analysis in terms of mechanistic models. However, most of the more interesting complex cognitive processes are more adaptive to cognitive, organismic models. Although it is not always clear what sort of model a particular researcher has adopted, most of the cognitive development research that is of particular interest for the learning and teaching of mathematics is based on organismic models, and they will be dealt with most completely in this chapter. For a more complete discussion of the mechanistic position with respect to cognitive development, see Baer (1970) or Bijou and Baer (1961).

Cognitive development is an extensive field that is impossible to characterize adequately here. Consequently, it is necessary to assume that the reader has some familiarity with the work in this area. Most of the research that has the greatest potential significance for the teaching and learning of mathematics has been based on the work of Piaget. Several excellent summaries of his voluminous works exist elsewhere, and no attempt has been made to duplicate or summarize these efforts. Piaget's basic positions have not changed significantly in recent years, and early studies on number, space, and geometry still provide the basis for much of the research on the teaching and learning of mathematics. Consequently, Flavell's (1963) summary is still one of the best statements of Piaget's basic theories and research available. For more recent and somewhat more general discussions of theories and research in cognitive development, see Flavell (1970, 1977), Gelman (1978), and Ginsburg and Koslowski (1976).

MAJOR PARADIGMS OF COGNITIVE DEVELOPMENT RESEARCH

Wohlwill (1973) has outlined a hierarchical model for the study of development problems which, with certain modifications, provides a useful framework for characterizing research in cognitive development in mathematics education. Wohlwill places certain restrictions on the criteria for suitable behavioral dimensions that would disallow many of the problems of central interest in mathematics education. In research that is primarily concerned with explaining the general cause of cognitive development, variables that develop independently of specific experiences or specific school curriculum are generally most appropriate. Although the foundations of many mathematical concepts may fit these criteria, most mathematical concepts are acquired under the influence of instruction. It can be argued that concepts influenced by instruction are not truly developmental, but this distinction does not seem very productive. If certain mathematical concepts show the same stagelike characteristics as pure developmental concepts, the paradigms and techniques of research in cognitive development can prove useful in their study and should be applied. Experience plays a role in the development of most concepts. When instruction is a factor, there is simply a greater potential for variability in the development of the given concepts. The important point is that at each level of Wohlwill's model, it is necessary to identify the specific effects of instruction when appropriate. If this attention to the effects of instruction is built into the model, Wohlwill's general model provides a useful framework to describe the major paradigms of basic research in the development of mathematical concepts.

Wohlwill identifies five basic phases in research on development: (a) the discovery and synthesis of developmental dimensions, (b) the descriptive study of change, (c) the correlational study of age change, (d) the study of the determinants of developmental change, and (e) the study of individual differences in development. Although there is an implied hierarchy, research has generally been conducted at each of the levels simultaneously. Ideally, the results at lower levels provide a foundation for research at higher levels, and conclusions reached at lower levels are consolidated and possibly revised on the basis of work at advanced levels.

The Discovery and Synthesis of Developmental Dimensions

The first task in investigating the development of mathematical concepts is to identify the dimensions to be used to describe development. In the study of the development of mathematical concepts, the specific variables to be investigated have been derived from two primary sources: (a) the mathematical axioms and theorems underlying the concepts under investigation and (b) the general study of cognitive development.

The study by Wagman (1975) is an example of an investigation employing variables derived from the mathematical structure of measuring area. Although the study is similar to those based on psychological considerations, Wagman maintains that most studies in the general cognitive development tradition have not investigated some of the significant aspects of measuring area. The implication is that by beginning with the mathematical foundations of a subject, one is more likely to provide a complete picture of the development of a mathematical concept. The studies reported by Lovell (1971a, 1971c) on the growth of the concept of a function and the development of the concept of mathematical proof provide additional examples of mathematically derived dimensions.

Most of the research on the development of mathematical concepts that has evolved from the general study of cognitive development has been based on the work of Piaget and his associates. For Piaget, certain logico-mathematical structures (e.g., groupings) provide excellent models of actual cognitive processes used by older children and adults. (For a more complete discussion of groupings, group-lattice structures, etc., see Flavell, 1963.) According to this theory, the major elements of cognitive development can ultimately be described in terms of the development of these logico-mathematical structures. Thus, for Piaget these structures provide the major dimensions for the study of cognitive development. However, although such structures are appealing for their mathematical elegance, to hypothesize the existence of these structures requires a high degree of inference, and their usefulness for explaining the development of basic mathematical concepts is open to question (Steffe, 1973).

Most research in the development of mathematical concepts has focused directly on principles like conservation, transitivity, seriation, and class inclusion, which are more readily observable than grouping structures.

However, although these principles are less obscure than grouping structures, researchers are still plagued by the problem of constructing criteria that are necessary and sufficient to establish whether or not a child has attained an operational level in applying them.

Developmental dimensions should be sufficiently situation independent to generate valid, reliable measures of development. Researchers are faced, however, with the well-documented problem of horizontal décalages. Although it seems that operations with the same logical structure would readily transfer from one problem situation to another, this is not the case. For example, conservation of mass is attained as young as 7 years, conservation of weight is not attained until at least 9 years, and volume is not conserved until 11 or 12 (Piaget & Inhelder, 1941; Elkind, 1961). Thus, although it is desirable to define developmental dimensions in terms as general as possible, some specification of the domain of application seems unavoidable. It is not sufficient to identify children as conservers; it is necessary to specify whether they conserve one-to-one correspondence, continuous quantity, weight, or volume.

Unfortunately, the problem does not disappear with the specification of the domain in which the operation is applied. Methodological variations account for significant differences in children's performance on tasks testing logical operations. Differences in the criteria for success, the use of verbal or nonverbal procedures, the presence or absence of conflict, and variations in materials or protocols all significantly affect the level of children's performance (e.g., see George, 1970; King, 1971; Sawada & Nelson, 1967; Shantz & Smock, 1966; Stone, 1972; Uzgiris, 1964). Furthermore, these differences are not trivial. Methodological variations account for a four-year age differential in the acquisition of transitivity (Bailey, 1971; Smedslund, 1963). This has led to sustained debate over appropriate research methodology (e.g., see Braine, 1959, 1964; Smedslund, 1963, 1965). Methodological issues frequently involve basic philosophic differences that seem to go back to fundamental mechanistic-organismic distinctions. This makes any empirical resolution virtually impossible.

One proposal for dealing with experimental variability and the décalage issue has been put forth by Flavell and Wohlwill (1969). The whole problem centers on what performance is necessary to demonstrate competence for a given logical operation. Flavell and Wohlwill propose that an analysis of cognitive development should incorporate a competence-performance distinction similar to Chomsky's model for language acquisition. The competence component of the model is the logico-mathematical structure of the domain, and the performance component represents the psychological processes by which the structures in the competence component are accessed and applied to specific tasks. The competence component is an idealized abstract representation of what is known or understood, whereas the performance component must account for the reality of stimulus variations, conflicting information, and memory limitations.

In Flavell and Wohlwill's model, a child's performance for a given operation should be specified in terms of three parameters: P_a, the probability that the operation will be functional in a given child; P_b, the probability of the operation's being applied to a given task; and k, the weight to be attached to P_b in a given child at a given age. The equation for the probability of a given child solving some particular task is

$$P(+) = P_a \times P_b{}^{1-k}.$$

Any description of development must account for P_b as well as P_a. In other words, developmental dimensions cannot be based completely on logical operations. They must also be defined in terms of attributes of potential problem situations that affect performance.

The Descriptive Study of Change

Once developmental dimensions have been selected, the task is to describe the course of development along these dimensions. This is the descriptive phase of the research program that characterizes the initial efforts in almost any field of scientific endeavor. Educational research in general has been marked by a disdain for this phase of the scientific process. Major curriculum projects and elaborate theories of instruction have been grounded on extremely limited empirical foundations. Rather than beginning with a careful observation of children learning mathematics, research has too often begun with narrowly defined hypotheses tested in carefully controlled settings using standardized, objective instrumentation. Standardization and experimental control certainly have their place in research. But if controlled experimentation is preceded by careful observation, the experimenter has a much better basis for explaining specific results. In addition, the experimenter should gain a clearer idea of what elements are not being tapped with the standardized instruments and be able to design items that get at the most significant variables.

In many scientific fields, carefully controlled research is not initiated until the experimenters have a sufficient empirical basis to be virtually certain of their results. That this paradigm has seldom been applied in educational research may in part account for the syndrome of *no significant difference* and the general lack of real progress in identifying significant educational variables.

Research in cognitive development has been somewhat less guilty in this regard than educational research in general. In fact, demonstrating the usefulness of clinical interview techniques and the wealth of information that is contained in incorrect responses may be one of the most significant contributions of Piaget to research in the learning of mathematics.

Ginsburg (1976) has made one of the strongest cases for the use of clinical-observational techniques in studying the learning of mathematics. He maintains that standard tests often misrepresent children's competence. Consequently, a greater emphasis on the flexible observation of children's mathematical thinking is required. This point is aptly illustrated by Erlwanger's (1973, 1975) evaluation of the Individually Prescribed Instruction (IPI) mathematics program using flexible interview techniques. Although standardized tests generally indicated that certain children were successfully progressing through the IPI program, clinical interviews uncovered a number of serious misconceptions that Erlwanger attributed to the program's specific nature.

Although the potential richness of clinical observation and interactive interview techniques is generally acknowledged, serious questions concerning their validity and reliability have been raised. To overcome these objections, most of the replication studies based on Piaget's original research have attempted to standardize protocols and procedures.

Frequently the standardized procedures impose less stringent conditions for assuming a child has attained a given operation, which results in identifying earlier ages of emergence of this operation. Piaget and his associates require that for a child to be judged operational for a given concept, the following criteria must be met:

1. They must make the correct judgment with respect to the given operation.

2. They must justify their response.

3. They must resist verbal countersuggestion.

4. Their performance must transfer to related tasks (Inhelder & Sinclair, 1969).

Brainerd (1973a, 1977) contends that these criteria are too restrictive and result in too many false negatives. He proposes that children be required only to give correct judgments and not to justify their answers. Others have proposed using nonverbal techniques that minimize verbalization on the part of the experimenter as well as on the part of children in their responses (Braine, 1959; King, 1971; Miller, 1976; Sawada & Nelson, 1967).

Although standardized techniques are definitely needed at some point in the research process, much of the richness uncovered using more subjective techniques is lost. Standardized protocols seldom uncover the transitional stages of performance on a given task that are identified by Piaget and others using interactive methods. The proponents of standardization could respond that these transitional stages are simply illusory anyway, whereas those favoring interactive procedures would maintain that the standardized techniques do not tap genuine operational competence.

This division tends to split along philosophical lines. Those favoring a mechanistic model believe that important cognitive outcomes should be specifiable in terms of overt behavior. Therefore they take a hard line on standardized techniques; those favoring interactive methods tend to fall in the organismic camp. To some degree these methodological issues present a false dichotomy; it is not a question of either-or. Both paradigms have their strengths and weaknesses. Some standardization is necessary in studies comparing instructional treatments and in studies comparing the relative difficulty of two or more tasks. In these kinds of studies, objectivity is of central concern. Standardization is also ultimately needed to test hypotheses and determine the prevalence of specific responses. However, interactive methods also have their place, and clinical case-study research should be recognized as legitimate research endeavor. Something is lost and something is gained with each paradigm, and both clinical and controlled studies are needed.

In both methods the goal of this phase in the research program is to describe the course of development along the dimensions that were laid out in the first phase discussed above. For the most part, the developmental dimensions that have been of greatest interest in describing learning in mathematics have been qualitative rather than quantitative. As a consequence, development cannot be described in terms of a mathematical function like one might generate from a test of word recognition. Instead, the problem becomes one of describing invariant sequential patterns of qualitatively different responses. The main task reduces to specifying the sequence in which behaviors appear during the course of development along with determining how invariant this sequence is for a given sample of children.

Some attempt has been made to establish age norms for the emergence of specific responses. However, in addition to the variance introduced through experimental variation, cultural and socioeconomic factors create an almost overwhelming obstacle in this regard. Although estimates of such age norms are useful as benchmarks and they do provide some measure of the duration of different stages of development, caution should be exercised in their application.

The Correlational Study of Development

The development of most mathematical concepts of real interest, like number or measurement, are not readily described along a single dimension. These concepts involve the synthesis of a number of logical operations, and therefore multiple measures are required. Furthermore, it is impossible to understand the development of a concept by considering it in terms of isolated, independent dimensions.

One of the major aims of cognitive-developmental study is to identify and interpret the temporal relations that may hold among conceptual acquisitions. For any pair of acquisitions A and B, the most interesting of such relations are invariant concurrence (A and B develop synchronously in all children) and invariant sequence (e.g., A develops earlier than B in all children). (Flavell, 1970, p. 1034).

Developmental sequences. By analyzing the structure of various problems, one can hypothesize that certain concepts must be learned before others because the development of the first mediates, or in some way contributes to the development of, the second. The difficulty is that by analyzing tasks in different ways, one can identify different sequences. For example, one can construct a reasonable argument for conservation preceding transitivity or for transitivity preceding conservation (cf. Brainerd, 1973d). For this reason logically derived sequences must be compared with the actual sequences of development so that hypotheses can be tested regarding factors that contribute to the development of a concept and the processes that a child is using to solve a given problem.

Although developmental sequences are an integral part of Piaget's theory, his method of comparing mean ages of development for different samples of children is inadequate for verifying the existence of such sequences. Repeated measures on the same subjects are required, the most effective of which would look for sequence reversals. If the development of B depends on the development of A, there should be an invariant A B sequence, and B should precede A only in cases of an error in measurement. Where more than two tasks have been involved, scalogram analysis techniques have frequently been applied (Kofsky, 1966; Wohlwill, 1960, 1973). Longitudinal design provides certain information that is inaccessible using cross-sectional methods, and invariant sequences identified in cross-sectional studies should be confirmed with longitudinal study, where the sequence of development can be observed directly within individual subjects. However, because of the practical problems involved, relatively few longitudinal studies relating to the development of mathematical concepts have been conducted (cf. Almy, Chittenden, & Miller, 1966; Almy, Dimitrovsky, Hardeman, Gordis, Chittenden, & Elliot, 1970; Carr, 1971; Dudek & Dyer, 1972; Little, 1972; Niemark & Lewis, 1968; Hooper & Klausmeier, 1973).

The objective of the study of developmental sequences is to establish some functional relationship between tasks that accounts for observed invariant sequences. A key problem in this endeavor is the sensitivity of the tasks used to measure the individual concepts. An observed A B sequence may simply result from the fact that the task measuring B is less sensitive than the task measuring A and consequently yields a greater number of false negatives. If there is sufficient time lag between the development of different concepts, as with conservation of mass, weight, and volume, there may be no serious problem. But most sequences of greatest interest occur over shorter periods of time.

For example, the sequence of the development of conservation and transitivity is of some potential significance for understanding the development of number concepts because it may reflect the ordinal-cardinal controversy (see Brainerd, 1976). Piaget and Inhelder (1941) initially proposed that the two concepts develop synchronously, but with the exception of a study by Lovell and Ogilvie (1961), the initial replications found that conservation develops before transitivity (Kooistra, 1964; McManis, 1969; Smedslund, 1961, 1963, 1964; Steffe & Carey, 1972). These studies, however, have been criticized by Brainerd (1973d) for failing to equate the relative sensitivities of the assessment tasks. Each of the studies employed perceptual illusion in the transitivity tasks. Using tasks that did not involve perceptual illusion, Brainerd (1973d) found that the development of transitivity precedes the development of conservation. It is not clear that Brainerd's procedures are any more equitable than the others, since the conservation tasks involved perceptual illusion and the transitivity tasks did not. At this point, the most reasonable conclusion seems to be that the sequence of development appears to depend on what evidence one requires for the respective operations. If one compares the standard conservation tasks to the weaker definition of transitivity, then it appears that transitivity develops earlier. If one insists on stronger criteria for transitivity, then it appears that conservation develops earlier. Unfortunately, there are no valid empirical procedures to resolve this issue. No task has any special claim to be the measure for a given operation. The competence-performance distinction is involved again, and it appears necessary to account for the performance dimension in the characterization and explanation of developmental sequences.

Developmental concurrences. Piaget's theory hypothesizes that new cognitive structures that can be applied to a wide range of problems emerge within a given stage of development. Furthermore, these operations are integrated into unified structural systems. This would seem to imply that development would be marked by the synchronous development of a variety of abilities, which should be manifested by consistent failure or success across a number of different tasks. Not only should tasks with the same inherent structure be mastered concurrently, but because of the hypothesized interconnectedness of logical operations, similar concurrences should be found for related operations.

The stage concept is potentially useful because it proposes to predict behavior over a wide range of tasks. Thus, performance on a small set of tasks should be sufficient to predict performance on a large domain of related tasks. Unless this sort of generalization is possible, the stage concept has little practical value for education. Unfortunately, very few consistent concurrences have been found. Although certain logical operations may ultimately be integrated into a *structure d'ensemble,* they appear to emerge asynchronously and initially generalize to a restricted number of problem situations.

In spite of the almost insurmountable obstacles in terms of horizontal décalages and methodological variability, the correlational study of development is central to applying research in cognitive development to education. Decisions involving the sequencing of content and matching instruction to appropriate levels of children's development both rest on such study.

For a more complete discussion of this topic, the reader is referred to the articles by Flavell (1970, 1971, 1972), Pinard and Laurendeau (1969), and Wohlwill (1973).

The Study of Developmental Change

The training study is the most widely used approach to investigate the factors affecting developmental change. Extensive reviews of Piagetian training studies can be found in articles by Beilin (1971), Brainerd (1973), Brainerd and Allen (1971), Hatano (1971), Glaser and Resnick (1972), Strauss (1972), and Wohlwill (1970). The typical training study has employed a relatively short period of training. Most treatments have consisted of a single short training session, and few have involved more than 10 half-hour sessions. Typically the treatments and pretests and posttests have been administered individually or in small groups, and training has involved a single logical operation, like conservation, seriation, or transitivity.

Beilin (1971) identifies three generations of training research. In the first generation, studies were designed to substantiate basic elements of Piaget's theory of cognitive development. One group of studies has attempted to induce logical operations by creating a state of disequilibrium with respect to the given operation. Other studies of this genre have focused on mental operations, such as addition-subtraction or reversibility, that are presumed to be involved in the natural development of the concept to be trained.

The second generation of training studies were based on the hypothesis that Piaget's stage theory is overly rigid in the limitations it places on cognitive development. A number of these investigators believe that the acquisition of logical structures can be accelerated, and they reject the equilibration model as the sole explanation for their acquisition. They do not accept, for example, that reversibility and compensation are the essential mechanisms leading to conservation. Some studies have trained children to attend to relevant attributes and disregard or ignore misleading perceptual cues. Another group of studies has relied on verbal rules or feedback in training. Others have employed techniques of conformity training, pairing nonconservers with conservers or exposing nonconservers to expert models.

Studies of this second type continue to be a major force in Piagetian research. However, there is a third generation of studies whose objectives are different from the other two. The aim of these studies, which are conducted by the Genevans themselves, is to investigate the psychological mechanisms that underlie the transitions between stages. These studies attend more closely to the stage of development their subjects have reached before training and specify in much greater detail than the earlier studies the specific effects of training. The perspective of these studies is that training only extends the domain of application of operational structures. It does not initiate the development of new operations. According to this view, "The development of operativity is malleable only within the limits imposed by the nature of development" (Beilin, 1971, p. 101). Evidence of the development of an early emerging operation like the conservation of number is prerequisite for successfully teaching more advanced concepts. In terms of the Flavell and Wohlwill (1969) model, training operates on the performance component rather than the competence component of the model.

Although many individual studies failed to demonstrate significant training effects, almost every type of training procedure has been able to accelerate the acquisition of logical operations. However, they have failed to identify the specific mechanisms that lead to the development of the operation. One difficulty is that researchers often fail to agree on the specific mechanism that is operating in a given training procedure. One researcher may attribute the effect of training to learning to attend to relevant dimensions, and another may identify latent reversibility training as the significant variable (cf. Brainerd & Allen, 1971).

Training studies have also failed to distinguish between necessary and sufficient conditions for the development of a given operation. Just because a training condition has been sufficient to accelerate the acquisition of an operation does not mean that condition is necessary for the development of the operation. With regard to this point Wohlwill (1973) reaches this conclusion:

> Thus, we have had a parade of training conditions which to varying extents and degrees of consistency have shown themselves to be sufficient to induce conservation, at least given a child within a particular age range. But the relationship between these conditions and the process of conservation as it takes place naturally—that is the question of the plausibility that these conditions could in fact have been operating in the child's extra laboratory experience—has rarely been examined. If it had been, it would quickly have become apparent that most of them, from rule learning to reversibility training, from

cognitive conflict to reinforced practice, are of dubious relevance to that experience. (p. 323)

Virtually all training studies have found that training transfers to novel
materials not used in the training procedure. This specific transfer applies
to situations in which the tasks are similar to those used in the training and
only the specific materials are changed. For example, toy cars may be used
in conservation training and poker chips in the specific transfer task.
Nonspecific transfer applies to situations in which the trained logical operation extends to a new domain of application (e.g., transfer of training on
length to area). This type of transfer has been more difficult to achieve,
although several studies have reported considerable success (e.g., Bearison,
1969; Gelman, 1969). The difficulty in finding nonspecific transfer is not
especially surprising given the prominence of observed décalages in the
natural development of operations. Transfer between logical operations
(e.g., conservation to transitivity) has been even more difficult to achieve.

Wohlwill (1970) proposes that cognitive development can be thought of
as a combination of horizontal and vertical transfer. The larger the number
of vertical steps the learner must climb to reach his goal, the narrower the
span of generalization or horizontal transfer. Wohlwill also observes that
the amount of transfer appears to be a function of the breadth and intensity of training.

Several studies have tested for retention over periods ranging from 1
to 7 months. Almost universally they have found that the trained concepts have been retained. The picture is somewhat different when a
specific effort is made to extinguish a given concept. According to the
stage theory of development, once an operation is fully attained, it should
be extremely resistant to extinction. An early study by Smedslund (1961)
found that trained conservers readily abandoned conservation judgments
when they were deceived with an example in which it appeared that weight
was not conserved. Natural conservers were much more resistant to such
extinction. This seemed to imply that the trained conservers were giving
only superficial responses and had not attained a genuine operational level.
Recent studies have failed to confirm these results. They have found no ap-
preciable differences between trained and natural conservers in their
resistance to extinction or countersuggestion. In general, earlier developing
concepts like number have proved to be quite resistant to extinction for
both groups, whereas later developing concepts like weight are quite easy
to extinguish for both natural and trained conservers (Brainerd, 1973c).

Although the goal of much of the training research has been to understand the specific mechanisms of development, not to accelerate development, a number of studies have been conducted whose only apparent goal
is to demonstrate that teaching a specific operation is possible. Many
studies conducted by researchers interested in problems dealing with the

learning of mathematics have been of this type. The assumption underlying these studies seems to be that a specific operation like conservation or seriation is apparently important for learning basic mathematical concepts. Therefore, if these operations can be successfully trained, the subsequent learning of basic mathematics will be facilitated. Although these studies have frequently been successful in training the specific operations, none have demonstrated that any significant transfer occurs in the learning of subsequent mathematical topics. In fact, in a follow-up to one of the more successful conservation training studies, Bearison (1975) concluded that the training had no effect on the subsequent learning of number skills.

Accelerating development has been a major issue in cognitive development. Piaget has questioned why Americans are so interested in accelerating development when the basic operations develop naturally anyway. This concern has been echoed by Glaser and Resnick (1972), who have questioned whether early stimulation will lead to richer growth or just faster growth. Elkind (1971) and Wohlwill (1970) have hypothesized that the longer formal instruction is delayed, up to reasonable limits, the longer the period of plasticity resulting in a richer ultimate level of achievement with greater flexibility and creativity. Elkind (1976) has also proposed that development is a whole-organism phenomenon and that accelerating any single part of it may encourage maladaptation. Both hypotheses remain to be proved, but at this point there is scant empirical evidence that any attempts to accelerate development result in any desirable educational outcomes.

It has been amply demonstrated that training is possible using a variety of different training procedures. Future training studies need to be designed so that they provide a greater understanding of the specific mechanisms of development. Such studies should provide answers to the following questions:

1. What are the prerequisites for attaining a given level of cognitive development?

2. What are the specific experiences that contribute to the development of a given concept?

3. To what extent does a concept generalize once it has been learned? This involves (a) measuring subjects' entering knowledge and level of development, (b) carefully designing training that is based on a reasoned theoretical rationale, and (c) measuring specific outcomes, including transfer and retention. Results should not be reported using global measures of group success or failure. Instead, some attempt should be made to account for the differential effects of instruction on individual subjects. Future training studies will contribute to our knowledge only in so far as

they can help us to understand how development proceeds in individual children.

An example of a study that incorporates many of the recommendations listed above is the "teaching experiment" of Steffe, Spikes, and Hirstein (1976). The purpose of their study was to investigate whether two clusters of Piagetian variables, class inclusion and conservation, are prerequisites for first-grade children's learning certain number concepts. Twenty-nine individual measures were clustered into the two readiness variables and seven achievement variables. Subjects were divided into two groups. For one group, instruction was carefully designed and monitored. The other group received regular classroom instruction. The treatment consisted of approximately 40 hours of instruction over a 3-month period. The results are complex and difficult to summarize, but evidence indicated that although conservation was not a prerequisite for learning some number skills, the learning of conservers was qualitatively different from the learning of non-conservers. Specifically, the conservers could transfer their learning to an unfamiliar task, whereas the nonconservers generally could not. This conclusion was possible only because of the completeness of the dependent and independent variables and the duration of the instructional treatment.

Individual Differences in Development

For the most part, individual differences have been virtually ignored in the study of cognitive development. Wohwill (1973) observes that "the real problem appears to be the failure of psychologists at either end to come to grips with the question, how developmental and differential foci may effectively be integrated into a coherent whole" (p. 333). Such an integration may take several forms. One involves the study of individual differences in development; a second involves the study of the development of individual differences. In the first, the variables of interest are those that have traditionally been of interest in the study of cognitive development. There is overwhelmimg evidence that individuals differ significantly in their cognitive development. This is attested to by the difficulty researchers have encountered in attempting to identify reliable stages of cognitive development. Any complete theory of cognitive development must include ways to account for and describe these individual differences. In the second type of study, the emphasis is on individual differences: What is the origin of individual differences? How do they develop? How consistent are they over the course of development?

Since individual differences are the subject of the chapter by Fennema and Behr in this volume, they are not discussed in any detail here. For a more complete discussion of individual differences in cognitive development, see Kagan and Kogan (1970) and Wohlwill (1973).

THE DEVELOPMENT OF MATHEMATICAL CONCEPTS

One of the unique features of research in cognitive development that has made it especially relevant for mathematics education is the fact that much of the research deals with the developmemt of specific concepts, many of them mathematical in nature. Although developmental psychologists are concerned with the development of cognitive structures that transcend the formation of any specific concept, many experiments are designed, at least in part, to describe the development of specific concepts. The development of number, measurement, space and geometry, and adolescent reasoning are areas that have received particular attention. What follows, by way of summary, is highly selective. For more complete accounts, see Brainerd (1973b, 1976), Bryant (1974), Churchill (1961), Flavell (1963, 1970), and Ginsburg (1975, 1977a) on number; Carpenter (1976) and Carpenter and Osborne (1976) on measurement; Lesh and Mierkiewicz (1977) and Martin (1976) on space and geometry; Flavell (1963, 1977) and Neimark (1975) on adolescent logical reasoning; and the general discussions by Beilin (1969) and Wallach (1969) on conservation.

Number

Much of the early research on number assessed children's ability to perform conventional arithmetical operations—counting, adding, subtracting, and so on (cf. Brownell, 1941). Current research is no longer concerned simply with identifying which problems are most difficult or how many children at a given age can solve a certain type of problem. The focus has shifted to an attempt to explain the development of basic number concepts and to characterize how children solve problems, not simply whether they can solve them.

The research takes two major lines of investigation. The first attempts to explain the development of primary number concepts in terms of the development of underlying logical operations. The second is based on the hypothesis that the development of number results from the integration of, or increasingly efficient application of, certain number skills like counting, estimating, "subitizing" (directly perceiving), comparing, and matching. Although there are prominent exceptions and some of the research is difficult to categorize, much of this research tends to be mechanistic in character, whereas number research based on primitive logic is almost exclusively organismic.

Logical foundations of number. Although McLellen and Dewey (1896) called attention to underlying mathematical assumptions over 80 years ago, it is the work of Piaget (1952) that provides the focus for current attempts to explain children's concept of number in terms of the development of logical reasoning abilities. Piaget's influence has been so great that it has led Flavell (1970) to observe, "Virtually everything of interest that we know about the early growth of number concepts grows out of Piaget's pioneer work in the area" (p. 1001).

For Piaget, number is a synthesis of class and asymmetrical relation. In assigning a cardinal number to a set, one disregards the differences between elements and treats all the elements of the set as though they were members of a common class, ergo the class or cardinal component of number. However, in counting the set to arrive at its cardinal value, it is necessary to order the set—count one element first, another second, and so on. This ordering represents an asymmetrical relation. As a consequence of this analysis, a principal focus of Piaget's research on the development of number has been the study of seriation and class inclusion and the coordination of cardinal and ordinal concepts. The segment of Piaget's investigation that has had the greatest impact on subsequent research involves the principle of conservation. Piaget contends that some form of conservation is necessary for any mathematical understanding, and almost a third of his book *The Child's Conception of Number* is devoted to studies of conservation of one kind or another.

Piaget describes a stagewise development of number concepts in which conservation, seriation, and class concepts develop in close synchrony. In the first stage, children are dominated by immediate perceptual qualities of an event and give little evidence of logical reasoning. Consequently, they do not conserve, are incapable of seriation, and do not understand simple class-inclusion relationships. At this stage, only gross quantitative judgments, based on dominant perceptual attributes, are possible. The second stage is a transitional stage. Some progress is made on all fronts, so that children can construct series and correspondences. But they still have difficulty when either is transformed. Cardinal and ordinal concepts have developed to a great extent, but since they have not been integrated, children cannot relate them to each other. Finally, in the third stage, the development of conservation, class inclusion, and seriation is complete, and the child achieves an operational concept of number.

Most of the replications of Piaget's research on number have concentrated on a single task, most frequently conservation. On the whole, these studies have confirmed Piaget's account of the progression of behaviors exhibited for each of the individual tasks. Furthermore, these replications have demonstrated that the errors exhibited by young children are not experimental artifacts and do not result simply from children's failure to understand the questions asked. However, studies that have included a variety of Piaget's number tasks have found a great deal less synchrony than that described by Piaget (cf. Dodwell, 1960, 1962; Wohlwill, 1960).

A different organization of the logical operations that underlie number is proposed by Brainerd (1973b, 1973e, 1976), who takes issue with Piaget's contention that an operational understanding of natural number results from the concurrent development of cardinal and ordinal concepts. He contends that such a theory is inadequate from a logical perspective and is contrary to the results of a number of empirical studies that he has conducted. Brainerd proposes that the concept of ordinal number is psychologically more basic than that of cardinal number, and that the former plays a more important role in the early growth of arithmetic concepts and skills than the latter. In fact, Brainerd proposes that much basic arithmetic is learned before cardinal concepts are acquired, and he concludes that the developmental sequence is ordinal number, natural number, and finally cardinal number.

These conclusions are based on a series of different studies. In one set of studies Brainerd found that children perceive ordinal sequences by 3 years of age, but cardinal number does not begin to emerge until about 5. In another set of studies, first graders were significantly more successful on ordinal tasks than on cardinal tasks, and ordinal number concepts (but not cardinal number concepts) were almost uniformly mastered by students who were proficient with basic addition and subtraction facts. Finally, in another set of studies, it was found that training was significantly more successful for ordinal number than for cardinal number concepts and that there was significantly greater transfer to basic arithmetic achievement.

Brainerd's results have uniformly supported his position. However, in spite of the range of experimental paradigms he has employed, he has tended to use the same basic items to characterize cardination and ordination. The ordination problems have generally involved some form of transitivity task; the cardination problems are a sort of pseudoconservation task in which subjects are asked to compare the number of elements in two sets arranged in what can best be characterized as the final state of a typical conservation task. It is questionable whether these tasks validly represent either cardinal or ordinal numbers.

Another basic question is whether the observed ordinal-to-cardinal sequence is a function of basic competence or simply reflects differences in difficulty of the selected tasks. Brainerd (1976) cites the results of a study by Gonchar (1975) as essentially supportive of his position. However, although Gonchar found the same developmental sequence for Brainerd's tasks, the sequence was reversed when more difficult ordinal tasks were used. This led Gonchar to conclude that Brainerd's ordinal-to-cardinal sequence is primarily a performance distinction between the tasks used to measure each concept.

Research based on number skills. In counterpoint to the logically based theories of Piaget and Brainerd, there is a growing body of research based on the assumption that the development of number concepts can best be explained in terms of the development of specific number skills. This may involve the hierarchical integration of a number of different skills, as illustrated by the work of Klahr and Wallace (1976) and Schaeffer, Eggleston, and Scott (1974), or it may involve the increasingly efficient application of a single skill or a small number of skills. This approach, which usually focuses on counting strategies, is illustrated by the work of Davydov (1975), Gelman (1972a, 1972b, 1977), and Ginsburg (1977a, 1977b).

The sequence of development of different number skills has not been clearly established. For example, Klahr and Wallace (1976) cite evidence to suggest that children "subitize" (directly perceive) the number of elements in small sets before they count. Gelman (1972a, 1972b, 1977), however, asserts that counting precedes subitizing.

Although there is no consensus on which skills are most productive to study or how different skills are hierarchically integrated, there is some agreement that the growth of the ability to count is a central factor in the acquisition of number concepts. Children first learn to count by memorizing a rote sequence of numerals (D'Mello & Willemsen, 1969; Wang, Resnick, & Boozer, 1971). They initially have a great deal of difficulty counting the number of elements in a set and make a variety of errors, like counting an element more than once, skipping an element, or counting on after all the elements in the set have been counted (Potter & Levy, 1968). Further, younger children do not recognize that the number of elements in a set is unaffected by the order in which the set is counted (Ginsburg, 1975). Children first learn to assign numbers to small sets and gradually extend their range (Gelman, 1972a, 1972b, 1977; D'Mello & Willemsen, 1969; Wang et. al., 1971). Once they can accurately assign numbers to sets of a given size, number becomes a salient feature of those sets and they have some understanding of the effect of different transformations on those sets (but not on larger ones). However, younger children still have some difficulty attending to relevant attributes in more complex situations, and counting does not insure correct responses in typical conservation problems (Carpenter, 1971).

Although this line of research does not accept that the development of basic number concepts depends on underlying logical operations, the existence of such constructs as conservation is generally acknowledged. In fact, these theories often try to explain the development of concepts like conservation in terms of the application of number skills. For example, Gelman (1969, 1972a, 1972b, 1977) hypothesizes that conservation failures do not reflect an immature conception of number but that they occur because children focus on different attributes of the array and do not attend to numerousness. Conservation emerges as the child learns to attend to the appropriate attribute. Gelman denies that conservation is a prerequisite for understanding basic number concepts, proposing instead that conservation develops through a growing sophistication to apply counting and estimating strategies. Instead of attributing to young children the very ephemeral conception of number that Piaget does, Gelman contends that number is a stable and salient property of a set, provided that the number of elements is within a range that a child can reliably count.

Gelman contends that children first learn to deal effectively with small numbers. Provided that they apply counting or estimating strategies, they will conserve and recognize the effect of adding or subtracting an element for sets with a small number of elements. They will fail, however, to generalize these operations to larger sets. In other words, these responses are restricted to a domain that the child can count. As the ability to count is extended to larger numbers, there is a commensurate increase in the domain of understanding the effect of different transformations. When children finally realize that numbers are infinitely constructible by the continued addition of units, they can generalize the basic operations and conserve number in all situations.

Gelman (1972b) makes a critical distinction between "estimators" and "operators":

> The cognitive processes by which people determine some quality, such as the numerosity of a set of objects, are termed *estimators*. The cognitive processes by which people determine the consequences of transforming a quantity in various ways are termed *operators*. (p. 116)

A similar distinction is made by Ginsburg (1975), who identifies three cognitive systems that children possess. System 1 includes conservation and other processes that are used to make quantitative judgments without counting. System 2 involves the various counting strategies that children develop independently of formal instruction. System 3 involves the formal knowledge transmitted through instruction. Ginsburg proposes that in individual children the three systems may be relatively independent of one another or may show some degree of integration. He suggests, however, that even though the study of System 2 and System 3 concepts will help explain children's learning of mathematics, the study of System 1 concepts is not productive in explaining children's learning of mathematics concepts.

The development of arithmetic operations. It is not immediately clear how the research of Piaget on the development of early number concepts might be extended to study children's acquisition of arithmetical operations. One attempt has involved the correlation of performance on a test of Piagetian tasks with some measure of mathematics achievement (cf. Cathcart, 1971; Dimitrovsky & Almy, 1975; Kaminsky, 1971; Kaufman & Kaufman, 1972; Nelson, 1970; Rohr, 1973; Smith, 1974; Steffe, 1970; LeBlanc, 1971). These studies have uniformly found high positive correlations, even when IQ is held constant (Kaminsky, 1971; Steffe, 1970; Le-Blanc, 1971). Furthermore, performance on Piagetian batteries administered in kindergarten appears to be an excellent predictor of mathematics achievement as much as two years later (Bearison, 1975; Dimitrovsky & Almy, 1975).

One limitation of correlational studies often overlooked in the rush to identify educational implications of research is that they do not specify cause-and-effect relationships. High positive correlations between performance on Piagetian tasks and arithmetic achievement does not imply that mastery of these tasks is a prerequisite for learning arithmetic skills. In fact, Mpiangu and Gentile (1975) found that training on arithmetic skills did not have a differential effect on the learning of conservers and nonconservers. In other words, although conservation was correlated with overall arithmetic achievement, nonconservers benefited as much from Mpiangu and Gentile's instruction as conservers. Thus, conservation was not necessary to benefit from instruction. However, to conclude on the basis of this study that the lack of conservation does not limit children's ability to learn computational concepts would be inappropriate. As most of the correlational studies did, Mpiangu and Gentile's study relied on superficial measures of arithmetic achievement. Even Piaget would not deny that nonconservers can be taught a variety of arithmetical calculations. From a Piagetian perspective, the important question is, What meaning do the operations have for children? This requires that the concepts have a certain degree of generalizability, transfer, and resistance to extinction.

The significance of the kind of learning measured is demonstrated by the teaching experiment by Steffe et al. (1976). Their results indicate that although nonconservers learned many of the same counting strategies as conservers, they learned them in a much narrower sense and could not transfer them to related problems. It is not clear what implications these results hold for instruction. There was no evidence that the nonconservers were harmed by instruction or would have benefited from having instruction deferred. A great deal more research is needed before we understand how the development of conservation affects the learning of other mathematical concepts and operations.

The link between the development of counting strategies and the learning of arithmetic operations is easier to establish. Children's earliest notions of addition and subtraction are built on counting, and even before they receive formal instruction in addition and subtraction, they can solve simple problems using a variety of counting strategies.

Even after several years of instruction on the addition and subtraction algorithms, children continue to employ a variety of counting and heuristic strategies. Different strategies involve varying degrees of sophistication and efficiency. For example, younger or less capable children tend to count all the elements in sets representing addition or subtraction problems, whereas older or more capable children may use appropriate *counting on* or *counting back* strategies.

Several techniques have been used to study the processes that children use to solve problems involving the application of arithmetic operations. Perhaps the most productive involves the use of clinical interview techniques (Davydov, 1975; Ginsburg, 1976, 1977a). A second approach has been to use response latencies to infer what sort of strategies children apply to the solution of different problems (cf. Groen & Parkman, 1972; Groen & Poll, 1973; Rosenthal & Resnick, 1974; Suppes, 1967; Suppes & Morningstar, 1972; Woods, Resnick, & Groen, 1975). This approach involves breaking operations down into a series of discrete steps (e.g., counting by ones). It is assumed that the time required to solve a given problem using a particular strategy is a linear function of the number of steps needed to reach the solution. By finding the best fit between response latencies for subjects solving a variety of problems and the regression equations of possible solution strategies, the most appropriate model can be inferred. For example, to solve $9 - 6$, children might count down 6 units from 9 or they might count up from 6 until they reach 9 and keep track of the number of units. For this particular problem, the latter strategy would require fewer steps; the counting down strategy would be more efficient for $8 - 2$. The evidence to date suggests that there is a developmental trend for children to move from using a single model exclusively to a more heuristic strategy by which they attempt to choose the most efficient strategy.

Most of the research on number has concentrated on the early development of number concepts. There have been only a few clinical studies of the processes that children use to solve more advanced problems (cf. Erlwanger, 1975; Lankford, 1972, 1974). Developmental psychologists tend to be primarily interested in concepts that develop somewhat independently of the school curriculum. Presumably this accounts for their singular lack of interest in all but the primary number concepts. This is one of the ways that the focus of research in cognitive development in mathematics education should be different from that in psychology. We are primarily interested in school learning; the limits that children's levels of cognitive development place on their ability to apply and understand algorithms for whole numbers, fractions, and decimals should be a central focus for such research.

Measurement

Although the development of measurement is frequently subsumed under the development of geometry, recent research in measurement seems, in many ways, more closely aligned with research on basic number concepts. The work of Piaget (Piaget, Inhelder, & Szeminska, 1960) also provides the focus for much of the recent research on the development of measurement concepts. He and his colleagues found that the general stages of development of number concepts also characterize major phases in the development of measurement. However, for measurement, the second and third stages are each divided into two substages and a fourth stage is added.

As with number, conservation is the central idea underlying all measurement. The attainment of conservation and the corresponding notion of transitivity is the hallmark of the first level of the achievement of measurement concepts (Stage IIIA). Measurement further depends on the synthesis of change of position and subdivision so that unit iteration is possible (Stage IIIB). Finally, the development of formal measurement operations is complete with the onset of the ability to coordinate the measures of several linear dimensions so that areas and volumes can be calculated directly from their respective linear dimensions (Stage IV).

Piaget et al. (1960) assessed this development with a great variety of measurement and premeasurement tasks. In the earliest stages children do not conserve and are unable to apply any sort of measurement operations correctly. In later stages they begin to apply some rudimentary forms of measurement, but they will use unreliable measures like the span of their arms and still rely extensively on visual comparisons. By trial and error they gradually discover that if it takes more units to cover A than B, then A is greater than B. But initially they fail to understand the importance of the size of the units and often count a fraction of a unit as a whole or equate two quantities that measure the same number of units with different-sized units of measure.

Conservation and transitivity are attained at about 7 to 8 years. Although this marks a significant stage in the development of measurement concepts, operational measurement is still not achieved. Children in this stage can use a moving middle term transitively, but only if it is as long as or longer than the original; they can conserve and therefore can compare units. Similarly, they recognize that a quantity is the sum of its unit covering. However, these ideas have not been fused; they continue to ignore the size and completeness of units of measure, and consequently unit iteration is not possible. It is also interesting that although children at this stage conserve included area and volume, they fail to conserve complementary area or occupied volume. In other words, they recognize the equality of areas and volumes contained within certain boundaries but do not recognize that the amount of space occupied by the object in relation to other objects around it must also be equal. The eventual coordination of change of position and subdivision makes unit iteration possible, but it is not until the onset of formal operations at the age of about 11 to 12 that development is complete and the calculation of areas and volumes is possible. As with their number research, Piaget and his colleagues' (1960) description of the range of children's responses to individual tasks involving conservation and transitivity has been confirmed, but the relationship between tasks and their place in the development of measurement has been questioned.

Some of the most interesting research on measurement has revolved around the use of different units of measure. A unique feature of the measurement process that distinguishes it from simply counting is the unit of measure. When a number is assigned to a set, the units are the individual elements of the set. However, in the measurement process the individual units that are counted may not be distinguishable, and different units may be used to measure the same quantity. This second feature of units of measure has been the subject of a variety of studies.

One study employed a series of conservation and measurement tasks in which children were provided both measurement and visual cues regarding the relationship between two liquid quantities (Carpenter, 1975). In some tasks children had to focus on the visual cues; the liquid was in identical containers and was measured with different units. In others the same unit was used, and children had to focus on the numerical cues, since the visual cues were misleading. This study found that, contrary to earlier hypotheses, virtually all first- and second-grade children respond to numerical measurement cues at least as readily as to perceptual cues. However, the majority still center on a single dominant dimension, numerical or perceptual, depending on the problem situation. This leads to both correct and incorrect judgments. But the errors appear to result from an inability to attend to the relevant cues, not misconceptions regarding the relevance of measurement operations. Almost all errors resulted from children responding to the most recent cues, whether they were numerical or perceptual. In fact, there was a tendency to focus on numerical rather than visual cues, and virtually all children correctly responded on the basis of number in the simplest measurement situations. These results are consistent with Gelman's (1972a) hypothesis that number is a salient property in arriving at quantitative judgments.

Furthermore, just as counting and estimating operations formed a basis for the development of conservation with discrete sets in Gelman's studies, there is evidence that measurement operations may extend this domain to include continuous quantity. Three of the most successful conservation training studies have used measurement activities to train conservation (Bearison, 1969; Fusaro, 1969; Inhelder et al., 1974). A longitudinal study by Wohlwill, Devoe, and Fusaro (1971) found a significant correlation between performance on a set of measurement tasks and performance on a conservation test administered approximately nine months later. Although the data are somewhat tenuous, they support the hypothesis that measuring activities actually contribute to the natural development of conservation and are not limited to laboratory training sessions.

All in all, a fairly consistent if somewhat illogical sequence emerges in the development of number and measurement concepts. It is clear that children's logic is not congruent with adult logic. Children who do not conserve length are also incapable of reasoning that this conservation failure should have any consequences for their measurement activities. If children are not asked specific conservation questions, the questions do not occur to them and they blissfully count the units just as any adult would do. Conservation, therefore, is not a prerequisite for successfully performing certain measurement tasks.

Children come to school with a well-established notion of counting. Number is a salient cue that children readily attend to. However, they still have difficulty controlling their attention and tend to center on a single dominant dimension, sometimes numerical and sometimes perceptual. This leads to a number of correct and a number of incorrect judgments.

Although measurement with a single unit is possible for quite young children, difficulties are encountered relating measures using different units. Here one of the incongruities in the development of measurement concepts is found. It seems logical that children would learn to identify the effect of measuring with different units by observing the results of actual measurement with different units. However, children know that an inverse relationship exists between the size of the unit and the number of units measured long before they are able to apply this knowledge to measurement problems involving several different units (Carpenter & Lewis, 1976). This may account in part for the equally incongruous finding of Inhelder et al. (1974) and Montgomery (1973) that measurement training involving comparisons of measures made with different units of measure are successful with relatively young children.

Space and Geometry

The work of Piaget and his colleagues (Piaget & Inhelder, 1956) also provides a central focus for much of the recent research on young children's spatial and geometric concepts. A central feature of Piaget's characterization of the development of spatial concepts is his distinction between perceptual and conceptual space. "Spatial concepts are internalized actions and not merely mental images of external things or events" (Piaget & Inhelder, 1956, p. 454). A young child might be able to perceive the differences between a circle and a triangle but be unable to deal with these differences conceptually. For example, the child may be unable to represent these differences in a drawing or to distinguish between the figures tactically.

Piaget and Inhelder describe three main series of spatial studies—one dealing with topological concepts, one dealing with projective concepts, and one dealing with Euclidean concepts. They propose that certain topological properties like proximity, separation, order, enclosure, and continuity are primitive spatial concepts from which projective and Euclidean concepts emerge. These properties are unaffected by a variety of transformations and, hence, do not require conservation. In projective space, objects are no longer considered in isolation but rather from particular points of view. Thus, the studies in this series characterize children's growing ability to describe objects viewed from a perspective other than their own. Since straight lines are preserved in a projective space, children's ability to construct straight lines is considered to be another measure of their knowledge of projective space.

From a Euclidean perspective, space is viewed as a common medium containing objects with well-defined spatial relationships between them. At an operational level, distance, area, and volume are conserved and measurement is possible. In addition to concepts of distance, relations between objects depend on a reference system of horizontal and vertical lines. Thus, for Piaget, the ability to conserve and measure and an understanding of the properties of horizontal and vertical lines are the hallmarks of the emergence of an operational view of Euclidean space.

Smock (1976b) characterizes the differences among the three spatial domains as follows: "In short, topological space deals with the internal relations of the isolated object. Projective space deals with the relations of objects to subjects. Euclidean space deals with the relations of objects to objects" (p. 48).

Because of the great variety of tasks Piaget used to assess children's concept of space and the concurrent development across three related spatial domains, it is even more difficult to characterize briefly Piaget's work in this area than in the areas of number and measurement. For a more complete account, see Smock (1976b).

Certain parallels exist between Piaget's research on number and measurement and his studies of spatial concepts. Whereas number concepts were grounded in basic, logical class and relational concepts, Euclidean space was built on the logically more basic concepts of topology. The course of development also follows parallel paths starting with a stage of gross global judgments and proceeding through an intuitive trial-and-error stage to a final operational stage. In fact, some of the same underlying factors seem to account for errors in all three realms.

A primary feature of development that seems to affect children's concepts in all areas is the growing ability to control attention, to attend to relevant attributes. Whereas difficulty in controlling attention leads to conservation errors in number and measurement problems, it also appears to contribute to children's difficulty constructing straight lines and their failures on tasks testing their ability to construct horizontal and vertical lines. Failures in both areas tended to result from their inability to ignore the irrelevant characteristics of the surrounding medium. Young children tended to construct "straight" lines following the edge of the table on which they were constructing them, even when the table was round, and they represented the level of water in a jar as being parallel to the bottom of the jar, even when the jar was tilted at an angle.

As with number and measurement, replications of the Piagetian tasks have found the same range of responses identified by Piaget. The tendency for replications to find a great deal less order and symmetry than described by Piaget holds true for spatial investigation (cf. Dodwell, 1963).

Several comprehensive attempts to expand Piaget's investigations of space have been reported. Laurendeau and Pinard (1970) describe a detailed experimental analysis of five tasks derived from Piaget's work in an attempt to construct a scale of spatial development. A second line of research has been conducted by the Genevans themselves. Laurendeau and Pinard's research has been directed at critically analyzing and validating the earlier work of Piaget and Inhelder (1956), whereas the recent work of the Genevans has attempted to expand the domain of the research to new tasks that deal with new concepts. These include the study of children's ability to deal with reflection and rotation transformations, several studies of their understanding of the relationship between changes in area and perimeter, and one dealing with their ability to describe the characteristics of a Möbius ring. Although the complete report of these studies is not available in English translation, a summary has been reported by Montangero (1976).

Another characterization of the development of geometry concepts has been proposed by the van Hieles (Freudenthal, 1973; Wirszup, 1976). They pick up where Piaget leaves off and describe a developmental sequence culminating in abstract geometric systems. They propose that the development of geometry proceeds through five levels: In Level I children perceive geometric figures in global terms. Although they recognize and can reproduce squares, rectangles, and parallelograms, they cannot isolate specific attributes of the figures. They are unable to identify relationships between different figures and do not recognize that all squares are rectangles, all rectangles are parallelograms, and so on. This is similar to Piaget's observation that young children have difficulty constructing class hierarchies in general.

At Level II children can isolate individual attributes of figures. But these are established empirically, and the child does not see that certain properties imply that other properties must also be present. In other words, children at Level II may recognize that the opposite sides of a parallelogram are both parallel and congruent but these properties are simply considered to occur concurrently. The child does not recognize that any quadrilateral with opposite sides congruent must be a parallelogram. Children at this level can identify the common attributes of different figures but still do not discern the class hierarchy between figures like squares, rectangles, and parallelograms.

Level III is a transitional level between the essentially empirical geometry of the first two levels and the formal systems of the next two. Deduction must be supplemented with empirical demonstration. Students at this stage see that certain properties must follow from others and understand the multiple classification of geometric figures. But the student's ability to use deduction is still limited and requires support from the teacher or text-book.

At Level IV a deductive system at the level of Euclid's *Elements* is complete. But it is not until Level V that an understanding of abstract systems divorced from concrete representations is acquired.

The van Hieles propose that there are distinct discontinuities between levels and that the levels cannot be skipped. Unlike Piaget, they propose that the levels develop primarily under the influence of school instruction. Therefore, instruction should be geared to lead students deliberately from one level to the next. Wirszup (1976) reports on the efforts of two Soviet researchers who have based a program of geometry instruction on the work of the van Hieles with striking success.

If the van Hieles' analysis is correct, it would have serious implications for instruction in geometry. Formal instruction in 10th grade geometry begins at Level IV and is preceded in earlier grades by relatively feeble efforts that certainly would be insufficient to lead students through Levels II and III. However, although there is an almost a priori logic to the sequence of development described by the van Hieles, it is not yet clear that the course of development is as rigid as they propose. At this point, relatively little research has been conducted to validate their conclusions. Although Wirszup reports that the Soviets have conducted extensive pedagogical investigations based on the van Hieles' work, it has yet to attract the attention of American researchers, and its implications for American curriculum are still unclear. It is clear, however, that many, if not most, students fail to master even the basic elements of formal geometry. The van Hieles' work provides a beginning framework for research in this area.

Adolescent Reasoning

Although the study of cognitive development in children is currently a major focus of research in both psychology and education, the parallel study of adolescence has not fared so well. In general, the study of adolescent reasoning is characterized, according to Neimark (1975), by "the paucity of systematic evidence, by the limited generality of what evidence there is, and by the almost complete failure to relate intellectual development to other concomitant developmental changes which mark this period'' (p. 541).

The scarcity of available research makes it impossible to specify with any confidence the precise nature of adolescent thinking. However, on the basis of a comprehensive review of current research, Neimark concluded that there is a stage of cognitive development beyond, and different from, the concrete operational stage of middle and late childhood. Although Piaget initially proposed that this stage begins between the ages of 12 and 15, it appears to develop later in many children. In fact, it is not attained at all by some individuals. Furthermore, there is a great deal more variability in the application of the formal reasoning structures of this period than for the concrete operations of earlier stages. Even adults operate at a formal operational level on some tasks but fail to do so on others. Piaget (1972) himself concedes that at this stage individual aptitude, interest, and experience appear to play a significant role in determining which tasks an individual can complete successfully. Although it is conceded that training should be a significant factor at this stage, the specific effects of training are largely unexplored.

The most fundamental property of formal thought is the ability to consider the possible rather than being restricted to concrete reality (Inhelder & Piaget, 1958). At this stage adolescents can identify all possible relations that can exist within a given situation and systematically generate and test hypotheses about these relations. They are capable of evaluating the logical structure of propositions independent of any concrete referents, and they are able to reflect on their own thought processes. Formal operations are also characterized by an ability to use more complex classification strategies and to shift the basis of classification more readily. In this stage adolescents are increasingly aware of the demands that tasks place on memory, and they use more efficient strategies for dealing with them. They also have much greater comprehension of key logical connectives and quantifiers.

In general, the capabilities of formal operational thought appear to be necessary for success in most mathematics beyond basic arithmetic. The construction of formal proofs and the learning of general heuristic strategies certainly appear to depend on formal reasoning processes. These are both areas in which many high school students experience little success. To what degree this failure results from their inability to operate at a formal operational level is largely a matter of conjecture, since there is little empirical evidence one way or another.

In many ways, the potential significance of research in cognitive development for education may be greater at adolescence than at the earlier stages, where it has been concentrated. Although concepts like conservation and transitivity are logical prerequisites for most of number and measurement, they are not an integral part of what children actually do when generating addition facts, learning algorithms, or making simple measurements. As a result, in spite of an overwhelming number of studies involving these concepts, their consequence for the learning of elementary mathematical concepts remains ambiguous. However, the abstract reasoning skills of the formal operational stage are precisely those that are needed for any real success in high school mathematics. Furthermore, the development of these skills in any given area appears to be much more a function of specific experience than in earlier stages, and so it is likely that specific, relatively short-term training should have a more profound effect than has been demonstrated by the myriad of conservation training studies. Since many adults fail to attain formal reasoning levels in many areas, it would also be easier to argue that such instruction has some educational value in its own right. It is generally conceded that experience and training should be a significant factor in the development of formal reasoning, but the specific effects of training are largely unexplored at this level.

The study of the development of formal reasoning is a potentially rich area for research. A number of individual studies have dealt with the development of various mathematical concepts at a formal operational level. For example, see the studies on proportionality by Ginsburg and Rapaport (1967), Lovell and Butterworth (1966), Lunzer and Pumfrey (1966), and Pumfrey (1968); the studies on probability by Lovell (1971d); the study of limits by Taback (1975); and the studies on the concept of a function by Lovell (1971c) and Thomas (1975). These studies have just begun to unravel the basic question of how the development of formal reasoning skills affects the learning of mathematics, and the study of formal operations should be a prime area for research in mathematics education in the future. One of the major problems in this regard is the construction of good measures of formal operational thought.

NEW DIRECTIONS

Recent research in cognitive development has been dominated by the research and theories of Piaget. In the areas of number, measurement, geometry, and formal reasoning, almost all the research of major interest has been conducted either on the basis of, or in reaction to, his theories (Flavell, 1970). His influence has been so extensive that it has led Neimark (1975) to observe: "There is only one comprehensive theory of cognitive development, Piaget's. All other contenders are so deeply influenced by and derived from the work of Piaget as to be better classified as shifts in focus or extensions" (p. 575).

Recently, however, several alternative approaches to the study of cognitive development have emerged. Klausmeier, Ghatala, and Frayer (1974) suggest that the general principles of concept learning outlined in their Concept Learning and Development model might be useful in studying the development of basic concepts; Scandura (1977) has proposed that structural learning theory may provide a productive framework for the analysis of developmental phenomena. Another interesting line of research is proposed by Wheatley, Mitchell, Frankland, and Kraft (1978), who have been examining the implications of hemispheric specialization for cognitive development. Recently translated Soviet research provides an especially rich source of ideas for research on cognitive development in mathematics education. Of special note are the recently available works of Vygotsky (1978) and Krutetskii (1976) and the 14 volumes of the Soviet Studies in the Psychology of Learning and Teaching Mathematics series (School Mathematics Study Group, 1969–75). Another potentially productive approach involves the application of information-processing theories to the study of cognitive development.

Soviet Studies

Like Piaget's research, much of the Soviet research has relied on qualitative methods and has focused on mental operations and other processes that children use to solve problems. However, whereas Piaget and most Western psychologists have focused on concepts that presumably develop independently of the school curriculum, the Soviets maintain that cognitive development and school learning are inexorably linked. "In the final analysis, a pupil's mental development is determined by the content of what he is learning. Existing intellectual capabilities must therefore be studied primarily by making certain changes in what children learn at school" (El'Konin & Davydov, 1975, p. 2). Thus, stages of development are not viewed as absolute, and it is believed that changes in the curriculum can result in significant changes in the developmental stages through which a child passes. The types of misconceptions that Piaget identifies in early stages of development are attributed to shortcomings in the curriculum, and much of the Soviet research is directed at identifying such misconceptions and reconstructing the curriculum so that they do not develop. The view is also held that the various logical reasoning processes used in mathematics are not strictly a function of maturation and general real-world experiences but can be learned through appropriate instruction. The instructional treatments that are used in Soviet research are not the short clinical studies typical of most Western research. Much of the instruction occurs in school settings over extended periods of time, sometimes an entire academic year.

The Soviet studies do not provide the unified theory found in the work of Piaget. Although 6 of the 14 volumes deal with issues involving cognitive development, the studies reported represent the work of many different authors attacking a variety of different problems. Only the work of Krutetskii (Krutetskii, 1976; Kilpatrick & Wirszup, 1969b), Vygotsky (1962, 1978), and possibly El'Konin and Davydov (Steffe, 1975) is presented in sufficient detail to provide anything approaching a unified theory.

Several examples that illustrate the general orientation and techniques of Soviet research follow. The first reports the results of a study by Gal'perin and Georgiev (1969) dealing with the learning of measurement concepts by young children. The second involves a discussion of several theoretical constructs of Vygotsky's that have potential implications for research in mathematics education. A brief summary of Soviet research in instructional psychology can be found in Volume 1 of the Soviet Studies series (Menchinskaya, 1969).

The study reported by Gal'perin and Georgiev clearly illustrates the difference between the Soviet and Piagetian points of view. Gal'perin and Georgiev identified many of the same type of conservation and measurement errors found by Piaget. But rather than accepting these errors as developmental phenomena, they attributed them to the traditional emphasis in school mathematics programs on number concepts, which incorrectly characterized units as discrete entities.

To test their hypothesis, they administered a series of measurement problems to the "upper group" of a Soviet kindergarten. They concluded that young children who are taught by traditional methods lack a basic understanding of a unit of measure, failing to recognize that each unit may not be directly identifiable as an entity and may, itself, consist of parts. Children are indifferent to the size and fullness of a unit of measure and have more faith in direct visual comparison of quantities than in measurement by a given unit.

On the basis of this study, Gal'perin and Georgiev devised a program of 68 lessons that focused on measurement concepts and systematically differentiated between units of measure and separate entities. The lessons were divided into three parts. The first part dealt with forming a mathematical approach to the study of quantities. This section focused on replacing the habit of direct visual comparison with systematic application of measuring units. Appropriate units for measuring different quantities were identified, and measuring skills were studied directly with special attention being directed to the deficiencies identified in the pretest. A variety of units were used, including units consisting of several parts (two or three matches, spoons, etc.) or some fractions of a larger object (half a mug or stick). All these concepts were presented without assigning numbers to the quantities.

Not until the second part was the concept of number introduced. Thus, Gal'perin and Georgiev introduced most of the basic measuring skills and spatial concepts before they introduced numbers. In the third part, they introduced the inverse relationship between the size of the unit and the number of units.

Although the investigation was not conducted with strict experimental controls, participating students showed striking gains over the performance of the previous year's students. In the previous year fewer than half could answer most of the items on the measurement test, but performance was close to 100% for the experimental group.

Another example of Soviet research that provides a counterpoint to Piaget is found in the work of Vygotsky (1962, 1978). Fuson (1977) has discussed at some length how Vygotskian theory might be applied to the study of number concepts. Several of Vygotsky's constructs may also provide a useful framework for research in cognitive development in other areas of mathematics education.

One potentially useful construct involves the distinction between *spontaneous* and *scientific* concepts. Spontaneous concepts are generated by each child on the basis of concrete experience and the child's own mental effort. Scientific concepts are the product of direct instruction or interaction with adults. Vygotsky proposes that it is the interplay between spontaneous and scientific concepts that leads to development. The formal structure of the scientific concepts helps to organize the child's spontaneous concepts into a coherent system, and the experiential basis of the spontaneous concepts gives meaning to the scientific concepts at a more elementary concrete level. The significant role attributed to instruction in this theoretical development is characteristic of Soviet psychology and offers a distinct alternative to Piagetian theory.

Another Vygotskian construct that has potential significance for research on cognitive development in mathematics education is the zone of proximal development. This is defined by Vygotsky (1962) as "the discrepancy between a child's actual mental age and the level he reaches in solving problems with assistance" (p. 103). This measure, which Vygotsky suggests is an excellent predictor of children's ability to learn from instruction, provides an alternative method of measuring and characterizing development that may be especially appropriate for educational applications.

A variety of other interesting studies deserve the attention of Western researchers. The work of El'Konin and Davydov (Davydov, 1975; Steffe, 1975) on children's early number concepts is especially noteworthy. Although the focus of Krutetskii's work is on individual differences, many of his techniques and results are of interest from the perspective of cognitive development (Krutetskii, 1976; Kilpatrick & Wirszup, 1969b). Volume 3 in the Soviet Studies series (Kilpatrick & Wirszup, 1969a) contains four papers discussing the thinking processes children use in arithmetic and algebra, and Volume 5 (Kilpatrick & Wirszup, 1971) is devoted to the development of spatial abilities.

Information Processing

Soviet research on cognitive development has operated from an entirely different perspective from Piaget's, but information-processing approaches have generally attempted to build on Piagetian research. The nature of this contribution is best understood in terms of Flavell and Wohlwill's (1969) performance-competence model. Whereas Piaget has been primarily concerned with questions of competence, information-processing approaches have attempted to incorporate the performance component of the model into their accounts of cognitive development. Instead of analyzing behavior in terms of the logical and algebraic properties of the problem, researchers analyze tasks in terms of their information-processing requirements.

> Tasks must be analyzed in much more detail than is provided by a description of their conventional logical structure. The general problem is to determine exactly how the input is encoded by the subject and what transformations occur between encoding and decoding. The objective task structure alone does not yield a valid description of the solution performance, and it is necessary to diagnose the actual psychological processes in great detail to obtain minute descriptions or well supported inferences about the actual sequences and content of the thinking process. (Klahr & Wallace, 1976, pp. 3–4)

A wide range of information-processing theories exist. Although they are all based on an analogy with the computer and are, therefore, essentially mechanistic, some carry this analogy farther than others. At the most task-specific level, the goal is to construct a running computer program that actually models some segment of behavior. At the other end of the continuum, the computer acts as a sort of metaphor to describe general processing mechanisms. The work of Klahr and Wallace (1970, 1972, 1973, 1976) is the most extensive attempt to generate computer simulations of developmental phenomena. Their general modus operandi can be described as follows:

> Faced with a segment of behavior of a child performing a task, we pose the question: "What would an information-processing system require in order to exhibit the same behavior as the child?" The answer takes the form of a set of rules for processing information: a computer program. The program constitutes a model of the child performing the task. It contains explicit statements about the capacity of the system, the complexity of the processes, and the representation of information—the data structure—with which the child must deal. (Klahr & Wallace, 1976, p. 5)

The prominent features of such a system include a short-term memory, which is extremely limited in capacity, and a long-term memory, which is potentially unlimited in capacity. The information-processing system also has access to the external environment and some sort of mechanism for controlling attention that determines which sensory information is selected for processing. The long-term memory contains conditions or rules for processing information. All processing occurs in the short-term memory, and information from the external environment or long-term memory must enter the short-term memory before it can be acted on.

The strategy is to produce programs that fit the general architecture of the processing system described above and accurately model the general patterns of success and failure at different stages in the development of a given task. Then the question becomes, What sort of transition mechanisms are necessary to transform one model into the next? Klahr and Wallace have been relatively successful in modeling different performance levels, but a number of questions regarding transition processes remain.

At the metaphorical level, one of the most viable information-processing models has been proposed by Pascual-Leone (1970, 1976). The principal focus of this theory regards the capacity of the central processor. Pascual-Leone (1970) hypothesizes that the basic intellectual limitation of children is the number of schemes, rules, or ideas they can handle simultaneously—a capacity that increases regularly with age. The maximum number of discrete chunks of information that a child can integrate simultaneously is assumed to grow linearly in an all-or-none manner as a function of age. From the early preoperational stage (3–4 years), a child's information-processing capacity, or M-power, grows at the rate of one chunk every two years until the late formal operational stage (about 15–16 years).

Children frequently do not operate at full capacity, and it is proposed that some children have a tendency to operate well below capacity. The ability to operate near capacity is hypothesized to be linked to individual differences in field dependence-independence (see the chapter by Fennema & Behr). Studies by Case (1972a, 1972b, 1974) and Scardamalia (1977) have provided substantial support for the predictive value of Pascual-Leone's model.

Information processing provides a fresh approach to the study of cognitive development that may help resolve some of the paradoxes that have plagued Piagetian theory. For example, by holding constant the information-processing requirements of the tasks, Baylor, Gascon, Lemoyne, and Pothier (1973) were able to eliminate the well-documented décalage between the seriation of length and the seriation of weight. Scardamalia (1977) was able to produce décalages in logically isomorphic tasks by varying the information-processing demands of the tasks.

Information-processing approaches may also help account for the rather illogical sequence of development of certain number and measurement concepts and children's ability to complete successfully certain instructional sequences for which they lack the logical prerequisites.

It might be hypothesized that the effectiveness of instruction is more a function of the information-processing demands of the specific tasks than of the development of logical prerequisite operations. In other words, children may benefit from instruction as long as the information-processing demands of the tasks do not exceed their limits, in spite of the fact that they do not possess the prerequisite logical operations. Children's logic is not the same as adult logic. Given appropriate instruction, they may be able to attend to certain relevant dimensions of a stimulus situation and ignore the fact that their judgments depend on certain prerequisite knowledge that they lack. For a further discussion of how the demands of instruction might be geared to the information-processing capacities of the learner, see Case (1975).

Finally, from an information-processing perspective of cognitive development, training studies potentially take on a different interpretation. Although a variety of training procedures have been successful in accelerating the acquisition of various Piagetian operations, there is no evidence that similar training can increase information-processing capacity. One might speculate that the traditional training studies have simply shifted the domain in which established information-processing levels can be applied. For example, one might hypothesize that a lack of sufficient information-processing capacity is the primary cause of conservation failure. Children fail to conserve because they are unable to focus on several dimensions simultaneously. They center on a single dominant dimension and fail to conserve. From this perspective it might be hypothesized that the successful training studies have simply taught children to focus on the appropriate attribute but have not accelerated cognitive development in the sense of actually changing basic cognitive structure.

An analysis of cognitive development in terms of information-processing variables seems especially well suited for dealing with educational problems. The emphasis on the existence of internal logical structures and the debate over what evidence is necessary to demonstrate the existence of these structures has never seemed especially germane to the problems in education. We are primarily interested in performance and can leave the question of underlying competence to the psychologists. Our primary concern is whether a child can attend to, and learn from, a particular instructional sequence. An analysis of both the mathematical skills and the instructional sequence in terms of their information-processing demands provides a potentially productive method for relating the mathematics curriculum to one measure of cognitive development.

Two information-processing variables that show clear developmental trends are children's memory and their ability to control attention (Flavell, 1977; Hagen, Jongeward, & Kail, 1975; Peck, Frankel, & Hess, 1975). Many errors in traditional concept-development tasks result from children attending to inappropriate dimensions of the problem. Individuals

are faced with an overwhelming quantity of information from the environment that must be routed through the central processor in order to be acted
on. This can create a tremendous bottleneck, and the selecting mechanisms
are exceedingly important in characterizing information-processing capacity. To plan instruction, it is essential to know what stimuli children can,
and naturally do, attend to and how capable they are of shifting their
attention from one dimension to another.

Memory is also an important information-processing variable. As children mature, they use increasingly efficient coding, storage, and retrieval
strategies and are increasingly aware of the demands that specific tasks
place on memory and their own abilities to handle these demands. Mathematical problems place significant demands on memory, and an inefficient
use of memory can clog the central processor when its full capacity may be
needed. For example, it is quite difficult for most adults to multiply in
base 8, even when they are given preliminary instruction in different number bases and are provided with a multiplication table. To some degree,
this simulates an inefficient memory strategy.

POTENTIAL EDUCATIONAL APPLICATIONS

Basic research and theory on cognitive development is not focused
primarily on educational practice or the teaching and learning of mathematics. However, since the study of cognitive development involves the
study of basic intellectual functioning in children and since the specific
content under investigation frequently has involved fundamental mathematical concepts, potential applications for the teaching and learning of
mathematics naturally come to mind. There are numerous general discussions of the relevance of this body of research for educational practice (e.g.,
Athey & Rubadeau, 1970; Beard, 1969; Brearly & Hitchfield, 1969; Bruner,
1960; Furth, 1970; Ginsburg & Opper, 1969; Hooper, 1968; Kohlberg,
1968; Schwebel & Raph, 1973; Sigel, 1969; Stendler, 1965; Sullivan, 1967;
Hooper & DeFrain, 1974; Klausmeier & Hooper, 1974). Others have specifically addressed its relevance for the teaching and learning of mathematics (e.g., Copeland, 1974; Huntington, 1970; Inskeep, 1972; Lovell,
1971b, 1972; Steffe, 1971).

Some authors have attempted to draw specific inferences for educational
practice directly from the general research in cognitive development (e.g.,
Copeland, 1974; Huntington, 1970). Sullivan (1967) and Weaver (1972)
have made a strong case that such extrapolation from pure research based
exclusively on psychological considerations is inappropriate. What is
needed is what Glaser (1976a, 1976b) calls a "linking science" to establish the relationship between the descriptive science of cognitive development and the prescriptive science of instructional design. In other words,

fundamental instructional issues cannot be resolved directly on the basis of pure research. Research on cognitive development is descriptive, not prescriptive. It does, however, provide a basis for initiating certain lines of instructional research that could address three basic curricular issues: (a) *what* content should be taught, (b) *when* it should be taught, and (c) *how* it should be presented. These issues will be discussed in the following three sections.

The Content and Sequencing of Mathematical Topics

The first issue—*what* to teach—involves content, of course, and also how that content should be sequenced. Kohlberg and Mayer (1972) argue that the aim of education should be to foster development and, insofar as possible, insure that students progress through the basic stages identified by Piaget, Kohlberg, and others. A similar argument is found in the van Hieles' proposals regarding the learning of geometric reasoning skills. Although certain elements of the assumptions on which these proposals are based are subject to empirical validation, the basic issue of what content is most important to teach seems to be based primarily on value considerations. Consequently, the implications of this issue for research are minimal.

The *sequencing* of content is more pedagogical, and it is of greater potential consequence for research in mathematics education. Once a specific objective has been identified, there is still the problem of choosing the most effective way to develop the topic mathematically. This involves choosing the approach, definitions, or models to be used and deciding how to sequence the topics. During the late 1950s and early 1960s this choice was based almost exclusively on the logical structure of the subject. There is a growing awareness, however, that one must also account for the psychology of the child learning the subject.

The basic paradigm involves attempting to trace the natural development of a concept in children and to reflect this natural development in constructing the curriculum. The assumption is that the foundations of many basic mathematical concepts develop naturally, independent of any specific instruction. Through careful investigation, one can identify this sequence and design a curriculum that builds on this basic foundation of what a child already knows. The task for research is to identify the approaches that are potentially the most productive.

Caution must be exercised in applying this paradigm. There is some question of whether one can identify natural foundation concepts that are independent of current school practice. If children's conceptions diverge significantly from the development in the school curriculum, a reasonable case can be made that this pattern of development is generally independent of the specific curriculum. But if the development of children's understanding of a mathematical concept parallels its development in the curriculum, it is difficult to separate the effects of the current curriculum. This might not be as great a problem as it appears: If children's development follows the curriculum, it may not be possible to isolate the specific contribution of the curriculum, but one can have some confidence that the curriculum is not in opposition to the natural sequence of development. Thus, curriculum changes would be needed only if children's patterns of learning differed significantly from the curriculum. However, any attempt to identify the "natural" development of a given concept should include a careful analysis of the potential contribution of the current school curriculum.

A line of investigation that illustrates the application of this paradigm is the work of Brainerd (1973b, 1973e, 1976, 1979), discussed above. He proposes that basic natural number concepts can be developed logically either from an ordinal perspective, as evidenced by the work of Dedekind and Peano, or from a cardinal perspective, in the tradition of Russell and Whitehead. On the basis of his research with young children, Brainerd concludes that ordinal number concepts develop before cardinal number concepts and that ordinal number concepts are more closely connected with the initial emergence of arithmetic. He recommends, therefore, that serious consideration be given to abandoning the traditional cardinal development of natural number in favor of ordinal definitions.

Even if Brainerd's conclusions regarding the sequence of ordinal and cardinal concepts were valid, his recommendations would represent unwarranted extrapolation. No attempt was made in his studies to design and test instruction based on the ordinal definition of number. Furthermore, the examples of ordinal and cardinal concepts included in these studies represent only a narrow sampling of the concepts involved in the development of either ordinal or cardinal numbers.

It might be more productive to design curriculum to take into account the explicit concepts, processes, and skills that children exhibit throughout their acquisition of a topic rather than attempt to completely redesign it to be consistent with the development of certain underlying logical concepts as proposed by Brainerd. One set of explicit strategies that might be incorporated in the mathematics curriculum involves children's use of various counting strategies to solve simple addition and subtraction problems. Instruction has traditionally failed to take into account the richness and growing sophistication of these strategies. As illustrated by the teaching experiment of Steffe et al. (1976), curricula could be developed to build on these strategies rather than portray operations exclusively in terms of set operations.

An alternative to focusing on children's naturally developed concepts and successful strategies is to analyze their errors. When educators identify serious misconceptions or significant prerequisite concepts or skills that children are failing to master, instruction can be designed to compensate for these deficiencies. The series of studies by Gal'perin and Georgiev (1969) discussed above is an excellent example of this type of research. Another example is provided by a study of Zykova (1969), in which children were found to lack certain geometric processing skills and then instruction was specifically designed to teach these skills.

Matching Instruction to Appropriate Levels of Development

A second potentially significant contribution of research in cognitive development for the teaching and learning of mathematics deals with the issue of readiness—*when* the content should be taught. The basic problem is to provide instruction that is appropriate for individual students' level of cognitive development. It is not a matter of constructing the sequence of instruction but rather of identifying the specific place in the instructional sequence that is appropriate for an individual student at a given stage of development.

From a mechanistic perspective, this becomes a problem of identifying a hierarchy of prerequisite skills—whether they are a knowledge of addition facts or an understanding of the principle of conservation—and insuring that students have mastered the essential *prerequisites*. From the organismic point of view, stages of development are a function of integrated cognitive structures that are not readily altered by instruction. Therefore, it is not sufficient simply to identify a sequence of prerequisite skills or knowledge and insure that a child has mastered it. One must also account for the child's ability to process information. The problem is to match instruction to a child's level of cognitive development rather than simply fit the child into the appropriate step in a sequence of instruction.

A critical difference between the two approaches is that mechanists believe that mental processes operate essentially unchanged throughout development, whereas the organismic view is that there are qualitative differences in the processes available to children at different stages of development. In the mechanistic approach, all learning and development is reducible to its component parts and is susceptible to instruction. In the organismic approach, certain fundamental processes, like conservation or transitivity, are representative of basic levels of cognitive functioning that are not reducible to isolated pieces or susceptible to instruction. The level of development puts certain limits on a child's ability to learn from particular instructional situations. These basic limitations cannot readily be removed by specific instruction. Therefore, the problem for research is to identify the specific limits for each stage of development and to describe how instruction that is consistent with these limits can be designed.

This endeavor involves three problems. First, it is necessary to specify the basic dimensions of the individual stages of development. Second, the cognitive developmental requirements of each mathematical topic must be identified so that individual topics can be matched with appropriate levels of cognitive development. Third, it is necessary to devise some means to insure that individual students are provided with instruction appropriate for their level of cognitive development.

This final task can be accomplished in several ways. One is to identify age norms for the attainment of given levels of development and then sequence the curriculum so that topics are taught in the appropriate grade. This approach is illustrated in the article by Huntington (1970) criticizing the grade placement of geometry topics in the School Mathematics Study Group's curriculum on the basis of Piaget, Inhelder, and Szeminska's (1960) description of children's development of measurement concepts.

A second approach deals with levels of development on an individual basis. Since it is generally recognized that there are wide individual differences in the rate of cognitive development, this approach should provide a much better match between an individual child's level of development and the child's mathematics instruction. The critical problem for this approach is to develop a valid, reliable measure of cognitive development.

A classic series of studies that addresses the problem of readiness is reported by Washburne (1939). Although these studies are dated and the methods and variables under investigation would not be considered the most appropriate today, the series is noteworthy for its comprehensive attack on the problem. Over 30 000 students participated in the studies over a period of more than 10 years. The purpose was to identify the appropriate placement of arithmetic topics in terms of individual children's levels of development. Development was defined in terms of mental age, and recommendations were based on the initial mental age at which 75 to 80% of the students successfully learned a controlled teaching unit on a specific topic.

The measure of mental age used by Washburne (1939) was, to some degree, a primitive measure of cognitive development. However, tasks used in instruments measuring mental age are chosen for their psychometric properties and may be based on a hodgepodge of different reasoning processess, and so it is not possible to characterize different levels of development in terms of specific cognitive skills. Therefore, Washburne was able to establish only an empirical relationship, not a logical one, between mental age and the ability to perform different mathematical tasks.

Current attempts to construct scales of development are based on theories of cognitive development (usually Piaget's) rather than on normative procedures. Piaget hypothesizes that intellectual development proceeds through an invariant sequence of stages. The stages are characterized by the emergence of integrated systems of new cognitive structures that can be applied to a wide range of problem situations. The hypothesized invariant sequence of development should allow the construction of a series of tasks that characterize sequential levels of development and form a good Guttman scale.

This means that the tasks can be sequenced in an ordinal scale so that it is possible to identify specific tasks an individual can and cannot do successfully by locating the student at a point on this scale. The student should be able to do all the tasks scaled below that point and none above it. Because individual tasks are representative of levels of development, these results should generalize to other problems that are characteristic of a given level of development. When mathematics topics have been analyzed in terms of their requirements in cognitive development, it should be possible to specify which ones are appropriate for an individual student's level of development.

Washburne's argument was somewhat circular and devoid of any cause-and-effect justification. Chronological age or height or weight could just as well have served as measures of development. The argument was simply that because a given topic was not mastered by most students until a given age, this was the appropriate age to teach the topic. Ordinal scales could potentially identify the presence or absence of specific logical reasoning processes that are necessary for learning a given topic.

That's the theory. In practice, it has proved a great deal more difficult to construct an ordinal scale of development than originally supposed. A number of researchers have been working on the problem for the last 10 to 15 years with only mixed success (Green, Ford, & Flamer, 1971; Pinard & Laurendeau, 1964; Pinard & Sharp, 1972). Standardized tests have been constructed (e.g., Goldschmid & Bentler, 1968) substituting Piagetian tasks for traditional psychometric items. However, they are not true Guttman scales, since the number correct is not reproducible from the ordinal position of the most difficult item passed.

There are two major problems. First, factor analytic research indicates that logical reasoning is not a one-dimensional domain (Kaufman, 1971; Stephens, McLaughlin, Miller, & Glass, 1972; Wohlwill, 1973). Therefore, it is unlikely that the major dimensions of cognitive development could be incorporated in a single scale. This problem could be resolved by profiling development in terms of several scales that measure different factors of cognitive development. Pinard and Sharp (1972) report an effort to coordinate five ordinal scales—space; causality; classification, seriation, and number; conservation; and time, movement, and speed—into an overall test of cognitive development.

The second problem is more severe. To scale any set of relevant tasks into an invariant sequence has proved extremely difficult. The problems of horizontal décalage and the variability introduced by methodological variations have created almost overwhelming difficulties. Tuddenham (1971) made the following observation:

> The evidence thus far obtained has about extinguished whatever hope we might once have held that we could place each child on a single developmental continuum equivalent to mental age, and from his score predict his performance on content of whatever kind. (p. 75)

This may be overly pessimistic. To date, all efforts to construct ordinal scales have been based on a purely Piagetian rationale. If information-processing variables or some measure of task difficulty are included in the equation, some of these problems may be at least partially resolved.

It is also not clear that task variability poses the same stumbling block for education that it does for psychology. The reason rests in a construct validity-predictive validity distinction. Psychologists have been intent on constructing a scale that locates a child at a given point in Piaget's sequence of developmental stages. They have felt constrained to develop an instrument that clearly identifies a given operation and have thus become enmeshed in competence-performance issues. Competence measures are unnecessary in identifying what mathematics a child is capable of attending to. All that is required is to identify a level of performance that generalizes to a range of mathematical tasks. Performance distinctions should be included in such a measure because they are also a part of the mathematical problems and the manner in which they are presented.

In addition, the variability that has been introduced through differences in experience and familiarity with different stimuli may pose less of a problem in constructing an ordinal scale for curriculum purposes. Psychologists, attempting to construct a reasonably pure scale (one that is minimally affected by variations in school curriculum), have used stimulus situations that are maximally independent of the content of the school curriculum. Children have a wide range of experiences outside of school, and this creates a great deal of variability in stimulus familiarity. By sticking closer to the curriculum and using terminology and stimulus materials that are part of it, one gains at least some control over one segment of experience and can, perhaps, eliminate some of the extraneous error.

If ordinal scales could be constructed, they might provide a relatively efficient measure of cognitive development, which would explicitly characterize individual children's ability to operate with a wide range of intellectual tasks. This characteristic would make them extremely attractive for application to school practice. But although the problems involved in constructing ordinal scales may not be insurmountable, they certainly are substantial, and little progress has been made in constructing ordinal scales that have potential for classroom use.

Although ordinal scales provide an appealing elegance and ease of interpretation, their construction is not the central problem. What is essential is the construction of good measures of children's thinking and the identification of specific relationships between performance on those measures and the learning of particular mathematical concepts. Whether these measures fall into an ordinal scale is not critical. It is important, however, that the measures of children's thinking predict with some accuracy children's ability to learn specific mathematical concepts and skills.

Several alternative directions for developing such measures are possible. They might be based on fundamental developmental variables like conservation, class inclusion, and transitivity, which are presumed to develop outside of formal instruction. As noted above, several of these measures have been shown to correlate highly with mathematical achievement. However, with the exception of the study by Steffe et al. (1976), little progress has been made in relating these measures to children's ability to learn specific mathematical concepts and skills. In other words, it is not sufficient to demonstrate that there is a difference in overall achievement between conservers and nonconservers. It is necessary to document exactly how they differ and what instruction is appropriate for each group.

A second alternative would be to focus more explicitly on the concepts and processes that children apply directly to the mathematics they are learning. This analysis should go beyond standardized aptitude or achievement tests. Even tests specifically constructed to measure whether children have mastered specific prerequisite skills are inadequate. What is needed are measures of the specific concepts and processes that children apply to the content of instruction and the specific errors they may make. It is very difficult to get this type of information from paper-and-pencil tests. An application of clinical interview techniques discussed by Ginsburg (1976) seems to be the most promising approach. However, in order for this approach to have any impact on educational practice, efficient procedures for applying it in educational settings need to be developed.

A third potential measure is Vygotsky's (1962, 1978) zone of proximal development. Since this measure actually involves adult interaction, which represents a form of instruction, it should provide an excellent measure of children's ability to benefit from instruction.

A closely related technique is the application of teach-test procedures to ascertain children's ability to deal with certain types of instruction. Teach-test procedures have frequently been used with mentally retarded children to measure their susceptibility to traditional forms of instruction (cf. Budoff, 1967) but have seldom been used with normal children. The basic format involves a short, controlled training session over certain novel and presumably unfamiliar tasks followed by a test on the instructed material. This differs from other measures in that the initial knowledge or ability to do the task is not the primary concern. What is of interest is the degree to which subjects are able to profit from the instructional sequence. By manipulating the form of the short training session, one can generate a measure of children's ability to attend to, and learn from, different instructional sequences.

A study that illustrates the application of this technique is reported by Montgomery (1973). This study was an aptitude-treatment interaction study that examined the interaction of second- and third-graders' ability to learn unit-of-length concepts with two treatments based on area and unit-of-area concepts. Aptitude was measured using a teach-test procedure that partitioned subjects on their ability to learn to compare two lengths measured with different units. Subjects were randomly assigned to one of two nine-day instructional treatments on measuring and comparing areas. The difference between the treatments was the emphasis placed on the unit of measure. In one treatment, subjects always measured with congruent units and compared regions covered with congruent units. In the other, subjects measured with noncongruent units and compared regions covered with different units. On both a posttest and a retention test, the treatment that used different units was significantly more successful in teaching children to assign a number to a region (measure) and to compare two regions using their measures. However, there was no significant difference between the two treatments on a transfer test that included problems involving measurement with different units, and no significant interactions were found between aptitude levels and treatments. The failure to find significant results may, in part, reflect certain anomalies in the development of measurement concepts that were not taken into account (see the discussion on measurement above). But this failure does illustrate the pitfalls in attempting to construct good measures in order to match children to appropriate instruction.

Given the difficulty in characterizing stages of development and constructing good measures of development, it is not surprising that little has been accomplished in analyzing specific mathematical topics in terms of their requirements in cognitive development. A very rough first approximation of this task is provided by the Nuffield *Checking Up* booklets (Nuffield Mathematics Project, 1970, 1972).

Choosing Instructional Strategies

The third potential application of theory in cognitive development to problems of education involves the issue of instructional strategies—*how* the content should be presented. Cognitive development theory, that of Piaget in particular, has been used to justify a wide range of instructional programs that are based on such approaches as open classrooms, discovery, or activity learning. Two of the most reasoned attempts to formulate general principles for instruction on the basis of cognitive development can be found in Elkind (1976) and Smock (1976a). Hooper and DeFrain (1974) report on a number of attempts to apply Piagetian theory to the design of preschool programs.

In general, relatively little is known about the specific mechanisms that contribute to cognitive development or how they operate; in spite of the fact that an abundance of training studies exist, even less is known about how instruction can be designed to take advantage of basic developmental mechanisms. Much more basic research is needed before any specific application of the theory to identify optimal instructional strategies is appropriate. On the whole, this does not appear to be one of the more productive avenues for research in cognitive development. Although instruction should be consistent with established theories, basic research in cognitive development cannot specify exactly what types of instructional strategies are most appropriate.

CONCLUSIONS

It has been observed that most research in cognitive development is only incidentally concerned with the learning of mathematics. Variables have been selected for their potential value in explaining the general course of cognitive development, and although mathematical topics have frequently been studied, researchers have not been motivated to include them by a desire to improve instruction in mathematics. In fact, specific content has been chosen for investigation because it is presumed to develop very much independently of the school curriculum, and much of the content of school mathematics has been virtually ignored.

Rohwer (1970) has argued that if research in cognitive development is going to have a significant impact on education, its theories will have to be recast in an educational context and principles of cognitive development will have to be applied directly to educationally significant questions. Thus, the objective for mathematics educators should not be to verify some aspect of a general theory of cognitive development; rather, we should attempt to identify how the theories and techniques of cognitive development can be applied to deal with issues that are significant for the teaching and learning of mathematics. Instead of selecting variables for investigation because of their independence of school experience, we should be primarily concerned with problems that are significant from the perspective of the school mathematics curriculum.

This refocusing of research should be aimed at the construction of what Shulman (1974) has called middle-range theories. Such theories fall between the task-specific working hypotheses that are generated to explain individual behaviors, errors, and the like and the comprehensive theories, such as those of Piaget, that attempt to encompass all of cognitive development. It is not clear that general cognitive structures like Piaget's groupings are especially useful in understanding children's learning of mathematics, and it is a profligate expenditure of limited resources for those of us in mathematics education to expend our energies identifying or validating the existence of such all-encompassing structures. If we can generate middle-range theories that can adequately explain aspects of children's mathematical behavior over limited periods of time, we shall have accomplished a great deal indeed.

For example, it should not be the role of mathematics educators to resolve the conflict between the theories of Brainerd and Piaget regarding the development of the logical foundations of early number concepts. A more important question for education is how useful are the theories in explaining children's learning of concepts that are part of the mathematics curriculum. Thus, the question is not whether conservation is a valid construct but whether it tells us anything about children's ability to learn and apply number and measurement skills.

Two general applications of research seem to hold the greatest promise for influencing educational practice. The first involves selecting and sequencing content. The second concerns individualizing instruction on the basis of each student's level of development of appropriate concepts and processes. Both applications require a good map of the cognitive development of key mathematical concepts and processes. This map must take into account both individual differences and the effects of instruction. Thus, a major objective for research in mathematics education should be to characterize the processes and concepts that children acquire at significant points in the learning of important mathematical topics. Furthermore, it should describe how these concepts and processes evolve over the course of instruction. This involves describing the different processes and errors that individual children exhibit on key tasks at each stage of instruction. It also should include an analysis of performance on related tasks. Although significant individual differences should be anticipated, it should be possible to identify clusters of children who exhibit similar profiles of performance over a range of tasks. If so, then key problems can be used to identify how individual children will perform over the complete range of tasks.

Finally, it is necessary to describe the change in concepts, processes, and errors over the course of instruction. Piaget assumes that all children go through essentially the same stages of development. Therefore, it is necessary only to characterize each stage to describe development. The evidence suggests, however, that there is a great deal of variation in the pattern of acquisition of most mathematical concepts. Consequently, to characterize development of these concepts it is necessary to describe how change takes place within individual children, or at least groups of children, over the course of instruction. This means analyzing how certain processes, concepts, or errors at a given stage have evolved from the processes, concepts, or misconceptions of earlier stages. For example, if a child makes certain errors at a given stage, will they be resolved as the child acquires more mature concepts and skills, or will these errors be magnified as new concepts are built on these earlier misconceptions?

To assess change effectively within individual children, it is necessary to follow them over the relevant instructional periods. This does not mean that the only appropriate studies are longitudinal ones that continue over the entire course of the development of a given concept. But any study that purports to measure intraindividual change must at least repeat measures on the same subjects over the time that change is being measured.

Individual children master concepts at different points in an instructional sequence. An important question is whether all children go through essentially the same basic sequence of development in learning certain concepts even though they may pass through a given stage at different points in the instructional sequence. In other words, are there certain key prerequisite concepts or processes that all children achieve before they master a given concept? Research should be especially sensitive to identifying such key prerequisites.

Teaching experiments seem especially appropriate for the research program outlined above. They may involve a few children or many. But they should systematically monitor children's progress through a carefully designed instructional sequence so that the children's specific experiences can be identified. In addition, the concepts that children have learned, the processes they are applying, and the systematic errors they are making should be regularly assessed. Clinical interview techniques seem most appropriate for this purpose. Finally, this research should not only describe children's knowledge or performance at a given point in time but also attempt to characterize their ability to attend to, and benefit from, instruction.

Assuming that it is possible to characterize the development of a given mathematical topic, it is not at all obvious how this information should be applied to the design of instruction. Consider the problem of selecting and sequencing appropriate content. Several alternatives are possible. One is to identify a minimum set of concepts and skills that all children exhibit at one point or another in the acquisition of a given topic and to build instruction around this basic set. This approach is not especially elegant and seems to reduce instruction to the least common denominator. However, one might assume that if one teaches the minimal set of skills that is logically complete and that can be understood by all students, the better students will continue to generate their own more complex strategies. A study by Groen and Resnick (1977) offers some support for this hypothesis.

An alternative approach would be to identify the most efficient processes that children use, or the processes that are used by the most capable students, and teach those specific processes. Although this approach has the appeal of attempting to make the most efficient strategies available to all the students, there are potential drawbacks. The slower students may not have the cognitive capacity to understand or apply the complex processes of the better students, and the complex processes may be very difficult to teach.

Clearly these extremes do not represent the only choices; there is a great deal of middle ground. Furthermore, as Resnick (1976) proposes, appropriate instruction should not necessarily copy the natural development of concepts in children. Instead, it should put learners in the best position to invent or discover appropriate strategies themselves. There is no simple answer to the question of how to select and sequence content, and it is unlikely that a single approach will be effective with all content or for all learners.

Similar problems exist with respect to problems of individualization. Should instruction be congruent with a child's level of development, so that the instructor can be sure the child can attend to the appropriate aspects of instruction, or should instruction lead development, as suggested by Vygotsky (1962) and others?

Research in mathematics education cannot stop with describing the development of mathematical concepts. We must initiate Glaser's (1976a, 1976b) linking research to establish how the descriptive information from research into children's thinking can be applied so as to prescribe instruction. Furthermore, this program of linking research cannot wait until a complete description of the development of a given concept is available. If viable programs of basic and applied research existed, they could interact to the mutual benefit of both. Research into children's thinking could provide the framework for initiating instructional research, and instructional research could identify the types of information about children's thinking that are most useful for making educational decisions.

Like most of the significant problems in education, the problems of characterizing children's thinking and applying this information to the design of instruction are not simple problems that can be answered by a collection of isolated studies. If any real progress is to be made toward resolving these problems, there is a critical need for coordinating the efforts of researchers, sharing ideas, identifying and attacking critical problems, and standardizing research techniques.

Four working groups that are dealing with problems relevant to the application of cognitive development to the learning of mathematics are currently operating under the general direction of the Georgia Center for the Study of Learning and Teaching Mathematics at the University of Georgia. They include a working group on number and measurement, one on rational numbers, one on space and geometry, and one on models for learning mathematics. These working groups, which constitute a somewhat loose consortium of individuals at different institutions, offer one of the best mechanisms currently available for unifying our attack on educational problems.

Papers from a series of research workshops at which these working groups were established have been published (Lesh, 1976; Martin, 1976; Osborne, 1976), and several monographs reporting the efforts of different working groups are in preparation.

Research on cognitive development in mathematics education must not just unify its efforts to attack significant educational problems; an effort must be made to insure that the results of this research have some impact on school practice. Rohwer (1970) has observed that "the relevance of cognitive development for education is easier to establish than the assertion that a substantial contribution to education will be made from its study" (p. 1380). Although we must avoid premature conclusions and clearly establish the links between cognitive development research and classroom practice, we must not bury our results in research journals. Part of the consortium orientation should be directed at including curriculum developers and developing curriculum materials. Unless we can convince teachers and curriculum developers to begin to see some of the problems of education in terms of cognitive development, the research will have little practical value for the teaching of mathematics.

REFERENCES

Almy, M., Chittenden, E., & Miller, P. *Young children's thinking.* New York: Teachers College Press, 1966.

Almy, M., Dimitrovsky, L., Hardeman, M., Gordis, F., Chittenden, E., & Elliot, D. *Logical thinking in second grade.* New York: Teachers College Press, 1970.

Athey, I. J., & Rubadeau, D. O. (Eds.). *Educational implications of Piaget's theory: A book of readings.* Waltham, Mass.: Blaisdell, 1970.

Baer, D. M. An age-irrelevant concept of development. *Merrill-Palmer Quarterly,* 1970, *16,* 238–245.

Bailey, J. H. The concept of transitivity in children (Doctoral dissertation, University of California, Los Angeles, 1970). *Dissertation Abstracts International,* 1971, *31,* 7618B. (University Microfilms No. 71-13,983)

Baylor, G. W., Gascon, J., Lemoyne, G., & Pothier, N. An information processing model of some seriation tasks. *Canadian Psychologist,* 1973, *14,* 167–196.

Beard, R. M. *An outline of Piaget's developmental psychology for students and teachers.* New York: Basic Books, 1969.

Bearison, D. J. Role of measurement operations in the acquisition of conservation. *Developmental Psychology,* 1969, *1,* 653–660.

Bearison, D. J. Induced versus spontaneous attainment of concrete operations and the relationship to school achievement. *Journal of Educational Psychology,* 1975, *67,* 576–580.

Beilin, H. Stimulus and cognitive transformation in conservation. In D. Elkind & J. Flavell (Eds.), *Studies in cognitive development: Essays in honor of Jean Piaget.* New York: Oxford University Press, 1969.

Beilin, H. The training and acquisition of logical operations. In M. F. Rosskopf, L. P. Steffe, & S. Taback (Eds.), *Piagetian cognitive development research and mathematical education.* Washington, D.C.: National Council of Teachers of Mathematics, 1971.

Bijou, S. W., & Baer, D. M. *Child development* (Vol. 1). New York: Appleton-Century-Crofts, 1961.

Braine, M. D. S. The ontogeny of certain logical operations: Piaget's formulation examined by nonverbal methods. *Psychological Monographs,* 1959, *73* (5, Whole No. 475).

Braine, M. D. S. Development of a grasp of transitivity of length: A reply to Smedslund. *Child Development,* 1964, *35,* 799–810.

Brainerd, C. J. Judgments and explantions as criteria for the presence of cognitive structures. *Psychological Bulletin,* 1973, *79,* 172–179. (a)

Brainerd, C. J. Mathematical and behavioral foundations of number. *Journal of General Psychology,* 1973, *88,* 221–281. (b)

Brainerd, C. J. Neo-Piagetian training experiments revisited: Is there any support for the cognitive-developmental stage hypothesis? *Cognition,* 1973, *2,* 349–370. (c)

Brainerd, C. J. Order of acquisition of transitivity, conservation, and class inclusion of length and weight. *Developmental Psychology,* 1973, *8,* 105–116. (d)

Brainerd, C. J. The origins of number concepts. *Scientific American,* 1973, *228,* 101–109. (e)

Brainerd, C. J. Analysis and synthesis of research on children's ordinal and cardinal number concepts. In R. A. Lesh (Ed.), *Number and measurement.* Columbus, Ohio: ERIC, 1976.

Brainerd, C. J. Response criteria in concept development research. *Child Development,* 1977, *48,* 360–366.

Brainerd, C. J. *The origins of the number concept.* New York: Praeger, 1979.

Brainerd, C. J., & Allen, T. W. Experimental inductions of "first order" quantitative invariants. *Psychological Bulletin,* 1971, *75,* 128–144.

Brearly, M., & Hitchfield, E. *A guide to reading Piaget.* New York: Schocken Books, 1969.

Brownell, W. A. *Arithmetic in grades I and II: A critical summary of new and previously reported research.* Durham, N.C.: Duke University Press, 1941.

Bruner, J. S. *The process of education.* Cambridge, Mass.: Harvard University Press, 1960.

Bryant, P. E. *Perception and understanding in young children.* London: Methuen, 1974.

Budoff, M. Learning potential as a supplementary strategy to psychometric diagnosis. *Learning Disorders,* 1967, *3,* 35.

Carpenter, T. P. *The role of equivalence and order relations in the development and coordination of the concepts of unit size and number of units in selected conservation type measurement problems* (Technical Report No. 178). Madison: Wisconsin Research and Development Center for Cognitive Learning, 1971.

Carpenter, T. P. Measurement concepts of first- and second-grade students. *Journal for Research in Mathematics Education,* 1975, *6,* 3–13.

Carpenter, T. P. Analysis and synthesis of existing research on measurement. In R. A. Lesh (Ed.), *Number and measurement.* Columbus, Ohio: ERIC, 1976.

Carpenter, T. P., & Lewis, R. The development of the concept of a standard unit of measure in young children. *Journal for Research in Mathematics Education,* 1976, *7,* 53–58.

Carpenter, T. P., & Osborne, A. R. Needed research on teaching and learning of measure. In R. A. Lesh (Ed.), *Number and measurement.* Columbus, Ohio: ERIC, 1976.

Carr, D. H. The development of number concept as defined by Piaget in advantaged children exposed to the Bereiter-Engelmann preschool materials and training (Doctoral dissertation, University of Utah, 1970). *Dissertation Abstracts International,* 1971, *31,* 3947A–3948A. (University Microfilms No. 71-3005)

Case, R. Learning and development: A neo-Piagetian interpretation. *Human Development*, 1972, *15*, 339–358. (a)

Case, R. Validation of a neo-Piagetian capacity construct. *Journal of Experimental Child Psychology*, 1972, *14*, 287–302. (b)

Case, R. Structures and strictures: Some functional limitations on the course of cognitive growth. *Cognitive Psychology*, 1974, *6*, 544–573.

Case, R. Gearing instruction to capacity. *Review of Educational Research*, 1975, *45*, 59–87.

Cathcart, G. W. The relationship between primary students' rationalization of conservation and their mathematical achievement. *Child Development*, 1971, *42*, 755–765.

Churchill, E. M. *Counting and measuring.* Toronto: University of Toronto Press, 1961.

Copeland, R. W. *How children learn mathematics.* New York: Macmillan, 1974.

Davydov, V. V. On the formation of an elementary concept of number by the child. In J. W. Wilson (Ed.), *Analyses of reasoning processes.* Soviet studies in the psychology of learning and teaching mathematics (Vol. 13). Palo Alto, Calif.: School Mathematics Study Group, 1975.

Dimitrovsky, L., & Almy, M. Early conservation as a predictor of arithmetic achievement. *Journal of Psychology*, 1975, *91*, 65–70.

D'Mello, S., & Willemsen, E. The development of the number concept. *Child Development*, 1969, *40*, 681–688.

Dodwell, P. C. Children's understanding of number and related concepts. *Canadian Journal of Psychology*, 1960, *14*, 191–205.

Dodwell, P. C. Relations between the understanding of the logic of classes and of cardinal number in children. *Canadian Journal of Psychology*, 1962, *16*, 152–160.

Dodwell, P. C. Children's understanding of spatial concepts. *Canadian Journal of Psychology*, 1963, *17*, 141–161.

Dudek, S. Z., & Dyer, G. B. A longitudinal study of Piaget's developmental stages and the concept of regression. *Journal of Personality Assessment*, 1972, *36*, 380–389.

Elkind, D. Children's discovery of the conservation of mass, weight, and volume: Piaget replication study II. *Journal of Genetic Psychology*, 1961, *98*, 219–227.

Elkind, D. Two approaches to intelligence: Piagetian and psychometric. In D. R. Green, M. P. Ford, & G. B. Flamer (Eds.), *Measurement and Piaget.* New York: McGraw-Hill, 1971.

Elkind, D. *Child development and education: A Piagetian perspective.* New York: Oxford University Press, 1976.

El'Konin, D. B., & Davydov, V. V. Learning capacity and age level: Introduction. In L. P. Steffe (Ed.), *Children's capacity for learning mathematics.* Soviet studies in the psychology of learning and teaching mathematics (Vol. 7). Palo Alto, Calif.: School Mathematics Study Group, 1975.

Erlwanger, S. H. Benny's conception of rules and answers in IPI mathematics. *Journal of Children's Mathematical Behavior*, 1973, *1*(2), 7–26.

Erlwanger, S. H. Case studies of children's conceptions of mathematics—Part I. *Journal of Children's Mathematical Behavior*, 1975, *1*(3), 157–283.

Fischbein, E., Pampu, I., & Manzat, I. Comparison of ratios and the chance concept in children. *Child Development*, 1970, *41*, 377–389.

Flavell, J. H. *The developmental psychology of Jean Piaget.* Princeton, N.J.: Van Nostrand, 1963.

Flavell, J. H. Concept development. In P. H. Mussen (Ed), *Carmichael's manual of child psychology* (Vol. 1). New York: Wiley, 1970.

Flavell, J. H. Stage-related properties of cognitive development. *Cognitive Psychology*, 1971, *2*, 421–453.

Flavell, J. H. An analysis of cognitive-developmental sequences. *Genetic Psychology Monographs*, 1972, *86*, 279–350.

Flavell, J. H. *Cognitive development.* Englewood Cliffs, N.J.: Prentice-Hall, 1977.

Flavell, J. H., & Wohlwill, J. F. Formal and functional aspects of cognitive development. In D. Elkind & J. H. Flavell (Eds.), *Studies in cognitive development: Essays in honor of Jean Piaget.* New York: Oxford University Press, 1969.

Freudenthal, H. *Mathematics as an educational task.* Dordrecht, Holland: D. Reidel, 1973.

Furth, H. G. *Piaget for teachers.* Englewood Cliffs, N.J.: Prentice-Hall, 1970.

Fusaro, L. A. *An experimental analysis of the roles of measurement and compensatory operations in the acquisition of conservation.* Unpublished master's thesis, Clark University, 1969.

Fuson, K. C. *Vygotskiian theoretical constructs related to research in the development of early number concepts.* Paper presented at the meeting of the Number and Measurement Working Group, Indianapolis, November 1977.

Gagné, R. M. Contributions of learning to human development. *Psychological Review,* 1968, *75,* 177–191.

Gagné, R. M. *The conditions of learning* (3rd ed.). New York: Holt, Rinehart & Winston, 1977.

Gal'perin, P. Ya., & Georgiev, L. S. The formation of elementary mathematical notions. In J. Kilpatrick & I. Wirzup (Eds.), *The learning of mathematical concepts.* Soviet studies in the psychology of learning and teaching mathematics (Vol. 1). Palo Alto, Calif.: School Mathematics Study Group, 1969.

Gelman, R. Conservation acquisition: A problem of learning to attend to relevant attributes. *Journal of Experimental Child Psychology,* 1969, *7,* 167–187.

Gelman, R. Logical capacity of very young children: Number invariance rules. *Child Development,* 1972, *43,* 75–90. (a)

Gelman, R. The nature and development of early number concepts. In H. Reese (Ed.), *Advances in child development and behavior* (Vol. 7). New York: Academic Press, 1972.(b)

Gelman, R. How young children reason about small numbers. In N. J. Castellan, D. P. Pisoni, & G. R. Potts (Eds.), *Cognitive theory* (Vol. 2). Hillsdale, N.J.: Lawrence Erlbaum Associates, 1977.

Gelman, R. Cognitive development. *Annual Review of Psychology,* 1978, *29,* 297–332.

George, L. O. Selected factors which affect young children's concepts of conservation of length (Doctoral dissertation, Indiana University, 1970). *Dissertation Abstracts International,* 1970, *31,* 2735A. (University Microfilms No. 70-23,358)

Ginsburg, H. Young children's informal knowledge of mathematics. *Journal of Children's Mathematical Behavior,* 1975, *1*(3), 63–156.

Ginsburg, H. Learning difficulties in children's arithmetic: A clinical cognitive approach. In A. R. Osborne (Ed.), *Models for learning mathematics.* Columbus, Ohio: ERIC, 1976.

Ginsburg, H. *Children's arithmetic: The learning process.* New York: Van Nostrand, 1977. (a)

Ginsburg, H. The psychology of arithmetic thinking. *Journal of Children's Mathematical Behavior,* 1977, *1*(4), 1–89. (b)

Ginsburg, H., & Koslowski, B. Cognitive development. In M. R. Rosenzweig & L. W. Porter (Eds.), *Annual Review of Psychology,* 1976, *27,* 29–62.

Ginsburg, H., & Opper, S. *Piaget's theory of intellectual development.* Englewood Cliffs, N.J.: Prentice-Hall, 1969.

Ginsburg, H., & Rapaport, A. Children's estimate of proportions. *Child Development,* 1967, *38,* 205–212.

Glaser, R. Cognitive psychology and instructional design. In D. Klahr (Ed.), *Cognition and instruction.* Hillsdale, N.J.: Lawrence Erlbaum Associates, 1976. (a)

Glaser, R. Components of a psychology of instruction: Toward a science of design. *Review of Educational Research,* 1976, *46,* 1–24. (b)

Glaser, R., & Resnick, L. B. Instructional psychology. In P. Mussen & M. Rosenzweig (Eds.), *Annual Review of Psychology,* 1972, *23,* 207–277.

Goldschmid, M. L., & Bentler, P. M. *Concept assessment kit-conservation.* San Diego: Educational and Industrial Testing Service, 1968.

Gonchar, A. J. *A study in the nature and development of the natural number concept: Initial and supplementary analyses* (Technical Report No. 340). Madison: Wisconsin Research and Development Center for Cognitive Learning, 1975.

Green, D. R., Ford, M. P., & Flamer, G. B. (Eds.). *Measurement and Piaget.* New York: McGraw-Hill, 1971.

Groen, G. J., & Parkman, J. M. A chronometric analysis of simple addition. *Psychological Review,* 1972, *79,* 329–343.

Groen, G. J., & Poll, M. Subtraction and the solution of open sentence problems. *Journal of Experimental Child Psychology,* 1973, *16,* 292–302.

Groen, G., & Resnick, L. B. Can preschool children invent addition algorithms? *Journal of Educational Psychology,* 1977, *69,* 645–652.

Hagen, J. W., Jongeward, R. H., & Kail, R. V. Cognitive perspective on the development of memory. In H. W. Reese & L. P. Lipsitt (Eds.), *Advances in child development and behavior* (Vol. 10). New York: Academic Press, 1975.

Hatano, G. A. A developmental approach to concept formation: A review of neo-Piagetian learning experiments. *Dikkyo University Bulletin of Liberal Arts Education,* 1971, *5,* 59–76.

Hooper, F. H. Piagetian research and education. In I. E. Sigel & F. H. Hooper (Eds.), *Logical thinking in children: Research based on Piaget's theory.* New York: Holt, Rinehart & Winston, 1968.

Hooper, F. H., & DeFrain, J. D. *The search for a distinctly Piagetian contribution to education* (Theoretical Paper No. 50). Madison: Wisconsin Research and Development Center for Cognitive Learning, 1974.

Hooper, F. H., & Klausmeier, H. J. *Description and rationale for longitudinal assessment of children's cognitive development and concept learning* (Working Paper No. 113). Madison: Wisconsin Research and Development Center for Cognitive Learning, 1973.

Huntington, J. R. Linear measurement in the primary grades: A comparison of Piaget's description of the child's spontaneous conceptual development and SMSG sequence of instruction. *Journal for Research in Mathematics Education,* 1970, *1,* 219–232.

Inhelder, B., & Piaget, J. *The growth of logical thinking from childhood to adolescence.* New York: Basic Books, 1958.

Inhelder, B., & Sinclair, H. Learning cognitive structures. In P. Mussen, J. Langer, & M. Covington (Eds.), *Trends and issues in developmental psychology.* New York: Holt, Rinehart & Winston, 1969.

Inhelder, B., Sinclair, H., & Bovet, M. *Learning and the development of cognition.* London: Routledge & Kegan Paul, 1974.

Inskeep, J. E. Building a case for the application of Piaget's theory and research in the classroom. *Arithmetic Teacher,* 1972, *19,* 255–260.

Kagan, J., & Kogan, N. Individual variation in cognitive process. In P. H. Mussen (Ed.), *Carmichael's manual of child psychology* (Vol. 1). New York: Wiley, 1970.

Kaminsky, M. A study of the status of conservation ability in relationship to arithmetic achievement (Doctoral dissertation, Wayne State University, 1970). *Dissertation Abstracts International,* 1971, *31,* 3341A. (University Microfilms No. 71-00,425)

Kaufman, A. S. Piaget and Gesell: A psychometric analysis of tests built from their tasks. *Child Development,* 1971, *42,* 1341–1360.

Kaufman, A. S., & Kaufman, N. L. Tests built from Piaget's and Gesell's tasks as predictors of first grade achievement. *Child Development,* 1972, *43,* 521–535.

Kilpatrick, J., & Wirszup, I. (Eds.). *Problem solving in arithmetic and algebra.* Soviet studies in the psychology of learning and teaching mathematics (Vol. 3). Palo Alto, Calif.: School Mathematics Study Group, 1969.(a)

Kilpatrick, J., & Wirszup, I. (Eds.). *The structure of mathematical abilities.* Soviet studies in the psychology of learning and teaching mathematics (Vol. 2). Palo Alto, Calif.: School Mathematics Study Group, 1969. (b)

Kilpatrick, J., & Wirszup, I. (Eds.). *The development of spatial abilities.* Soviet studies in the psychology of learning and teaching mathematics (Vol. 5). Palo Alto, Calif.: School Mathematics Study Group, 1971.

King, W. L. Nonarbitrary behavioral criterion for conservation of illusion distorted length in five-year-olds. *Journal of Experimental Child Psychology,* 1971, *11,* 171–181.

Klahr, D., & Wallace, J. G. An information processing anaylsis of some Piagetian experimental tasks. *Cognitive Psychology,* 1970, *1,* 358–387.

Klahr, D., & Wallace, J. G. Class inclusion processes. In S. Farnham-Diggory (Ed.), *Information processing in children.* New York: Academic Press, 1972.

Klahr, D., & Wallace, J. G. The role of quantification operators in the development of conservation of quantity. *Cognitive Psychology,* 1973, *4,* 301–327.

Klahr, D., & Wallace, J. G. *Cognitive development: An information processing view.* Hillsdale, N.J.: Lawrence Erlbaum Associates, 1976.

Klausmeier, H. J., Ghatala, E. S., & Frayer, D. A. *Conceptual learning and development: A cognitive view.* New York: Academic Press, 1974.

Klausmeier, H. J., & Hooper, F. H. Conceptual development and instruction. In F. Kerlinger & J. B. Carroll (Eds.), *Review of research in education* (Vol. 2). Itasca, Ill.: Peacock, 1974.

Kofsky, E. A scalogram study of classificatory development. *Child Development,* 1966, *37,* 191–204.

Kohlberg, L. Early education: A cognitive-developmental view. *Child Development,* 1968, *39,* 1013–1062.

Kohlberg, L., & Mayer, R. Development as the aim of education. *Harvard Educational Review,* 1972, *42,* 449–496.

Kooistra, W. H. Developmental trends in the attainment of conservation, transitivity, and relativism in the thinking of children: A replication and extension of Piaget's ontogenetic formulations (Doctral dissertation, Wayne State University, 1963). *Dissertation Abstracts International,* 1964, *25,* 2032. (University Microfilms No. 64-9538)

Krutetskii, V. A. *The psychology of mathematical abilities in schoolchildren.* Chicago: University of Chicago Press, 1976.

Lankford, F. G. *Some computational strategies of seventh grade pupils* (U.S.O.E. Project No. 2-c-013). Charlottesville: University of Virginia, 1972.

Lankford, F. G. What can a teacher learn about a pupil's thinking through oral interviews? *Arithmetic Teacher,* 1974, *21,* 26–32.

Laurendeau, M., & Pinard, A. *The development of the concept of space in the child.* New York: International Universities Press, 1970.

LeBlanc, J. F. *The performance of first-grade children in four levels of conservation of numerousness and three IQ groups when solving subtraction problems* (Technical Report No. 171). Madison: Wisconsin Research and Development Center for Cognitive Learning, 1971.

Lesh, R. A. (Ed.). *Number and measurement.* Columbus, Ohio: ERIC, 1976.

Lesh, R., & Mierkiewicz, D. (Eds.). *Recent research concerning the development of spatial and geometric concepts.* Columbus, Ohio: ERIC, 1977.

Little, A. A longitudinal study of cognitive development in young children. *Child Development,* 1972, *43,* 1024–1034.

Lovell, K. The development of the concept of proof in abler pupils. In M. F. Rosskopf, L. P. Steffe, & S. Taback (Eds.), *Piagetian cognitive development research and mathematical education.* Washington, D.C.: National Council of Teachers of Mathematics, 1971.(a)

Lovell, K. *Intellectual growth and understanding in mathematics: Kindergarten through grade three.* New York: Holt, Rinehart & Winston, 1971. (b)

Lovell, K. Some aspects of the growth of the concept of a function. In M. F. Rosskopf, L. P. Steffe, and S. Taback (Eds.), *Piagetian cognitive development research and mathematical education.* Washington, D.C.: National Council of Teachers of Mathematics, 1971. (c)

Lovell, K. Proportionality and probability. In M. F. Rosskopf, L. P. Steffe, & S. Taback (Eds.), *Piagetian cognitive development research and mathematical education.* Washington, D.C.: National Council of Teachers of Mathematics, 1971. (d)

Lovell, K. Intellectual growth and understanding mathematics: Implications for teaching. *Arithmetic Teacher,* 1972, *19,* 277–282.

Lovell, K., & Butterworth, I. B. Abilities underlying the understanding of proportionality. *Mathematics Teaching,* 1966, *37,* 5–9.

Lovell, K., & Ogilvie, E. A study of the conservation of weight in the junior school child. *British Journal of Educational Psychology,* 1961, *31,* 138–144.

Lunzer, E. A., & Pumfrey, P. D. Understanding proportionality. *Mathematics Teaching,* 1966, *34,* 7–12.

McLellan, J. A., & Dewey, J. D. *The psychology of number and its application to methods of teaching arithmetic.* New York: Appleton, 1896.

McManis, D. L. Conservation and transitivity of weight and length by normals and retardates. *Developmental Psychology,* 1969, *1,* 373–382.

Martin, L. (Ed.). *Space and geometry.* Columbus, Ohio: ERIC, 1976.

Menchinskaya, N. A. Fifty years of Soviet instructional psychology. In J. Kilpatrick & I. Wirszup (Eds.), *The learning of mathematical concepts.* Soviet studies in the psychology of learning and teaching mathematics (Vol. 1). Palo Alto, Calif.: School Mathematics Study Group, 1969.

Miller, S. A. Nonverbal assessment of Piagetian concepts. *Psychological Bulletin,* 1976, *83,* 405–430.

Montangero, J. Needed research in space and geometry based on recent results in Geneva. In L. Martin (Ed.), *Space and geometry.* Columbus, Ohio: ERIC, 1976.

Montgomery, M. E. The interaction of three levels of aptitude determined by a teach-test procedure with two treatments related to area. *Journal for Research in Mathematics Education,* 1973, *4,* 271–278.

Mpiangu, B. D., & Gentile, R. J. Is conservation of number a necessary condition for mathematical understanding? *Journal for Research in Mathematics Education,* 1975, *6,* 179–192.

Neimark, E. D. Intellectual development during adolescence. In F. D. Horowitz (Ed.), *Review of child development research* (Vol. 4.). Chicago: University of Chicago Press, 1975.

Neimark, E. D., & Lewis, N. Development of logical problem solving: A one year retest. *Child Development,* 1968, *39,* 527–536.

Nelson, R. J. An investigation of a group test based on Piaget's concepts of number and length conservation and its ability to predict first grade arithmetic achievement (Doctoral dissertation, Purdue University, 1969). *Dissertation Abstracts International,* 1970, *30,* 3644A. (University Microfilms No. 70-3948)

Nuffield Mathematics Project. *Checking up I.* New York: Wiley, 1970.

Nuffield Mathematics Project. *Checking up II.* New York: Wiley, 1972.

Osborne, A. R. (Ed.). *Models for learning mathematics.* Columbus, Ohio: ERIC, 1976.

Pascual-Leone, J. A mathematical model for the transition rule in Piaget's developmental stages. *Acta Psychologica,* 1970, *63,* 301–345.

Pascual-Leone, J. A view of cognition from a formalist's perspective. In K. F. Riegel & J. Meacham (Eds.), *The developing individual in the changing world.* The Hague: Mouton, 1976.

Peck, A. D., Frankel, D. G., & Hess, U. L. Children's attention: The development of selectivity. In E. M. Hetherington (Ed.), *Review of child development research* (Vol. 5). Chicago: University of Chicago Press, 1975.

Piaget, J. *The child's conception of number.* New York: Humanities Press, 1952.

Piaget, J. Intellectual evolution from adolescence to adulthood. *Human Development*, 1972, *15*, 1–12.

Piaget, J., & Inhelder, B. *Le développement des quantiés chez l'enfant.* Neuchâtel: Delachaux et Niestlé, 1941.

Piaget, J., & Inhelder, B. *The child's conception of space.* London: Routledge & Kegan Paul, 1956.

Piaget, J., Inhelder, B., & Szeminska, A. *The child's conception of geometry.* New York: Basic Books, 1960.

Pinard, A., & Laurendeau, M. A scale of mental development based on the theory of Piaget: Description of a project. *Journal of Research in Science Teaching*, 1964, *2*, 253–260.

Pinard, A., & Laurendeau, M. "Stage" in Piaget's cognitive-developmental theory: Exegesis of a concept. In D. Elkind & J. H. Flavell (Eds.), *Studies in cognitive development: Essays in honor of Jean Piaget.* New York: Oxford University Press, 1969.

Pinard, A., & Sharp. E. IQ and point of view. *Psychology Today*, June 1972, pp. 65–68; 90.

Potter, M. C., & Levy, E. L. Spatial enumeration without counting. *Child Development*, 1968, *39*, 265–273.

Pumfrey, P. The growth of the scheme of proportionality. *British Journal of Educational Psychology*, 1968, *38*, 202–204.

Reese, H. W., & Overton, W. F. Models of development and theories of development. In L. R. Goulet & P. B. Baltes (Eds.), *Lifespan developmental psychology: Research and theory.* New York: Academic Press, 1970.

Resnick, L. B. Task analysis in instructional design: Some cases from mathematics. In D. Klahr (Ed.), *Cognition and instruction.* Hillsdale, N.J.: Lawrence Erlbaum Associates, 1976.

Rohr, J. A. G. The relationship of the ability to conserve on Piagetian tasks to achievement in mathematics (Doctoral dissertation, University of Tennessee, 1973). *Dissertation Abstracts International*, 1973, *34*, 2398A. (University Microfilms No. 73-27,743)

Rohwer, W. Cognitive development and education. In P. H. Mussen (Ed.), *Carmichael's manual of child psychology* (Vol. 1). New York: Wiley, 1970.

Rosenthal, D. J. A., & Resnick, L. B. Children's solution processes in arithmetic word problems. *Journal of Educational Psychology*, 1974, *6*, 817–825.

Sawada, D., & Nelson, L. D. Conservation of length and the teaching of linear measurement: A methodological critique. *Arithmetic Teacher*, 1967, *14*, 345–348.

Scandura, J. M. Structural approach to instructional problems. *American Psychologist*, 1977, *32*, 33–53.

Scardamalia, M. Information processing capacity and the problem of horizontal decalage: A demonstration using combinational reasoning tasks. *Child Development*, 1977, *48*, 28–37.

Schaeffer, B., Eggleston, V., & Scott, J. L. Number development in young children. *Cognitive Psychology*, 1974, *6*, 357–379.

Schwebel, M., & Raph, J. (Eds.). *Piaget in the classroom.* New York: Basic Books, 1973.

Shantz, C., & Smock, C. Development of distance conservation and the spatial coordinate system. *Child Development*, 1966, *37*, 943–948.

Shulman, L. S. The psychology of school subjects: A premature obituary? *Journal of Research in Science Teaching*, 1974, *4*, 319–339.

Sigel, I. E. The Piagetian system and the world of education. In D. Elkind & J. H. Flavell (Eds.), *Studies in cognitive development: Essays in honor of Jean Piaget.* New York: Oxford University Press, 1969.

Smedslund, J. The acquisition of substance and weight in children: II. External reinforcement of conservation of weight and the operations of addition and subtraction. *Scandinavian Journal of Psychology*, 1961, *2*, 71–84.

Smedslund, J. Development of concrete transitivity of length in children. *Child Development*, 1963, *34*, 389–405.

Smedslund, J. Concrete reasoning: A study of intellectual development. *Monographs of the Society for Research in Child Development*, 1964, *29* (2, Serial No. 93).

Smedslund, J. The development of transitivity of length: A comment on Braine's reply. *Child Development*, 1965, *36*, 577–580.

Smith, G. J. The development of a survey instrument for first grade mathematics based on selected Piagetian tasks (Doctoral dissertation, University of Montana, 1973). *Dissertation Abstracts International*, 1974, *34*, 7056A. (University Microfilms No. 74-11,637)

Smock, C. D. A constructivist model for instruction. In A. R. Osborne (Ed.), *Models for learning mathematics*. Columbus, Ohio: ERIC, 1976. (a)

Smock, C. D. Piaget's thinking about concepts and geometry. In L. Martin (Ed.), *Space and geometry*. Columbus, Ohio: ERIC, 1976. (b)

Steffe, L. P. Differential performance of first-grade children when solving arithmetic addition problems. *Journal for Research in Mathematics Education*, 1970, *1*, 144–161.

Steffe, L. P. Thinking about measurement. *Arithmetic Teacher*, 1971, *18*, 332–338.

Steffe, L. P. An application of Piaget-cognitive development research in mathematical education research. In R. Lesh (Ed.), *Cognitive psychology and the mathematics laboratory*. Columbus, Ohio: ERIC, 1973.

Steffe, L. P. (Ed.). *Children's capacity for learning mathematics*. Soviet studies in the psychology of earning and teaching mathematics (Vol. 7). Palo Alto, Calif.: School Mathematics Study Group, 1975.

Steffe, L. P., & Carey, R. L. Equivalence and order relations as interrelated by four- and five-year-old children. *Journal for Research in Mathematics Education*, 1972, *3*, 77–88.

Steffe, L. P., Spikes, W. C., & Hirstein, J. J. *Summary of quantitative comparisons and class inclusion as readiness variables for learning first grade arithmetical content*. Athens: The Georgia Center for the Study of Learning and Teaching Mathematics, 1976.

Stendler, C. B. Aspects of Piaget's theory that have implications for teacher education. *Journal of Teacher Education*, 1965, *16*, 329–335.

Stephens, B., McLaughlin, J. A., Miller, C. K., & Glass, G. Factorial structure of selected psycho-educational measures and Piagetian reasoning assessments. *Developmental Psychology*, 1972, *6*, 343–348.

Stone, G. E. G. Three approaches to assessing the conservation of weight concept (Doctoral dissertation, Iowa State University, 1972). *Dissertation Abstracts International*, 1972, *33*, 199A. (University Microfilms No. 72-19,528).

Strauss, S. Inducing cognitive development and learning: A review of short-term training experiments. *Cognition*, 1972, *1*, 329–357.

Sullivan, E. *Piaget and the school curriculum—A critical appraisal*. Toronto: Ontario Institute for Studies in Education, 1967.

Suppes, P. Needed research in the learning of mathematics. *Journal of Research and Development in Education*, 1967, *1*, 1–47.

Suppes, P., & Morningstar, M. *Computer assisted instruction at Stanford, 1966–68*. New York: Academic Press, 1972.

Taback, S. The child's concept of limit. In M. F. Rosskopf (Ed.), *Children's mathematical concepts: Six Piagetian studies in mathematics education*. New York: Teachers College Press, 1975.

Thomas, H. L. The concept of function. In M. F. Rosskopf (Ed.), *Children's mathematical concepts: Six Piagetian studies in mathematics education*. New York: Teachers College Press, 1975.

Tuddenham, R. D. Theoretical regularities and individual idiosyncracies. In D. R. Green, M. P. Ford, & G. B. Flamer (Eds.), *Measurement and Piaget*. New York: McGraw-Hill, 1971.

Uzgiris, I. C. Situational generality of conservation. *Child Development*, 1964, *35*, 831–841.

Uznadze, D. N. *The psychology of set*. New York: Plenum Press, 1966.

Vygotsky, L. S. *Thought and language*. Cambridge, Mass.: M.I.T. Press, 1962.

Vygotsky, L. S. *Mind in society: The development of higher psychological processes*. Cambridge, Mass.: Harvard University Press, 1978.

Wagman, H. G. The child's conception of area measure. In M. F. Rosskopf (Ed.), *Children's mathematical concepts: Six Piagetian studies in mathematics education*. New York: Teachers College Press, 1975.

Wallach, L. On the basis of conservation. In D. Elkind & J. H. Flavell (Eds.), *Studies in cognitive development: Essays in honor of Jean Piaget*. New York: Oxford University Press, 1969.

Wang, M. C., Resnick, L. B., & Boozer, R. F. The sequence of development of some early mathematics behavior. *Child Development*, 1971, *42*, 1767–1778.

Washburne, C. The work of the Committee of Seven on grade placement in arithmetic. In G. M. Whipple (Ed.), *Thirty-eighth yearbook of the National Society for the Study of Education* (Pt. 1). Bloomington, Ill.: Public School Publishing Co., 1939.

Watson, J. S. Conservation: An S-R analysis. In I. E. Sigel & F. H. Hooper (Eds.), *Logical thinking in children: Research based on Piaget's theory*. New York: Holt, Rinehart & Winston, 1968.

Weaver, J. F. Some concerns about the application of Piaget's theory and research to mathematical learning and instruction. *Arithmetic Teacher*, 1972, *19*, 263–270.

Wheatley, G. H., Mitchell, R., Frankland, R. L., & Kraft, R. Hemispheric specialization and cognitive development: Implications for mathematics education. *Journal for Research in Mathematics Education*, 1978, *9*, 20–32.

White, S. H. Evidence for hierarchical arrangement of learning processes. In L. P. Lipsett & C. C. Spiker (Eds.), *Advances in child development and behavior* (Vol. 2). New York: Academic Press, 1965.

Wirszup, I. Breakthroughs in the psychology of learning and teaching of geometry. In L. Martin (Ed.), *Space and geometry*. Columbus, Ohio: ERIC, 1976.

Wohlwill, J. F. A study of the development of the number concepts by scalogram analysis. *Journal of Genetic Psychology*, 1960, *97*, 345–377.

Wohlwill, J. F. The place of structured experience in early cognitive development. *Interchange*, 1970, *1*, 13–27.

Wohlwill, J. F. *The study of behavioral development*. New York: Academic Press, 1973.

Wohlwill, J. F., Devoe, S., & Fusaro, L. *Research on the development of concepts in early childhood* (Final Report for NSF Grant G-5855). University Park: Pennsylvania State University, 1971.

Woods, S. S., Resnick, L. B., & Groen, G. J. An experimental test of five process models for subtraction. *Journal of Educational Psychology*, 1975, *1*, 17–21.

Zykova, V. I. Operating with concepts when solving geometry problems. In J. Kilpatrick & I. Wirszup (Eds.), *The Learning of Mathematical Concepts*. Soviet studies in the psychology of learning and teaching mathematics (Vol. 1). Palo Alto, Calif.: School Mathematics Study Group, 1969.

8

Skill Learning

Marilyn N. Suydam
Ohio State University
Donald J. Dessart
University of Tennessee

ONE of the most frequently stated goals of mathematics instruction involves the development of skills. Skills are comparatively easy to describe or specify, to teach, and to evaluate. A skill is what a learner should be able to *do*. Skills arise from concepts and principles and provide a foundation for the development of other concepts and principles. Conceptual throught is derived in part from the understanding attained as skills are developed. And it is also apparent that skills are pragmatically purposeful—that is, they are perceived as being useful and therefore valued by society.

Skills are generally characterized in terms of (a) proficiency or accuracy and (b) efficiency or speed. When mastered, skills require relatively little reflection. In effect, they become reflexes, to be exercised at a subconscious level. Just as a child learns to tie shoelaces without thinking, so he or she is to learn to—

- subtract a two-digit number from a three-digit number;
- make plausible estimates;
- complete the square of a quadratic equation;
- plot ordered pairs of integers on a Cartesian plane;
- specify the product of two binomial expressions;
- multiply two two-digit numbers;
- reduce a fraction to lowest terms;
- add two rational numbers.

In each example, the student is to become proficient and efficient with a particular procedure or algorithm.

Practice is obviously one component of learning a skill. It is simply not efficient to perform most skills in other than a routine way, and practice aids in their mastery for routine use. Sometimes this is interpreted to mean that skills should be taught by rote procedures emphasizing drill. But understanding what makes a procedure work—including the application of concepts and principles—is a necessary concomitant to skill learning. Attaining competency with a skill is "the second half of a two-stage learning process; the first half of the process involves a form of understanding" (Henkin, 1975, p. 75).

There is currently debate over the term *basic skills:* does the term mean only computational skills, or does it include broader mathematical goals? Participants in the National Institute of Education (NIE) Conference on Basic Mathematical Skills and Learning (1975) were asked to develop broad interpretations; thus Gibb proposed the following:

> (1) Understandings of mathematical concepts and techniques of computation, (2) skill in using these understandings in computation, (3) skill in problem solving, and (4) skill in thinking creatively. (1975, p. 57)

Rising summed up the various points in this comment: "Basic mathematical skills are those mathematics-related abilities that should be attained in order to function as a citizen" (1975, p. 149). A similar intent to define basic skills broadly is evident in the *Position Paper on Basic Mathematical Skills* prepared by the National Council of Supervisors of Mathematics (NCSM, 1976). These definitions are responses to the popular use of vaguely defined terminology.

As the definition of skills appropriate for this chapter was considered, it became evident that a skill involves a learner's behavior in using facts, concepts, principles, algorithms, or problem solutions. For this reason, it was difficult to determine the extent to which many studies focused on skill learning. The base for much of the research on skill learning has been formed in both classical and current educational psychology. However, we found it difficult to develop this chapter in terms of psychological terms. The research is neither definitive nor exclusive in relation to such terms. After an explanation of how the evidence is organized, the status of research will be reviewed in order to indicate the scope of what has been studied about skill learning within mathematics education. No attempt is made to be comprehensive in citing studies; rather, some evaluative criteria were applied to select studies indicative of a particular focus. The directions taken in research investigations, problems evidenced in the design of studies, and gaps in the research evidence will be indicated. In the following two sections, trends and issues will be discussed briefly. Finally, recommendations for new directions for research on skill learning will be described.

REVIEW OF THE SCOPE OF RESEARCH ON SKILL LEARNING

As the body of research on skill learning in mathematics education is examined, one is clearly impressed with the fact that such research has attempted to deal with problems of the classroom. This is a noble goal, which no one should dispute as being an unreasonable direction to pursue. Surely research in mathematics education is designed to foster better learning and better classroom instruction. As Sparks (1967) noted,

> The scholar engaged in continuing study of his discipline encounters questions which need answering; or he becomes convinced by his work and study that a certain concept has validity and can be translated into an observable activity; or he seeks a way to test his theoretical position; or a problem which seems answerable in terms of his discipline is posed to him. Of course, the list is not exhaustive; but the items in it have common characteristics: research developing out of a knowledge of the theoretical state and/or practical developments in the discipline and a personal engagement in research relevant to these. (p. 1)

Because of the concern with classroom application, research on the learning of skills appears to be organized around subject-matter considerations. Researchers in the past have focused their attention on counting, place value, basic facts, algorithms for whole numbers or fractions, and so forth. Their intent was to provide teachers with better and more efficient ways of working with children, and teachers hope that researchers can provide this assistance. Consequently, the two points of view are compatible and mutually reinforcing.

However, many critics of research in mathematics education feel that an emphasis on skill learning merely in relation to categories of mathematical content will contribute little to a basic understanding of the psychological principles that may be inherent in skill learning and thus can have only a very limited effect on advancing the field of understanding of skill learning in mathematics education. Such a viewpoint would suggest that research on skill learning should become independent of the particular content that is being taught. One might counter that an emphasis on skill study independent of content belongs in the domain of the educational psychologist rather than the mathematics education researcher. Perhaps so, but if research in skill learning is to make genuine advances, such an emphasis appears necessary.

Mathematics education researchers who adopt the basic viewpoint that skill study should be independent of content may be interested in questions regarding the differences that exist between *fact learning,* which includes such skills as $8 + 5 = 13$, $\pi = 3.14\ldots$, $\frac{1}{2} = 0.5$, and $\sin 45° = 0.707\ldots$, and *algorithmic learning,* which includes such skills as the addition of whole numbers, the addition of fractions, the long division algorithm, and the

Euclidean algorithm for finding the greatest common divisor of two natural numbers. One might view these two types of learning as merely progressive stages; that is, the pupil must master "facts," which are later used in chains of facts called algorithms. But one might also argue that algorithmic learning contains another ingredient, the *gestalt* or matrix that cements the facts into algorithms. If so, the student who merely memorizes facts will surely miss the forest because of the trees!

The hierarchical approach to research on skill learning as advocated by Gagné (1970) and others may also contribute to research in this direction. The organization of hierarchies of skills provides researchers with a convenient framework through which to focus their attentions in attempting to understand the processes of skill learning. For example, suppose one were to organize a hierarchy of skills related to finding the sum of two fractions using the least common denominator method as opposed to employing a procedure that uses the algorithm represented by

$$\frac{a}{b} + \frac{c}{d} = \frac{ad + bc}{bd}, \quad b \neq 0, d \neq 0$$

(see Suydam & Dessart, 1976, p. 33). In learning this skill, does the student reach the stage in which a different kind of learning (trial and error, for example) dominates, thereby presenting a new and distinctive challenge to the learner? Even more basically, does this phenomenon exist in all forms of algorithmic learning?

Questions related to the role of practice in the learning of any skill are worthy of study. Is practice necessary? If so, does its effectiveness vary according to the complexity of the skill or the inherent capabilities of the learner both? Does the rehearsal of a skill, whether it be the long division algorithm or the side stroke in a swimming lesson, produce a more satisfying learning experience? Does practicing the skill in an unusual setting, such as a game of "Battleship" to practice plotting points on a Cartesian plane or water basketball to practice swimming, enhance the efficiency of practice? Answers to these and related questions may contribute to a better understanding of skill learning.

Before turning to a review of the current status of research in skill learning, we shall challenge researchers to consider future efforts in seeking answers to basic questions that are related to skill learning and independent of particular content. This may require the cooperation of psychologists using a team approach to research. A continued emphasis on "applied" research to deal with the immediate concerns of teachers should not be discouraged, but attention to the more basic questions may prove more fruitful to the future of research on skill learning.

Now we turn to a review of research on skill learning by mathematical category.

Counting and Place-Value Skills

Counting is a prerequisite skill for work with arithmetic operations. From individual instances and from research (e.g., Ilg & Ames, 1951), we know that children begin to associate number with objects (that is, develop the concept necessary for counting) before the age of 2; rote counting, or the procedure of naming numbers in their successive order, generally begins before the child is 3. By the time formal schooling begins in kindergarten, almost all children can count to about 20, although there is wide variance in how far they can count and in the development of rational counting (e.g., Brace & Nelson, 1965; Rea & Reys, 1970; Schwartz, 1969).

Counting is frequently used by young children (aged 3 to 5) in determining the size of a group, with perceptual recognition of a group of objects used more frequently as they grow older. Studies (e.g., Khan, 1973; Maertens, Jones, & Waite, 1977; Siegel, 1974) have indicated the importance of the arrangement of objects used in counting. The arrangement of sub-groups in identifiable patterns facilitates accurate counting more than a random arrangement does. Most studies have focused, however, not on the child's *skill* in counting, but on counting as one aspect of the child's *concept* of number (e.g., Gelman & Tucker, 1975; Piaget, 1952).

Many questions about counting skills have been unasked, such as—

- Why do children start to count? To what extent do parental or societal influences affect the process?
- Is there a relationship between rote counting and rational counting that is reflected in later achievement?

Place value has consumed relatively little attention from researchers—despite its importance, despite the difficulty many teachers experience in teaching it, despite the fact that assessment evidence (e.g., Glennon, 1949; Callahan, 1967) indicates that the knowledge of place value is poorer than should be expected. (Hope has been expressed that the hand-held calculator will be used to increase place-value understanding.)

It would seem that establishing a hierarchy of place-value tasks would not be difficult. Yet little attention has been directed toward establishing the particular points at which students meet difficulty. In one such study (Smith, 1972), certain place-value skills were found to be difficult at the second-grade level: (a) interpreting the value of each place in a two-place numeral, (b) counting by tens, (c) interpreting 10 ones as 1 ten and 1 ten as 10 ones, (d) exchanging tens for ones and ones for tens, and (e) naming the same number in different ways.

Only recently has research considered the appropriate time and sequence for introducing place-value ideas. Rathmell (1973) focused on the effects of grouping and the early or late introduction of base representations. Those pupils given lessons on reading and writing numerals *before* instruction on grouping had consistently higher means than those given grouping experiences first. Thus, introducing two-digit symbols without regard to tens-and-ones meaning appeared not to be detrimental. However, Barr (1976, 1978) found that retention was enhanced when two-digit numeration was introduced by counting by tens as well as by ones. Yet many of the pupils he studied could already write two-digit numerals. Two conflicting studies provide insufficient evidence for decision making; it is obvious that the question of sequence should be carefully considered.

Basic Facts

Basic facts have been studied in a number of ways. In a descriptive study, Marotta (1974) used textbooks to trace how the addition facts were taught from colonial times to 1950. He noted that the drill theory predominant in nearly all elementary school teaching before 1900 reached a peak around 1920. Arithmetic was fragmented into minute parts to be taught and learned separately; drill was emphasized and the structural properties of mathematics were ignored. Dissatisfaction with the drill method led to the theory of incidental learning: a skill was to be taught only when a need for it arose. Then in 1935, Brownell proposed the meaning theory, with emphasis on meaningful approaches involving materials and discussion. Drill was shown to be necessary, but research clearly indicated that it should follow the development of meaning.

Surveys and correlational studies predominated in the research on basic-fact instruction through the 1940s. Particular attention was devoted to the relative difficulty of the facts to be learned. For the most part, the surveys were conducted when stimulus-response theories of learning were prevalent, under the assumption that the time needed to memorize facts could be reduced if they were sequenced appropriately. Varying procedures used to ascertain the difficulty level resulted in a lack of agreement among the studies. Some common findings were evident, however; most related to the size of the addend or factor, the inverse and commutative forms, and the doubles. Thus:

> Two findings that were frequently cited in the early studies on multiplication were (1) that combinations involving zero presented difficulty and (2) that the size of the product was positively correlated to difficulty. (Suydam & Dessart, 1976, p. 14)

It is apparent that

> in the past decade, there has been a recurrence of interest in difficulty levels. For example, Suppes and Groen (1967), Smith and Shaw (1969), and Jerman (1970) have used the data-gathering ability of the computer to explore the relative difficulty of both facts and problems. The findings have been used to sequence programs for drill and practice . . . available commercially in books, in kit form, and for administration by computer-assisted instruction. (p. 14)

Swenson (1949) questioned whether results on relative difficulty obtained under drill-oriented methods of learning are valid when applied in learning situations not drill oriented. She concluded that the order of difficulty seemed to be at least in part a function of the teaching method. More recently, Marotta (1974) noted that the teacher should provide specific learning experiences for individual students, realizing that the basic facts

> may be organized for instruction in many different ways, using different approaches and materials, and different means to achieve the goal of computational skill with understanding. (p. 3701)

Information about the difficulty of various facts was also an outcome of other studies. Some of these focused on mathematical sentences and in particular on the difficulty children have in completing sentences with the placeholder in various positions. A synthesis of investigations by Aims (1971), Engle and Lerch (1971), Groen and Poll (1973), Grouws (1972, 1974), Grouws and Good (1976), and Weaver (1971, 1972, 1973) suggests that—

1. open subtraction sentences are more difficult to solve than open addition sentences;
2. sentences of the form $\Box - b = c$ or $c = \Box - b$ are clearly the most difficult of all types;
3. sentences with the operation sign on the right-hand side of the equals sign are more difficult than those with the operation sign on the left-hand side;
4. sentences with numbers between 20 and 100 are more difficult than those that are within the context of basic facts;
5. children's methods of solving open sentences vary from type to type; and
6. they also vary within each particular type. (Suydam & Weaver, 1975, p. 6-3)

Many of the studies on basic facts have been experiments conducted to ascertain feasible procedures for teaching the basic facts. Some of the studies conducted since 1950 are listed in Table 1. They provide support for—

1. the use of concrete materials in teaching basic facts before moving to pictorial and symbolic approaches (Babb, 1976; Nichols, 1972; Norman, 1955; Punn, 1974);
2. the use of a developmental discovery approach over an expository approach (Fullerton, 1955; Nichols, 1972);
3. the postponement of drill from Grades 1 or 2 to Grades 3 and 4 (Davidson, 1975);
4. the use of calculators rather than paper and pencil for immediate acquisition and short-term retention (Hohlfeld, 1974);
5. emphasis on such structural elements as closure, properties, the

identity element, the inverse, and place value (Gray, 1965; Uprichard & Collura, 1974).

Table 1
Experimental Studies on Basic Facts

Researcher	Date	Operation	Grade	n^*	Length
Babb	1976	multiplication	2	3c, 76p	23 days
Brown	1976	multiplication, addition	4–6 3	1526p	
Davidson	1975	addition, subtraction	1–9	35c, 1007p	2 weeks
Fullerton	1955	multiplication	3	30c	8 days
Gray	1965	multiplication	3	22c, 480p	18 days
Hall	1967	multiplication	3	30c, 701p	36 days
Hohlfeld	1974	multiplication	5	7c, 84p	25 days
Nichols	1972	multiplication, division	3	10c, 267p	15 days
Norman	1955	division	3	24c	8 days
Pace	1967	multiplication	4–6(MR)	6c, 81p	2 weeks
Pincus	1956	addition, subtraction	3	4c	12 weeks
Punn	1974	multiplication	3	90p	9 weeks
Sandefur	1966	addition, subtraction	3	520p	30 days
Spencer	1968	addition, subtraction	1–2	4c	4 weeks
Uprichard/ Collura	1974	addition	2		

*c = classes; p = pupils

In another study of potential significance, Spencer (1968) explored retroactive, proactive, and associated effects for sequencing addition and subtraction. He reported that there were both some intertask interference and some facilitation for each of the sequences.

Earlier studies (Brownell, 1928, 1941; Brownell & Carper, 1943; Brownell & Chazal, 1935; Buckingham, 1927; Courtis, 1909; McConnell, 1934; Olander, 1931; Overman, 1930; Thiele, 1939; Thorndike, 1921; Wilburn, 1942; Wilson, 1930; Woody, 1930) provide information on patterns for instruction and practice. Many of these supported the drill theory of instruction. Others echo Brownell and Chazal's (1935) conclusion that drill does not guarantee immediate recall; moreover, drill in itself contributes little to growth in quantitative thinking, since it fails to develop more mature ways of dealing with numbers.

To determine what drill and practice procedures are most effective has been the object of research both inside and outside of mathematics education. Many studies have been conducted with basic facts, although the results may be generalized to other aspects of instruction. Davis (1978) summarized his own research and the evidence from psychological studies in the form of the following principles for drill:

- Children should attempt to memorize material they reasonably understand. (p. 52)
- Have children begin to memorize basic arithmetic facts soon after they demonstrate an understanding of symbolic statements. (p. 52)
- Children should participate in drill with the intent to memorize. (p. 54)
- During drill sessions, emphasize remembering—don't explain! (p. 54)
- Keep drill sessions short, and have some drill almost every day. (p. 55)
- Try to memorize only a few facts in a given lesson, and constantly review previously memorized facts. (p. 55)
- Express confidence in your students' ability to memorize—encourage them to try memorizing and see how fast they can be. (p. 56)
- Emphasize verbal drill activities and provide feedback immediately. (p. 56)
- Vary drill activities and be enthusiastic. (p. 57)
- Praise students for good efforts—keep a record of their progress. (p. 58)

Studies that have explored the ways in which children obtain answers have a particular significance for both practice and research. Brownell (1928, 1941) and McConnell (1934) reported that pupils used various ways to obtain answers to combinations—guessing, counting, solving from known combinations, as well as immediate recall. Brownell felt that this was a natural process, with children attaining a mastery level only after a period in which they used procedures that were less advanced—but to them more meaningful—than automatic responses. Grouws (1974) verified that these processes are still used frequently, but his list of methods used by third graders to solve open addition and subtraction sentences included others: addend-sum relationship, equivalent sentences, random or systematic substitution, counting on or back, tallying, inverse relationship, and simplifying.

Jerman (1970) added data on pupils in Grades 3 through 6, reporting that they used different strategies for different multiplication combinations and that the strategy used may have been a function of the combination itself. Strategies used in Grade 3 appeared to be the ones used for the same combinations in Grade 6 in 72% of the cases. Groen and Poll (1973) and Woods, Resnick, and Groen (1975) reported that most pupils counted either down from the larger number or up from the smaller, depending on which procedure required the fewer steps.

In another study with information-processing models, Hamrin (1975) reported that the learning of number facts was a reconstructive process in which students applied a learned rule to retrieve a fact from memory. Peck and Jencks (1976) used interviews to elicit two strategies for finding answers to missing addend examples. The first graders who used counting were able to solve examples posed with concrete materials, whereas pupils who relied on memory were unable to do so.

It is easy to find flaws in the studies on basic facts; they are indicative of the range of problems that plague researchers. For example:

- Babb himself taught the three classes in his study, with no control for bias. However, his avowed bias was with the group using mnemonics, and this group did not achieve as well as the group using manipulative materials. Sometimes biases are counteracted; perhaps the small sample size failed to provide a clear test of the hypothesis.

- Nichols confounded the independent variables of method and materials. But she reported unusually high differences favoring the discovery-with-manipulative-materials group. Careful analysis of the study failed to indicate what might have led to such scores, unless it was the specificity of the treatment. Studies need to be designed so that the variables are clear and tested, and the report of the study also needs to be clear and explicit.

- Davidson reported little about the actual drill procedure he used, beyond the fact that it was administered using the overhead projector. However, he was interested in establishing trends and obtaining correlational data to ascertain how the pupils scored from grade to grade. He might have incorporated interviews to check on his statements that "the results are consistent with what one would expect if first grade students had not formed the concept of addition with reversibility." Almost every study could be improved if researchers took the time to question the students that form their samples.

- Norman reported that "relatively little control was applied to the textbook method"; teachers were asked to teach using their usual procedures, whereas the developmental method involved the use of various materials. This, too, is a fault in many studies: the treatment is controlled, the control is not; the treatment is unusual, the control is not.

In most of the studies, the selection of the sample fits the pattern that mathematics education researchers have come to expect in school-based studies: the sample could not be randomly selected. But in most studies, the treatment was randomly assigned. The length of time varied: some researchers appeared to anticipate such powerful treatments that the study could be concluded in a few days. Retention data were obtained only weeks later; it has come to be accepted that long-term retention is a variable that must be assessed in ways other than through the vehicle of a dissertation. For these studies, the tests were appropriate, since, of course, tests on basic facts take comparatively little effort to devise.

A large number of the studies—although not all—fit the most important criterion of all: they were based on a problem about which information was needed. As other studies are analyzed, similar criteria should be applied.

Although much is known about the teaching of basic facts, many aspects related to this specific type of skill instruction have not been studied. For example:

- What is the optimal sequencing and timing of introductory activities and of practice for varying groups of children?
- How do manipulative materials interact with learning the facts?
- How does the use of calculators affect learning the facts? (There is unpublished evidence that children continue to learn facts as they use calculators; replication and publication of such investigations would seem to be essential.)

Skill Learning with Algorithms for Whole Numbers

Algorithms are specified procedures that may involve facts, concepts, and procedures. We have attempted to cite illustrations of the diversity of approaches and outcomes that have resulted from relatively uncoordinated studies.

Skill in working with algorithms for whole numbers was compared in many studies, especially algorithms for subtraction and division. For subtraction, the advantages and disadvantages of the equal additions algorithm (in common use up to the 1940s) and the decomposition algorithm (in common use today) were the focus of attention. A study by Brownell (1947; Brownell & Moser, 1949) did much to affirm the use of the decomposition algorithm, although the data indicated that either algorithm, decomposition or equal additions, taught with meaning (rationally) was superior to the same algorithm taught mechanically (by rote). The decomposition algorithm taught rationally was superior to either procedure with the equal additions algorithm on most measures of understanding and transfer, whereas the decomposition algorithm taught mechanically was poorer than either procedure with the equal additions algorithm. However, children with limited arithmetic backgrounds did better with the decomposition algorithm. Such indication of the effectiveness of an algorithm under varying conditions provides information by which decisions can be made. In a more recent investigation, Trafton (1971) found that additional time spent in developing the decomposition algorithm was more effective than a procedure that included work with concepts and the use of the number line before the algorithm was taught.

Other studies that have compared algorithms are listed in Table 2. Several involve comparisons of the distributive and subtractive algorithms for division. The findings are mixed, depending in part on the dependent variable. Burkhart (1968) reported that the distributive form was favored

Table 2
Experimental Studies on Algorithms with Whole Numbers

Researcher	Date	Operation	Grade	n^*	Length
Boyle	1975	multiplication	elem.		
Burkhart	1968	division	4		
Cuevas	1976	division	5	66p	9 days
Dashiell	1975	addition	2–6	333p	
Dilley	1970	division	4	10c	1 semester
Hilker	1976	addition	4	60p	8 days
Hughes (see also Hughes/Burns)	1973⎱ 1975⎰	multiplication	4	12c, 264p	15 days
Hutchings	1973	addition	5	5 schools	
Jones	1976	division	5–6	108p	21 days
Kratzer (see also Kratzer/ Willoughby	1972⎱ 1973⎰	division	4	12c	
Schrankler	1967	multiplication	4	23c, 608p	6 weeks
Wheatley	1976	addition	4	4c, 92p	2 weeks
Wheeler	1972	addition, subtraction	2	144p	

*c = classes; p = pupils

over the subtractive on immediate measures of computational skill, under-standing, and application, as well as retention. Jones (1976) found the distributive form was preferable for computation, and Kratzer (1972; Kratzer & Willoughby, 1973) found it was preferable on transfer measures. Dilley (1970) also reported differences favoring the distributive algorithm for retention but found that the subtractive algorithm was better for ap-plications.

As with the studies on the algorithms for subtraction and division, Schrankler (1967) reported the following varying results on the measure of different dependent variables with two multiplication algorithms:

	Indented Algorithm	Partial Products Algorithm
Multiplication Facts	Immediate computational speed and accuracy	Retention and computational speed
	Knowledge of facts	
Properties	Retention on computation and problem solving	Immediate understanding and problem solving

Such results require some analysis for interpretation, especially when they must be compared with the results of other studies. But they also provide information on which to make decisions in terms of the goals of mathematics programs and the needs of individual students.

Various "low stress" algorithms have been explored in several studies (Boyle, 1975; Dashiell, 1975; Hilker, 1976; Hutchings, 1973). Claims for these algorithms, which require more recording and less mental recall, have been enthusiastic, but it is difficult to locate the data that support the claims.

Research on other algorithms has been limited. Thus, the lattice method for multiplication was compared with the distributive algorithm in only one study (Hughes, 1973; Hughes & Burns, 1975); the lattice method was better on measures of time and accuracy. As another example, the direct method for column addition resulted in greater accuracy and speed than the grouping-to-tens method (Wheatley, 1976). The lack of replication and extension of such studies makes them more like single raindrops than a steady shower of information.

For other topics, attention has been more continuous. Many studies have focused on the skill of estimating the quotient (e.g., Carter, 1960; Flournoy, 1959a; Grossnickle, 1931; Hartung, 1957). The Grossnickle study is one in which 44 550 examples were analyzed to determine the probability of errors. One of a set dealing with slightly varying samples, it is research that probably does not need replication, although it may need reinterpretation.

Some of the most interesting research on skill learning has been conducted in relation to division. Brueckner and Melbye (1940) reported that long division is not a single general ability but a process that consists of a considerable variety of skills found in combinations varying widely in difficulty. Examples in which the apparent quotient is the true quotient were much easier than those that required correcting.

Brownell (1953) explored division in terms of subordinate skills. He found that practice in dividing two-place numbers had no single, uniform, predictable results as far as proficiency in subskills was concerned. In general, the oldest and best-established subskill (subtraction) seemed less subject to change than subskills more recently taught, whereas the subskill (simple division) most like the complex skill seemed to be less stable. Children with the lowest degree of proficiency in subskills made relatively little improvement on them while working on the complex skill.

The algorithm-selection process is related to the attainment of skills. The preferred algorithms are those that (a) are easiest for the learner to conceptualize and understand, (b) will be attained most readily and efficiently, (c) can be generalized and transferred to other algorithms, (d) can be applied readily to solve problems, *and* (e) can be mastered and retained with speed and accuracy. The search and testing of algorithms will continue, with the calculator potentially exerting influence on decisions. In the course of the search thus far, research has disclosed—

1. some of the strengths and weaknesses of each algorithm or of procedures connected with teaching each algorithm (e.g., the decomposition algorithm seemed easier to explain meaningfully than the equal additions algorithm);
2. some of the concomitants that may affect or facilitate the teaching of particular algorithms (e.g., the use of manipulative materials);
3. some indication that one algorithm may be better for one type of learner and another for other learners (e.g., the decomposition algorithm for low achievers);
4. one algorithm may be better for immediate learning, and another may be better for retention.

The function of research is apparent through such instances: it gives educators the knowledge from which to make a more informed decision by disclosing factors to be considered as an educational choice is made. Procedural and sampling differences in the studies led to variance in findings. Coordinated studies, built from these efforts, could provide more definitive information about anticipated outcomes for each type of algorithm.

Skill Learning with Algorithms for Fractions

Fractions are the focus of the studies listed in Table 3. The results of these investigations can be summarized in terms of four categories: sequence, approach, the type of algorithm, and the use of materials. Variability and lack of precision are evident.

When *sequence* was considered, conceptual work followed by late presentation of the algorithm for comparing fractions was better than three other combinations (Choate, 1975). The rule-first sequence resulted in higher achievement on skills items; the model-first sequence was better for understanding (Ellerbruch, 1976). A number of other studies have sought to develop hierarchies of skill with fractions (e.g., Novillis, 1976; Phillips & Kane, 1973; Uprichard & Phillips, 1977).

When *approach* was considered, individual studies revealed the following information:

1. For addition and subtraction, the subset-ratio method was favored over the "usual" method (Stenger, 1972); the region method was favored over the ratio method (Coburn, 1974).
2. For finding the least common denominator, no significant differences were found between using rows of equivalent fractions and factoring

Table 3
Experimental Studies on Algorithms with Fractions

Researcher	Date	Operation	Grade	n*	Length
Anderson	1966	addition	5	26c, 599p	15 days
Bat-haee	1969	addition, subtraction	5	6c, 112p	11 days
Bidwell	1968	division	6	448p	8 days
Bisio	1971	addition, subtraction	5	29c, 501p	
Bohan	1971	addition, subtraction, multiplication	5	6c, 171p	6 weeks
Capps	1960 1962 1963	multiplication, division	6	20c	3 weeks
Choate	1975	addition, subtraction	elem.	8c	
Coburn	1974	addition, subtraction	4	12c	6 weeks
Ellerbruch	1976	addition, subtraction	4	4c, 77p	25 days
Green	1970	multiplication	5	480p	12 days
Stenger	1972	addition, subtraction	5	2c, 81p	16 days

*c = classes; p = pupils

denominators (Anderson, 1966); the factoring method was better than the inspection method (Bat-haee, 1969).

3. For multiplication, the area approach was favored over the finding-a-part-of approach (Green, 1970).

When the *type of algorithm* was considered, Capps (1960, 1962, 1963) found no significant difference between common denominator and inversion algorithms on addition, subtraction, and division with fractions, but the inversion algorithm was better for multiplication with fractions. Bidwell (1968) reported that the inversion algorithm was favored, followed by the complex fraction and common denominator algorithms.

When the *use of materials* was examined, the passive use of manipulative materials appeared to be as effective as their active use and better than nonuse (Bisio, 1971). When paper folding was compared with a property-of-one procedure, no significant differences were found except for retention, where paper folding was favored (Bohan, 1971). No significant differences were found by Green (1970) between the use of diagrams and materials.

The need for planned, coordinated efforts on research with fraction skills was evident: many of these studies were conducted at the University of Michigan under the direction of Payne. Such continuing emphasis gives promise of providing instructional applicability (e.g., see Ellerbruch & Payne, 1978) as well as evidence on how children learn.

Skill Learning with Algorithms for Decimals

The studies that relate to the development of skills for learning algorithms with decimals are listed in Table 4. Sequencing was the subject of three of them (Faires, 1963; O'Brien, 1967; Willson, 1969, 1972). Faires's data favored a sequence based on the orderly extension of place-value ideas with no reference to common-fraction equivalents rather than teaching fractions before decimals. In a study with admitted faults, O'Brien found that the decimal-numeration approach was less effective than procedures based on the relation between decimals and fractions or on rules or procedures with no mention made of fractions or of principles of decimal numeration. Willson, however, found no significant differences in achievement between fraction-decimal or decimal-fraction sequences.

Table 4
Experimental Studies on Decimals

Researcher	Date	Grade	$n*$	Length
Bauer	1975	7	18c, 568p	15 days
Faires	1963	5	8c	
Flournoy	1959b	5	6c, 137p	
Kuhn	1954	6	18c	5 days
O'Brien	1968	6	36c	
Willson	1969, 1972	5	112p	14 weeks

*c = classes; p = pupils

In two studies on how to determine where the decimal point should be placed in the quotient, Flournoy (1959b) favored the use of multiplying by a power of ten over the subtractive method, whereas Kuhn (1954) found that expressing the quotient in terms of the smallest decimal place in the divisor was better than the power-of-ten method.

Bauer (1975) studied common-fraction equivalents, expanded exponential notation, and number-line approaches, finding no significant differences in achievement among them. Although research has provided no clear indication of the most logical approach to use, it does indicate that (in the words used at one time or another by every researcher) "more research is needed."

Skill Learning with Other Mathematical Content

There is a decline in the interest of researchers in skill learning with other mathematical topics. This has been noted before in connection with research on secondary school mathematics: more attention is devoted to broader areas of concern, such as the evaluation of a course, or to seeking an answer to a particular problem, such as the need to predict achievement, than to such concerns as skill learning.

Teaching and learning skills with integers has been given little attention from researchers. One example is the study by Coltharp (1969), in which no significant differences were found between abstract and concrete approaches for addition and subtraction of integers with 79 sixth graders. Using seventh graders, Sawyer (1973, 1974) reported no significant differences in computation between the complement method of subtracting integers and the related facts method. The complement method was favored in a second study when it was compared to the systems method.

For geometry, one study by Campbell (1972) seems to focus on skill learning. He identified three to six variables at each grade level, 3 through 6, which accounted for 38 to 60% of the variance when predicting geometry achievement.

Two studies on algebra involved ninth graders. Brandner (1976) reported the type of solution and the format both affected the correct solution of linear equations. Many of the 177 boys surveyed were competent only with a guess-and-test strategy. In a comparison of three sequences for solving simultaneous linear equations, Shafer (1976) found that student performance did not decline when a second method was introduced, regardless of the order or the timing. No significant difference in success or the choice of algorithm was found.

Skill Learning with Other Topics

The vast majority of research on skill learning is concerned with computational algorithms and their prerequisite basic facts. But there are a few studies involving other skills. For instance, Nelson (1967) and Paull (1972) reported that students in Grades 4, 6, and 11 varied in their ability to use estimation skills. Sutherlin (1977) explored the teaching of decimal estimation skills with calculators; no significant differences were found between groups given and not given an estimation unit. Ibe (1973) indicated that instruction on estimation skills was better than no instruction—always a comforting finding! Similarly, research indicates that instruction is effective in helping students attain better mental computation skills (e.g., Flournoy, 1954; Grumbling, 1971; Rea & French, 1972).

One of the ways in which skill learning can be readily critiqued is through error analysis. In addition to brief analyses that appear as one component of many studies, a number of major efforts have been undertaken to provide broad analyses (see Table 5).

The findings of such studies have differed in nonsignificant ways over the years: the major errors made under the drill theory of instruction tend to occur today when attempts are made to make instruction more mean-

Table 5
Studies on Error Analysis

Researcher	Date	Grade	n*	Focus**
Baxter	1974	6	96p	a, s, m, d
Brueckner	1928a	5–7		fractions
	1928b	6–8	300p	decimals
Burge	1932	4–6	2577p	m
Buswell/John	1926	3–6	61p	a, s, m, d
Cox	1975	2–6	744p	a, s, m, d
Ellis	1972	6	690p	a, s, m, d
Grossnickle	1941	6–9	761p	d with
	1943		400p	decimals
Grossnickle/ Snyder	1939	4–8	500p	a, s, m, d
Guiler	1945	9	937p	fractions
	1946a	9	936p	decimals
	1946b	9	936p	decimals
Lankford	1972	7	176p	a, s, m, d, fractions
Logan	1976	4	200p	s
Roberts	1968	3	148p	a, s, m, d
Smith	1969	3–4	523p	s

*c = classes; p = pupils
**a, s, m, d = addition, subtraction, multiplication, division with whole numbers

ingful. The nature of the content seems to create the situation for errors rather than merely the way the material is presented. In a summary of many studies, it has been noted that the most frequently found errors made by pupils are these (Suydam & Dessart, 1976, p. 22):

- Errors with basic facts for each operation
- Errors with zero for each operation
- Subtracting the minuend from the subtrahend
- Adding a carried number later
- Adding carried numbers before multiplying
- Carrying the wrong number in multiplication
- In division, errors on subtraction and multiplication

Errors with basic facts and with regrouping are noted frequently in recent studies, including data analyses from the National Assessment of Educational Progress (NAEP) (Carpenter, Coburn, Reys, & Wilson, 1978).

Assessments of Skill Learning

Whether a skill has been attained can be assessed by having students demonstrate that they can perform the skill. An understanding of the procedure, the ability to select appropriate applications, the ability to transfer to new applications, the ability to generalize to expanded forms—all are irrelevant when we simply want to assess whether or not, or how well, a skill has been attained. Understanding, transfer, applicability, and generalizing are important to consider in selecting the procedure that is the means to attain the skill. But in the end, what is of concern is that the learner has mastered the skill. It matters not that one uses the decomposition algorithm or the equal additions algorithm; what matters is that when confronted with an example requiring the subtraction of a three-digit number from a three-digit number, one can attain the correct answer.

Skill learning, then, is assessed by giving a test in which the learner must demonstrate mastery. Standardized tests, national and state assessment tests, city and district tests, and classroom tests all include sections that test skills. Some tests, unfortunately, assess only skills; many tests assess only computational skills.

Bright (1978) compared data on computation with whole numbers and fractions from the National Longitudinal Study of Mathematical Abilities (NLSMA), NAEP, and several state assessments. He stated the following conclusions:

- Overall, several patterns in the data seem to support clear conclusions. First, there is general improvement in performance across grades. This result is not unexpected, and it is consistent with the results of the grade-equivalent studies discussed earlier. Second, the levels of performance decrease as the items become more complex. Third, performance tends to stabilize. For the areas discussed in this article, stabilization seems to occur during the junior high school years. . . . Fourth, stabilization of performance for whole-number computation occurs earlier and at a higher level than for fractional-number computation. . . . Fifth, for all computation skills considered, there is no decline—or at least no important decline—in the performance of adults in comparison to that of high school students. In the context of improvement of skill performance across grades, this suggests that once skills are mastered, they are not forgotten.

- Computation skills are not acquired on the basis of initial instruction. Instruction over several years is needed to reach stability, and in every area examined there is still room for improvement.

- It is important to note that the data presented here refute the notion that students generally do not acquire basic computation skills. In fact, some skills (e.g., addition and subtraction without regrouping) are almost universally acquired, whereas others (e.g., division of decimal fractions) are not. Any meaningful discussion of the performance of students in basic computation skills must be a discussion of specific skills rather than skills in general. (p. 160)

A statement by Carpenter et al. (1975) relative to the NAEP data adds another dimension to Bright's summary:

Many students master subtraction some time after the primary emphasis on instruction in subtraction algorithms has been completed. It is also interesting to observe that performance on subtraction computation improves from ages 13 to 17, even though very little systematic drill on whole-number subtraction is provided in the high school curriculum. (p. 654)

These analyses provide some response to those who argue that students are not attaining competency with the traditional computational skills. The NAEP data also indicate, however, that other skills, such as estimation, are not being learned well (Carpenter et al., 1978).

Summary

In this section the research on skill learning was summarized in relation to counting and place value; basic facts; algorithms for whole numbers, fractions, and decimals; other content; other topics; and assessments.

- More attention has been given to the concepts involved in counting than to the skills.
- Little attention has been given to place-value skills.
- Basic facts have received continuing attention over the years, with a focus on difficulty level.
- Continuing attention has also been given to algorithms for whole numbers and fractions.
- Very little attention has been given to algorithms for decimals or other mathematical topics.
- Results of error analysis over the years can be readily summarized.
- Means of assessing skills are briefly discussed, and evidence is summarized.

Difficulties of research design are noted in connection with particular studies. In addition, gaps in the research should be readily apparent; the need for coordinated studies is reaffirmed.

TRENDS IN RESEARCH ON SKILL LEARNING

Many early studies on skills focused on such factors as the difficulty level of basic facts, patterns of effective drill, the errors pupils make, and the potential errors inherent in the content. Studies on factors associated with various algorithms gradually became of greater interest. The range of dependent variables increased, including the speed and accuracy criteria essential as measures of skill attainment but also encompassing understanding, transfer, retention, and similar criteria.

What will influence research on skill learning in the coming years? In addition to trends that will affect all research, one technological development will directly influence research on skills, and a second factor will demand pragmatic attention.

Calculating Power

Calculating power never before available is now available at the touch of each person's fingers. The calculator is the forerunner of computing tools that are bringing mathematics closer to the lives of everyone. Today's calculators have the computing power of the computers of 20 years ago. Virtually unlimited computing power is being brought within the grasp of each person, which promises (or threatens) vast changes in technology for businesses, homes, and—yes—schools. We have the tool: We must determine how it can best be used in the mathematics classroom.

It seems evident that the calculator can have a profound effect on how computational skills are taught. However, little is known about how the calculator affects learning: Evidence suggests only that learners who have used calculators for mathematics instruction score on paper-and-pencil achievement tests at least as well or better than students who have not used calculators for instruction (Suydam, 1978). Preliminary evidence suggests further that the calculator appears to help many pupils in learning basic facts, possibly because it provides immediate feedback. Little is known about how the calculator affects the teaching of algorithms. Little is known about what algorithms might be more effectively taught given the existence of the calculator. Research is obviously needed on the effects of the calculator on skill learning.

Competency Testing

In one form or another, whether by minimal competency tests or progress assessments, skill learning is being—and will continue to be—measured. Public attention is directed toward the products of instruction. Standardized tests have been oriented toward the measurement of skills; frequently, even those subtests labeled "concepts" or "problem solving" assess skill learning. It is easier to measure skills and to write items with good item statistics; in addition, certain skills are of public concern.

Competency testing will emphasize the need for better ways to develop skills. Researchers, who have for years pursued research on improving skill learning, will therefore have renewed approbation for their efforts.

ISSUES IN RESEARCH ON SKILL LEARNING

Issues about skill learning are related to internal and external factors. The internal issues are those involving the nature of skill learning and how to teach skills more effectively. The latter, in particular, is derived from an external issue, the "back to the basics" movement.

A proportion of the research in mathematics education has always been devoted to societal concerns and frequently interacts with a concern reflected by the prevailing learning theory. Thus in the early years of this century, when stimulus-response was the accepted notion of how children learn, the societal need to provide increased numbers of children with a basic public school education lent support to the research on efficient teaching procedures. The shock of learning how poorly military forces tested in arithmetic (in 1918) led to further exploration of drill techniques. When the emphasis on social utility superceded the fragmented drill approach, the way was paved for studies ascertaining what arithmetic was really needed in various occupations.

The first emphasis was on sequencing for efficiency, the second on necessary content. With the third phase on meaning, the emphasis shifted to the instructional process. Society sanctioned the shifts in great part because of pervading concern over the rigidity of drill and the permissiveness of social utility. Similarly, the concern over a lack of pressure led to an acceptance of the "new math," where the emphasis was once again on content. As the glow from change faded, concern for the "basics" is again reflected; the issue has become one of content once again, with underlying tones of both sequence and instructional procedure.

A number of issues about skill learning have been raised in recent years. A list of such issues would include the following:

- Should it be assumed that the principles that apply to skill learning in general (or in other subject areas) apply to mathematical skills, or are there features unique to mathematical skill learning?

- Should skills be given primary emphasis or a less dominant emphasis in the mathematics program?

- Should competency on measures of immediate learning be the primary goal in selecting procedures for teaching skills, or should transfer, retention, or other goals be primary?

- Should preschool children learn rote counting, or should they be discouraged from counting without meaning?

- Should basic facts be taught meaningfully (e.g., with manipulative materials) or rotely (e.g., with drill exercises)?

- Should learning the meaning of skills precede practice for mastery, or should mastery be attained and then meaning developed?

- Should some skills be taught only rotely and others with meaning?

- Should skills be taught discretely or should they be taught within a cohesive framework?

- Should a skill be practiced until it is mastered before moving to another topic, or should students be at different levels of attainment on several skills at the same time?

- Should computational skills be mastered before students leave the elementary school, or should the secondary school accept responsibility for having students attain mastery?
- Should calculators be used beginning in the primary grades to teach counting, basic facts, and other skills, or should their use be postponed until at least the intermediate grades?
- Should competency with algorithms be attained before calculators are used, or should calculators be used in developing competency with algorithms?
- Should skills be taught to the point of recall from memory, or should most skills be taught only up to a point and then calculators or computers used as needed?
- Should traditional algorithms (i.e., algorithms that parents were taught) be learned, or should new algorithms (e.g., algorithms appropriate for use with calculators) be learned?
- Should a child learn one "standard" algorithm directly, or should developmental algorithms be used to build understanding and competency?

Research cannot answer the question of "should"; research can identify probability-of-success levels. Research cannot attack all the issues directly; it may provide information related to most of them. The evidence is weighed in relation to philosophical beliefs as decisions are made about what, when, and how skills are to be taught and learned. It seems obvious that research can provide only fragmentary evidence for some of the issues above. Several seem of more immediate concern than others: those dealing with the role of meaningful instruction and those relating to the use of the calculator. Decision making about methods and materials should not proceed independently of the evidence that research can provide.

All research on skill learning need not be related to prevalent issues: The need to know more about the learning process should be the motive directing the majority of investigations. There is a need for studies to provide current information on what skills students are achieving. There is a need for studies that provide information on the effectiveness of procedures under specified conditions. But the predominant need is for studies that will build an understanding of how skills are learned. We need such information in order to ascertain what really makes a difference in teaching and learning.

It should not escape attention that most of the research to date has been on computational skills at the elementary school level. There is a need for more knowledge on the range of skills at all levels.

NEW DIRECTIONS FOR RESEARCH ON SKILL LEARNING

The development of arithmetic skills in pupils, with an emphasis on speed and accuracy, has been, historically, a goal accepted by teachers. In the preface of the *American Calculator,* published in 1831, Slocum commented on rules for calculation by observing that—

> these questions should be repeated, till the learner is able to answer them readily, not only in the natural order in which they stand, but also when put promiscuously, embracing several rules in the same lesson. (Bidwell & Clason, 1970, p. 4)

In 1924, Thorndike stated, "The bonds in question clearly must be made far stronger than they now are. They should in fact be strong enough to abolish errors in computation except for those due to temporary lapses" (Bidwell & Clason, 1970, p. 467). With the current interest in the "basics," we may see a resurgence of emphasis on skill learning with speed and accuracy as cherished outcomes of learning.

In light of the demands placed on teachers to develop skills in pupils, it is not surprising that researchers in mathematics education have focused on questions related to speed and accurate skill learning in a classroom setting. From a review of the research completed, and especially through an examination of Tables 1–5, one cannot escape the conclusion that researchers have been far more concerned with the applicability of their findings to immediate classroom practice than with searching for basic, psychological understandings of the processes of skill learning.

Against this background of concern for an immediate usefulness of research findings for classroom teachers arises a new philosophical viewpoint of the goals of research in mathematics education. This point of view, sparked largely by an interest in establishing basic, underlying psychological principles in learning, calls for a search for answers to broader questions that can be generalized to many areas of skill learning, including mathematics education. This chapter would not be complete without describing the flavor of this outlook and presenting a challenge to researchers in mathematics education to consider quite carefully the implications of this philosophy.

A Model for Research

A theory for skill development in an educational setting would involve a study of at least three facets: (a) the attributes of those who are asked to perform the skill, (b) the characteristics of the skill, and (c) the program of activities designed to teach the skill. Such a comprehensive theory would be complex indeed and may be too much to hope for in the foreseeable future.

However, researchers could focus primarily on the learner under well-defined conditions and raise the question, "How do the actions of the learner in this particular situation result in the ability to perform a skill with a minimal involvement of attention?", or as Whitehead said, "without thinking." Perhaps initial research efforts in establishing such a theory would involve extensive clinical investigations to generate hypotheses for rigorous testing. Without such hypotheses, rigorous experimentation would be premature in contributing to a viable theory of skill learning.

In considering a clinical model for studying the learner, we can view skill development in four progressive stages: (a) the *preparation* stage, (b) the *active learning* stage, (c) the *practice or use* stage, and (d) the *retention, decay, or loss* stage.

In illustrating questions that may be investigated at each of these stages, we have selected a particular skill. This skill, the factoring of the differences of two squares, could have been any other skill, such as adding two fractions, differentiating a polynomial equation, or even throwing a baseball at a target. It is felt that similar questions could be raised about each of these skills.

The Preparation Stage

When students are first informed that a new skill is to be learned, there is a period of time during which they brace or prepare themselves for the learning experience. This period may be of very short duration and has not usually been studied in past research efforts.

During this period of preparation, questions similar to the following may be raised: Do the learners attempt to recall applicable information? Do they recall facts, concepts, or principles? If so, which? What is the nature of the recalled information, and when was it learned? How was it learned? How much time do learners spend searching their memory? Should they be permitted to spend more time? Less time?

One could also investigate a variety of physical changes in the learners during this period. Do they become tense? Bored? Indifferent? Does the heartbeat increase? Does the blood pressure increase? In other words, an attempt would be made to ascertain as much as possible about what actually occurs in the learner during the period between the announcement of a skill-learning experience and the onset of the actual episode of skill development.

The Active Learning Stage

Following a consideration of the stage in which the learner prepares for the learning episode, one might focus on problems associated with the actual mastery of a skill. During this stage, interest centers on the learner interacting with the elements of a learning strategy designed to bring him or her to the state of being able to perform the skill. In the preparation stage, interest centered on actions of the learner; in the active learning stage, the learner as well as the strategies of learning are studied.

Returning to a consideration of the skill of factoring the difference of two squares, the researcher might investigate the effects of symbolic versus physical emphases. For example, which of the strategies is most effective in advancing the learner to the mastery of a skill: (a) a symbolic experience, (b) a symbolic followed by a physical experience, or (c) a physical followed by a symbolic experience?

If the experience is primarily symbolic, a strategy might include the presentation of the basic identity, $x^2 - y^2 = (x - y)(x + y)$, with all subsequent exercises related to that identity. In this strategy, $16^2 - 9^2$ becomes the special case in which $x = 4$ and $y = 3$, and $(m + n)^2 - (p + q)^2$ is the case in which $x = m + n$ and $y = p + q$. Each new exercise would involve an interpretation of that example as a special case of the identity.

A physical experience, however, could include a model for developing the concept of the difference of two squares (Figure 1). In such a model, a square whose area is designated by y^2 is placed on a square whose area is x^2, so that the shaded portion shown in (a) is a representation of $x^2 - y^2$. The shaded region is subdivided as shown in (b) and rearranged as in (c) to illustrate that $x^2 - y^2 = (x - y)(x + y)$. A physical experience of this type could precede, follow, or be integrated into a symbolic experience.

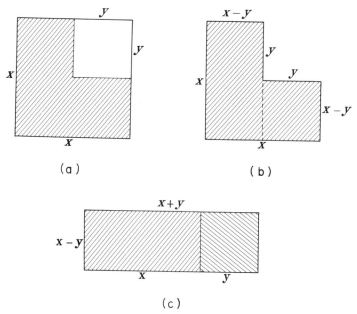

Figure 1.

At this point, the researcher could assume a fixed time period for the learning episode. Suppose that a total of 30 minutes is available and that strategies of symbolic, symbolic followed by physical, or physical followed by symbolic are employed for various intervals of the time period. Interest could center on determining which strategy brings the learner most effectively to a criterion of skill mastery.

Furthermore, when considering a fixed time period for skill mastery, one might also raise questions as to whether rapid, repetitive, symbolic presentations are more effective than slower, repetitive, symbolic presentations. This would be of particular interest if one is primarily concerned with producing rapid skill performance in learners; that is, do rapid learning strategies tend to reinforce the speed of performance more effectively than slower learning strategies?

Turning aside from strategies, the researcher may also consider the characteristics of the learner interacting with the strategy employed. Partitioning samples of learners on the basis of sex, IQ, and mathematical achievement are common ways of viewing characteristics of learners, and such partitions are very appropriate and most worthy of consideration. In addition to those characteristics, there are more novel characteristics, such as field independence versus field dependence, reflectivity versus impulsivity, and high anxiety versus low anxiety (see the chapter by Fennema & Behr), to provide additional categories of classification.

Studying $m \times n$ partitions of samples with m dimensions of learner characteristics and n dimensions of teaching strategies in a clinical, laboratory type of setting with well-defined skills seems to be an effort worthy of pursuit. Initial investigations would be devoted primarily to attempts to observe phenomena that could be studied later under more rigorous, tightly controlled settings.

Defined strategies designed to bring the learner to skill mastery would provide interesting avenues of investigation. One might also consider the relationships of strategies. The researcher might wish to consider the interacting effects of presenting two closely related skills at one time. Interest could center on determining whether or not an attempt to master two skills simultaneously provides too much competition for the student's memory and learning capacities. For example, suppose the learning episode includes determining the solution set of an equation, such as $x^2 - 4 = 0$, as well as factoring the difference of two squares. Since these are closely related skills, would learning them together tend to reinforce the learning of each skill? Or, suppose two dissimilar skills, such as factoring the difference of two squares and finding the common logarithms of numbers, were presented. It seems reasonable to expect that these two would tend to overburden the pupil's memory and probably result in the inefficient learning of both skills.

The Practice or Use Stage

Once a skill has been mastered, it must be practiced or used in order to be retained by the learner. As noted earlier, the skill should be performed in an automatic manner if it is to be used in other processes, such as problem solving. Surely if the problem-solving process calls for the factoring of the difference of two squares, one would hope that the student could perform this skill rapidly without much reflection so that the mind could be kept free to dwell on the problem-solving process. Consequently, skill retention is an important goal of learning.

The practice of the skill could (a) occur in terms of reviewing patterns that were part of the initial learning strategy; (b) be part of a strategy employing the skill as a subskill—for example, using the factoring of two squares in finding the solution set of a quadratic equation, such as $x^2 - 9 = 0$; or (c) occur in a novel setting, such as a game. The inherent attractiveness of games is undoubtedly a motivating factor with students, but one might question whether the game tends to compete for the attention of the student and thus to promote inefficient habits of practice.

It might also be observed that practice can be overdone. It has been claimed that students can acquire mental sets if routine skills are practiced too extensively (Luchins & Luchins, 1950). This implies that they become so persistent in wishing to apply a given skill that they refuse to adopt an alternative route or strategy. An example of this may occur in having students find the diagonal of the rectangle in the circle given in Figure 2. The first reaction of many students is to use a skill acquired from the Pythagorean theorem to determine the diagonal; if they would give the matter a little reflection, they might easily see that the diagonal is equal to r, the radius of the circle.

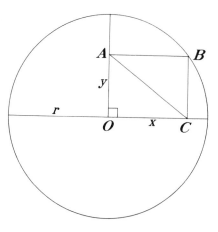

Figure 2.

The Retention, Decay, or Loss Stage

Finally, after a skill has been mastered and used or practiced, a period of disuse is inevitable. What happens to a learner who was able to perform a skill at an earlier time but is unable to perform the skill readily at a later time? Probably he or she has "forgotten" the skill, and interest could focus on the manner in which the skill is recalled from memory. One would certainly suspect that the passage of time influences recall, but other factors related to the initial learning episode may also affect recall.

Of interest would be the actions of the learner in the recall or reconstruction episode. Precisely what does the student initially recall in attempting to remember the skill? In the example of the skill related to the difference of two squares, does the learner attempt to recall "x^2," "y^2," "$x^2 - y^2$," " $=$," " $+$," the exponent "2"? As the student is attempting to recall information, how does the search of memory proceed? Is it organized, random, of some combination of factors? If the skill was initially learned by a symbolic experience, is the recall primarily symbolic? If the skill was learned through a physical experience, is the recall effort related to physical factors?

In recalling skills, the student may employ cues to jog the memory. In attempting to recall the title of a book, some have found that often the color of the book may be the first conscious cue in the recall experience. Suppose a skill was initially acquired with an emphasis on color in the learning episode; that is, suppose a red pencil was used with yellow paper. Would the colors "red" or "yellow" provide cues at a later stage of recall? Surely, if more were known about the mechanism of recall, the initial learning episodes could be designed to accommodate these factors.

Summary

In this section an attempt has been made to describe a clinical research model for developing a skill theory in mathematical learning. Efforts could focus on viewing the process of skill development occurring in four stages: (a) the preparation stage, (b) the active learning stage, (c) the practice or use stage, and (d) the retention, decay, or loss stage. Initial efforts in this direction would employ clinical approaches in which attempts would be made to observe phenomena that may evolve into a refined theory of skill development in mathematics education.

REFERENCES

Aims, B. D. A study of selected relationships between solution time and five characteristics of arithmetic drill problems (Doctoral dissertation, Memphis State University, 1970). *Dissertation Abstracts International,* March 1971, *31,* 4373A.

Anderson, R. C. A comparison of two procedures for finding the least common denominator in the addition of unlike, unrelated fractions (Doctoral dissertation, University of Iowa, 1965). *Dissertation Abstracts,* April 1966, *26,* 5901.

Babb, J. H. The effects of textbook instruction, manipulatives and imagery on recall of the basic multiplication facts (Doctoral dissertation, University of South Florida, 1975). *Dissertation Abstracts International,* January 1976, *36,* 4378A.

Barr, D. C. A comparison of three methods of introducing two-digit numeration and the effects of these methods on certain groups of children (Doctoral dissertation, University of Illinois at Urbana-Champaign, 1975). *Dissertation Abstracts International,* March 1976, *36,* 5799A.

Barr, D. C. A comparison of three methods of introducing two-digit numeration. *Journal for Research in Mathematics Education,* January 1978, *9,* 33–43.

Bat-haee, M. A. A comparison of two methods of finding the least common denominator of unlike fractions at fifth-grade level in relation to sex, arithmetic achievement, and intelligence (Doctoral dissertation, Southern Illinois University, 1968). *Dissertation Abstracts,* June 1969, *29,* 4365A.

Bauer, J. L. The effect of three instructional bases for decimals on computation skills of seventh-grade students (Doctoral dissertation, Ohio State University, 1974). *Dissertation Abstracts International,* May 1975, *35,* 7024A.

Baxter, M. M. Prediction of error and error type in computation of sixth grade mathematics students (Doctoral dissertation, Pennsylvania State University, 1973). *Dissertation Abstracts International,* July 1974, *35,* 251A.

Bidwell, J. K. A comparative study of the learning structures of three algorithms for the division of fractional numbers (Doctoral dissertation, University of Michigan, 1968). *Dissertation Abstracts,* September 1968, *29,* 830A.

Bidwell, J. K., & Clason, R. G. (Eds.). *Readings in the history of mathematics education.* Washington, D.C.: National Council of Teachers of Mathematics, 1970.

Bisio, R. M. Effect of manipulative materials on understanding operations with fractions in grade V (Doctoral dissertation, University of California, Berkeley, 1970). *Dissertation Abstracts International,* August 1971, *32,* 833A.

Bohan, H. J. A study of the effectiveness of three learning sequences for equivalent fractions (Doctoral dissertation, University of Michigan, 1970). *Dissertation Abstracts International,* June 1971, *31,* 6270A.

Boyle, M. L. Effects of social reinforcement under simulated test and non-test conditions on the computational rate and accuracy of children using either the conventional algorithm or the Hutchings' "low-stress" algorithm (Doctoral dissertation, University of Maryland, 1975). *Dissertation Abstracts International,* December 1975, *36,* 3499A.

Brace, A., & Nelson, L. D. The preschool child's concept of number. *Arithmetic Teacher,* February 1965, *12,* 126–133.

Brandner, R. J. Testing for the analytic strategy for solving linear algebraic equations (Doctoral dissertation, University of Cincinnati, 1976). *Dissertation Abstracts International,* July 1976, *37,* 164A–165A.

Bright, G. W. Assessing the development of computational skills. In Marilyn N. Suydam (Ed.), *Developing computational skills,* NCTM 1978 Yearbook. Reston, Va.: National Council of Teachers of Mathematics, 1978.

Brown, R. E. Effects of an elementary school principal systematically reinforcing students for learning multiplication facts (Doctoral dissertation, University of Kansas, 1975). *Dissertation Abstracts International,* July 1976, *37,* 485B.

Brownell, W. A. *The development of children's number ideas in the primary grades* (Supplementary Educational Monographs, No. 35). Chicago: University of Chicago Press, 1928.

Brownell, W. A. Psychological considerations in the learning and the teaching of arithmetic. In *The teaching of arithmetic,* Tenth Yearbook of the National Council of Teachers of Mathematics. New York: Bureau of Publications, Teachers College, Columbia University, 1935.

Brownell, W. A. *Arithmetic in grades I and II* (Duke University Studies in Education, No. 6). Durham, N.C.: Duke University Press, 1941.

Brownell, W. A. An experiment on "borrowing" in third grade arithmetic. *Journal of Educational Research,* November 1947, *41,* 161–171.

Brownell, W. A. The effects of practicing a complex arithmetical skill upon proficiency in its constituent skills. *Journal of Educational Psychology,* February 1953, *44,* 65–81.

Brownell, W. A., & Carper, D. V. *Learning the multiplication combinations* (Duke University Studies in Education, No. 7). Durham, N.C.: Duke University Press, 1943.

Brownell, W. A., & Chazal, C. B. The effects of premature drill in third-grade arithmetic. *Journal of Educational Research,* September 1935, *29,* 17–28.

Brownell, W. A., & Moser, H. E. *Meaningful vs. mechanical learning: A study in grade III subtraction* (Duke University Studies in Education, No. 8). Durham, N.C.: Duke University Press, 1949.

Brueckner, L. J. Analysis of errors in fractions. *Elementary School Journal,* June 1928, *28,* 760–770. (a)

Brueckner, L. J. Analysis of difficulties in decimals. *Elementary School Journal.* September 1928, *29,* 32–41. (b)

Brueckner, L. J., & Melbye, H. O. Relative difficulty of types of examples in division with two-figure divisors. *Journal of Educational Research,* February 1940, *33,* 401–414.

Buckingham, B. R. Teaching addition and subtraction facts together or separately. *Educational Research Bulletin,* May 1927, *6,* 228–229; 240–242.

Burge, L. V. Types of errors and questionable habits of work in multiplication. *Elementary School Journal,* November 1932, *33,* 185–194.

Burkhart, L. L. A study of two modern approaches to the development of understanding and skills in division of whole numbers (Doctoral dissertation, Case Western Reserve University, 1967). *Dissertation Abstracts,* April 1968, *28,* 3877A.

Buswell, G. T., & John, L. *Diagnostic studies in arithmetic* (Supplementary Educational Monographs, No. 30). Chicago: University of Chicago Press, 1926.

Callahan, L. G. A study of knowledge possessed by elementary school teachers, in-service and in-training, of the cultural, psychological, and mathematical foundations of the elementary school mathematics program (Doctoral dissertation, Syracuse University, 1966). *Dissertation Abstracts,* June 1967, *27,* 4149A–4150A.

Campbell, B. L. Prediction of elementary pupils' scores on a test of cognitive skills in geometry achievement (Doctoral dissertation, Pennsylvania State University, 1971). *Dissertation Abstracts International,* July 1972, *33,* 69A.

Capps, L. R. A comparison of the common denominator and inversion method in teaching division of fractions (Doctoral dissertation, University of Minnesota, 1960). *Dissertation Abstracts,* October 1960, *21,* 819–820. *See also: Journal of Educational Research,* July-August 1963, *56,* 516–522; *Arithmetic Teacher,* January 1962, *9,* 10–16.

Carpenter, T. P., Coburn, T. G., Reys, R. E., & Wilson, J. W. Subtraction: What do students know? *Arithmetic Teacher,* December 1975, *22,* 653–657.

Carpenter, T., Coburn, T. G., Reys, R. E., & Wilson, J. W. *Results from the first mathematics assessment of the National Assessment of Educational Progress.* Reston, Va.: National Council of Teachers of Mathematics, 1978.

Carter, M. K. A comparative study of two methods of estimating quotients when learning to divide by two-figure divisors (Doctoral dissertation, Boston University, School of Education, 1959). *Dissertation Abstracts,* February 1960, *20,* 3317.

Choate, S. A. The effect of algorithmic and conceptual development for the comparison of fractions (Doctoral dissertation, University of Michigan, 1975). *Dissertation Abstracts International,* September 1975, *36,* 1410A.

Coburn, T. G. The effect of a ratio approach and a region approach on equivalent fractions and addition/subtraction for pupils in grade four (Doctoral dissertation, University of Michigan, 1973). *Dissertation Abstracts International,* February 1974, *34,* 4688A.

Coltharp, F. L. A comparison of the effectiveness of an abstract and a concrete approach in teaching of integers to sixth grade students (Doctoral dissertation, Oklahoma State University, 1968). *Dissertation Abstracts International,* September 1969, *30,* 923A–924A.

Courtis, S. A. Measurement of growth and efficiency in arithmetic. *Elementary School Teacher,* 1909, *10,* 58–74; 177–199.

Cox, L. S. Diagnosing and remediating systematic errors in addition and subtraction computations. *Arithmetic Teacher,* February 1975, *22,* 151–157. *See also:* Systematic errors in the four vertical algorithms in normal and handicapped populations. *Journal for Research in Mathematics Education,* November 1975, *6,* 202–220.

Cuevas, G. J. The effects of precise thinking algorithmic exercises and cognitive style on fifth grade student's ability to perform the division algorithm (Doctoral dissertation, University of Miami, 1975). *Dissertation Abstracts International,* March 1976, *36,* 5896A.

Dashiell, W. H. An analysis of changes in affect and changes in both computational power and computational stamina occurring in primary and elementary school children after instruction in Hutchings' low fatigue addition algorithm, practice with unusually large examples, and exposure to one of two alternative performance options (Doctoral dissertation, University of Maryland, 1974). *Dissertation Abstracts International*, June 1975, *35*, 7740A.

Davidson, T. E. The effects of drill on addition-subtraction fact learning; with implication of Piagetian reversibility (Doctoral dissertation, Utah State University, 1975). *Dissertation Abstracts International*, July 1975, *36*, 102A.

Davis, E. J. Suggestions for teaching the basic facts of arithmetic. In Marilyn N. Suydam (Ed.), *Developing computational skills*, NCTM 1978 Yearbook. Reston, Va.: National Council of Teachers of Mathematics, 1978.

Dilley, C. A. A comparison of two methods of teaching long division (Doctoral dissertation, University of Illinois at Urbana-Champaign, 1970). *Dissertation Abstracts International*, November 1970, *31*, 2248A.

Ellerbruch, L. W. The effects of the placement of rules and concrete models in learning addition and subtraction of fractions in grade four (Doctoral dissertation, University of Michigan, 1975). *Dissertation Abstracts International*, April 1976, *36*, 6441A–6442A.

Ellerbruch, L. W., & Payne, J. N. A teaching sequence from initial fraction concepts through the addition of unlike fractions. In Marilyn N. Suydam (Ed.), *Developing computational skills*, NCTM 1978 Yearbook. Reston, Va.: National Council of Teachers of Mathematics, 1978.

Ellis, L. C. A diagnostic study of whole number computations of certain elementary students (Doctoral dissertation, Louisiana State University and Agricultural and Mechanical College, 1972). *Dissertation Abstracts International*, November 1972, *33*, 2234A.

Engle, C. D., & Lerch, H. H. A comparison of first-grade children's abilities on two types of arithmetical practice exercises. *School Science and Mathematics*, April 1971, *71*, 327–334.

Faires, D. M. Computation with decimal fractions in the sequence of number development (Doctoral dissertation, Wayne State University, 1962). *Dissertation Abstracts*, May 1963, *23*, 4183.

Flournoy, M. F. The effectiveness of instruction in mental arithmetic. *Elementary School Journal*, November 1954, *55*, 148–153.

Flournoy, F. Children's success with two methods of estimating the quotient figure. *Arithmetic Teacher*, March 1959, *6*, 100–104. (a)

Flournoy, F. A consideration of pupils' success with two methods for placing the decimal point in the quotient. *School Science and Mathematics*, June 1959, *59*, 445–455. (b)

Fullerton, C. K. A comparison of the effectiveness of two prescribed methods of teaching multiplication of whole numbers (Doctoral dissertation, State University of Iowa, 1955). *Dissertation Abstracts*, November 1955, *15*, 2126–2127.

Gagné, R. M. *The conditions of learning* (2nd ed.). New York: Holt, Rinehart & Winston, 1970.

Gelman, R., & Tucker, M. F. Further investigations of the young child's conception of number. *Child Development*, March 1975, *46*, 167–175.

Gibb, E. G. Response to questions for discussion at the conference on basic mathematical skills and learning. In *Volume I: Contributed Position Papers, Conference on Basic Mathematical Skills and Learning, Euclid, Ohio*. Washington, D.C.: National Institute of Education, 1975.

Glennon, V. J. A study of the growth and mastery of certain basic mathematical understandings on seven educational levels. *Harvard Educational Review*, Winter 1949, *19*, 62–64.

Gray, R. F. An experiment in the teaching of introductory multiplication. *Arithmetic Teacher*, March 1965, *12*, 199–203.

Green, G. A. A comparison of two approaches, area and finding a part of, and two instructional materials, diagrams and manipulative aids, on multiplication of fractional numbers in grade five (Doctoral dissertation, University of Michigan, 1969). *Dissertation Abstracts International*, August 1970, *31*, 676A–677A.

Groen, G. J., & Poll, M. Subtraction and the solution of open sentence problems. *Journal of Experimental Child Psychology,* October 1973, *16,* 292–302.

Grossnickle, F. E. How to estimate the quotient figure in long division. *Elementary School Journal,* December 1931, *32,* 299–306.

Grossnickle, F. E. Types of errors in division of decimals. *Elementary School Journal,* November 1941, *42,* 184–194. *See also:* Kinds of errors in division of decimals and their constancy. *Journal of Educational Research,* October 1943, *37,* 110–117.

Grossnickle, F. E., & Snyder, J. H. Constancy of errors to basic facts in the fundamental operations in arithmetic. *Journal of Educational Research,* January 1939, *32,* 336–344.

Grouws, D. A. Differential performance of third-grade children in solving open sentences of four types (Doctoral dissertation, University of Wisconsin, 1971). *Dissertation Abstracts International,* January 1972, *32,* 3860A. *See also:* Open sentences: Some instructional considerations from research. *Arithmetic Teacher,* November 1972, *19,* 595–599. *See also:* Solution methods used in solving addition and subtraction open sentences. *Arithmetic Teacher,* March 1974, *21,* 255–261.

Grouws, D. A., & Good, T. L. Factors associated with third- and fourth-grade children's performance in solving multiplication and division sentences. *Journal for Research in Mathematics Education,* May 1976, *7,* 155–171.

Grumbling, B. N. An experimental study of the effectiveness of instruction in mental computation in grade IV (Doctoral dissertation, University of Northern Colorado, 1970). *Dissertation Abstracts International,* February 1971, *31,* 3775A–3776A.

Guiler, W. S. Difficulties in fractions encountered by ninth-grade pupils. *Elementary School Journal,* November 1945, *46,* 146–156.

Guiler, W. S. Difficulties in decimals encountered by ninth-grade pupils. *Elementary School Journal,* March 1946, *46,* 384–393. (a)

Guiler, W. S. Difficulties in percentage encountered by ninth-grade pupils. *Elementary School Journal,* June 1946, *46,* 563–573. (b)

Hall, K. D. An experimental study of two methods of instruction for mastering multiplication facts at the third-grade level (Doctoral dissertation, Duke University, 1967). *Dissertation Abstracts,* August 1967, *28,* 390A–391A.

Hamrin, J. M. Information-processing models for addition, subtraction, and multiplication in the mentally retarded and non-retarded (Doctoral dissertation, Columbia University, 1974). *Dissertation Abstracts International,* April 1975, *35,* 5155B–5156B.

Hartung, M. L. Estimating the quotient in division (a critical analysis of research). *Arithmetic Teacher,* April 1957, *4,* 100–111.

Henkin, L. Skills and skills. In *Volume I: Contributed Position Papers, Conference on Basic Mathematical Skills and Learning. Euclid, Ohio.* Washington, D.C.: National Institute of Education, 1975.

Hilker, D. L. The effects of increasing addition skill on self-concept in children (Doctoral dissertation, University of Maryland, 1976). *Dissertation Abstracts International,* December 1976, *37,* 3078B.

Hohlfeld, J. F. Effectiveness of an immediate feedback device for learning basic multiplication facts (Doctoral dissertation, Indiana University, 1973). *Dissertation Abstracts International,* February 1974, *34,* 4563A.

Hughes, F. G. A comparison of two methods of teaching multidigit multiplication (Doctoral dissertation, University of Tennessee, 1973). *Dissertation Abstracts International,* November 1973, *34,* 2450A–2461A. *See also:* Hughes, F. G., & Burns, P. C. Two methods of teaching multidigit multiplication. *Elementary School Journal,* April 1975, *75,* 452–457.

Hutchings, L. B. An examination, across a wide range of socioeconomic circumstance, of a format for field research of experimental numerical computation algorithms, an instrument for measuring computational power under any concise numerical addition algorithm, two experimental numerical addition algorithms and equivalent practice with the conventional addition algorithm (Doctoral dissertation, Syracuse University, 1972). *Dissertation Abstracts International,* March 1973, *33,* 4678A.

Ibe, M. D. The effects of using estimation in learning a unit of sixth grade mathematics (Doctoral dissertation, University of Toronto, 1971). *Dissertation Abstracts International,* March 1973, *33,* 5036A.

Ilg, F., & Ames, L. B. Developmental trends in arithmetic. *Journal of Genetic Psychology,* September 1951, *79,* 3–28.

Jerman, M. Some strategies for solving simple multiplication combinations. *Journal for Research in Mathematics Education,* March 1970, *1,* 95–128.

Jones, W. L. An experimental comparison of the effects of the subtractive algorithm versus the distributive algorithm on computation and understanding of division (Doctoral dissertation, University of Maryland, 1976). *Dissertation Abstracts International,* December 1976, *37,* 3395A–3396A.

Khan, A. Children's use of perceptual groupings in counting (Doctoral dissertation, University of Oregon, 1972). *Dissertation Abstracts International,* March 1973, *33,* 4944A.

Kratzer, R. O. A comparison of initially teaching division employing the distributive and Greenwood algorithms with the aid of a manipulative material (Doctoral dissertation, New York University, 1971). *Dissertation Abstracts International,* April 1972, *32,* 5672A. See *also:* Kratzer, R. O., & Willoughby, S. S. A comparison of initially teaching division employing the distributive and Greenwood algorithms with the aid of a manipulative material. *Journal for Research in Mathematics Education,* November 1973, *4,* 197–204.

Kuhn, J. N. A comparison of the effectiveness of the *power of ten* and *same decimal unit* methods as applied to introductory work in the division of decimals (Doctoral dissertation, State University of Iowa, 1954). *Dissertation Abstracts,* October 1954, *14,* 1644.

Lankford, F. G., Jr. *Some computational strategies of seventh grade pupils.* Charlottesville, Va.: University of Virginia, 1972. (ERIC Document Reproduction Service No. ED 069 496)

Logan, H. L. A study of the effects of examples, non-examples and a mix of the two on computational skills in subtraction for systematic and non-systematic error groups among fourth grade children (Doctoral dissertation, University of Iowa, 1976). *Dissertation Abstracts International,* November 1976, *37,* 2621A.

Luchins, A. A., & Luchins, E. S. New experimental attempts at preventing mechanization in problem solving. *Journal of General Psychology,* April 1950, *42,* 279–297.

Maertens, N. W., Jones, R. C., & Waite, A. Elemental groupings help children perceive cardinality: A two-phase research study. *Journal for Research in Mathematics Education,* May 1977, *8,* 181–193.

Marotta, G. A. A survey of the teaching of the basic addition facts in elementary school mathematics in the United States (Doctoral dissertation, Rutgers University—The State University of New Jersey, 1973). *Dissertation Abstracts International,* January 1974, *34,* 3700A–3701A.

McConnell, T. R. *Discovery and authoritative identification in the learning of children* (University of Iowa Studies in Education, No. 9). Iowa City: University of Iowa, 1934.

National Council of Supervisors of Mathematics. *Position paper on basic mathematical skills.* Minneapolis: Author, 1976. (ERIC Document Reproduction Service No. ED 139 654)

Nelson, N. Z. The effect of the teaching of estimation on arithmetic achievement in the fourth and sixth grades (Doctoral dissertation, University of Pittsburgh, 1966). *Dissertation Abstracts,* June 1967, *27,* 4172A.

Nichols, E. J. A comparison of two methods of instruction in multiplication and division for third-grade pupils (Doctoral dissertation, University of California, Los Angeles, 1971). *Dissertation Abstracts International,* May 1972, *32,* 6011A.

Norman, M. Three methods of teaching basic division facts (Doctoral dissertation, State University of Iowa, 1955). *Dissertation Abstracts,* November 1955, *15,* 2134.

Novillis, C. F. An analysis of the fraction concept into a hierarchy of selected subconcepts and the testing of the hierarchical dependencies. *Journal for Research in Mathematics Education,* May 1976, *7,* 131–144.

O'Brien, T. C. An experimental investigation of a new approach to the teaching of decimals

(Doctoral dissertation, New York University, 1967). *Dissertation Abstracts*, May 1968, *28*, 4541A–4542A.

Olander, H. T. Transfer of learning in simple addition and subtraction. I. *Elementary School Journal*, January 1931, *31*, 358–369. II. *Elementary School Journal*, February 1931, *31*, 427–437.

Overman, J. R. An experimental study of the effect of the method of instruction on transfer in arithmetic. *Elementary School Journal*, November 1930, *31*, 183–190.

Pace, R. E. The effects of tangible reinforcement on the efficiency in which E.M.R. pupils memorize selected multiplication facts (Doctoral dissertation, Brigham Young University, 1967). *Dissertation Abstracts*, December 1967, *28*, 2100A–2101A.

Paull, D. R. The ability to estimate in mathematics (Doctoral dissertation, Columbia University, 1971). *Dissertation Abstracts International*, January 1972, *32*, 3567A.

Peck, D. M., & Jencks, S. M. Missing-addend problems. *School Science and Mathematics*, December 1976, *76*, 647–661.

Phillips, E. R., & Kane, R. B. Validating learning hierarchies for sequencing mathematical tasks in elementary school mathematics. *Journal for Research in Mathematics Education*, May 1973, *4*, 141–151.

Piaget, J. *The child's conception of number.* London: Routledge & Kegan Paul, 1952.

Pincus, M. An investigation into the effectiveness of two methods of instruction in addition and subtraction facts (Doctoral dissertation, New York University, 1956). *Dissertation Abstracts*, August 1956, *16*, 1415.

Punn, A. K. The effects of using three modes of representation in teaching multiplication facts on the achievement and attitudes of third grade pupils (Doctoral dissertation, University of Denver, 1973). *Dissertation Abstracts International*, May 1974, *34*, 6954A–6955A.

Rathmell, E. C. The effects of multibase grouping and early or late introduction of base representations on the mastery learning of base and place value numeration in grade one (Doctoral dissertation, University of Michigan, 1972). *Dissertation Abstracts International*, May 1973, *33*, 6071A–6072A.

Rea, R. E., & French, J. Payoff in increased instructional time and enrichment activities. *Arithmetic Teacher*, December 1972, *19*, 663–668.

Rea, R. E., & Reys, R. E. Mathematical competencies of entering kindergarteners. *Arithmetic Teacher*, January 1970, *17*, 65–74.

Rising, G. R. What are the basic skills of mathematics? In *Volume I: Contributed Position Papers, Conference on Basic Mathematical Skills and Learning, Euclid, Ohio.* Washington, D.C.: National Institute of Education, 1975.

Roberts, G. H. The failure strategies of third grade arithmetic pupils. *Arithmetic Teacher*, May 1968, *15*, 442–446.

Sandefur, E. W. Experimental study of two methods of drill for mastering addition and subtraction facts (Doctoral dissertation, Duke University, 1965). *Dissertation Abstracts*, February 1966, *26*, 4401.

Sawyer, R. C. *Evaluation of alternative methods of teaching subtraction of integers in junior high school.* 1973. (ERIC Document Reproduction Service No. ED 073 944) *See also:* Evaluation of alternative methods of teaching subtraction of integers in two junior high schools (Doctoral dissertation, University of Idaho, 1973). *Dissertation Abstracts International*, May 1974, *34*, 6958A.

Schrankler, W. J. A study of the effectiveness of four methods for teaching multiplication of whole numbers in grade four. (Doctoral dissertation, University of Minnesota, 1966). *Dissertation Abstracts*, June 1967, *27*, 4055A.

Schwartz, A. N. Assessment of mathematical concepts of five-year-old children. *Journal of Experimental Education*, Spring 1969, *37*, 67–74.

Shafer, B. L. A comparison of three sequences of methods for teaching the solving of simultaneous linear equations in ninth grade algebra (Doctoral dissertation, Ohio State University, 1975). *Dissertation Abstracts International*, February 1976, *36*, 5179A.

Siegel, L. S. Heterogeneity and spatial factors as determinants of numeration ability. *Child Development*, June 1974, *45*, 532–534.

Smith, C. W., Jr. A study of constant errors in subtraction and in the application of selected principles of the decimal numeration system made by third and fourth grade students (Doctoral dissertation, Wayne State University, 1968). *Dissertation Abstracts International*, September 1969, *30*, 1084A.

Smith, R. F. A diagnostic study of pupil performance on a test of skills relevant to the mastery of place-value tasks (Doctoral dissertation, Fordham University, 1972). *Dissertation Abstracts International*, July 1972, *33*, 87A–88A.

Sparks, J. N. *Design paradigms*. University Park: Pennsylvania State University, 1967. (Multilith)

Spencer, J. E. Intertask interference in primary arithmetic (Doctoral dissertation, University of California, Berkeley, 1967). *Dissertation Abstracts*, January 1968, *28*, 2570A–2571A.

Stenger, D. J. An experimental comparison of two methods of teaching the addition and subtraction of common fractions in grade five (Doctoral dissertation, University of Cincinnati, 1971). *Dissertation Abstracts International*, January 1972, *32*, 3676A.

Sutherlin, W. N. The pocket calculator: Its effect on the acquisition of decimal estimation skills at intermediate grade levels (Doctoral dissertation, University of Oregon, 1976). *Dissertation Abstracts International*, March 1977, *37*, 5663A.

Suydam, M. N. *State-of-the-art review on calculators: Their use in education*. Columbus, Ohio: Calculator Information Center, 1978.

Suydam, M. N., & Dessart, D. J. *Classroom ideas from research on computational skills*. Reston, Va.: National Council of Teachers of Mathematics, 1976.

Suydam, M. N., & Weaver, J. F. *Using research: A key to elementary school mathematics*. Columbus, Ohio: ERIC Center for Science, Mathematics, and Environmental Education, 1975.

Swenson, E. J. Organization and generalization as factors in learning, transfer, and retroactive inhibition. In *Learning theory in school situations* (University of Minnesota Studies in Education, No. 2). Minneapolis: University of Minnesota Press, 1949.

Thiele, C. L. *The contribution of generalization to the learning of the addition facts* (Contributions to Education, No. 763). New York: Teachers College, Columbia University, 1939.

Thorndike, E. L. The psychology of drill in arithmetic: The amount of practice. *Journal of Educational Psychology*, April 1921, *12*, 183–194.

Trafton, P. R. The effects of two initial instructional sequences on the learning of the subtraction algorithms in grade three (Doctoral dissertation, University of Michigan, 1970). *Dissertation Abstracts International*, February 1971, *31*, 4049A–4050A.

Uprichard, A. E., & Collura, C. *The effect of emphasizing mathematical structure in the acquisition of whole number computation skills (addition and subtraction) by seven- and eight-year-olds: A clinical investigation*. 1974. (ERIC Document Reproduction Service No. ED 088 716)

Uprichard, A. E., & Phillips, E. R. An intraconcept analysis of rational number addition: A validation study. *Journal for Research in Mathematics Education*, 1977, *8*, 7–16.

Weaver, J. F. Some factors associated with pupils' performance levels on simple open addition and subtraction sentences. *Arithmetic Teacher*, November 1971, *18*, 513–519. *See also:* The ability of first-, second-, and third-grade pupils to identify open addition and subtraction sentences for which no solution exists within the set of whole numbers. *School Science and Mathematics*, November 1972, *72*, 679–691. *See also:* The symmetric property of the equality relation and young children's ability to solve open addition and subtraction sentences. *Journal for Research in Mathematics Education*, January 1973, *4*, 45–56.

Wheatley, G. H. A comparison of two methods of column addition. *Journal for Research in Mathematics Education*, May 1976, *7*, 145–154.

Wheeler, L. E. The relationship of multiple embodiments of the regrouping concept to children's performance in solving multidigit addition and subtraction examples (Doctoral dissertation, Indiana University, 1971). *Dissertation Abstracts International,* February 1972, *32,* 4260A.

Wilburn, D. B. A method of self-instruction for learning the easier addition and subtraction combinations in grade I. *Elementary School Journal,* January 1942, *42,* 371–380.

Willson, G. H. A comparison of decimal-common fraction sequence with conventional sequence for fifth grade arithmetic (Doctoral dissertation, University of Arizona, 1969). *Dissertation Abstracts International,* December 1969, *30,* 1762A. *See also:* Decimal-common fraction sequence versus conventional sequence. *School Science and Mathematics,* October 1972, *72,* 589–592.

Wilson, G. M. New standards in arithmetic: A controlled experiment in supervision. *Journal of Educational Research,* December 1930, *22,* 351–360.

Woods, S. S., Resnick, L. B., & Groen, G. J. An experimental test of five process models for subtraction. *Journal of Educational Psychology,* February 1975, *67,* 17–21.

Woody, C. *Some investigations resulting from the testing program in arithmetic: An investigation to determine the transfer effects of three different methods of teaching three different types of examples in two-place addition* (Indiana University School of Education Bulletin, No. 6). Bloomington: Indiana University, 1930.

9

Concept and Principle Learning

Larry Sowder
Northern Illinois University

E VERYONE agrees that the learning of concepts and principles is important, but there is considerable variation in how the words *concept* and *principle* are used. Accordingly, the first part of this chapter deals with the meanings that are associated with these terms. An overview of typical research variables is presented next, and a short section on trends and issues in the learning of concepts and principles follows. The final section of the chapter suggests areas of research that need to be investigated.

DEFINITIONS

Concepts

Flavell (1970) considered several definitions of the term *concept* and summarized his search by noting that "their most important similarity is their inadequacy" (p. 983). Perhaps our best starting point is the view adopted by Pikas: a concept has been formed when a common response is given to dissimilar stimuli (1966, p. 228). A student who says "primes" and points to 5, 17, and 109 in a list containing 27, 39, and 119 would certainly be regarded as having formed a concept. The attractiveness of Pikas's view is that the giving of a common response to dissimilar stimuli seems to lie in the intersection of different opinions about what a concept is. Yet, the view also allows people to interpret it to fit their own ideas of the definition of a concept. For example, those who feel that a concept is a mental construct can interpret "response" to fit that meaning; a model of

The Editorial Panel, John Dossey, James Lockwood, and my colleagues at Northern Illinois University—Jeffrey Barnett, George Bright, and Ed Silver—gave very helpful reactions to earlier versions of this chapter. Any shortcomings remaining are undoubtedly due to my failure to heed their suggestions.

a trapezoid will arouse some internal entity. Those who feel that a verbal label is a necessary part of a concept can interpret the view to mean that the response will be the proper word; students will say "trapezoid" when they see a model of a trapezoid.

Since most concepts used in mathematics do have verbal labels associated with them, it is convenient to give examples of concepts in terms of these labels. Each of these terms deals with a concept: point, polygon, real number, function, equation. "Pythagoras," however, is not associated with a concept in the spirit of Pikas's view. Several dissimilar questions might indeed be answered correctly by responding "Pythagoras," but the intended meaning of "dissimilar stimuli" is "examples." One can give several examples of polygons or functions, but there was only one Pythagoras. (One way out of this possible confusion is to speak of *singular concepts*—concepts that have only one example. See, for example, Henderson, 1970.)

For the researcher in mathematics education, a more important question than "Precisely how shall I define 'concept'?" is "How shall I decide whether the concept has been learned?" Researchers in concept learning must know what they will accept as evidence that a concept has been learned. Klausmeier, Ghatala, and Frayer (1974), for example, offer a model of conceptual learning and development that would enable one to speak in operational terms about *levels* of concept learning and that could improve communication among researchers. Here is a brief description of the evidence of concept learning at each of their four levels:

Level 1 (Concrete). The student recognizes an example that has been experienced earlier. (The child says "trapezoid" when shown a trapezoid seen yesterday.)

Level 2 (Identity). In addition to Level 1, the student recognizes an example encountered earlier even though the example "is observed from a different spatio-temporal perspective or sensed in a different modality" (Klausmeier, 1976, p. 8). (The child still calls the figure a trapezoid, even when the figure is turned sideways, for example, on a later occasion.)

Level 3 (Classificatory). In addition to Levels 1 and 2, the student can distinguish between examples and nonexamples. (The child picks out all the trapezoids from a collection of different figures.)

Level 4 (Formal). In addition to Levels 1, 2, and 3, the student can state a definition of the concept.

Concepts that have examples in the child's environment may require little instruction for attaining the first two levels, as Klausmeier notes (1976, p. 18). A verbal label must be present at the formal level; it may be present at any level. It must be emphasized that Level 4 includes more than the statement of a definition; evidence of understanding that goes beyond rote recitation of a definition is required. A definition of a concept is not the concept, even though the definition may play an important role in teaching the concept.

The level at which one would expect the student to produce an example is not obvious in the preceding model. Since giving an example is a reasonable expectation with many mathematical concepts, it might be helpful to make explicit the following level and insert it into the model:

Level 3.5 (Production). In addition to Levels 1–3, the student can give (a) any example and (b) a new example of the concept.

Henderson (1970) discusses an excellent taxonomy of concepts. Let us examine just one possible pair of subcategories: concrete vs. abstract concepts. Concrete concepts are those with examples that are physically real —for example, algebra book, ruler, geoboard. Abstract concepts are those that do not have such examples. Most of the concepts encountered in mathematics—fractional number, complex number, infinity, line, polygon, randomness, and so on—are, in fact, abstract concepts. Numbers and geometric figures, however, do admit physically real representations— sets of objects, colored rods, pieces of string, soda straw figures, drawings —that give them an air of concreteness. Since such concrete representations of abstract concepts often exist, a dichotomy more serviceable to a researcher might be based on familiarity. The fractional number ¾ might be abstract (and unfamiliar) to second graders but quite familiar to high school students. Similarly, a student struggling with the unfamiliar concept of "group" may profit from exposure to the more familiar (but also abstract) additive group of integers.

Readers accustomed to mathematical precision may be uneasy because no careful definition of *concept* has been given. For those readers, two definitions, chosen as examples with no assertion of their superiority, are given: (a) "A concept consists of a set of objects, symbols, or events (referents) which have been grouped together because they share some common characteristics (attributes). Concepts are usually referenced by some concept name" (Merrill & Wood, 1974, p. 19); and (b) ". . . we define a concept as ordered information about the properties of one or more things —objects, events, or processes—that enables any particular thing or class of things to be differentiated from and also related to other things or classes of things" (Klausmeier et al., 1974, p. 4).

Principles

A principle is a relationship involving two or more concepts. For example, the following statement expresses a principle, since it relates the concepts of the parabola and eccentricity of a conic: If the eccentricity of a conic is 1, then the conic is a parabola. Any theorem gives a relationship among concepts and so could be called a statement of a principle. Although there is little agreement about the meaning of "concept," there is much more agreement that "principle" refers to a relationship involving two or more concepts, although some writers use terms such as *rule* or *generalization*. By using "rule" in the sense of "rule-governed," however, some writers—notably Scandura (1971, 1976)—ascribe a central role to rule learning and envelop concept and principle learning, among other types, under that rubric. For example, Scandura asserts that "all mathematical behavior is a rule-governed activity and the basic underlying constructs are rules" (1976, p. 235). To Scandura, "concepts are simply rules in which each stimulus in a class is paired with a common response" (1976, p. 228).

Researchers need operational evidence that a principle has been learned, just as they need evidence that a concept has been learned. However, there seems to be no published parallel to the levels of attainment for concepts described by Klausmeier et al. (1974). A parallel can easily be hypothesized, however, by imitating part of their hierarchy. Suppose a statement of the principle has an "if" part and a "then" part (e.g., *if* a triangle is equilateral, *then* it is equiangular).

Level 1. The learner observes the *then* part in a specific instance of the principle. (The learner notices the congruent angles in an equilateral triangle.)

Level 2. The learner applies the *then* part to a new instance (generalizes). (The learner declares that the angles are congruent in another, not necessarily equilateral, triangle.)

Level 3. The learner classifies a situation as satisfying or not satisfying the *if* part (generalizes correctly). (The learner checks for congruent sides before asserting that the angles are congruent.)

Level 4. The learner produces a specific instance. (The learner sketches an equilateral triangle and then asserts congruence of the angles.)

Level 5. The learner states the principle.

In order to be judged proficient at one level, the learner would be required to exhibit proficiency at all lower-numbered levels in this hypothesized description. In particular, mere verbalization of the principle should not be accepted as indicating proficiency at the lower-numbered levels.

Fuzziness

Even at the risk of belaboring terminology, there is perhaps enough fuzziness in the general use of the words *concept* and *principle* to justify further commentary. People sometimes use "concept" in the sense of "ability to use" or "ability to carry out an algorithm for," as in "the student has no concept of fractions," or "the student has a good concept of multiplication." Such ambiguous use of terms sometimes occurs even in research reports, as when a "concepts posttest" actually involves the statement or application of principles. Increasingly, however, mathematics education researchers are treating the terms *concept* and *principle* in the technical sense of this chapter.

Principles necessarily involve concepts; concepts may involve principles. For example, commutativity of addition of whole numbers, commutativity of multiplication of real numbers, and commutativity of composition of translations are just three of many principles that may be subsumed under the concept of commutativity. Or, the principles stated in the Pythagorean theorem, the law of cosines, and Parseval's identity might suggest a concept called Pythagorean relationships. When a concept is built from principles, it may not be clear what is meant by "example" or "instance." In a further effort to clarify terminology, Cooney, Davis, and Henderson (1975) suggest that a specific case of a principle be called an *instance* of the principle, but any one of the many cases that may be associated with a concept would be called an *example* of the concept. Hence, 3 + 6 = 6 + 3 would be an instance of commutativity of addition (a principle), and commutativity of addition would be an example of commutativity (a concept). These restrictions of "example" to concepts and of "instance" to principles are not widespread. In most contexts "example" and "instance" can be used interchangeably without confusion.

Equating a concept with its definition can lead to some confusion. If a particular concept is defined by a word statement, and thus as a relationship among other concepts, one might argue that such a concept is a principle. Certainly a concept can be *learned* from a definition (an example of Gagné's "rule learning," 1970), but that does not mean that the concept *is* the word definition. Similarly, a principle should not be equated with a verbal statement of the principle, even though the verbal statement may play some role in the learning of the principle. Some additional guidance to the distinction between concepts and principles lies in an analogy with the components of a formal mathematical system: undefined terms, defined terms, postulates, and theorems. In this chapter, concepts are analogous to the undefined and defined terms, whereas principles are analogous to the postulates and theorems.

As a final point, principles provide the mathematical rationale for algorithms. Properties of operations, laws of exponents, statements about equivalent fractions—all principles—are used in algorithms even though their presence may not be continually emphasized. For instance, distributivity of multiplication over addition (a principle) lies behind the usual algorithms for calculating 3×21 or $(x + 5)(x + 3)$. Algorithms can be learned as rote procedures, as the SMSG Panel of Research (1972) points out while arguing against such learning (see also the chapter by Suydam & Dessart). But algorithms can also be learned by building on concepts and on principles like the distributive, commutative, and associative properties. Most mathematics teachers would be disappointed if a child made a passing score on an addition-of-fractions test but had no idea of what "add" means and no grasp of the principles of equivalent fractions underlying the algorithm. One can forcefully argue that a skill without a foundation in appropriate concepts and principles is an empty skill.

TYPICAL RESEARCH VARIABLES
IN CONCEPT LEARNING STUDIES

The following descriptions of variables in research on concept and principle learning are neither exhaustive nor the result of carefully sieved selections. The wealth of reported studies on concept learning in the psychological literature alone precludes a comprehensive review and analysis in this chapter. Excellent reviews of research in concept learning, although of course without an orientation toward mathematics, can be found in Bourne, Ekstrand, and Dominowski (1971); Clark (1971); Klausmeier et al. (1974); and the periodic reviews in *Annual Review of Psychology* (e.g., Bourne & Dominowski, 1972, or Neimark & Santa, 1975). Or see Flavell (1970) for a Piagetian-oriented review of studies on concept development.

Concept learning is treated in this section; principle learning will be covered in the next section, but in less detail, since the variables are much the same. The discussion on concept-learning studies is organized around task variables, treatment (or instructional) variables, subject variables, and dependent variables; occasionally a specific variable might well have been placed in some other category. Some variables have "obvious" consequences that have been verified, but then at one time it was "obvious" that a heavy stone should fall faster than a lighter one.

Task Variables

In the 1960s many of the studies dealing with concept learning were engendered by the now classic work of Bruner, Goodnow, and Austin (1956). The following task variables seem to have been foci: task content, the structure of definition, types of task learning, and the number of relevant or irrelevant attributes. A mode-of-representation variable has been added as another task variable. This lengthy catalogue may be made more endurable by considering the sample task in Figure 1. What concept is suggested by the information there? (This task will be referred to throughout this section on task variables.)

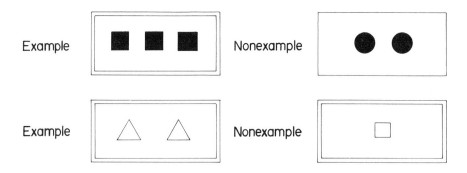

Figure 1. An example of the classicial psychological concept-learning task.

What task content? The content of a task in a typical study of the type conducted by Bruner et al. involves a collection of cards with different numbers of differently colored shapes on them, perhaps with distinctive borders. (Dimensions such as number, color, and shape are called attributes.) The concept "two red triangles" might describe a subset of the cards, which then serve as examples of the concept. The remaining cards are nonexamples of the concept. Except to the most naive subject, a task based on such a domain is clearly contrived and artificial; however, such material does give well-defined, easily replicable tasks to which subjects probably bring a uniform background.

However, tasks that are, or closely resemble, typical school tasks can also be used. For example, the tasks investigated by Shumway (1971, 1974, 1977) involved numerical-algebraic material, and Trudnak (1975) and Bailey (1975) used concepts from probability. There is an "in between" area of contrived tasks that seem to be very schoollike—for example, Dossey and Henderson's "prifor," a natural number that is either prime or has a units digit of four (1974, p. 10). The content of such tasks is apt to be "real" enough for subjects of limited background to regard the concepts as being a legitimate part of mathematics.

Extrapolating across domains of task content may be risky. Only limited and tentative direct comparisons of performance on artificial tasks and performance on "real" tasks are available (Securro & Wallis, 1971; Sowder, 1975b). Differences may occur even with schoollike tasks; performance on geometric tasks may be higher than that on similar numerical tasks (Dossey & Henderson, 1974).

What structure of definition? The logical form of the definition of a concept has also received a great deal of attention. An example card for a "two red triangles" concept must contain shapes that are two in number *and* red *and* triangular. This last statement makes clear the conjunctive rule. Regular polygons—polygons that are equilateral *and* equiangular—

give an example of a conjunctive concept in mathematics. This way of looking at concepts suggests an analysis according to the logical structure of the definition (or rule) for the concept. (Or, as in the psychological studies, one generates a concept by making a rule from some choice of attributes and a logical connective.) Concepts can then be categorized as to whether their rules are conjunctive (. . . and . . .), inclusive disjunctive (. . . or . . . or both), exclusive disjunctive (. . . or . . . but not both), negative (not . . .), conditional (if . . . then . . .), and so on. The concept in Figure 1 follows a disjunctive rule. The difficulty of learning concepts of different logical structures is usually found to follow this order (easiest to hardest): conjunctive, exclusive disjunctive, inclusive disjuntive, conditional (e.g., Neisser & Weene, 1962). The most common of these structures in mathematics seems to be the conjunctive form, although one can certainly find examples of other forms: a polynomial is a monomial *or* a sum of monomials (exclusive disjunctive).

Another set of concepts—the set of *relational* concepts— noted by Bruner et al. (1956, p. 43), has been somewhat disparaged by Henderson (1970, p. 172) but seems important to others (Carroll, 1964). Complementary angles, orthogonal vectors, proportion, "less than," and "is congruent to" might suggest relational concepts, since examples for each involve a particular relationship not describable with the usual logical connectives. The values of the relevant attributes in a relational concept may vary. For instance, the degree measures of the angles in different pairs of supplementary angles may all be different, and yet in each pair the sum is 180. It is this *relationship* of the values that is the same from example to example rather than the presence of such particular values as "red" or "equilateral." In view of their frequency in mathematics, it is unfortunate that relational concepts have not been investigated as extensively as concepts describable with logical connectives. Only a few studies have given attention to relational concepts (e.g., Braley, 1963; Bruner & Kenney, 1966; Catanzano & Godwin, 1977).

What type of task learning? The psychologists' work with rules and attributes over artificial domains has led them to three types of task learning; these types vary in what information is given about the rule form and the relevant attributes. Let us consider a task in an artificial domain such as that suggested earlier. Suppose the subjects are to learn a concept based on examples and nonexamples shown to them. The logical form of the rule can be specified ahead of time; then a subject must ascertain only the relevant attributes. After Figure 1 was described as illustrating a disjunctive concept, all that remained was to find the correct combination of attributes: Is it "shaded or squares"? or Is it "shaded or triangles"? This type of learning is called *attribute identification.* Otherwise, the pertinent attributes (say, triangular shapes, three shapes) may be identified ahead of time, with the subject's task being to determine what logical connective or other relationship enables one to distinguish between examples and nonexamples (Is it "three shapes *and* triangular shapes"?; Is it "if triangles, then three"?). This type of task learning is usually called *rule learning* (note the narrow context; Gagné, 1970, uses "rule learning" in quite a different sense, for example). Finally, information about neither the attributes nor the rule need be given to subjects, as when Figure 1 was first presented; such task learning is usually called *complete learning*. See Haygood & Bourne, 1965, for a more complete treatment of these types of task learning.)

How many attributes? The number of *relevant* attributes involved in a concept is naturally related to the ease with which the concept can be learned. There were two relevant attributes in Figure 1—shape and number of shapes. The more attributes one has to heed, the harder the concept is to learn. The concept of "triangle" should be more easily learned than that of "regular polygon," for instance. Yet the number of *irrelevant* attributes present in examples of a concept may also affect the learning of the concept, especially if some values always appear or appear frequently (cf. Shumway & White's "prevalence," 1977). If, for instance, young learners see as examples of triangles only drawings in red ink of right triangles with one leg always parallel to the top of the paper, they may not be certain whether an equilateral triangle drawn in black ink in some other orientation is indeed a triangle. The fact that scarcely any reader would be mystified if asked to sketch an "upside-down trapezoid" is another illustration of the influence of prevalent irrelevant attributes: drawings of trapezoids ordinarily have the parallel sides horizontal and the longer parallel side at the bottom; yet both of these attributes are irrelevant to a figure's being a trapezoid. Klausmeier et al. (1974) note that in instructional settings one may naturally control the number of irrelevant variables by using more abstract representations (p. 208). For example, a plastic triangular region might serve as a model for a triangle—with the accompanying irrelevant attributes of being a region and having thickness—whereas a drawing of a triangle or the even more abstract word "triangle" with a definition might enable one to ignore the attributes of thickness and possessing interior.

What mode of representation? As suggested above, the concept of triangle may be communicated in several ways: concretely (as a plastic triangular region), pictorially (as a drawing), and symbolically (as a definition). These different modes of representation are also possible with many other mathematical concepts. The spirit of the times, influenced by Piaget (e.g., 1974) and by Bruner (1964) through his enactive, iconic, and symbolic levels of knowing, decrees that experience with concrete, or at least pictorial, representations should precede symbolic work, especially with young learners. The research findings for studies involving the concrete mode (manipulatives) are mixed, as noted by Kieren (1969), Wilkerson (1974), and Higgins (1976).

Treatment (or Instructional) Variables

Many of the task variables previously cited were drawn from the psychological literature. In contrast, the variables in this section come mainly from school-oriented studies.

Attainment or assimilation? This first variable might well have been joined with the type-of-task-learning variable. The version here, however, is more directly related to school situations than the psychologists' types-of-task learning. An inductive approach to the learning of a concept is common in the literature: several examples and perhaps nonexamples are presented with the criterion being the proper classification of new examples or possibly a verbal description or definition, as in Figure 1. This approach will be called *concept attainment.* Note that concept attainment corresponds to the psychologists' "complete learning" mentioned earlier. Gagné's (1970) concept learning is the same as concept attainment, with the classification of new examples and nonexamples as the criterion. "Induction" and "discovery" are terms sometimes used instead of "concept attainment."

One may criticize a concept-attainment task as being unnaturally contrived. The typical concept-attainment setting *is* more structured than that in which many concepts are naturally developed; for example, dogs and nondogs are not systematically paraded past a young child. Pikas (1966, chap. 6) points out that concept attainment in experimental settings is actually a type of problem solving. As in Figure 1, subjects know that there is some relationship among the (well-known) attributes and that their job is to find it. Hence, "concept attainment" is actually (to Pikas) a misnomer. In contrast, the act through which classes are formed—*concept formation*—is the proper province of study in Pikas's view. In a related study Collis (1971) devised a card-sorting technique for studying the evolution of selected mathematical concepts. Students periodically sort, as they see fit, a set of cards with examples of concepts on them; the results are interpreted in terms of the concepts embedded in subsets of the cards. This concept-evolution technique would seem to fall, in terms of naturalness, somewhere between a study of the elusive concept formation and the fabricated concept-attainment task. Describing a concept-attainment task as fabricated is not intended to be disparaging; much of what takes place in instructional settings is fabricated by design.

A few school concepts are usually taught to older learners through concept-attainment approaches. Alternate interior angles and proof are examples of concepts that are most often taught through examples and nonexamples. Concept attainment does not, however, occur as often in instructional settings with older students as *concept assimilation* does (Ausubel & Robinson, 1969). In concept-assimilation approaches a definition or verbal description of the concept plays a central role, perhaps accompanied by examples and nonexamples to aid in the assimilation. Thus, a concept-assimilation approach is a less "pure" strategy than a concept-attainment approach—an observation that is relevant to the researcher, who must give careful thought to planning and reporting any concept-assimilation strategy. An assimilation strategy might range from just a verbal exposition with no examples ("A prime is a whole number that has exactly two factors") to a verbal exposition with several examples ("Notice that 17 has exactly two factors, 1 and 17. Such whole numbers are called primes. Another prime is 5. Is 11 a prime? Is 100?"). Terms such as "expository teaching" or "rule learning" (Gagné, 1970) are often used for assimilation strategies that rely heavily or totally on verbalizations. The influence of the Bruner et al. (1956) concept-attainment approach over research in concept learning is reflected in the fact that concept assimilation has only recently been studied by researchers (e.g., as reported in Klausmeier et al., 1974, pp. 259–261). It should be pleasing to the school-oriented researcher that Markle (1975) can refer to "a thundering herd of studies" dealing with concept assimilation (p. 5).

Reception or selection? The researcher of a concept-attainment task may choose the particular examples and nonexamples given to the subject (a *reception* paradigm) or may permit the subject to specify which case is to be tested next as an example or nonexample (a *selection* paradigm). A reception paradigm was used in Figure 1. The control of information possible with a reception paradigm and its suitability for group-administered treatments have made it highly attractive to researchers, but a selection paradigm would seem to have promise as a low-verbal way to study the *processes* of concept attainment. Briggs (1976) has altered the usual selection paradigm to allow the subject to seek information about either another example or a definition (the results suggest three different learning styles: one in which the subject seeks many definition statements, another in which no definitions are sought, and a third in which examples are mainly sought). However, the reception paradigm can also be used to study processes if subjects are asked to state their description of the concept or what they are thinking as each example is presented. (See Bourne et al., 1971, pp. 224–230, or Bruner et al., 1956, chaps. 4 and 5, for discussions of different strategies used by subjects in the classical concept-attainment tasks.) The reception paradigm probably is most common in classroom and other real-life situations.

Successive or simultaneous presentation? Researchers may choose to reveal only one example or nonexample at a time (successive presentation) to gain some control over what the subject might be perceiving or even to force a "cognitive strain" so that subjects will adopt—and perhaps by their responses reveal—their natural strategies for processing information. For instructional purposes, however, all the examples and nonexamples are usually left in view as they are introduced (simultaneous presentation) or, if not in view, are available so that the student can refer back to them. Figure 1 offers a simultaneous presentation.

Tell the objective? Any researcher preparing a learning task will almost certainly give thought to the behavioral objectives to be attained. Another variable arises from the question, Should the learners be told what these (behavioral) objectives are? Walbesser and Eisenberg (1972) review the research dealing with this question (the answer is a cautious yes) and other questions related to behavioral objectives. The SMSG Panel on Research argued implicitly that objectives should be revealed to the learner, since they included a statement of the objective as one of the variables in their research-oriented "canonical teaching procedures" (1972).

Tell the label? The Panel on Research also suggested that telling the name of the concept is a variable for which there is some support (p. 17). Whether the name serves as a "hook," signals that something nameworthy is developing, or plays some other role, its presence does seem to facilitate concept learning, and it certainly helps in communicating the concept later. To digress to principle learning, it is curious that the role of labels for principles does not seem to have been investigated. For example, the Pythagorean theorem, commutativity of addition, the fifth postulate, and SAS are all labels for principles, but most principles (e.g., theorems) do not have labels. If labels do improve the learning or retaining of principles, their use should become more widespread.

Use a rational set? If students feel that some nonexamples of a concept are examples, they have *overgeneralized* (or failed to discriminate). It makes sense that a student would be helped in learning to discriminate among examples and nonexamples—and thus helped to avoid overgeneralizing—by seeing some nonexamples. Conversely, if students identify some examples as being nonexamples, they have *undergeneralized*. Suppose that a student has seen the altitudes of triangles always oriented vertically (an irrelevant attribute for an altitude of a triangle). It would be understandable that such a student might view verticalness as a necessary condition for an altitude and thus fall prey to undergeneralizing. It seems, then, that the undergeneralizer would profit if irrelevant attributes (such as the orientation of an altitude) were varied as much as possible. Not only do the provision of nonexamples and the variation of irrelevant attributes seem sensible, but their positive role in concept learning has also been confirmed (Klausmeier & Feldman, 1975; Shumway, 1971, 1974). There are, however, some puzzling results on the role of nonexamples (e.g., Benton, 1977; Dossey & Henderson, 1974; Shumway & White, 1977); nonexamples have not always facilitated learning in the predicted way. Despite these results, references are now made to a *rational set of examples and nonexamples* (Markle & Tiemann, 1969).

To illustrate this concept, let us consider drawings for a rational set of examples and nonexamples for the concept of "square." Suppose the definition to be used is that a square is a rhombus with a right angle. Note that two relevant attributes of this (conjunctive) concept must be present in examples: being a rhombus and having a right angle. A rational set should then include at least two nonexamples—say, a nonsquare rhombus and a nonsquare rectangle—that systematically omit each of these relevant attributes (see Figure 2, drawings d and e). However, a drawing will include irrelevant attributes such as orientation, size, and thickness of sides. A rational set must include enough examples of these irrelevant attributes for them to be varied and thus not be accepted as necessary for squareness. Hence, tilted squares of varied sizes, and lines of varied thickness should be included as examples. In addition, Tennyson, Woolley, and Merrill (1972) have found evidence to support (a) the matching of an example with a non-example so that their irrelevant attributes are as alike as possible (in our illustration one square should be nearly the same size as the rhombus, their sides should be the same thickness, and their orientations should be similar; see a-d and b-e in Figure 2), and (b) the pairing of two examples so that their irrelevant attributes differ as much as possible (one square could be tilted, large, and thin-sided; another could have horizontal sides and be small and thick-sided; see b-c in Figure 2).

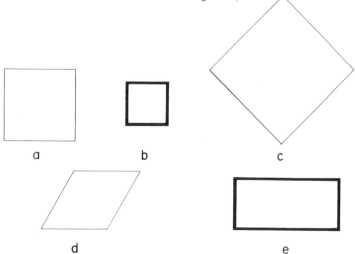

Figure 2. One rational set of examples (a, b, c) and nonexamples (d, e) for the concept of "square."

What mode of representation? Several lines of inquiry have been pursued in work with the mode of representation as a treatment variable. Several studies have, in fact, dealt with different sequences of modes. These studies have addressed this sort of question: If students succeed when they are given a stimulus in one mode—for example, 5 blocks (concrete)—and are asked for a response in another mode—for example, the numeral 5 (symbolic)—does this ensure success when the modes are reversed—stimulus, the numeral 5; response, 5 blocks? Affirmative answers have clear curricular implications; a mode sequence that is learned automatically from its reversal might not need to be taught explicitly. Some findings have been affirmative; others have not (Farris, 1973; Hirschbuhl, 1973; Klein, 1973; for more background see Heimer & Lottes, 1973). In another direction, Dienes's notion that exposure to several types of concrete representations of a concept (multiple embodiments) enhances understanding has also been tested, again with mixed results (e.g., Beardslee, 1973; Gau, 1973). In still another area, Behr (1976) has noted that second graders do not automatically link work with concrete materials to the corresponding symbolic manipulations. Finally, how a hands-on experience compares with, say, watching a demonstration or looking at pictures has been studied. Although the dependent measures in their study may not have been devoted entirely to concept learning, Vance and Kieren (1972) found that those subjects who merely witnessed demonstrations by the teacher with concrete materials did as well as, or better than, those subjects who had hands-on experience. With older subjects, Barnett and Eastman (1978) and Eastman and Barnett (in press) found that preservice elementary teachers who had hands-on work with manipulatives plus some workbook (pictorial) practice surpassed on only one occasion (a test of properties of operations) those subjects who witnessed teacher demonstrations and had the workbook practice.

Pacing? The psychologists' work with pacing variables, usually different delays of feedback or intervals between cases, does not seem particularly applicable to classroom instruction, primarily because of the artificiality of the tasks studied. (Bourne et al., 1971, pp. 274–280, report some of this work.) What might prove of interest, however, is a study such as that of Rowe (1974), in which she found that "wait times" after teachers asked questions (and also after students had responded) were astonishingly short. When these wait-times were lengthened, the quantity and quality of student responses and questions increased, although no measures of learning were used.

Advance organizer? The well-turned phrase "advance organizer" (Ausubel, 1963) has the drawback of not having been operationally defined. The notion of providing "ideational scaffolding" at a high level of generality so that new material can be related to a student's cognitive structure is attractive. But so few researchers have managed to exhibit effective advance organizers that Barnes and Clawson (1975), after reviewing several studies, concluded that "advance organizers, as presently constructed, generally do not facilitate learning" (p. 651), but compare the replies by Ausubel (1978) and Lawton and Wanska (1977). Some studies that found effects attributable to advance organizers seem to have devoted a substantial portion of the treatment time to the study of the advance organizer (Lesh, 1976a, 1976b; Lesh & Johnson, 1976).

Use a "moves" analysis? Interest in the "moves" approach to instructional strategies has grown during the last ten years. Several categories of "moves" have been identified through analyses of what teachers do in the classroom. Briefly, in teaching a concept a teacher might describe some or all of the defining attributes of the concept (*characterization* moves) and might include several examples and nonexamples, perhaps accompanied by justifications (*exemplification* moves). More detailed breakdowns of moves in teaching concepts can be found in Henderson (1970) or Cooney, Davis, and Henderson (1975, chap. 5). The complete sequence of moves used to teach a concept is called a *strategy.* For example, concept attainment involves a strategy using only exemplification moves; characterization moves would play a major role in concept assimilation.

To date, the "moves" studies have focused on the sequence of moves (e.g., should characterization moves precede, follow, or be intermingled with exemplification moves?) and on the number of moves in strategies. Within reasonable bounds, the length of a strategy seems not to be a factor when characterization moves are included in the strategy (Dossey, 1975; Frayer, 1970). When variations within a sequence have produced strategies of different effectiveness, the strategies that seem superior are those in which characterization moves appear early, or early and late (e.g., Dossey & Henderson, 1974). Such results have been noted primarily with disjunctive concepts.

There is some evidence (Gaston & Kolb, 1973) that performance on the criterion measure reflects what appears in the strategy, as Dossey points out in his survey of research on strategies for concept learning (1976). Turner (1976) also points out the probable relevance of the type of moves to the measure (p. 126). For example, a strategy with several characterization moves would probably lead to a better performance on a posttest calling for definitions than would a strategy consisting solely of exemplification moves. This you-learn-what-you-do observation and the general failure of researchers to detect different effects for different strategies may have led Kolb to his model for research on teaching strategies (1977a), discussed later in the section on possible research areas.

Dependent Variables

Not enough can be said about the importance of choosing the dependent measures for a study and clearly communicating what they are. The use of a validated, reliable standardized achievement test of some sort may militate against the chances that a study will reveal actual differences, since these differences may be obscured by the general nature of such tools. Hence, ad hoc instruments must be created, but space restrictions in journals may not allow the printing of such instruments, with the result that a reader can only guess at what was measured.

Basic measures. Dependent measures in psychological concept-attainment tasks usually are (a) the number of trials (examples or nonexamples presented) required to reach some correct-classification criterion, (b) the number of incorrect classifications that occur before reaching the criterion, and (c) occasionally the time required to reach the criterion. The ability to classify correctly appears in Level 3 of the school-oriented model designed by Klausmeier et al. (1974). Requiring a statement of a definition (Level 4 behavior) or the production of an example (Level 3.5 in the augmented model) is not characteristic of the psychological concept-attainment task, but studies dealing with strategies have incorporated measures of these variables. Perhaps in response to Turner's (1976) remark that a carefully developed taxonomy of measures ("indicators") for concept learning had not been developed, Cooney and Dossey (1978) have developed a preliminary list of measures. They include the correct classification and production of examples and nonexamples as well as the recognition and production of a suitable definition. Their list also includes, among other measures, the giving of subordinate and supraordinate concepts, sample "higher order" measures that are treated in the next paragraph.

Higher-level measures. For several years it has been common for researchers to design measures based on (especially) the hierarchy of Bloom and others (1956). Klausmeier et al. (1974, chap. 6), however, have found it convenient to speak of "uses" of attained concepts without implying a hierarchical relationship among them (p. 230). Beyond the ability to classify examples and nonexamples correctly, their uses include dealing with (a) supraordinate, subordinate, and coordinate concepts; (b) principles that involve the concept; and (c) problems that involve the concept. For example, the uses for the concept of equilateral triangle could include these: (a) the student can state that equilateral triangles are special triangles or polygons (supraordinate concepts) and that quadrilaterals (a coordinate concept) are another kind of polygon; (b) the student can state the relationship among the angles of an equilateral triangle; and (c) given the sum of the degree measures of the angles of an equilateral triangle, the student can tell the size of each angle of the triangle. "Equilateral triangle" does not suggest a subordinate concept; rectangles provide an example of a concept that is subordinate to the concept of parallelogram.

Overgeneralizing and undergeneralizing. Results of classification tests are not always analyzed in terms of overgeneralizing or undergeneralizing, but such an analysis could be done so easily that it seems that it *should* be done. Identifying nonexamples as examples indicates overgeneralizing; identifying examples as nonexamples indicates undergeneralizing. It is, of course, possible to design a specific test for overgeneralizing (or undergeneralizing), as Shumway (1971) did.

Process. The Bruner et al. (1956) reports of the learner's attempted process of solution in concept attainment are fascinating. These processes are usually called strategies, but to avoid confusion with the teaching strategies associated with moves, that term is not used here. The considerable subsequent work with these processes is summarized by Bourne et al. (1971, pp. 223-234). Let us point out only that subjects seem to approach disjunctive concept-attainment tasks just as they do conjunctive ones. Since such approaches are not well suited to disjunctive tasks, Bruner et al. concluded that "most people are told about [disjunctive concepts] rather than having to attain them" (p. 172).

Subject Variables

Since individual differences are discussed at length in the chapter by Fennema and Behr, we shall mention only a few subject variables here.

IQ and achievement. As one would predict, a student who has a high IQ or prior achievement generally achieves a high performance level on a concept-learning task. When the opposite happens, the explanation may involve some fresh insight. For example, in presenting concept-attainment tasks with several irrelevant attributes, Osler and Trautman (1961) found that their average-IQ subjects performed better than their high-IQ subjects. The explanation? High-IQ students attacked the tasks by generating hypotheses, whereas the other youngsters looked for attributes common to examples. Since many irrelevant attributes were involved, the possibility of many hypotheses resulted in a less efficient performance for the high-IQ students.

Age. Age is an obvious variable, so obvious that it is somewhat disquieting to note that many studies use college-age subjects. Even if the IQ of the average college student were not greater than that of the average fourth or ninth grader, the college student's greater experience at learning and presumed greater language facility may make extrapolations to different age groups extremely dubious. Vygotsky (1962) even asserted that "the intellectual functions that in a specific combination form the psychological basis of the process of concept formation [attainment?] ripen, take shape, and develop *only at puberty*" (p. 58, emphasis added). Researchers on strategies (in the sense of the "moves" approach) have been doing much of the recent research on concept assimilation in mathematics; it is encouraging that some are using younger subjects (e.g., Lockwood, 1977, eighth and tenth graders; Swank, 1976, eighth graders). Part of the attractiveness of the Klausmeier et al. model (1974) is that there is some cross-sectionally longitudinal support for it (Klausmeier, 1976).

Cognitive style. Several of the many aspects of cognitive style (see the chapter by Fennema & Behr) are of possible interest in concept-learning studies. Messick (1976, pp. 14–18) catalogs several: conceptualizing style, breadth of categorization, conceptual integration, and cognitive complexity vs. simplicity. None of these cognitive styles seem to have been pursued by researchers in mathematics education, although other dimensions of cognitive style such as field dependence-independence and reflectivity-impulsivity have been investigated (e.g., Pendleton, 1973, with number theory–based concepts; Threadgill, 1977, with graph-traversing principles). Brigg's work (1976), which suggests the three learning styles, has been mentioned; these styles could be significant if they prove to persist over tasks and occasions.

Socioeconomic status. Finally, socioeconomic status would seem to be a worthwhile moderator variable, since it carries some information about children's out-of-school experiences and, in general, their backgrounds. Earlier contact with examples of concepts and instances of principles cannot be assumed for many children. As Stephens (1967) has noted, there are often out-of-class influences that are quite likely to overwhelm our brief and puny (in contrast) teaching efforts. Isolating such influences and devising ways to overcome them will be a difficult chore.

SELECTED RESEARCH VARIABLES
IN PRINCIPLE LEARNING STUDIES

Many of the variables involved in concept learning are, with suitable modification, also of concern in principle learning. For example, one may consider whether to present a principle in a concrete, a pictorial, or a symbolic mode. A classification of "moves" for teaching principles has also been designed (Cooney, Davis, & Henderson, 1975, chap. 6; Cooney, Kansky, & Retzer, 1975). Because principles are general statements, they, like concepts, can be illustrated by specific instances; hence one can study overgeneralizing, undergeneralizing, or the influence of noninstances. Rather than repeating the variables listed for concept learning, then, this section focuses briefly on selected variables that, although not unique to principle learning, have received special attention in that context.

Three Treatment Variables

Attainment vs. assimilation again. The first variable is the parallel of the distinction between concept attainment and concept assimilation. Recall that an inductive approach is followed in the typical concept-attainment task: present an example or nonexample; subject categorizes or verbalizes the rule; subject then receives feedback, with repetition until she or he gives a certain number of correct responses. Such a procedure can also be followed in the learning of principles; it is often called learning through *discovery* (although that word can vie with "concept" and "principle" for the honor of having the greatest number of interpretations). To maintain a parallel with concept attainment, "principle attainment" will be used here. Hence, both concepts and principles can be induced through attainment strategies. Nonetheless, this fact seems to make the maintaining of a distinction between concepts and principles more than mere semantic swordplay. In a concept-attainment task, the subjects must receive feedback on the correctness of their responses from an external source, whereas in a principle-attainment task, the subjects *themselves* can check their responses. Students trying to induce the meaning of "rhombus" through examples and nonexamples must have their responses judged by the teacher or some other external method, but students seeking a shortcut for squaring a number ending in 5 can *themselves* check whatever ideas they have. (Admittedly, checking an instance like $2^{54} \times 2^{73} = 2^{127}$ is not a practical undertaking; such instances need not be used, of course, in a reception approach. In passing, let us note that Wills, 1970, suggested the use of such computationally forbidding instances as "target tasks" to define and effect appropriate attainment tasks.)

The counterpart of concept assimilation in teaching principles, where verbal statements of the principle play an important role, is often called *expository* teaching. Again, for no reason other than consistency, the "principle assimilation" terminology will be adopted here. Although a teaching strategy may be said to focus on attainment or assimilation, many gradations occur. Providing selected instances in an attainment task gives some degree of guidance, and scarcely anyone would use *only* verbalizations of a statement of a principle to teach that principle. Hence, researchers in this area should be extremely attentive to a careful description of their teaching procedure. Shulman and Keislar (1966) and Bittinger (1968) cover some of the issues and give somewhat dated reviews of research in "discovery" teaching. Ausubel's articulate defense (1963) of "expository" teaching is well known.

Subject verbalization. A second variable that has received attention for its role in attainment settings is the requirement of subject verbalization. Despite some early reports of the deleterious effect of asking students to verbalize a recently discovered generalization (Hendrix, 1947; Schwartz, 1955), most studies have not confirmed those results (Albig, 1973; Hanson, 1967; Retzer, 1969; Sowder, 1974, 1975a). (Schwartz's tasks and some of Hanson's tasks involved concept, rather than principle, attainment.) Indeed, if one looks beyond principle learning and the verbalization of the principle, certain studies indicate that verbalizing (talking aloud) during learning may enhance performance (Gagné & Smith, 1962). The results of a study by Pereira (1973) suggest that *when* a subject talks may be more important than *whether* the subject talks.

Learning hierarchies. Careful preparation for teaching a principle demands that all content prerequisites be provided. One way to arrange these prerequisites is to analyze the principle and draw up a *learning hierachy,* a lattice of capabilities deemed necessary for mastery of the principle (Gagné, 1970, chap. 9). A learning hierarchy is usually generated by a knowledgeable person, of course, but it may nonetheless fail to describe capabilities that do, in fact, enable a student to master the task. Accordingly, different criteria may be applied to measure the suitability of a hierarchy. For example, is the hierarchy "adequate" in the sense that students who do exhibit the prerequisite capabilities also master the task (Eisenberg & Walbesser, 1971)? Learning hierarchies can also be devised for concepts (and for skills—see Gagné, 1970, p. 255). Novillis (1976) gives a hierarchy for the fraction concept. See Walbesser and Eisenberg (1972) for an impressive review of studies involving learning hierarchies and White (1973) for a commentary on methodology in research on learning hierarchies.

Dependent Variables for Principle Learning

What can someone who has "learned a principle" do? The capabilities in the parallel to the levels of concept learning given by Klausmeier et al. (1974)—the ability to apply the principle to a routine situation, to give an instance of the principle, or to state the principle—are minimal. Concepts organize stimuli, whereas principles make assertions about stimuli. These assertions may be quite fertile. Think of the many challenging problems that can be built using the principle that the sum of the degree measures of the angles of a triangle is 180, particularly when this principle is embedded in a context where other principles, such as the theorems about angles in parallel lines, also apply. The point is, "learning a principle" might be interpreted to mean far more than the basic performances listed. Kolb (1977b) includes the following as increasingly advanced evidence of one's grasp of a principle: (a) recognizing paraphrases of the principle, (b) solving problems requiring more than one principle, and (c) solving nonroutine problems.

TRENDS AND ISSUES

The waxing promise of, for example, "discovery," concrete materials, behavioral objectives, advance organizers, structure of the intellect (Guilford, 1967), aptitude-treatment interaction (see the chapter by Fennema & Behr), or clinical studies is, alas, frequently followed by waning interest when the often ambiguous and unsupportive research reports come in. Hence, the identification of trends may be unduly affected by the excitement attached to an idea on the upsurge. Identifying important issues that are not already familiar to workers in a particular field is also difficult. For example, the issue of whether the results of studies using programmed materials can be extended to "regular" instructional settings is well known. Such observations provide a framework for the following comments on trends and issues in research on mathematics concept and principle learning.

School Tasks and Subjects

More work seems to be done with classroomlike tasks than with materials such as the classical concept-attainment cards. The interest in concept assimilation (recall Markle's reference to a "thundering herd of studies") no doubt has forced the change. In the setting of the typical psychological concept-attainment study, to state "The concept is two red triangles" would result in instant learning! Thus, less artificial settings, in which the defining concepts are not too basic, must be used in concept-assimilation studies. Extrapolation to school situations is certainly more persuasive from a study that has dealt with concepts such as trapezoids and equilateral triangles than from a study that has featured such concepts as "three large shapes, with red borders."

Whatever the setting, the important thing is the subject's feelings about the tasks: Are these tasks ones I should take seriously and learn so that I can remember them, or are they unimportant and worthy of, at most, short-term memory? It may be that seriousness of intent, motivation, immediate learning, retention, and transfer are the same for artificial tasks as for regular school tasks. If so, the greater control possible with artificial tasks almost demands their use in experiments. Provocative and important findings from such experiments should, of course, be cross-validated with school tasks.

It is most comforting when both school tasks and schoolchildren appear in the same study, although one could scarcely identify a trend toward involving both schoolchildren and mainline content in research studies. College students make up the groups most accessible to researchers. They also make up a group of much more experienced, if not more sophisticated, learners than the students in an elementary or secondary school classroom.

(It is acknowledged that this issue is platitudinous and that there are numerous, pleasing examples of studies with both school tasks and school-children, as illustrated in Payne's 1975 paper.)

Moves

In research on teaching strategies, the number of studies based on Henderson's (1970) analysis of moves would seem to signal a trend. The many kinds of concepts, their varied levels of difficulty, and the differences among learners may preclude the formulation of concise general guidelines for planning instruction, but the use of the notion and vocabulary of moves should enable researchers and teachers to communicate better. In particular, researchers in concept and principle learning should adopt descriptions of the moves of the instruction. To suggest that there is a trend toward an analysis of moves in research on instructional strategies is not to suggest that earlier research was worthless. It would seem, however, to be a worthwhile undertaking to analyze earlier studies in terms of the moves used. These results could then be added to those obtained from studies initially couched in terms of moves or be matched against theoretical predictions (see the model designed by Kolb, 1977a, in a following section).

The taxonomies of moves for teaching concepts and principles (Cooney, Davis, & Henderson, 1975) seem to need some refinement; "introduction moves" are mentioned for the teaching of principles but not for the teaching of concepts. One would eventually expect to find categories of moves that would be applicable to all types of subject matter—for example, "reinforcement moves" or explicit "interaction-reversal moves" or even "humor moves." There is always the danger of destroying the molecule by pulling it apart to examine its atoms.

Issue: What Does Attainment Yield?

Since concept attainment depends heavily on external feedback, why not use this external source for a definition and adopt the concept-assimilation approach, which is probably more time-efficient, in research? One might offer these reasons for choosing the concept-attainment approach: (a) a primary aim might be to give experience in recognizing different attributes and in discriminating among them; (b) the learner may have a very limited language capability; or (c) the concept may be difficult to describe in words (e.g., corresponding angles of parallel lines cut by a transversal). One might also argue for the concept-attainment approach on the grounds that (d) attained concepts are retained better than assimilated concepts or (e) the subject learns concept-inventing processes. Whether these last two claims are, in fact, true is an important issue. Similarly, claims of superior retention, superior transferability, and "learning to learn" for the principle-attainment approach over the principle-assimilation approach remain unsubstantiated.

Clinical Studies and Teaching "Experiments"

More researchers now regard clinical studies and teaching "experiments" (Johnson, "Types of Research") as legitimate research efforts than in the past, perhaps because tightly controlled, experimental studies have not yet yielded revolutionary findings. Although it is difficult to carry out an in-depth, probing interview, one need look only at Piaget and his colleagues' work to find samples of the insights that a flexible interaction can yield. Furthermore, researchers interested in instruction no doubt find the idea of a teaching "experiment" attractive. As Vygotsky (1962) pointed out, "Studying child thought apart from the influence of instruction, as Piaget did, excludes a very important source of change and bars the researcher from posing the question of the interaction of development and instruction peculiar to each age level" (p. 117). Even researchers who prefer experimental studies undoubtedly see merit in these practices: (a) examining their own experiences and questioning several other teachers about common misconceptions or difficulties if a schoollike task is involved, (b) adopting the outlook of a clinical study or of a teaching "experiment" in carrying out one or more pilot studies, and (c) including interviews as a part of the collection of posttreatment data. Designs that include periodic interviewing of samples of the subjects are also possible and worth considering.

POSSIBLE RESEARCH AREAS

A few areas inviting research have been touched on obliquely in earlier sections of this chapter; some of these areas are repeated here. Other research areas in this section have been selected from the literature (e.g., Klausmeier et al., 1974, pp. 267-275). Many of the choices are obvious; all, of course, reflect the writer's biases and limited vision.

The topics are classified, again loosely, under the subsections used earlier: task variables, treatment variables, dependent variables, and subject variables. The areas within a subsection are roughly ordered, with "favorites" listed first. A suggestion on the importance of these areas across subsections is made in the concluding remarks.

Task Variables

Content. There is one body of content—logic—that seems to warrant special mention. Specifically, "logic" is to be interpreted as the concepts associated with the logical connectives and the principles of logical reasoning (inference patterns such as modus ponens). The earlier remarks about task content have centered on contrasting schoollike tasks with the artificial type of task invented by the psychologists. No particular attention has been paid to content areas within school mathematics, but this omission must not be allowed to imply a lack of importance. A program of studies within a single content area is certainly a worthwhile effort; one convenient example is the series of studies on fractional numbers by Payne (1975) and his students.

The content area of logical concepts and principles has been chosen for emphasis here for two reasons: (a) their importance in mathematics and their value in everyday life and (b) the astonishingly low level of students' grasp of the concepts and principles (see Jansson, 1974, for a review). One can point to the widespread, everyday use of "or" in the exclusive sense and of "if . . . , then . . ." in the "if and only if" sense as explanations for some of the incorrect uses, called "child's logic" or "quasi-child logics" by Shapiro and O'Brien (1973). Here are examples of these everyday uses: "Abe will wear the white shirt or the orange one," and "If someone leaves the door open, then mosquitoes will get in."

Ennis (1975) has critiqued some of Piaget's work; certain researchers have interpreted Piaget's findings as asserting that pre-formal-operational thinkers cannot use logical reasoning. There may be truth about the use of logic in Vygotsky's assertions about concept acquisition: "We found that instruction usually precedes development" (1972, p. 101). "The only good kind of instruction is that which marches ahead of development and leads it; it must be aimed not so much at the ripe as at the ripening functions" (p. 104). Can we identify the ripening of aspects of logical concepts and principles?

Whatever the answer, Jansson (1974) was able to say, "The paucity of sound research into instruction in the use of deductive reasoning is evident" (p. 25). Since the studies are few in number and inconsistent in their findings, a first priority might be to find out *what* instruction in logic can accomplish *when,* that is, with students of different ages. An important special case would be investigations of the effect of instruction that deals with negations; people's ability to use logical principles involving negations is amazingly low (e.g., see Eisenberg & McGinty, 1974; Miller, 1968; Wason & Johnson-Laird, 1972).

Relational concepts. Carroll (1964) pointed out that little research had been done with relational concepts. Some relational concepts in mathematics are common enough to merit attention, for example, perpendicular lines, factorable polynomial, simplest fraction, reciprocal, and similarity. The relatively uncommon (in mathematics) disjunctive concept has received much more attention than the relational concept, probably because of the provocative work in the psychological literature. This is an argument for attention to relational concepts, not an argument against the study of disjunctive concepts. Disjunctive concepts seem to be relatively difficult, and as Turner (1976) argues, "Selecting difficult concepts, principles, or skills is desirable because 'easy' ones are by definition those that can be learned about equally well under any teaching strategy" (p. 119). Note, however, that generalizing from studies of strategies for disjunctive concepts to other kinds of concepts would be risky; the main value of studies of disjunctive concepts may lie in determining how people deal with "negative information" such as nonexamples.

Concept/principle difficulty. One might be concerned about the difficulty of a concept or a principle for purposes other than that of research. There may be much educational value in learning whether the difficulty of a concept (or a principle) can be established on a priori grounds. For example, the number of examples and nonexamples in a rational set has been suggested as a criterion. It seems to be well established that conjunctive concepts are more easily learned than disjunctive ones, especially inclusive-disjunctive concepts. The payoff might ensue from suggesting which view, whenever two or more views of a concept are possible, could lead to "improved" learning of the concept. For example, intuitive congruence might be viewed as a conjunctive "same size and same shape" concept or a relational "one figure can be moved to match the other one" concept. If it were established that relational concepts are more easily learned than conjunctive concepts, one would probably choose the relational view.

The whole question of the relative difficulty of principles seems to be uninvestigated, as are most questions dealing with principles. Perhaps one can derive a "rational set of instances and noninstances" for a principle and judge the difficulty of the principle according to the size of the set. Or, if difficulty measures can be assigned to concepts, perhaps the difficulty of learning a principle can be inferred according to the difficulties of the concepts it involves. In another approach each principle could be stated in a canonical if-then form; its difficulty would then be based on logical forms of the hypothesis and the conclusion.

Artificial vs. real. Finally, it seems important that researchers confront the issue of whether research with the typical contrived concepts gives information that one can extrapolate to school tasks with some degree of faith. The observation was made earlier that very little seems to have been done to address this issue. The contrived type of concept used by Dossey and Henderson (1974)—a preve is a natural number that is either a prime or an even number—is similar to school concepts in the following ways: (a) it has a label; (b) its definition uses concepts less familiar than color, shape, and number of objects; and, perhaps most important, (c) its content is sufficiently rich to permit its use in principles and defined concepts. Concepts such as the preve concept could also be used in studies on both attainment and assimilation. In contrast, "red triangle" is a remarkably sterile concept, even if one attaches a label like "kul" to it. Nonetheless, it is possible that performances on all these tasks may be correlated or that results with artificial tasks may generalize to at least a few settings (e.g., the game Mastermind) of potential interest to mathematics teachers.

Treatment Variables

Kolb's model for teaching strategies. The first several studies that analyzed teaching strategies on the basis of the moves involved did not yield a clear-cut winner. Even if an apparently superior strategy had emerged, the question of *why* the strategy was superior would have remained to be investigated. Kolb's (1977a) model represents a major contribution to the thinking in research on teaching strategies; instead of searching for the most successful "recipe" (strategy), he suggests that examining the "ingredients" and how they interact may lead, if not to a best recipe, at least to a means of deciding what recipes to use in a study of strategies. "Experiments should be devised where there is a basis or rationale for picking specific strategies and where the rationale can be used to make predictions about which strategy should be superior" (p. 3).

Three comments are appropriate before describing Kilb's model.

1. Working without a theoretical base should not be shunned. For example, Kolb might not have devised his model if the early studies had not been done. The state of knowledge about concept and principle learning still permits (demands?) exploratory, clinical, and status studies, that is, studies to suggest the "big picture." (To be fair to the strategies researchers, their work is not without a carefully developed foundation; nevertheless, the foundation is not theoretical.)

2. A theoretical framework, when available, provides an outline of this big picture. It suggests studies that either paint in part of the picture or force one to admit that this big picture is not suitable. Kolb (1977a) reminds us that

> a mental device such as this model is not right or wrong, but rather it is useful or not useful. It is useful to the extent that it explains observations from experiments and permits data to be synthesized into generalizations. This model will be useful if it is rich in generating hypotheses and predictions that can be supported or refuted by experiments. As empirical evidence accumulates, the model may be supported, may require refinements, may need a drastic overhaul, or it may be cast aside in favor of a new conception. (p. 20)

The model already suggests a question: Is there a Kolbian model for principle learning?

3. Teachers who do not do research are perhaps more interested in superior recipes than in intriguing analyses of ingredients. It behooves

ingredients researchers, when communicating with such teachers, to make clear how these ingredients can contribute to a successful recipe.

Here is an outline of Kolb's model of strategies for teaching concepts. His first step is to examine two "ingredients"—(a) learners do bring different degrees of knowledge of prerequisites to a learning task, and (b) performance on a particular dependent variable may depend on the particular combination of types of moves (exemplification or characterization). He then looks at the simplest strategies—the single-move strategies. Kolb next builds on that model to predict the learning for multiple-move strategies made up of moves of only one type. His final step is to extend the analysis to a strategy that uses both types of moves. Let us adopt the usual shorthand of E for an exemplification move and C for a characterization move. Thus, the sequence EECEE describes a strategy that has one characterization move sandwiched between two pairs of exemplification moves. The discussion here treats only a dependent variable of classification ability; Kolb's coverage is more extensive.

Figure 3 presents the model for a strategy using a single move. The model reflects the observation that for a learner who does not know much about the terms being used (i.e., has a low knowledge of prerequisites), a single C-move will not result in much learning. However, a learner who has a high degree of knowledge of prerequisites should learn a great deal from a single C-move. Since a single E-move does provide some information about a concept, even the learner with a low knowledge of prerequisites may acquire a slight amount of classificatory ability. Although slight, this learning should be greater than that which would result from a C-move containing terms that are virtually meaningless to this learner.

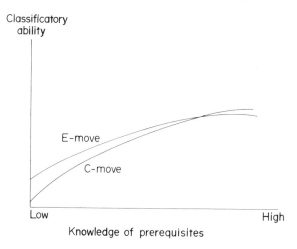

Figure 3. The interaction of single-move strategies with knowledge of prerequisites in producing classificatory ability. (Adapted from Kolb, 1977a, p. 8.)

A learner with a high knowledge of prerequisites, however, could not acquire as much explicit information from a single E-move as from a single C-move; thus, in Figure 3 the curve for the C-move strategy at some degree of knowledge of prerequisites rises above the curve for the E-move strategy.

The second step is to extend the model to strategies using several moves, but moves of only one type. This model is summarized in Figure 4. With an increased number of E-moves (the typical concept-attainment strategy), one would expect to find increasingly greater amounts of classificatory ability, even for learners with a low knowledge of prerequisites. For learners with a high knowledge of prerequisites, several E-moves should provide enough information for them to perform nearly as well as they would have with several C-moves. Given an even greater number of C-moves, however, the learner who has a low degree of knowledge of prerequisites may not learn much. Thus, the model points out the importance of the learner's knowledge of prerequisites—a point that seems not to have been considered in earlier studies of teaching strategies. If for some reason a student were allowed only one type of move, the student who does not have a good background should learn more from E-moves; the student who has a good background may profit more from C-moves.

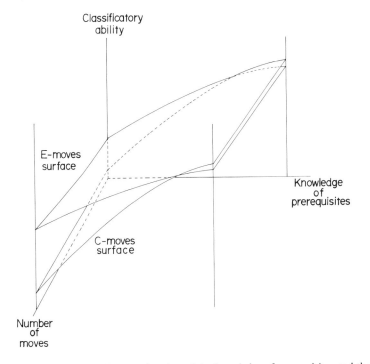

Figure 4. Classificatory ability as a function of the knowledge of prerequisites and the number of moves for pure, multiple-move strategies. (Adapted from Kolb, 1977a, p. 14.)

The final step is to use the graphs of Figure 4 in describing mixed-move strategies—strategies that contain both E and C moves. For a strategy such as EEECCEEC, the graph suggests what level a learner with a certain knowledge of prerequisites would have attained after the sequence of the first three E-moves. The key question, then, is how to place the learner on the C-graph so that the effect of the next two moves, CC, can be predicted. (Note that a similar question occurs each time a strategy involves a change from one type of move to the other.) Kolb's technique involves two procedures: (a) equating a sequence of moves of one type to a *one*-move strategy of that type and (b) equating one-move strategies of different types.

1. The importance of different amounts of knowledge of prerequisites becomes evident when one equates a sequence such as EEE to a single E-move strategy. An EEE sequence for a learner with a certain knowledge of prerequisites should result in the same classificatory ability (z_1 in Figure 5) as a *single* E-move produces for a learner *with a greater knowledge of prerequisites* ($z'_1 = z_1$ in Figure 5). The same technique, of course, could be applied to strategies made up solely of C-moves by using the C-surface in Figure 4.

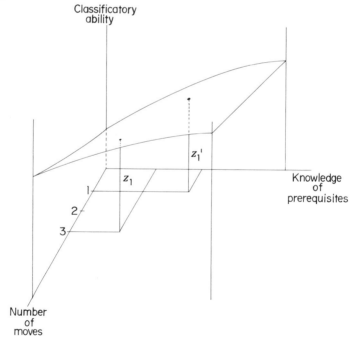

Figure 5. Finding a combination of a single E-move and a degree of knowledge of prerequisites that yields classificatory ability equal to an EEE strategy ($z_1 = z_1'$) with a different degree of knowledge of prerequisites.

2. An ordered pair is convenient notation for linking a strategy with a degree of knowledge of prerequisites: (strategy, degree of KP). Once a sequence such as EEE has been "reduced" to (E, some level of KP), that combination in turn is equated to the pair (C, some level of KP). This last combination can be determined as in Figure 6. A given (C, degree of KP) combination can be treated in the same way to yield an equivalent (E, degree of KP) combination.

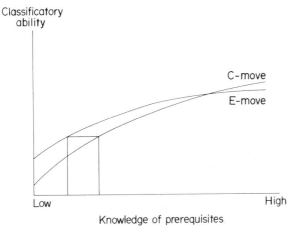

Figure 6. Finding a combination of a C-move and a degree of knowledge of prerequisites that yields classificatory ability equal to a combination of an E-move and a degree of knowledge of prerequisites.

In toto, given a strategy, one can use the procedures above to find a single-move strategy for some degree of knowledge of prerequisites that is equivalent to the given strategy with respect to the learning it produces. For example, the strategy EEECCEEC would undergo the transformations suggested by this notation:

$$EEECCEEC \rightarrow E\,'CCEEC \rightarrow C\,'CCEEC \rightarrow C''EEC \rightarrow$$
$$E''EEC \rightarrow E'''\,C \rightarrow C'''\,C \rightarrow C''''$$

Each step would probably involve a different degree of knowledge of prerequisites. This canonical (single-move, degree of KP) combination could then be used to predict how two strategies compare or should compare, thus providing a rationale for choices of strategies.

Inasmuch as models are simplifications, one can raise charges of oversimplification. For example, will degrees of knowledge of prerequisites and of the dependent variable be sufficiently measurable to permit testing the model? A claim that every E-move (or sequence of E-moves) is as effective as every other E-move (or sequence of E-moves) is dubious (e.g., Lockwood, 1977; Shumway & White, 1977). Thus, the surfaces in the model may be too "strategy specific" to be generalizable. Kolb's treatments of disjunctive concepts and nonexamples may be too brief (pp. 9–10); he argues that the surfaces will be much the same, with the graphs intersecting at a lower degree of KP. It may be necessary to insist that strategies contain a rational set of examples and nonexamples.

Despite these quibbles, the model is provocative enough, rich enough, and, admittedly, new enough to serve as a reference point for researchers of strategies. To quote Kolb (1977a):

> The ability to evaluate mixed move strategies allows one to determine the effects of any strategy. Obviously, the effects of one strategy can be compared to the effects of another strategy, and in this way a prediction can be made concerning the expected outcome of an experiment with the two strategies. Therefore, the model provides the means to suggest relationships, select appropriate strategies to compare in an empirical test, and predict what kind of an outcome would conform to the model. . . .
>
> Clearly, the first test of the model must be with strategies consisting solely of E-moves or C-moves. Only when the surfaces are established will it be possible to make predictions about mixed strategies. In fact, good clean predictions on mixed-moves may not be possible until the functions are established whose graphs are the surfaces. (pp. 19–20)

An ambitious goal!

Nonexamples. The frequently noted reluctance or inability of students to process the information in nonexamples needs investigation, particularly when instruction on using nonexamples seems ineffective (Malo, 1975). Presumably the same phenomenon would hold for noninstances of principles. This topic is, of course, related to the call for research on the teaching of logic. Perhaps an explicit foundation in logic would better equip and dispose students to use negative information. Whether an extensive, explicit treatment of logic is required or whether a long-term exposure to nonexamples and noninstances in learning is sufficient remains to be seen. In a related area, the role of counterexamples (examples or nonexamples that show the falsity or incompleteness of an inadequate definition or statement of a principle) seems to be uninvestigated. Who generates the inadequate statements—the student or the experimenter—might be an important variable in studies of counterexamples.

Language. The nature of the language used in research on learning concepts and principles offers another variable. Van Hiele and van Hiele (1959) expressed the concern that too often the level of teachers' language is *not* the level that would expedite the students' grasp of the concept or principle. (Students have also made this claim!) Markle (1975) notes that an expert in a given subject might classify examples or nonexamples of a concept in a manner quite different from that way suggested by the formal definition that the same expert would teach. Do we decide whether something is a square by looking for "a rhombus with a right angle" or "a rectangle with two adjacent sides congruent" or even a figure with "all right angles and symmetric with respect to each diagonal"? If "square" indeed connotes, say, an equilateral quadrilateral with all right angles, perhaps that definition would lead to better learning. If students who have not been given a definition but have exhibited correct classificatory capabilities for a concept are asked to tell their criteria, their statements might generate a "folk definition" for the concept. If the folk definition differs from a usual formal definition, it could prove valuable to determine whether concept assimilation, when based on the different definitions, leads to different performance in classifying, producing examples, or using the concept. Vygotsky (1962) calls the following statement an "indisputable fact": "Thought development is determined by language, i.e., by the linguistic tools of thought and by the sociocultural experience of the child" (p. 51). If the statement is true, then investigations into the language of learners (or the language of teachers, as in Gregory & Osborne, 1975) must be carried out.

Off the deep end? An intriguing notion that does not seem to have been researched is Dienes and Golding's "deep end" hypothesis (1971). They suggest that perhaps instruction should start with more advanced forms rather than follow the usual practice of going from the simple to the more complex. For example, a study of congruence could start with general figures and then specialize to polygons, angles, and segments rather than proceed according to the usual segments-angles-triangles sequence, which may or may not be continued to other polygons and figures. Or, perhaps there would be some benefit in earlier work with graphs of *nonlinear* functions or with the distributivity of multiplication over *several* addends. It is not clear how advance organizers are related to the deep-end hypothesis. They may be paraphrases of each other, but the deep-end approach seems to expect that more study at the complex end would precede the simpler forms.

Classroom interaction. The qualitative and quantitative aspects of the teacher-student interaction involved in questioning would seem to be important, since questioning is perhaps the easiest route to overt responses. ("Questioning" should be interpreted to include such imperative statements as "Give an example of an irrational number.") It is striking that only 1.3% of the questions asked in several geometry classes were above the applications level in the Bloom (1956) taxonomy (Friedman, 1973). When Rowe's (1974) teachers increased the length of the question-to-response and the response-to-next-question intervals, their students gave more and better answers, the students *asked* more questions, and the teachers asked more advanced-level questions. This promising study should be repeated with mathematical concepts and principles at several grade levels.

Since the level of language used by teachers may occasionally be inappropriate and since student involvement is usually highly regarded, it may be worthwhile to investigate concept and principle learning in small groups. Some work has indicated a probable positive effect (Bierden, 1970; Pearl, 1967); it is difficult to sort out what role any small-group work plays from reports on studies with mathematics laboratories. It would be worthwhile to study the language used by small groups of students as they work through lessons on concepts or principles, with the lessons involving different strategies or different levels of language.

Review. How often should concepts and principles be formally reviewed? Classroom practice is often controlled by the textbook, which in turn seems to be based on the authors' hunches rather than on the scanty research (e.g., Gay, 1973). The question of *how* the material should be reviewed is also interesting, but the results have not been encouraging and seem at best to offer trends rather than significant differences (e.g., Pence, 1975; Thomas, 1975).

Rational sets. The notions of rational sets of examples and nonexamples, matched pairs of examples and nonexamples, and divergent examples touched on earlier seem so reasonable that it is disappointing that so little research using these notions with mathematical concepts has been reported. One might expect that such reasonable ideas would be tested whenever a concept-learning study is carried out because some ideas that seem reasonable may be adopted without question when in fact they may not be better than anything else. Thus, these "reasonable" ideas should especially be put to thorough research tests rather than assumed.

Dependent Variables

What is learned by discovery? One of the many claims of supporters of attainment strategies has been that such strategies help students "learn to learn." The practice in gathering data, generating hypotheses, and testing hypotheses should carry over into other learning situations, according to the claims. After practice, subjects do seem to become more proficient with the typical psychological concept-attainment task (Clark, 1971, p. 260). Wills (1967), too, has presented some encouraging evidence that experience with principle-attainment tasks can transfer to new settings. Nonetheless, such an important variable deserves much more attention, especially in the area of principle learning. (Since discovery may be viewed as problem solving, see also the chapter by Lester.)

"Systems" of concepts and principles. In sharp contrast to artificial con-

cepts, "real" concepts are most often related to other concepts and incorporated into a body of principles. A student who has studied triangles throughout a high school geometry course certainly has a richer concept of "triangle" than an elementary school student who has not, even though each might be equally good at classifying triangles and nontriangles. A student who recognizes that a theorem about parallelograms may be applicable in situations dealing with rectangles has, in some sense, a better grasp of the theorem than a student who does not. Much of this richness derives from experience with the concept or principle in the context of other concepts and principles rather than from isolated ideas associated with a vocabulary word or a page in another chapter.

Zykova (1969) has touched on one aspect of a "system of concepts" (p. 93). In some settings an object can exemplify two concepts that are ordinarily unrelated. For example, in a complicated figure a transversal for two parallel lines might also be an angle bisector. Zykova notes that students may not use the second concept after noticing the first and calls this phenomenon the "braking" effect of the first concept. Zykova reports some success in loosening students' mind sets by giving instruction that incorporates a variety of examples and a discussion of the possible multiple roles of an object. The ability to see multiple roles of an object might serve as one index of a learner's grasp of a "system" of concepts—as a dependent measure of learning—as opposed to the mere "mastery" of concepts in isolation. Another aspect of "richness" might be found in the limit of a student's ability to generalize a concept or a principle. For example, will a pupil who endorses commutativity of multiplication for small whole numbers be willing to assume commutativity of multiplication for large whole numbers, mixed numbers, or decimals—or for *division* of small whole numbers? Perhaps Collis's (1971) method of studying the evolution of a concept could be used to suggest how a student's system of concepts changes.

Vygotsky's experiments several decades ago led him to assert, "We can now reaffirm on a sound basis of data that the *absence of a system* is the cardinal psychological difference distinguishing spontaneous [attained in natural settings] from scientific [instructed] concepts" (1962, p. 116). Whether Zykova's and Vygotsky's "systems of concepts" are the same is not clear, but the phrase is a valuable reminder that the classification or production of an example or an instance is a limited measure of a student's grasp of a concept or principle. How, for example, might the surfaces in Figure 4 appear if an ultimate dependent measure dealt with the acquisition of a principle related to the concept?

Long-term retention. Since many studies of concept learning have dealt with artificial tasks, performance has usually been measured immediately after the treatment period or a week later at most. When nonartificial concepts or principles are used in research, long-term performance should be studied. Results over a longer term are occasionally surprising; Scott, Frayer, and Klausmeier (1971) found that the performance of a discovery group went *up* after a 21-day interval! Before becoming too encouraged by such results, researchers should use designs that allow the posttest practice effects to be analyzed.

Subject Variables

Developmental level, mode of representation interaction. Some aspects of a student's developmental level might well be related to a need for a concrete or iconic representation of a concept or principle. For example, a concrete-operational student might profit more from such representations than a formal-operational student. Armstrong's study (1972) with retarded subjects indicated that the type of task is also an important variable in such work. A narrower aspect of development that might be an important variable is the child's use of language. When (or whether) students' language capabilities permit a change in teaching strategies could be explored. It is possible that a study of master teachers at several grade levels might suggest an evolution of effective strategies. However, there is probably too much within-grade-level variation to identify a predominant strategy, even with a restriction to master teachers.

Dimensions of cognitive style. As Fennema and Behr point out in their chapter, research with cognitive styles is in general at the fledgling stage. Whether the area holds promise is a moot question because of measurement problems. Yet the notion of identifying characteristics of learners that reveal strengths or weaknesses in how they process information is so compelling—and might offer such great payoff—that Messick's (1976) list cited earlier on page 261 must be pursued. Certain features of mathematics —its logical structure, the variety of modes of representation often possible, its compact symbolism—may interact with such traits as conceptualizing style or hemispheric predominance.

CONCLUDING REMARKS

It appears safe to make these general observations about concept and principle learning. The terms *concept* and *principle* should not be used interchangeably; in mathematics education, at least, there seems to be reasonable uniformity along the lines of the usage in this chapter. The extensive work with concept attainment by psychologists has emphasized a careful analysis of a concept in terms of its attributes and the logical form of the concept's defining rule. Most of the psychologists' work has involved artificial concepts like "red triangle," which are limited to concept-attainment strategies, play no part in a system of concepts and principles, and may not give results generalizable to "real" concepts. Educational psychologists do offer the logical but minimally tried-and-proved idea of a rational set of examples and nonexamples. A moves analysis of a teaching strategy offers at least a means of clearer communication among researchers and teachers, particularly when dealing with assimilation strategies; Kolb's model offers a rationale for choosing a strategy. Few studies have dealt with principle learning, despite its importance.

Several areas for research on concept or principle learning have been mentioned in this chapter. A researcher might well make a major contribution to knowledge about concept or principle learning by exploring the following areas:

1. Can instruction in logical concepts and principles, especially those that involve negation, be effective with students of different ages and developmental levels? An important special issue is whether one can facilitate students' use of the negative information contained in nonexamples, noninstances, and counterexamples.

2. Predictions from Kolb's model for concept learning should be tested. Perhaps post hoc analyses of some completed studies could yield information about the model. If nothing else, Kolb's model reminds us of the importance of the degree of prerequisite knowledge, a variable that should undoubtedly play a major role in studies of principle learning or in the development of a Kolbian-inspired model for principle learning.

3. Do attainment strategies teach anything about the attainment process? Researchers in heuristics (see the chapter by Lester) often address questions about the learning of processes. Since attainment tasks can be viewed as problems, the heuristics researchers may have much to offer researchers in concept and principle attainment and vice versa.

4. What can be said about the learning of relational concepts? When alternative definitions are possible, are they assimilated equally well?

Concepts and principles are the foundations of knowledge. Any research results that give information about how students learn concepts and principles or how teachers can go about teaching them is certainly valuable. Even though hypotheses are not always affirmed, the prospect of making even small contributions to theoretical foundations and classroom practices should be exciting and heartening to researchers.

REFERENCES

Albig, D. L. A study of the effects of verbalization on concept formation in mathematics (Doctoral dissertation, Florida State University, 1973). *Dissertation Abstracts International,* 1973, *34,* 632A. (University Microfilms No. 73–18,303)

Armstrong, J. R. Representational modes as they interact with cognitive development and mathematical concept acquisition of the retarded to promote new mathematical learning. *Journal for Research in Mathematics Education,* 1972, *3,* 43–50.

Ausubel, D. P. *The psychology of meaningful verbal learning.* New York: Grune & Stratton, 1963.

Ausubel, D. P. In defense of advance organizers: A reply to the critics. *Review of Educational Research,* 1978, *48,* 251–257.

Ausubel, D., & Robinson, F. *School learning.* New York: Holt, Rinehart & Winston, 1969.

Bailey, H. J. Toward a theory of sequencing: Study 4-1: An examination of the effects of a particular canonical teaching procedure on concept attainment and generalization in mathematics (Doctoral dissertation, Pennsylvania State University, 1974). *Dissertation Abstracts International,* 1975, *36,* 98A. (University Microfilms No. 75–15,786)

Barnes, B. R., & Clawson, E. U. Do advance organizers facilitate learning? Recommendations for further research based on an analysis of 32 studies. *Review of Educational Research,* 1975, *45,* 637–659.

Barnett, J. C., & Eastman, P. M. The use of manipulative materials and student performance in the enactive and iconic modes. *Journal for Research in Mathematics Education,* 1978, *9,* 94–102.

Beardslee, E. C. Toward a theory of sequencing: Study 1-7: An exploration of the effect of instructional sequences involving enactive and iconic embodiments on the ability to generalize (Doctoral dissertation, Pennsylvania State University, 1972). *Dissertation Abstracts International,* 1973, *33,* 6721A. (University Microfilms No. 73-13,953)

Behr, M. J. Personal communication, September, 1976.

Benton, E. R. The relationship between the number of attributes and the number of moves in conjunctive concept teaching strategies (Doctoral dissertation, Texas A & M University, 1976). *Dissertation Abstracts International,* 1977, *37,* 4927A. (University Microfilms No. 77-2591)

Bierden, J. E. Behavioral objectives and flexible grouping in seventh grade mathematics. *Journal for Research in Mathematics Education,* 1970, *1,* 207–217.

Bittinger, M. L. A review of discovery. *Mathematics Teacher,* 1968, *61,* 140–146.

Bloom, B. S. (Ed.). *Taxonomy of educational objectives, handbook 1: Cognitive domain.* New York: David McKay, 1956.

Bourne, L. E., Jr., & Dominowski, R. L. Thinking. In P. Mussen & M. Rosenzweig (Eds.), *Annual review of psychology* (Vol. 23). Palo Alto, Calif.: Annual Reviews, 1972.

Bourne, L. E., Jr., Ekstrand, B. R., & Dominowski, R. L. *The psychology of thinking.* Englewood Cliffs, N. J.: Prentice-Hall, 1971.

Braley, L. S. Strategy selection and negative instances in concept learning. *Journal of Educational Psychology,* 1963, *54,* 154–159.

Briggs, J. E. *Teaching moves elicited by student questions in minimally-directed study of mathematical concepts.* Unpublished master's thesis, Illinois State University, 1976.

Bruner, J. S. The course of cognitive growth. *American Psychologist,* 1964, *19,* 1–15.

Bruner, J. S., Goodnow, J. J., & Austin, G. A. *A study of thinking.* New York: Wiley, 1956.

Bruner, J. S., & Kenney, H. J. On relational concepts. In J. Bruner, R. Olver, & P. Greenfield (Eds.), *Studies in cognitive growth.* New York: Wiley, 1966.

Catanzano, R., & Godwin, W. Comparative effectiveness of three sequences of moves for teaching conjunctive and relational mathematical concepts to college students. *Journal for Research in Mathematics Education,* 1977, *8,* 33–47.

Carroll, J. B. Words, meanings, and concepts. *Harvard Educational Review,* 1964, *34,* 178–202.

Clark, D. Teaching concepts in the classroom: A set of teaching prescriptions derived from experimental research. *Journal of Educational Psychology,* 1971, *62,* 253–278. (Monograph)

Collis, K. F. A technique for studying concept formation in mathematics. *Journal for Research in Mathematics Education,* 1971, *2,* 12–22.

Cooney, T. J., Davis, E. J., & Henderson, K. B. *Dynamics of teaching secondary school mathematics.* Boston: Houghton Mifflin, 1975.

Cooney, T. J., & Dossey, J. A. *A system of concept acquisition indicators.* Manuscript submitted for publication, 1978.

Cooney, T., Kansky, R., & Retzer, K. *Protocol materials in mathematics education: Selection of concepts* (Report No. 7). Bloomington, Ind.: National Center for the Development of Training Materials in Teacher Education, 1975. (ERIC Document Reproduction Service No. ED 106 124)

Dienes, Z. P., & Golding, E. B. *Approach to modern mathematics.* New York: Herder & Herder, 1971.

Dossey, J. A. *The differential effect of venture length in concept teaching strategies for disjunctive mathematical concepts.* Unpublished manuscript, 1975.

Dossey, J. A. The role of relative efficiency studies in the development of mathematical concept teaching strategies: Some findings and some directions. In T. Cooney (Ed.), *Teaching strategies.* Columbus, Ohio: ERIC Center for Science, Mathematics, and Environmental Education, 1976.

Dossey, J. A., & Henderson, K. B. The relative effectiveness of four strategies for teaching disjunctive concepts in mathematics. *Journal for Research in Mathematics Education,* 1974, *5,* 6–19.

Eastman, P. M., & Barnett, J. C. The interaction between spatial visualization abilities and the use of manipulative materials in the enactive and iconic modes for preservice elementary teachers. *International Journal of Mathematical Education in Science and Technology,* in press.

Eisenberg, T. A., & McGinty, R. L. On comparing error patterns and the effect of maturation in a unit on sentential logic. *Journal for Research in Mathematics Education,* 1974, *5,* 225–237.

Eisenberg, T. A., & Walbesser, H. H. Learning hierarchies—Numerical considerations. *Journal for Research in Mathematics Education,* 1971, *2,* 244–256.

Ennis, R. H. Children's ability to handle Piaget's propositional logic: A conceptual critique. *Review of Educational Research,* 1975, *45,* 1–41.

Farris, D. C. Study 1-2: An exploration of selected relationships among the enactive, iconic, and symbolic modes of representation. *Journal for Research in Mathematics Education,* 1973, *4,* 104–105.

Flavell, J. H. Concept development. In P. Mussen (Ed.), *Carmichael's manual of child psychology.* New York: Wiley, 1970.

Frayer, D. A. *Effects of number of instances and emphasis of relevant attributes on mastery of geometric concepts by fourth- and sixth-grade children* (Technical Report No. 116). Madison: Wisconsin Research and Development Center for Cognitive Learning, 1970. (ERIC Document Reproduction Service No. ED 040 878)

Friedman, M. The development and use of a system to analyze geometry teachers' questions (Doctoral dissertation, Columbia University, 1972). *Dissertation Abstracts International,* 1973, *33,* 4215A–4216A. (University Microfilms No. 73-2593)

Gagné, R. M. *The conditions of learning* (2nd ed.). New York: Holt, Rinehart & Winston, 1970.

Gagné, R. M., & Smith, E. C., Jr. A study of the effects of verbalization on problem-solving. *Journal of Experimental Psychology,* 1962, *63,* 12–18.

Gaston, J. A., & Kolb, J. R. A comparison of three strategies for teaching a selected mathematical concept to students in college algebra. *Journal for Research in Mathematics Education,* 1973, *4,* 177–186.

Gau, G. E. Toward a theory of sequencing: Study 1-6: An exploration of the effect of instructional sequences involving enactive and iconic embodiments on the attainment of concepts embodied symbolically (Doctoral dissertation, Pennsylvania State University, 1972). *Dissertation Abstracts International,* 1973, *33,* 6728A. (University Microfilms No. 73-13,980)

Gay, L. Temporal position of reviews and its effect on the retention of mathematical rules. *Journal of Educational Psychology,* 1973, *64,* 171–182.

Gregory, J. W., & Osborne, A. R. Logical reasoning ability and teacher verbal behavior within the mathematics classroom. *Journal for Research in Mathematics Education*, 1975, *6*, 26–36.

Guilford, J. P. *The nature of human intelligence*. New York: McGraw-Hill, 1967.

Hanson, L. E. Inductive discovery learning, reception learning, and formal verbalization of mathematical concepts (Doctoral dissertation, Florida State University, 1967). *Dissertation Abstracts*, 1967, *28*, 1731A–1732A. (University Microfilms No. 67–14451)

Haygood, R. C., & Bourne, L. E., Jr. Attribute- and rule-learning aspects of conceptual behavior. *Phychological Review*, 1965, *72*, 175–195.

Heimer, R. T., & Lottes, J. J. The theoretical model and a synopsis of the first two years of the research program. *Journal for Research in Mathematics Education*, 1973, *4*, 85–93.

Henderson, K. B. Concepts. In M. Rosskopf (Ed.), *The teaching of secondary school mathematics*, Thirty-third Yearbook of the National Council of Teachers of Mathematics. Washington, D.C.: The Council, 1970.

Hendrix, G. A new clue to transfer of training. *Elementary School Journal*, 1947, *48*, 197–208.

Higgins, J. L. Personal communication, April, 1976.

Hirschbuhl, J. J. Study 1-5: An exploration of selected transitivity and conjunctive relationships among the enactive, iconic, and symbolic modes of representation. *Journal for Research in Mathematics Education*, 1973, *4*, 113–115.

Jansson, L. C. *The development of deductive reasoning: A review of the literature, preliminary version*. Paper presented at the annual meeting of the American Educational Research Association, Chicago, April 1974. (ERIC Document Reproduction Service No. ED 090 034)

Kieren, T. E. Activity learning. *Review of Educational Research*, 1969, *39*, 509–522.

Klausmeier, H. J. Conceptual development during the school years. In J. Levin & V. Allen (Eds.), *Cognitive learning in children*. New York: Academic Press, 1976.

Klausmeier, H. J., & Feldman, K. V. Effects of a definition and a varying number of examples and nonexamples on concept attainment. *Journal of Educational Psychology*, 1975, *67*, 174–178.

Klausmeier, H. J., Ghatala, E. S., & Frayer, D. A. *Conceptual learning and development*. New York: Academic Press, 1974.

Klein, P. A. Study 1-1: An exploration of selected relationships among the enactive, iconic, and symbolic modes of representations. *Journal for Research in Mathematics Education*, 1973, *4*, 94–103.

Kolb, J. R. A predictive model for teaching strategies research. Part I: Derivation of the model. Report from the Georgia Center for the Study of Learning and Teaching Mathematics, 1977. (a)

Kolb, J. R. Teaching and testing for comprehension of principles. *Frostburg State College Journal of Mathematics Education*, 1977, (14), 14–29. (b)

Lawton, J. T., & Wanska, S. K. Advance organizers as a teaching strategy: A reply to Barnes and Clawson. *Review of Educational Research*, 1977, *47*, 233–244.

Lesh, R. A., Jr. The influence of an advanced [sic] organizer on two types of instructional units about finite geometries. *Journal for Research in Mathematics Education*, 1976, *7*, 82–86. (a)

Lesh, R. A., Jr. The influence of two types of advanced [sic] organizers on an instructional unit about finite groups. *Journal for Research in Mathematics Education*, 1976, *7*, 87–91. (b)

Lesh, R. A., Jr., & Johnson, H. Models and applications as advanced [sic] organizers. *Journal for Research in Mathematics Education*, 1976, *7*, 75–81.

Lockwood, J. R. *The effect of varying quality of examples on a strategy for teaching a concept in mathematics*. Unpublished manuscript, 1977.

Malo, G. E. Differential treatments in learning disjunctive concepts in mathematics (Doctoral dissertation, University of Illinois, 1974). *Dissertation Abstracts International*, 1975, *35*, 4051A. (University Microfilms No. 75-363)

Markle, S. M. They teach concepts, don't they? *Educational Researcher*, 1975, *4*, 3–9.

Markle, S. M., & Tiemann, P. W. *Really understanding concepts: Or in frumious pursuit of the jabberwock*. Champaign, Ill.: Stipes, 1969.

Merrill, M. D., & Wood, N. D. *Instructional strategies: A preliminary taxonomy*. Columbus, Ohio: ERIC/SMEAC, 1974.

Messick, S. Personality consistencies in cognition and creativity. In S. Messick & Associates (Ed.), *Individuality in learning*. San Francisco: Jossey-Bass, 1976.

Miller, W. A. The acceptance and recognition of six logical inference patterns by secondary students (Doctoral dissertation, University of Wisconsin, 1968). *Dissertation Abstracts*, 1968, *29*, 1685A–1686A. (University Microfilms No. 68-13,651)

Neimark, E., & Santa, J. Thinking and concept attainment. In M. Rosenzweig & L. Porter (Eds.), *Annual review of psychology* (Vol. 26). Palo Alto, Calif.: Annual Reviews, 1975.

Neisser, V., & Weene, P. Hierarchies in concept attainment. *Journal of Experimental Psychology*, 1962, *64*, 644–645.

Novillis, C. F. An analysis of the fraction concept into a hierarchy of selected subconcepts and the testing of the hierarchical dependencies. *Journal for Research in Mathematics Education*, 1976, *7*, 131–144.

Osler, S. F., & Trautman, G. E. Concept attainment: II. Effect of stimulus complexity upon concept attainment at two levels of intelligence. *Journal of Experimental Psychology*, 1961, *62*, 9–13.

Payne, J. N. Review of research on fractions. In R. Lesh (Ed.), *Number and measurement: Papers from a research workshop*. Columbus, Ohio: ERIC/SMEAC Science, Mathematics, and Environmental Education Information Analysis Center, 1975.

Pearl, A. W. A study of the effects on students' achievement and attitudes when they work in academic teams of three members (Doctoral dissertation, Cornell University, 1967). *Dissertation Abstracts*, 1967, *28*, 59A–60A. (University Microfilms No. 67-6432)

Pence, B. J. *Small group review of mathematics: A function of the review organization, structure, and task format*. Paper presented at the annual meeting of the National Council of Teachers of Mathematics, Denver, April 1975.

Pendleton, J. M. Mathematical concept attainment of sixth grade students in relation to their cognitive style (Doctoral dissertation, University of Texas at Austin, 1972). *Dissertation Abstracts International*, 1973, *33*, 5043A. (University Microfilms No. 73-7617)

Pereira, W. C. *The relationship between girls' overt verbalization, performance, retention, rules and strategies as they learn a mathematical structure: A study based on elements of a potential theory which relates thinking, language and learning* (Technical Report No. 293). Madison: Wisconsin Research and Development Center for Cognitive Learning, 1973. (ERIC Document Reproduction Service No. ED 098 081)

Piaget, J. Foreword. In M. Schwebel & J. Raph (Eds.), *Piaget in the classroom*. London: Routledge & Kegan Paul, 1974.

Pikas, Anatol. *Abstraction and concept formation*. Cambridge, Mass.: Harvard University Press, 1966.

Retzer, K. A. *Effects of precise verbalization of discovered mathematical generalizations on transfer* (Final report, OE Bureau of Research, Project No. 8-E-019), 1969. (ERIC Document Reproduction Service No. ED 040 849)

Rowe, M. B. Wait-time and rewards as instructional variables, their influence on language, logic, and fate control: Part one—Wait-time. *Journal of Research in Science Teaching*, 1974, *11*, 81–94.

Scandura, J. M. A theory of mathematical knowledge: Can rules account for creative behavior? *Journal for Research in Mathematics Education*, 1971, *2*, 183–196.

Scandura, J. M. A theory of structural learning. *Journal of Structural Learning*, 1976, *5*, 251–329.

Schwartz, B. D. Certain relations between verbalization and concept formation (Doctoral dissertation, Princeton University, 1948). *Dissertation Abstracts,* 1955, *15,* 453. (University Microfilms No. 11023)

Scott, J. A., Frayer, D. A., & Klausmeier, H. J. *The effects on short- and long-term retention and on transfer of two methods of presenting selected geometry concepts.* Paper presented at the annual meeting of the American Educational Research Association, New York, February 1971.

Securro, S., Jr., & Wallis, R. T. Concept attainment of culturally advantaged and disadvantaged children utilizing artificial and lifelike stimulus tasks. *Journal of Educational Psychology,* 1971, *62,* 531–538.

Shapiro, B. J., & O'Brien, T. C. Quasi-child logics. *Educational Studies in Mathematics,* 1973, *5,* 181–184.

Shulman, L. S., & Keislar, E. R. *Learning by discovery: A critical appraisal.* Chicago: Rand McNally, 1966.

Shumway, R. J. Negative instances and mathematical concept formation: A preliminary study. *Journal for Research in Mathematics Education,* 1971, *2,* 218–227.

Shumway, R. J. Negative instances in mathematical concept acquisition: Transfer effects between the concepts of commutativity and associativity. *Journal for Research in Mathematics Education,* 1974, *5,* 197–211.

Shumway, R. J. Positive versus positive and negative instances and the acquisition of the concepts of distributivity and homomorphism. *Journal of Structural Learning,* 1977, *4,* 331–348.

Shumway, R. J., & White, A. L. *Prevalent levels of irrelevant attributes: A potentially important variable in mathematical concept learning.* Unpublished manuscript, Ohio State University, 1977.

SMSG Panel on Research. Final report of the SMSG Panel on Research. *Newsletter No. 39,* August, 1972. (ERIC Document Reproduction Service No. ED 088 706)

Sowder, L. The influence of verbalization of discovered numerical- or sorting-task generalizations on short-term retention in connection with the Hendrix hypothesis. *Journal for Research in Mathematics Education,* 1974, *5,* 167–176.

Sowder, L. Further work on verbalization of discoveries. *Journal for Research in Mathematics Education,* 1975, *6,* 222–227. (a)

Sowder, L. Transfer between two settings for some concept attainment tasks. *Journal of Educational Psychology,* 1975, *67,* 905–908. (b)

Stephens, J. M. *The process of schooling.* New York: Holt, Rinehart & Winston, 1967.

Swank, E. W. An empirical comparison of teaching strategies where the amount of content information and teacher-pupil interaction is varied. In T. Cooney (Ed.), *Teaching strategies.* Columbus, Ohio: ERIC Center for Science, Mathematics, and Environmental Education, 1976.

Tennyson, R. D., Woolley, F. R., & Merrill, M. D. Exemplar and nonexemplar variables which produce correct concept classification behavior and specified classification errors. *Journal of Educational Psychology,* 1972, *63,* 144–152.

Thomas, S. H. *A comparison of two review strategies for reviewing mathematics.* Paper presented at the annual meeting of the National Council of Teachers of Mathematics, Denver, April 1975.

Threadgill, J. A. The relationship of analytic-global cognitive style and two methods of instruction in mathematical concept attainment (Doctoral dissertation, University of Oregon, 1976). *Dissertation Abstracts International,* 1977, *37,* 5664A. (University Microfilms No. 77-4766)

Trudnak, J. L. Toward a theory of sequencing: Study 4-2: The relative effectiveness of four canonical teaching procedures for concept attainment and generalization in mathematics (Doctoral dissertation, Pennsylvania State University, 1974). *Dissertation Abstracts International,* 1975, *36,* 114A. (University Microfilms No. 75-15,799)

Turner, R. L. Design problems in research on teaching strategies. In T. Cooney (Ed.), *Teach-*

ing strategies. Columbus, Ohio: ERIC Center for Science, Mathematics, and Environmental Education, 1976.

van Hiele, P., & van Hiele, M. La pensée de l'enfant et la géométrie. *Bulletin de l'Association des Professeurs de Mathématiques de l'Enseignement Public,* 1959, *38,* 199–205.

Vance, J., & Kieren, T. Mathematics laboratories—More than fun? *School Science and Mathematics,* 1972, *72,* 617–623.

Vygotsky, L. S. [*Thought and language*] (E. Hanfmann & G. Vakar, Eds. and trans.). Cambridge, Mass.: M.I.T. Press, 1962.

Walbesser, H. H , & Eisenberg, T. A. A review of research on behavioral objectives and learning hierarchies. Columbus, Ohio: ERIC Information Analysis Center for Science, Mathematics, and Environmental Education, 1972. (ERIC Document Reproduction Service No. ED 059 900)

Wason, P. C., & Johnson-Laird, P. N. *Psychology of reasoning, structure and content.* Cambridge, Mass.: Harvard University Press, 1972.

White, R. T. Research into learning hierarchies. *Review of Educational Research,* 1973, *43,* 361–375.

Wilkerson, J. D. A review of research regarding mathematics laboratories. In W. Fitzgerald & J. Higgins (Eds.), *Mathematics laboratories: Implementation, research, and evaluation.* Columbus, Ohio: ERIC Information Analysis Center for Science, Mathematics, and Environmental Education, 1974.

Wills, H. III. Transfer of problem solving ability gained through learning by discovery (Doctoral dissertation, University of Illinois, 1967). *Dissertation Abstracts,* 1967, *28,* 1319A–1320A. (University Microfilms No. 67-11,937)

Wills, H. Generalizations. In M. Rosskopf (Ed.), *The teaching of secondary school mathematics,* Thirty-third Yearbook of the National Council of Teachers of Mathematics. Washington, D.C.: The Council, 1970.

Zykova, V. I. [The psychology of sixth-grade pupils' mastery of geometric concepts.] In J. Kilpatrick and I. Wirszup (Eds.), *Soviet studies in the psychology of learning and teaching mathematics* (Vol. 1). Stanford, Calif.: School Mathematics Study Group, 1969.

10

Research on Mathematical Problem Solving

Frank K. Lester, Jr.

Indiana University

S TUDY the diagram below and read the statement that follows it. (A minor variation of this problem is discussed by Henderson and Pingry, 1953).

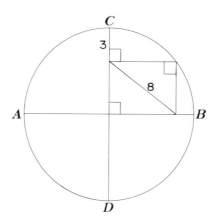

AB and *CD* are diameters of the circle.
How long is the radius of the circle?

Your reaction to this problem may have been one of the following:

1. I never have been good at geometry. I don't think I'll bother.
2. It's a trick problem; otherwise he wouldn't have stated it.
3. Interesting! I'll have to spend some time on this later.

4. Hmm! If I draw a diameter parallel to the segment that is known to be 8 units, then . . .

5. Trivial! The radius is obviously 8 units, since the given diagonal of the rectangle is 8 units and the other diagonal is a radius.

6. I've seen this before. The answer is 8 units.

The point of all this is that problem solving is a very personal type of activity. A particular problem may evoke reactions ranging from utter delight to total boredom or complete frustration. Also, the way a problem is presented and the type of information provided may significantly influence success in solving it. A few of the many other factors that play a role in mathematical problem solving include previous experience, mathematical background, level of interest, motivation, and problem structure. In short, problem solving is an extremely complex area of human behavior.

Before proceeding further, we shall define the terms *problem* and *problem solving:* "A *problem* is a situation in which an individual or group is called upon to perform a task for which there is no readily accessible algorithm which determines completely the method of solution" (Lester, 1978, p. 54). It follows that problem solving is the set of actions taken to perform the task (i.e., solve the problem). This definition is consistent with definitions presented by several others (e.g., Bourne, Ekstrand & Dominowski, 1971; Brownell, 1942; Duncker, 1945; Henderson & Pingry, 1953; Kinsella, 1970; Newell & Simon, 1972; and Resnick & Glaser, 1976). It should be added that this definition assumes a desire on the part of the individual or group to perform the task. Otherwise the situation cannot be considered a problem.

The fact that problem solving has been the object of so much research, a focal point for several curriculum-development efforts, and the subject of innumerable books, articles, and conference reports attests to its importance in the study of mathematics. Indeed, there is substantial support for the notion that the ultimate aim of learning mathematics at every level is to be able to solve problems. Despite this well-recognized importance, the role problem solving should play in the mathematics curriculum is less clear. A cursory look at the most popular mathematics textbooks gives ample evidence of the lack of generally accepted tenets about the role of problem solving. For example, elementary textbook series continue to devote almost exclusive attention to the development of computational skills, and high school algebra books are concerned primarily with imparting a collection of algorithmic techniques and other procedures for manipulating algebraic expressions. In brief, all too often mathematics is taught using a "paint by number" model that provides little opportunity for students to develop whatever natural creative abilities they may have. This is unfortunate but understandable. It is one thing to recognize the importance of problem solving and quite another to know how to develop the abilities associated with it. The proper domain of mathematical problem-solving research is in establishing a body of knowledge about the nature of problem solving that can be used to assist students in developing their maximum potential as problem solvers.

This chapter is divided into three main sections: the nature of mathematical problem solving, representative research and current trends, and key issues for future efforts.

The first section is brief, since it is intended as a means for structuring the discussion of the other two sections rather than as a substantive analysis of problem solving. The research cited in the second section is restricted primarily to efforts conducted between 1970 and 1979. The few earlier studies that are included represent problem-solving research that has been particularly influential in determining the direction of current inquiry. No attempt has been made to provide an exhaustive review of the literature. Rather, the intent is to discuss those investigations that help paint a reasonably clear picture of the state of the art and to point out trends. The final section raises a few critical issues that will confront researchers in the near future in their efforts to add to the existing body of knowledge about mathematical problem solving.

THE NATURE OF
MATHEMATICAL PROBLEM SOLVING

The problem at the beginning of this essay illustrates the multitude of factors involved in problem solving. I asked several adults, including mathematics educators, doctoral students in mathematics education, preservice elementary teachers, and a few persons who were not associated with education in a professional way, to solve this problem. For some there was an immediate shifting of gears as they tried to recall relevant theorems about circles. (As it happens, this approach will not yield a very elegant solution to the problem.) For these problem solvers, their previous mathematical training may have actually hampered their progress. Such situations as this make it extremely difficult to isolate the key ingredients for successful problem solving. Mathematical problem solving appears, to a certain extent, to be so complex and subtle as to defy description and analysis. However, there are four types of factors associated with problem solving, all inextricably linked, with each type involving many parts. The "radius of the circle" problem illustrates these four types.

The Problem Itself: Task Variables

Of course, the problem itself influences success. Spatial problems may be quite difficult for individuals who have an analytic orientation. The mathematical content of the problem is also important (e.g., Would a person who didn't know that the diagonals of a rectangle have the same length have much hope for success?). Other problem-related factors include problem format and problem structure.

Characteristics of the Individual: Subject Variables

Various characteristics of the individual play an important role in his or her ability to solve the circle problem. Such characteristics include *conceptual style* (e.g., Does the individual tend to be analytically, spatially, or intuitively oriented?); *previous mathematical background* (e.g., Has the individual previously studied about circles?); *reaction under stress or pressure* (e.g., Does the individual feel pressed to get a quick solution if the problem poser is watching?); and (valuable for this problem) *field independence* (e.g., Does the solver have the ability to ignore distracting information?).

Problem-solving Behavior: Process Variables

The third category, closely tied to both the characteristics of the solver and the nature of the problem, involves factors related to the individual's behavior during problem solving: the manner of organizing and processing information, the types of cognitive strategies used to plan and carry out the attack, and the methods used to evaluate what was done.

Environmental Features: Instruction Variables

The fourth category includes those features of the problem-solving environment external to the problem and the problem solver. (One individual felt compelled to obtain a quick solution to the problem because of external pressures.) Instructional factors comprise the most important class of factors within this category. Consequently, our discussion will be restricted to instruction variables only.

In summary, the nature of problem solving involves at least four interacting categories of factors (variables):

1. *Task variables:* Factors associated with the nature of the problem.
2. *Subject variables:* What the individual brings to the problem.
3. *Process variables:* The overt and covert behavior of the individual during problem solving.
4. *Instruction variables:* Actually a subclass of environmental variables. How individuals can be helped to become better problem solvers.

REPRESENTATIVE RESEARCH AND CURRENT TRENDS

During the 1970s, mathematics education researchers devoted more attention to problem solving than to any other topic in the mathematics curriculum. There is every indication that this trend may continue for some time to come (Suydam, 1976). It is difficult to synthesize the myriad studies that have been conducted because of such factors as a lack of agreement of what constitutes problem solving, how performance should be measured, what tasks are appropriate, and what the key variables are that influence behavior. Indeed, there has been little unanimity of opinion regarding which are the most important issues to investigate.

A recent review of psychology research on thinking and problem solving suggests that problem solving may be the most chaotic of research areas in psychology (Dodd & Bourne, 1973). Reviews of the research have appeared periodically in both the mathematics education and psychology literature. Notable among these are the reviews by Bourne and Dominowski (1972), Davis (1966, 1973), Gorman (1968), Green (1966), Kilpatrick (1969), and Shulman and Elstein (1975). In addition, a number of problem-solving monographs have been published under the auspices of ERIC (viz., Goldin & McClintock, in press; Hatfield & Bradbard, 1978; and Lesh, Mierkiewicz, & Kantowski, in press).

The discussion here focuses on representative research efforts that exemplify the range of current research on mathematical problem solving. An attempt has been made to classify studies in such a way as to provide a clear picture of the scope of the research, indicate discernible trends, and highlight the key issues. Four categories of research are considered, corresponding to the four types of variables identified in the preceding section. These categories do not partition the set of contemporary research studies nor do they classify all types of investigations. Rather, they serve to classify the preponderance of research in a natural and useful way.

Task Variables

A primary reason it is difficult to draw any general conclusions about mathematical problem solving is that a wide diversity of problems have been used in the research. Tasks range from direct computations to puzzle problems of the Tower of Hanoi and tangram varieties and from standard textbook problems involving a one-step translation to "project" problems involving group efforts over an extended period of time. In addition, the mathematical content of a problem is linked closely to such factors as the problem solver's motivation, cognitive processes, heuristic strategies, and background, and the complexity of the task. Consequently, since research tasks have come from arithmetic, geometry, algebra, and calculus as well as other areas, the possibility of generalizing results is severely limited.

A final serious limitation of much of the problem-solving research has been identified by Lesh (1979), who insists that the types of problems used in the research have been primarily of the "puzzle problem" (e.g., Tower of Hanoi) and simple translation story problem varieties. Indeed, research has lacked problems with substantive mathematical content or realistic situations. He suggests that the processes and skills needed to solve real-world problems are not necessarily the same as those that are typically considered in problem-solving research. Consequently, there is a need for research involving problem-solving situations that "focus on *real people, real problems* involving *real mathematics* content, and *realistic situations*" (p. 87).

There is general agreement that the task confronting a problem solver has a significant influence on performance. Consequently, a substantial amount of research has focused on various characteristics of problem tasks, such as the mathematical content, problem representation, method of presentation, and structural parameters inherent in the problem. The main goals have been to isolate the key determinants of problem difficulty and to identify the problem features that influence the solution process.

Unfortunately, no sets of variables have been clearly established as the most important determinants of problem difficulty. For example, beyond the almost obvious statement that children cannot solve a problem if they cannot read it, there is conflicting evidence regarding the effect of reading ability on problem-solving performance. Linville (1970) found that the difficulty level of the syntax has a significant effect on the solution of the problems. However, Knifong and Holtan (1976) contend that on the basis of their analysis of children's solutions to word problems "it is difficult to attribute major importance to reading as a source of failure" (p. 111). They found computational errors to be the most important deterrent to success.

A number of investigators have focused on the effect of the complexity of the structure of tasks (e.g., complexity of syntax, underlying computational structure, and information) on problem-solving performance. One approach employed by researchers interested in variables associated with problem structure (i.e., structural variables) has been to apply multiple linear regression techniques to identify sets of variables that accurately predict problem-solving performance. The series of investigations conducted by Jerman to determine linguistic and computational variables that are predictors of students' error rates on verbal arithmetic problems typifies the best work in this area (Jerman, 1973, 1974; Jerman & Rees, 1972). Results of Jerman's efforts indicate that although there does not appear to be a universal set of linguistic variables (e.g., problem length, parts of speech, punctuation) that serves to predict student performance, there is evidence to suggest that linguistic predictor variables are age or grade-level specific. That is, the set of "good" predictors changes with increasing age. At the same time it appears that the importance of computational variables as predictors decreases from being very important in the intermediate grades to having very little value as predictors for college students (Jerman,

1974). A limitation that Jerman recognizes in this type of research is that there is no theory to use to determine optimal weights to give to the variables or to "account for the accuracy of the predictors" (p. 360).

An alternative to the multiple regression approach for investigating structural variables is to hold constant all variables that are relevant to the solution of the task but whose effects are not to be considered. This is the procedure used by Caldwell (1977) in a study designed to determine the relative difficulties of different types of word problems at different ages. Problems were designed to be the same with respect to such factors as length, syntactic structure, vocabulary level, underlying algebraic equation, sequencing of information, and types of numbers involved. Problems differed with respect to two dichotomous experimental variables: abstract versus concrete, and factual versus hypothetical. Among the significant results were that subjects in elementary grades solved more hypothetical than factual problems, abstract problems were more difficult than concrete ones across grade levels, concrete/factual problems were the easiest for all grade levels, and there was a significant interaction between the level of abstractness and the degree of factualness for elementary and junior high school subjects but not for senior high school subjects.

In the process of developing a large bank of problems for use in the intermediate grades, the staff of the Mathematical Problem Solving Project (MPSP) devoted considerable attention to the development of a scheme for categorizing problems to facilitate efficient retrieval (Lester, 1978). As a result of prolonged observation of children as they solved problems and interviews with a large number of children after problem-solving sessions, a theoretical categorization scheme was devised. This scheme consisted of four dimensions: setting of the problem, structure and mathematical complexity, mathematical content, and strategies applicable for solving a problem. A key feature of this scheme is that reading and computational factors comprise a relatively small portion of the complexity dimension. Other factors include the complexity of the focusing process during problem solving, the complexity of the solution process, and the complexity of evaluation and generalization. The work of the MPSP on problem categorization cannot be classified as experimental research in the classical sense, but it represents an attempt to evolve a theory of mathematical problem solving from which testable hypotheses can be formed.

The research studies discussed in the foregoing paragraphs employed different research methods and were designed for different purposes. Nevertheless, they share a common goal of assisting teachers and curriculum developers in the selection of sets of problems of predictable levels of difficulty for a given grade level or for a given instructional objective. Barnett (1975a) attempted to apply the results of research on structural variables to the development of instructional materials for improving problem-solving ability. He used four sets of structural variables (linguistic, operational, computational, and procedural) that are predictors of problem difficulty and "account for a significant portion of variance in observed proportion correct, and . . . are highly reliable over different problem sets" (Barnett, 1975b, p. 4). He sought to determine whether problem-solving ability can be improved by instruction directed at overcoming difficulties caused by these variables. Barnett designed a study employing a pretest-posttest control group design with repeated measures with pre-service elementary teachers as subjects. The results indicated that instructional strategies based on particular structural variables can enhance problem-solving behavior, but the amount of variance in the proportion correct accounted for by these variables did not appear to change as a result of the instruction.

Goldin and Luger (1974, 1975) and Luger (1974) have applied certain artificial intelligence techniques to the study of problem-solving behavior, but they have not focused on determining which factors influence problem difficulty and complexity. Using *state-space* representations of a problem, they were able to describe the algorithmic and logical structure of the problem in order to investigate patterns in subjects' problem-solving behavior. (Briefly, a *state-space* representation of a problem is a diagrammatic illustration of the set of all states reachable from the initial state. A *state* is the set of all expressions that have been obtained from the initial statement of the problem up to a given moment. For a discussion of state-space representations, the reader is referred to Nilsson, 1971.) They have investigated such behaviors as goal-directedness, the role of subgoal states, the solution of subproblems, the tendency toward congruence of successive moves for isomorphic subproblems, the effect of problem symmetry on problem solving, and the transfer of learning from one problem to an isomorphic problem (Goldin & Luger, 1974). The state-space approach not only presents a complete analysis of the algorithmic and logical structure of problems but also provides a means for systematically studying the effect of this structure on subjects' problem-solving behavior.

An ultimate aim of most mathematical problem-solving research is to discover means for improving students' abilities to solve problems. An important component of realizing this aim is the systematic study of factors that make problem solving difficult or factors that in some way interact with subjects' behaviors. If instruction is to be optimally effective, problems having the appropriate content, context, level of difficulty, and interest for students must be carefully selected. In addition, if the teacher is interested in demonstrating the usefulness of a particular heuristic, care must be taken to choose problems that can elicit that heuristic. Thus it is important to gain as much information as possible on task variables. The status of the task variables research is quite healthy. Besides the research already discussed, studies by Days, Wheatley, and Kulm (1979), Ingle (1975), and Nesher (1976) are representative. A "Task Variables Working Group," formed as a result of a workshop on mathematical problem-solving research conducted at the University of Georgia in 1975, illustrates this healthy state (Hatfield, 1976). Among the activities of this working group has been the formation of the National Collection of Research Instruments for Mathematical Problem Solving (Goldin, McClintock, & Webb, 1977). A primary purpose of the collection is to serve as a resource for mathematical problems that have been used in at least one research study. Problems are carefully documented with respect to data on subject, treatment, and task variables. The collection provides a medium for communication among researchers in problem solving in addition to serving as a depository for problem-solving research instruments. The monograph on research on task variables written by several members of the Task Variables Working Group analyzes the key issues and describes some of the current research (Goldin & McClintock, in press).

Trend. The individual and cooperative efforts spawned by the Task Variables Working Group promise to provide a wealth of information. Both the regression model (e.g., Jerman's approach) and the process-tracing model (e.g., Goldin & Luger's approach) should continue to be popular and valuable research modes. Hatfield (1976) suggests there will be special interest in examining task variables in the context of experiments focusing on instruction in heuristic methods or the development of specific problem-solving skills.

Subject Variables

What traits do good problem solvers possess that poor problem solvers do not? Why is it that a person can solve certain kinds of problems but not others? (E.g., why are some people good at algebra problems but not geometry problems?) What are the appropriate times to attempt to teach students how to solve particular types of problems or how to use certain heuristic techniques?

These questions and other similar ones are fundamental to the study of mathematical problem solving. In particular, such questions focus on variables directly associated with the problem solver (e.g., sex, age, socioeconomic status, spatial ability, memory, self-concept, anxiety, and cognitive style). Although only a small portion of the research has been devoted exclusively or primarily to a consideration of subject variables, most studies do consider various subject variables as independent variables. ("Independent variables" are variables used to predict behavior.)

Before we look at specific studies, it may be useful to categorize subject variables. In a recent analysis of variables and methodologies in problem-solving research, Kilpatrick (1978) classified subject variables as being either *organismic* or *trait* variables. Organismic variables, such as sex, age, and socioeconomic status, are generally used to describe subjects; trait variables, such as abilities, attitudes, and personality factors, are open to some modification and require a sample of behavior. A third category proposed by Kilpatrick includes variables that describe the *instructional history* of subjects. Although these variables constitute a subcategory of organismic variables, it seems appropriate to draw special attention to them, since the instruction that subjects have received significantly influences results of research on developmental changes, individual differences, attitudes, and perhaps even abilities. This categorization of subject variables serves to organize the consideration of research relating the characteristics of problem solvers to their performance.

Developmental Changes in Problem-solving Behavior

It is necessary to identify (a) which processes subjects use naturally, (b) when they acquire these capabilities, and (c) which processes they can be taught to use in order to maximize instructional effectiveness. Developmental analyses of problem solving are scarce. Most studies use only a limited age range, making comparisons across ages difficult. Of course, the classic work of Piaget (e.g., Inhelder & Piaget, 1958) and the lesser-known developmental studies of Weir (1964) and Neimark and Lewis (1967) have been invaluable sources of information regarding the cognitive development of children and its relation to problem-solving ability. Recent research suggests the existence of some key developmental changes with respect to subjects' attention to irrelevant information and mental processes used.

Stevenson's review of research in children's learning and cognitive development points out that younger children tend to focus on irrelevant attributes of a problem situation, thereby making errors (Stevenson, 1975). Bana and Nelson (1978) support Stevenson's claim. They investigated the effects of "distractors" in different problem settings on the problem-solving behavior of children in Grades 1–3 and found that irrelevant information does affect problem-solving performance and that in particular spatial-numerical distractors were the most troublesome. In addition, attention to distractors decreased with increasing age. The belief that the presence of irrelevant data significantly influences problem difficulty is indicated by the work of the Mathematical Problem Solving Project (MPSP) on the development of a problem categorization scheme. A part of this scheme is a "complexity of the problem" dimension. The MPSP theorized that the "complexity of the focusing process" of a problem is determined in part by the "number of bits of irrelevant data" (Lester, 1978).

My study of developmental changes in problem-solving behavior involving students in Grades 1 through 12 (Lester, 1975) was one of the few such studies specific to mathematics education. A key result was the observation that younger children (Grades 1–3) often used a previously successful response regardless of whether or not the response was appropriate. In addition, children as young as 6 could solve problems of the proof type. The main differences between younger and older children was in the amount of time required, the number of errors made, and a tendency among younger children to rely exclusively on a trial-and-error strategy. Not only was the proclivity for trial-and-error behavior inversely related to age, but younger subjects did not appear to profit as readily from mistakes as older ones. This result is consistent with the conjecture posed by the MPSP that "children (Grade 5) without training use only a trial-and-error strategy in solving process problems" (Stengel, LeBlanc, Jacobson, & Lester, 1977, p. 46).

Individual Differences and Characteristics of Successful Problem Solvers

A fundamental question in problem-solving research is "Why is it that some people are good problem solvers and others are not?" The trivial answer "because people are different" offers little help beyond pointing to the need to tailor problem-solving instruction to individual abilities. Unfortunately, as Scandura (1977) points out, "Individual differences measurement is a relatively neglected aspect of human problem solving" (p. 493).

Individual differences such as sex, cognitive ability, mathematical aptitude, and attitude toward mathematics and the relationship of these differences to problem-solving ability have been investigated by a few researchers. Dodson (1972) sought to determine discriminating characteristics of successful problem solvers and thereby to form hypotheses concerning variables that might be determinants of success. Using data from the NLSMA Z-population, Dodson attempted to characterize successful "insightful" problem solvers in terms of four categories of variables: (a) mathematics achievement; (b) cognitive and affective variables; (c) variables of teacher, background, and attitude; and (d) variables of school, community, and curriculum. Results indicated that good problem solvers differed from poor ones in several ways. Among the most prominent differences were that good problem solvers are superior with respect to (a) overall mathematics achievement, (b) verbal and general reasoning ability, (c) spatial ability, (d) positive attitudes, (e) resistence to distraction, (f) level of field independence, and (g) divergent thinking.

Meyer (1978) attempted to determine a structure of intellectual abilities related to mathematical problem solving. She concluded that mathematical ability is specific among all intellectual abilities and although prerequisite mathematical concepts and skills are related to problem-solving success, a knowledge of these concepts and skills is not sufficient for successful problem solving.

Several researchers have considered differences between males and females in problem-solving ability (Fennema, 1974). The results are inconclusive; some studies indicate males to be superior to females (e.g., Wilson, 1972), and others conclude that males do not typically perform better than females (e.g., Fennema & Sherman, 1978). Since sex-related differences appear to increase with age, the number of years of studying mathematics may play an important part in determining the extent of the difference. In fact, when the factor of sex was controlled, the main differences between sexes lay with two affective variables, confidence in learning mathematics and mathematics as a male domain (Fennema & Sherman, 1978).

Computational skill and reading ability are two commonly considered correlates of problem-solving success. The relationship between problem-solving ability and computational skill seems to vary with age. More specifically, computational ability is closely related to problem-solving ability for young children, but there is only a remote relationship for college-age students (Dodson, 1972; Jerman, 1974). The role of reading ability is less clear. Whereas there is considerable evidence to suggest reading ability to be directly associated with performance on standard word problems (e.g., Chase, 1960; Linville, 1970; Martin, 1964), there is also support for the belief that reading plays only a minor role in determining problem-solving success (e.g., Balow, 1964; Knifong & Holtan, 1976).

The work of Krutetskii (1963, 1969, 1976) is most notable among recent studies of individual mathematical problem-solving abilities. A primary goal of his more recent work (1976) was "to clarify the features that characterize the mental activity of mathematically gifted pupils as they solve various mathematical problems" (p. 78). Additional aims related to problem-solving abilities and individual differences were to determine typological differences in the structure of mathematical abilities and to investigate age-related changes in mathematical abilities. In an earlier study (1963) Krutetskii found that students with some incapacity in mathematics could be grouped into six categories with respect to their visual and verbal abilities: (a) low visual ability and low verbal ability; (b) low visual ability and low verbal ability, but stronger visual ability; (c) clear predominance of visual ability over verbal ability; (d) equal abilities visually and verbally, but only average in both; (e) well-developed verbal ability; and (f) well-developed visual ability. In his classic twelve-year study (1976), he attempted to apply this categorization scheme to all students. He concluded that there appear to be three types of students: *analytic, geometric,* and *harmonic* (a combination of the other two types). This conclusion is amazingly similar to that of Haecker and Ziehen (1931), who also determined that there were three types of students: (a) abstractly dominant students (even geometric problems solved abstractly); (b) visually dominant students (even abstract problems solved visually); and (c) those students for whom abstract and visual components are in equilibrium.

Another important feature of Krutetskii's studies (1976) was his investigation of the relationship between problem-solving ability and perceptions of problem structure. He found that a major difference between good and poor problem solvers lies in their perception of the important elements of problems. Good problem solvers typically had certain abilities that poorer problem solvers lacked: (a) the ability to distinguish relevant from irrelevant information, (b) the ability to see quickly and accurately the mathematical structure of a problem, (c) the ability to generalize across a wide range of similar problems, and (d) the ability to remember a problem's formal structure for a long time.

Silver (1979) concurred with Krutetskii's conclusion that good problem solvers are superior to poor problem solvers in their ability to perceive the mathematical structure of a problem and to generalize to problems having similar structure. More specifically, he found that the extent to which individuals sorted problems on the basis of mathematical structure was related to their problem-solving ability as well as to their general verbal and mathematical abilities.

Krutetskii's work is generally not quantitative and does not adhere to standard tenets of experimental design. However, his use of clinical interviews and other nonexperimental procedures may prove to be the aspects of his investigations that will have the biggest impact on mathematical problem-solving research.

In addition to Krutetskii, several American researchers have investigated the role of spatial ability in problem solving (Moses, 1977; Schonberger, 1976; Wheatley, Mitchell, Frankland, & Kraft, 1978; Wilson & Begle, 1972). Moses found empirical evidence of a strong correlation between spatial ability and problem-solving ability, a result in agreement with earlier NLSMA findings (Wilson & Begle). The relationship between spatial ability and problem-solving ability is at least implicit in the work of Wheatley and his associates.

Another psychological characterisitc that appears to be related to problem-solving ability is field independence. Dodson (1972) concluded that field independence was one of the strongest characteristics of successful problem solvers. Blake (1977) found not only that good problem solvers were field independent but also that field independent students used a greater variety of heuristics and were more willing to change their mode of attack than field dependent students. These observations help explain the high correlation between field independence and problem-solving success.

There is an urgent need for work relating individual differences and characteristics and problem-solving abilities if viable theories are to be developed that consider the interrelationships among problem tasks, problem solvers, processes, and the task environment. The theory development efforts of Scandura (1977) and Resnick and Glaser (1976) support this notion. For Scandura a consideration of individual differences along with content and cognition is vital to gaining a better understanding of problem-solving behavior. He calls for the development of diagnostic methods for isolating the problem-solving processes that individuals can learn to use.

Resnick and Glaser contend that problem-solving success is a function of (a) competency on task-specific skills; (b) facility with strategies related to problem detection, feature scanning, and goal analysis; and (c) the features of the task environment. Furthermore, they believe the second category includes the primary competencies in which individuals differ and that the way these strategies are carried out distinguishes the good from the poor problem solver. Thus for Scandura, Resnick and Glaser, and other researchers in sympathy with their ideas, it appears that the most important individual differences are associated with the ability to use various cognitive processes (a type of trait variable).

Affective Variables

No one doubts the importance of variables such as interest, motivation, confidence, perseverance, and a willingness to take risks. Unfortunately, because of the elusiveness of these variables and the lack of reliable instruments, there is little conclusive information regarding their specific roles in mathematics in general or problem solving in particular. For example, after a careful review of the literature on problem solving and a year of observing over 700 intermediate grade children solving problems, the staff of the Mathematical Problem Solving Project (MPSP) decided that willingness, perseverance, and self-confidence were three of the most important influences on problem-solving performance (Webb, Moses & Kerr, 1977). However, the MPSP was unable to develop an attitude instrument to measure adequately the extent to which these three factors changed over time, even though the staff and classroom teachers were confident that very definite changes had occurred. Robinson (1973) studied the problem-solving behavior of sixth graders and found that good problem solvers had higher self-esteem than poor problem solvers, a result that supports the belief in the importance of developing students' self-confidence in order to enhance problem-solving success.

In a review of 155 studies involving the relationship between various psychological traits and problem solving, Trimmer (1974) observed intrinsic motivation and having enough time to complete a complex task to be the best facilitators of learning how to solve problems. In addition, he concluded that impulsivity is useful in producing hypotheses but reflexivity is better for evaluating hypotheses. That is, concentration and persistence are keys to making real progress in solving problems. Other conclusions drawn by Trimmer were that confidence, lack of anxiety, flexibility, lack of rigidity, and an ability to cope with uncertainty were traits associated with successful problem solving.

Trends. Studies like those of Dodson (1972) and Meyer (1978), which attempted to identify characteristics of good problem solvers using various multivariate statistical procedures, have been valuable inasmuch as they provide reasonable bases on which to formulate conjectures about the essential problem-solving skills and abilities. These studies are basically atheoretical but serve to establish guidelines for theory development. It is expected that although investigations like these will continue to be conducted, emphasis will shift toward linking problem solvers to the types of mental processes they employ during problem solving. Recent studies (e.g., Kantowski, 1974; Moses, 1977; Putt, 1978) indicate an interest in observing students closely over prolonged periods of time in an effort to identify processes as they develop or change. This new direction in research on subject variables is due in large measure to the influence of Krutetskii (1976), the urging of noted authorities like Shulman (1970), and a general trend toward mounting a systematic, concerted effort to link problem solvers to the processes they use.

Process Variables

The cognitive processes used during problem solving have been the object of a substantial amount of study in recent years. This interest is due in large part to the now generally accepted view that a knowledge of the processes used to solve a problem is more important than noting simply that the problem was or was not solved, how much time was taken, how many errors were made, and so on. Perhaps problem-solving research gets its reputation for being a chaotic area of investigation because such a wide range of mental activities are involved. Cognitive processes include all thinking done during problem solving and range over such diverse behaviors as working backward, simplifying, and deducing to drawing pictures, solving equations, and using trial and error. Indeed, the very fact that such a large variety of activities must be considered in the study of problem-solving behavior may be a major reason research on mental processes has only recently become acceptable in the psychological literature.

The preponderance of research into problem-solving processes can be classified as the "process tracing" variety. According to Shulman and Elstein (1975), "process-tracing approaches ... attempt to describe the intellectual processes used by subjects as they render judgments and make decisions or solve problems" (p. 4). This approach aims to describe human problem solving in terms of certain elementary cognitive activities by analyzing verbal, or otherwise manifest, protocols. Although this research is largely atheoretical, the intent is to gain the sort of insights about problem-solving behavior that will facilitate the generation of theory.

Clarification of Terms

The complexity of problem-solving processes has caused considerable confusion regarding the meanings of the various types of processes involved. *Heuristics, key organizers,* and *tool skills* are among the many terms used in the literature. Polya (1957) describes a *heuristic* as a planned action or series of actions performed to assist in the discovery of a solution to a problem. He suggests that "heuristical reasoning is reasoning not regarded as final and strict but as provisional and plausible only, whose purpose is to discover the solution of the present problem" (p. 113). For Polya the word *heuristic* is used to refer to mental operations only. However, it appears that such different actions as drawing a diagram, looking for a pattern, and solving an equation have been classified as heuristics by some researchers. Goldin and Luger (1975) give a more technical but still rather general definition of heuristic. Using the language of information-processing theorists, they consider a heuristic as a path taken by a problem solver within a state-place. The advantage of this view of heuristics is that it is an operational definition lending itself to tangible analysis. Terms like "key organizers," "tool skills," and "skills" typically refer to actions and abilities that facilitate the use of a strategy. For example, since "making a table" often helps organize information that can then aid in the "looking for a pattern" strategy, "making a table" is considered a "key organizer" or "tool skill."

Techniques for Studying Processes

Data-gathering techniques. A number of different approaches have been employed to study problem-solving processes, but the most common has been the *thinking aloud* technique. This method involves having the subject verbalize the ideas and questions that occur during problem solving. Typically an audiotape or videotape recording is made, and a trained observer uses a protocol-coding procedure to record certain aspects of the subject's behavior.

Other techniques, less frequently used, are introspection, retrospection, and written problem-solving inventories. Introspection differs from thinking aloud in that it requires subjects to analyze their thinking as they attempt to solve a problem. Retrospection requires analysis by the subject *after* the problem is solved and often involves a discussion between subject and interviewer. Written inventories usually attempt to incorporate aspects of one technique or some combination of the other three techniques into a written form, thereby eliminating the need for audiotaping and protocol coding. In addition, with written instruments data can be collected from a relatively large number of subjects in a relatively short period of time.

Each of these techniques has certain inherent weaknesses and relative strengths. Presently, all the process-tracing methods "involve at least as much art as science, with few well-calibrated procedures available for use" (Shulman & Elstein, 1975, p. 30).

Data-analysis techniques. The difficulties surrounding the accurate observation and recording of cognitive processes are compounded by the problems involved in analyzing the data. The most popular method of analyzing subjects' problem-solving protocols has been to employ a checklist and a coding scheme to record the sequence of processes used. Unfortunately, among all the studies involving protocol analysis, only Kantowski (1977) and Putt (1978) have attempted to identify patterns of behavior. As Hatfield points out (1978), most investigators have been content to study the type and frequency of occurrence of certain heuristic strategies.

A different approach to analyzing cognitive processes is the *state-space* analysis technique used by Goldin and Luger (1975). They prefer to regard a problem and the problem solver as two separate but interacting systems. A complete discussion of state-space analysis is found in the ERIC monograph on task variables (Goldin & McClintock, in press).

Representative Research on Process Variables

The wide range of processes considered by researchers on problem solving is clearly evident from a scrutiny of recent studies. In a review of eight selected studies and one literature review that focused on problem-solving processes, Webb (1977) found little commonality regarding the processes studied. Types of processes included such diverse behaviors as divergent thinking, blind guessing, identifying a pattern, ability to employ abstract analytical reasoning, making use of drawings, and looking carefully at details. Such diversity may account in large part for the lack of conclusive results regarding the processes that successful problem solvers use, which processes can be taught, and how and when problem-solving processes develop. Another reason for this unfortunate state of affairs is that subjects have ranged from the primary grades through college with few replicative efforts having been made with subjects of the same age. Thus, although it might be possible to discern developmental changes, it is not possible to generalize observations for a particular age group.

A final reason, discussed earlier, for the difficulty in consolidating results across studies can be found in the crudeness of existing methodology for observing and recording problem-solving behaviors. There would be significantly more commonality in the types of processes studied if there were a framework for organizing and codifying them.

Some promising research on process variables has been conducted in recent years. Selected studies discussed in the following paragraphs can be placed in two broad categories: (a) research to identify the processes that subjects use and (b) research involving the development of instruments.

Process identification. Protocol analysis has been the most popular approach taken to study processes used during problem solving. Kilpatrick (1967) used the "thinking aloud" technique with eighth-grade students of above-average ability as they solved word problems. He devised a coding system and applied it to tape-recorded protocols. Reliably coded protocols were drawing a figure, using successive approximations, questioning the existence or the uniqueness of a solution, using deduction, using an equation, using trial and error, and checking the solution. The only process found to have a significant correlation with the total score on a problem-solving test was using successive approximations. An especially interesting result was that subjects who used the most trial and error were higher in mathematics achievement and quantitative ability than subjects who used less trial and error.

Kilpatrick's methodology has been used in modified forms by several researchers, notably Goldberg (1974), Lucas (1974), Webb (1975), Kantowski (1977), and Putt (1978). With the exception of Webb's research each study involved the effectiveness of instruction in heuristics. Associated with these studies have been attempts to identify processes used in solving problems and to measure processes as a part of overall problem-solving performance. Certain of these studies are discussed in more detail in the section on instructional variables. Kantowski's study deserves special comment because of her methodology. By employing a clinical paradigm in working with a small group of ninth-grade students of comparable ability, she was able to observe in depth the behavior of the students as they solved problems in geometry. Furthermore, longitudinal observations during the course of the study allowed variation in processes or sequences of processes to be monitored as problem-solving ability developed. Results indicated that problems with scores above the median for each subject showed evidence of a consistent use of heuristics in general and goal-oriented heuristics in particular. Kantowski raised a concern regarding the thinking-aloud technique, which she used, and called for research into the development of a valid, reliable, less time-consuming method of process analysis.

In addition to the research into measuring the processes that subjects use before and after instruction in heuristics, a number of studies have focused sole attention on the types of processes subjects use without instructional intervention. Webb (1975) studied the processes used by high school students of second-year algebra in an attempt to discern the relationships of cognitive, affective, and process variables to each other and to problem-solving ability. In addition he sought to determine which heuristics are problem-specific and which are general strategies, and which problem-solving modes groups of students tend to use. As previously mentioned, Webb used a modification of Kilpatrick's coding system. Among his findings were that the better problem solvers generally used a wide range of heuristic strategies and that most heuristics were problem specific. Also, subjects who used a moderate amount of trial and error did better than those who used a substantial amount of trial and error. This result was somewhat in conflict with Kilpatrick's observation regarding the value of trial and error. Other investigations of the processes subjects use without instruction are those of Sanders (1973), Hollander (1973), and the Mathematical Problem Solving Project (LeBlanc & Kerr, 1977; Lester, 1978). Sanders' study is noteworthy in that it has been one of the few to rely solely on retrospection to gather information about subjects' solution strategies for arithmetic word problems.

The staff of the Mathematical Problem Solving Project devoted considerable attention to observing students as they worked on problems either individually or in small groups in order to determine if intermediate-grade students employ any strategies as they solve problems. Over 100 fourth- and fifth-grade students were observed over a 2-year period. Conclusions drawn from these observations and several follow-up interviews related to the use of processes were as follows: (a) Students generally do not use any strategies (although a few tried to identify patterns for some problems), (b) trial and error was the most prevalent behavior exhibited if a computation did not lead directly to an answer, and (c) most students had difficulty retaining and coordinating multiple conditions present in a problem (Lester, 1978).

Just as Kilpatrick's coding system established a starting point for mathematics education researchers interested in developing accurate techniques for analyzing protocol, the work of various Soviet researchers has had a seminal influence on American problem-solving research in mathematics. Hatfield (1978) suggests that the Soviet Studies series (Kilpatrick & Wirszup, 1969–75) has fostered substantial interest in clinical investigations specifically designed to probe into children's mental processes. The enthusiastic acceptance of the methodology that Krutetskii (1976) used in his 12-year study is reflected in the research of Kantowski (1977) and Putt (1978), among others.

Instrument development. The difficulty of scoring and analyzing the solution of a problem is well recognized. Each of the techniques used in current research has serious limitations. Introspection and "thinking aloud" can be attacked on the ground that requiring subjects to talk while they solve problems may have a deleterious effect on their performance. At the same time there may be a tendency for subjects to talk only about actions they believe to be safe or correct. Kantowski (1977) and Krutetskii (1976) discuss the limitations of these approaches in more depth. Retrospection is often criticized as being unreliable inasmuch as subjects are not likely to be able to reconstruct accurate accounts of their behaviors. In addition to these weaknesses, each of these techniques is very time-consuming.

Because of these apparent shortcomings, some investigators have designed process inventories of problem solving that do not involve protocol analysis or that can be used to supplement protocol analysis. Smith (1973), Vos (1976), and the Mathematical Problem Solving Project (Proudfit, 1977) have undertaken attempts in this vein. Smith, in order to increase his confidence in his own analysis of subjects' written solutions to several problems, devised an eight-item questionnaire to serve as a written retrospective account of how each subject reasoned while solving the problems. He found the questionnaire and accompanying interviews quite valuable for identifying which heuristics his subjects used. Vos's Problem Solving Approach Test did not require subjects to solve problems but rather to choose from a list of five approaches to each problem the best and next-best approach. The Mathematical Problem Solving Project attempted to develop a paper-and-pencil instrument that would not only determine the processes used in solving problems but also be practical for classroom use. The final instrument produced by their efforts contained multiple-choice items corresponding to four stages in problem solving: comprehension, planning, carrying through a plan, and evaluation. Although this process-evaluation test was found to need much refinement, Proudfit (1977) concluded that it did yield useful information concerning processes used.

Valid and reliable methods for detecting processes are urgently needed. As a result of a research workshop held in 1975 at the University of Georgia under the auspices of the National Science Foundation, a team of researchers has been working at refining Kantowski's protocol-coding scheme. The members of this team have conducted a series of longitudinal clinical studies across age levels using a common set of problems and a common coding scheme (Kantowski, Branca, Goldberg, Kellogg, Lucas, Miller, Rachlin, & Smith, 1978; Smith, Branca, Goldberg, Kellogg, & Lucas, 1977). Preliminary indications are that their work will provide the research community with some valuable insights into the way processes develop and, perhaps more importantly, add more accurate data-gathering and analysis instruments.

Trends. As noted earlier, there has been a definite shift in emphasis toward linking problem solvers to the types of cognitive processes they employ. Toward this end research on process variables is likely to focus on creating techniques for accurately recording problem-solving behavior and on the subsequent analysis of this data. The bulk of this development will probably concentrate on designing and refining schemes of protocol analysis, although efforts to devise suitable paper-and-pencil inventories will continue.

Researchers interested in task variables will continue to pursue their interest in the interaction between the intrinsic structure of a problem and problem-solving behavior using techniques like state-space analysis. However, since it is difficult to render state-space representations for most mathematics problems, substantial modifications in present state-space analysis procedures must be made if this approach is to have general applicability.

Instructional Variables

Pursuing a fuller understanding of problem solving as a category of human learning leads naturally to an interest in the extent to which a person can be trained to be a better problem solver and in the conditions that most enhance success. A number of quite different views regarding problem-solving instruction have been proposed in recent years, the most common being those based on the extensive writings of Polya (1957, 1962, 1965). Although Polya's work has influenced the study of problem-solving processes, its most profound impact has been on the study of instruction in heuristic methods. Polya's prescriptive ideas help students become better problem solvers by suggesting a four-stage model with direct applicability to instruction.

In discussing instruction in heuristical methods, Hatfield (1978) has provided a useful characterization of problem-solving instruction. He distinguished among three types of instruction: teaching *for* problem solving, teaching *about* problem solving, and teaching *via* problem solving. The first, most often emphasized in current mathematics textbooks, focuses on the learner's acquisition of math concepts and skills that are useful for solving problems. The second typically involves a teacher modeling good problem-solving behavior or directing students' attention to salient procedures and strategies. The third involves presenting mathematics content in the context of problems to be solved. It is this third type of instruction that Polya encourages and that has been exemplified most recently in the work of Wickelgren (1974) and the research studies of Lucas (1974), Smith (1973), Goldberg (1974), Kantowski (1977), and Putt (1978).

A slightly different categorization of instruction will be used for purposes of discussing particular instruction-related problem-solving research. This categorization sorts the major research thrusts related to instruction and includes instruction designed to (a) develop specific tool skills (e.g., making tables, estimating, solving equations), (b) develop master thinking processes (e.g., skills and strategies useful for solving problems in any content area), (c) teach task-specific heuristics (i.e., advice not readily generalizable), (d) teach general heuristics (i.e., advice applicable to a wide range of tasks), and (e) involve students extensively in solving problems without direct teacher intervention.

Developing Master Thinking Skills

The Productive Thinking Program developed by Crutchfield and Covington (1963) was designed to develop rather general problem-solving skills and strategies that could be used in any content area. They evaluated the program by testing three pairs of fifth- and sixth-grade classes. Experimental classes were found to be superior to control classes in measures of divergent thinking, originality, and perceived value of problem solving (Covington & Crutchfield, 1965). In a later evaluation, Olton, Wardrop, Covington, Goodwin, Crutchfield, Klausmeier, and Ronda (1967) investigated the extent to which the thinking and problem solving of fifth-grade students could be improved using the Productive Thinking Program. Results from 44 fifth-grade classes ($N = 704$) showed statistically significant increases in thinking and problem-solving performance. Still later, Treffinger (1969) sought to determine the effectiveness of the Productive Thinking Program in developing verbal creativity and problem-solving ability in children from Grades 4–7. He sought, among other things, to determine the transfer of problem-solving skills from the program materials to an arithmetic puzzles test. At each grade level, significant differences favoring the experimental groups were found in pupils' attitudes toward creative thinking and problem solving. A comparison of pretest and posttest scores showed no result indicating that the program developed skills or abilities that transferred to the arithmetic problem-solving tests used in the study.

In line with Treffinger's results, Jerman (1971) found no significant difference between fifth-grade classes on an arithmetic word problem test when he compared the Productive Thinking Program with a Modified Wanted-Given Program (based on Wilson, 1964). He did, however, find a significant difference in favor of the wanted-given program on a follow-up test of word problems. He concluded that either approach to problem solving is more effective than providing no systematic instruction at all. Although Jerman's results showed that a program aimed at developing master strategies was no more effective than instruction focusing more specifically on mathematics, it would be interesting to see a replication of his study using less standard, less routine types of word problems. It may be that the type of problem task is a critical variable.

Developing Specific Tool Skills

Instruction focusing on developing specific tool skills is basically the same as Hatfield's instruction *for* problem solving and is common in many current mathematics textbooks. The instructional method proposed by Dahmus (1970) illustrates instruction that emphasizes skill development. Dahmus claimed that the study from which his method evolved was conducted over a 25-year period and involved the examination of over 300 references and 50 mathematics texts. His method emphasizes a translation of a verbal problem to mathematical-symbol statements in a manner as "direct, piecemeal, pure, and complete as possible" (p. 123). To use this method, the student must be able to translate each phrase into symbolic form. Thus, it is usually necessary to teach students how to translate key phrases. For example, "increased by" becomes "plus." A comparison of Dahmus's translation approach with a strategy purportedly based on the work of Polya was done by Bassler, Beers, and Richardson (1975). The second strategy stressed the four steps in problem solving proposed by Polya. The study involved individualized instruction with ninth-grade algebra students using teaching machines. Results, although subject to several serious limitations, favored the Polya method.

Vos (1976) investigated the relative effectiveness of three instructional strategies on the acquisition of five problem-solving behaviors across Grades 9, 10, and 11. The five problem-solving behaviors were (a) drawing diagrams, (b) approximating, (c) constructing equations, (d) classifying data, and (e) constructing charts. These behaviors can be considered *tool skills* in the sense described earlier in this section. The three instructional treatments were

- Repetition (R)—subjects were asked to solve problems without instruction;
- List (L)—subjects were given the same problems as in treatment R but in addition a checklist of suggested procedures to follow was provided, written instruction in one of the five problem-solving behaviors that could aid in solving the problem was given, and finally, subjects were allowed to return to the task of solving the problem;
- Behavior Instruction (B)—subjects were given the same written instruction as in treatment L but not the checklist, and following the instruction, subjects were given the problem.

Twenty problems were administered through self-instructional materials over a period of 15 weeks. Vos tentatively concluded that instruction in the use of specific problem-solving behaviors increases the successful use of those behaviors. Of particular interest in his study were two tests developed by Vos, the Problem-Solving Test (PST) and the Problem-Solving Approach Test (PSAT). The PST contained seven written problems that subjects were to solve in any way they chose. They were encouraged to write down all their thoughts about the problem. The test was scored using a modification of the scoring scheme devised by Kilpatrick (1967) as well as correct-incorrect response. The PSAT did not involve finding the solutions to a set of problems but rather required subjects to decide which of five approaches (the five treatment behaviors) could be used to solve a particular problem. In addition, Part 2 of the PSAT sought to measure some transfer of ability in using different problem-solving approaches (viz., recalling a formula, searching for a pattern, constructing a physical model, asking a missing question, and solving a related but simpler problem). It appears that whereas the five behaviors used in instruction can be classified as tool skills, at least some of the behaviors considered in the transfer test are, in fact, heuristical strategies (e.g., searching for a pattern, solving a simpler problem).

Major focuses of the Mathematical Problem Solving Project (MPSP) were the development, implementation, and evaluation of "skills" booklets for use in intermediate-grade mathematics classrooms (LeBlanc & Kerr, 1977). The word *skill*, as used by the MPSP, refers to techniques that must be mastered in order to use a particular strategy. Three skills booklets were created: "Using Guesses to Solve Problems" (guess-and-test skill), "Using Tables to Solve Problems" (table-making skill), and "Organizing Lists" (organized-listing skill). Each booklet was pilot tested, revised, and finally implemented over a 2-year period. Summative evaluation of the booklets involved over 700 students in Grades 4, 5, and 6. Trends in the data indicated that students using the skills booklets performed better than control students in solving process problems and at least as well as control students in solving standard textbook problems (Webb & Charles, 1977). It should be pointed out that these results suggest that systematic instruction in specific skills enhances problem-solving performance among intermediate-age students. They do not imply that such an approach to problem-solving instruction is preferred over other systematic approaches.

General or Task-specific Heuristics

Wilson (1967) hypothesized that high school students given instruction in task-specific heuristics would perform better on the training tasks but more poorly on transfer tasks than similar students given instruction in the use of general planning and means-end heuristics. This hypothesis was not confirmed, and Wilson found that the planning heuristics led to better performance on a training task than the corresponding task-specific heuristic. A possible explanation of the result could be the short duration of the treatment (two 3-hour sessions), which did not give sufficient practice of the general heuristics.

In a similar study, Smith (1973) gave greater emphasis to the generality of the general heuristics and used more task environments during the training phase to enable subjects to practice the general heuristics in a wide variety of settings. Results of this study were similar in some respects to those in Wilson's (1967) study. The evidence gleaned from these two studies indicates that the general heuristic does not possess the strong transfer power sometimes attributed to it.

Post and Brennan (1976) sought to determine the effects of methods of instruction in general heuristic processes on the problem-solving ability of 10th grade students. Subjects in the experimental group were instructed in the use of a general heuristic procedure consisting of four phases: a recognition, clarification, and understanding of the problem phase, a plan-of-attack phase, a productive phase, and a validating phase. Within each phase, subjects were given specific instructions (e.g., "Read the problem carefully" and "State the problem in your own words" in Phase 1) or questions (e.g., "Do you know a related problem?" in Phase 3 and "Can you use the result or method for some other problem?" in Phase 4). The four-phase procedure was similar to the procedure used by Post (1967) in an earlier study and contained several features of Polya's four-stage model. Results indicated that instruction in a general heuristic procedure had no significant effect on problem-solving performance. This observation was consistent with Post's 1967 study, leading the authors to suggest that specific instruction in general heuristic processes is not effective in increasing problem-solving ability.

Lucas (1974) used a modified version of Kilpatrick's (1967) system for coding and analyzing protocols of college students following the teaching of heuristics in calculus. During an 8-week period of instruction, one class was taught using a heuristic style based on Polya's writings. They also received papers that defined and demonstrated heuristic strategies as well as problem assignments that encouraged the use of these strategies. Another class learned calculus without attention to heuristics.

Since the study was exploratory, Lucas was interested in identifying variables for further study rather than in testing hypotheses. When the problems were scored on approach, plan, and result, subjects from the heuristic treatment were judged superior in their ability to solve calculus problems. These subjects used the following heuristics more frequently: working backward, using methods or results of related problems, devising workable plans, and organizing and introducing mnemonic notation. Lucas further concluded that heuristics can be taught without infringing on normal content, but for the experimental group, written instruction in heuristics was reserved for extraclass time.

Goldberg (1974) investigated the effects of instruction in heuristics on the ability of non–mathematics majors to construct proofs in number theory. Two sets of self-instructional booklets were used with 238 subjects in nine number theory classes. Classes were randomly assigned to one of three different treatments: reinforced heuristic, unreinforced heuristic, and non-heuristic. Six weeks of experimental treatment were followed by posttests on number theory concepts, proof construction, attitudes toward the self-instructional booklets, and attitudes toward problem solving. There was some evidence, but not at a statistically significant level, that reinforced heuristic instruction was the most beneficial of the three methods. For students with high ability, results favored reinforced heuristic instruction over the other two methods with respect to understanding concepts and constructing proofs. Students of high ability who were given nonheuristic instruction had a more positive attitude toward the self-instructional booklets and toward the problem-solving process than students given the other two methods of instruction. In addition, Goldberg applied a coding system to the written proofs of the students who scored in the top one-third on the proofs posttest. She found that students given reinforced heuristic instruction used the greatest variety of heuristics and used them most frequently. She concluded that instruction in some heuristics of proof with reinforcement through class discussion is effective for some students.

A modified version of Kilpatrick's (1967) coding scheme was used by Kantowski (1974) for analyzing protocols of eight ninth-grade algebra students of high ability. The study was composed of four phases: a pretest, a readiness instruction phase, an instruction (in geometry) phase using heuristic instructional techniques, and a posttest. During each phase, the subjects thought aloud while they solved problems and their protocols were recorded simultaneously.

Kantowski used a clinical methodology in this exploratory study working with a small group of students of comparable ability. In this way she could observe in detail the behavior of subjects as they solved problems. Furthermore, longitudinal observations during the course of the study allowed variation in processes or sequences of processes to be monitored as the students' problem-solving ability in geometry developed.

The modified coding scheme allowed for the calculation of a process-product score for each problem. A median decimal score for each of the eight subjects was then found from his or her own distribution of process-product scores. Results indicate that problems with scores above the median for each subject showed (a) evidence of the use of goal-oriented heuristics and (b) evidence of the consistent use of heuristics in obtaining solutions. A marked increase in the use of goal-oriented heuristics from pretest to posttest was attributed to the two instructional phases of the study.

Probably the most significant aspect of this study is the set of hypotheses generated for future studies. Kantowski suggested that the effects of heuristic instruction versus expository instruction should be investigated with the use of heuristics as the dependent variable. Studies should also be carried out in content areas other than geometry, with younger and older subjects, and with subjects of different levels of ability. Looking-back strategies were not used extensively by the subjects in the study even though their use was emphasized in the instruction. Hence, Kantowski suggests investigations to explore any relationships between looking-back strategies and success in problem solving. Some concern was also raised regarding the use of the thinking-aloud technique in determining processes, and a call was made for the development of a valid, reliable, and less time-consuming method of process analysis.

Schoenfeld (1978) conducted a small-scale study with seven science and mathematics college students to investigate the impact that instruction in heuristics had on performance. Specifically, the heuristics were (a) drawing a diagram, (b) induction, (c) proof by contradiction, (d) reducing the number of variables, and (e) establishing subgoals. He found students ($N = 4$) who had been instructed in the use of these heuristics to be superior to students ($N = 3$) who worked on problems without instruction. More significantly, he observed that students cannot be expected to intuit useful heuristics; they must be given explicit instruction. Perhaps the most valuable aspect of Schoenfeld's research lies with his discussion of a schematic outline of a "managerial" strategy for problem solving and how to train students to use it.

One of the few instruction-related studies at the elementary level in recent years was conducted by Putt (1978), who compared the effects of two methods of problem-solving instruction with the effects of no special instruction in problem solving on the behavior of fifth-grade students solving process problems (i.e., problems that lend themselves to exemplifying the nonalgorithmic procedures inherent in problem solving). In addition, he compared the two methods of instruction in problem solving. Both instructional methods were based on Polya's four-stage model but were different in two respects: (a) the role of the teacher and (b) the behaviors expected of students during problem solving. One treatment used an approach integrating Polya's model and a model of learning based on information-processing tenets. In this treatment the teacher was required to make the students aware of the heuristic strategies (in the Polya sense) at each of the four stages in the process of solving problems. The second treatment did not involve any direct heuristic teaching; students were simply given problems to solve. The teacher's role was primarily to clarify words or terms and to provide feedback on potential solutions. No attempt was made to teach heuristic strategies or generalize solutions. An especially important feature of Putt's research was that he made no attempt to control the teacher variable by using self-instructional materials as was done by several other researchers (e.g., Bassler et al., 1975; Lucas, 1974; Vos, 1976; Webb & Charles, 1977). Instead he conducted a "teching experiment" in an effort to observe processes as they developed and to make instruction as natural as possible. Putt focused primarily on qualitative information obtained from students' responses to certain parts of a posttest and from classroom observations of problem-solving lessons made by him and two trained observers. These are among the key results:

1. Students in the heuristic treatment named Polya's four stages as helpful steps in solving problems, whereas the students who simply solved problems or received no instruction tended to name the four arithmetic operations as helpful steps.

2. Students in the heuristic treatment used some of the strategies highlighted during instruction more frequently than the nonheuristic students.

3. When asked to do so, students in the heuristic treatment were able to write significantly more questions for understanding the problem than students in the other two treatments.

4. Students who were not taught any specific strategies used a wider variety of strategies for some problems than students who were taught specific strategies.

Putt concluded that fifth-grade students can learn to solve process problems in a relatively short period of time (four weeks). Also, he found that students can be taught to ask themselves questions that might help in understanding a problem and that they can be taught to use specific strategies for solving problems.

Trends. Clinical studies of the effectiveness of instruction in heuristics of the type conducted by Kantowski (1977) and Putt (1978) are replacing studies comparing methods of instruction in general heuristics with instruction in task-specific heuristics. The trend toward employing "teaching experiments" to make possible the collection of qualitative data regarding students' problem-solving behavior will necessitate an end to the tendency to control for the effect of the teacher. Instead the teacher will need to be considered a vital part of the task environment. This trend has both positive and negative features. Kantowski (1978) points out that such methodology introduces threats to the validity of the research that are quite unacceptable by current American standards. However, it allows the researcher "to observe how a subject is operating and to determine levels of sophistication . . . instead of mere numbers of correct solutions. Such diagnostic techniques permit the discovery of erroneous concepts as well as 'strokes of genius' " (p. 49).

KEY ISSUES FOR FUTURE EFFORTS

Several promising developments have occurred in mathematical problem-solving research in recent years. The shift in emphasis from concentrating solely on collecting quantitative information about problem-solving performance to focusing on the way problem solvers proceed in analyzing and attacking problems is among the most prominent. The interest in qualitative aspects of problem-solving behavior has been accompanied by a recognition of the importance of investigating the interactions among the characteristics of problem solvers, the processes they use, the variables associated with problems, and environmental factors such as instruction.

The growing support for qualitative research to supplement or, in many cases, to replace quantitative research has resulted in an increased awareness of the need for better instrumentation. That is, if qualitative methods such as clinical interviews and "teaching experiments" are to be employed, better methods are required for recording and analyzing protocols of problem-solving episodes. It is safe to say that the establishment of a commonly accepted body of knowledge about mathematical problem solving will be delayed until valid and reliable instruments and techniques exist for collecting and analyzing information. Progress is being made in this direction.

Another encouraging trend is the growing recognition of the value of theory-based and theory-development research. The extreme complexity of problem solving makes a theory orientation a must for at least three reasons. First, a theory serves as a means to explain observed phenomena. It is one thing to conduct careful interviews with problem solvers and quite another to make sense of the observations. A theory is extremely useful in this regard. A second reason is that a theory enables the investigator to make predictions about yet unobserved relationships and phenomena. Finally, a theory structures the conduct of inquiry by guiding the researcher in the process of asking questions, formulating hypotheses, and determining what key variables and relationships to investigate.

Perhaps the most promising development of all is the evidence of cooperative, well-conceptualized efforts among groups of mathematics educators, mathematicians, and psychologists. Although this is not unique to problem-solving research, it seems to be particularly apparent in this area.

The research discussed here not only highlights the trends in the current literature and points out promising directions but also raises a number of issues that must be confronted by future researchers. The following issues are among the most important and deserving of attention during the next 20 years. These issues can be placed in three broad categories: theory-related issues, instruction-related issues, and research methodology issues.

Theory-related Issues

In view of the increasing awareness of the need for theory-based problem-solving research, three key issues are apparent.

Issue 1

Past problem-solving research in mathematics has suffered from the absence or neglect of theory. The shift toward a theory orientation raises two questions:

1. Is there a real need for theories of mathematical problem solving?
2. If there is a need for theories, will any of the various psychological theories of problem solving suffice or must specialized theories for mathematics evolve? That is, are certain fundamental problem-solving skills and processes unique to mathematics?

Issue 2

Problem solving is a chaotic area of inquiry largely because of the widely diverse types of tasks used. The tasks used in problem-solving research significantly affect the generalizability of results. With this in mind, researchers must consider the following questions:

1. Are the tasks that are being used appropriate for the purpose of the study?
2. What research questions are best addressed by content from the standard mathematics curriculum, and what questions are best addressed by puzzle problems?
3. Is there a need for a core of research tasks (i.e., a collection of research instruments) to be used by all problem-solving researchers?

Issue 3

Characteristics of problem solvers greatly affect behavior and consequently severely limit the generalizability of results. What kinds of subject to use in problem-solving research is a topic of much discussion. For example, although knowledge about the processes that good problem solvers use is clearly important, it is less clear that problem solvers of average ability can be taught to use these processes. Should subjects be "mathematically talented" or of "average" ability?

Instruction-related Issues

I have every reason to believe that a substantial portion of future problem-solving research will focus on instruction. For this reason, it is appropriate to point out the key issues directly associated with instruction.

Issue 4

There is little agreement regarding how best to improve problem-solving performance beyond the obvious fact that *attempting* to solve problems is a necessary ingredient. Common points of view regarding problem-solving instruction include the following:

1. Having students solve many problems with no direct instruction
2. Teaching unitary skills (tool skills)
3. Teaching heuristic strategies
4. Modeling good problem-solving behavior and having students imitate this behavior
5. Some combination of the above

Issue 5

In addition to a lack of consensus regarding the best ways to enhance problem solving, there is no accord about the nature of improvement in problem solving. Some researchers interested in problem-solving instruction have focused on the improvement of students' abilities to use particular strategies or skills, and others have considered improvement only in terms of an increase in the number of correct solutions. Also, in many cases no attention has been given to whether newly acquired facility in solving a particular type of problem transfers to solving a different type of problem. Indeed, the extent to which various types of transfer of training should be expected is an open question.

Issue 6

The extent of instructional treatments in recent research varies from about one week to several months, with relatively short treatments being the most common. Treatments should be extensive enough not only to allow for full explication of ideas and procedures but also to provide ample opportunity for students to practice the procedures they are being taught.

Research Methodology Issue

There is a single issue related to research methodology. Typically, methodological issues become less important when a sound theoretical basis guides the conduct of inquiry. However, the present lack of adequate theories makes Issue 7 a current, although possibly short-term, concern. This issue is not the unique domain of problem-solving researchers nor is it of the same level of importance as the first six issues, but it is important enough to warrant serious attention.

Issue 7

No generally accepted methods or instruments for measuring performance or observing behavior during problem solving are clearly reliable and valid. Thus, the kind of instrumentation that is appropriate for a particular purpose remains an issue. The most popular instruments are of two types: paper-and-pencil tests and protocol analysis based on "thinking aloud" or retrospection. Each of these types has serious weaknesses. Paper-and-pencil tests are notoriously unreliable measures and often use only routine problems. Protocol analysis suffers equally serious limitations. Requiring problem solvers to think aloud may have a deleterious effect on their performance; typically they are unable to articulate all, or even the most important, thought processes. Retrospective analysis is often criticized as being unreliable. Should more or less emphasis be given to the development of paper-and-pencil tests? Should more or less emphasis be placed on the development of procedures for collecting and analyzing problem-solving protocols?

Individual researchers must make personal decisions regarding some, or all, of these issues before undertaking their research. At the same time, the problem-solving research community as a whole should give overt attention to discussing the controversies involved with these issues. It is only through the open exchange of ideas and viewpoints that progress can be made toward building a large and stable body of knowledge about mathematical problem solving.

FINAL COMMENTS

A brief discussion of mathematical problem solving has been presented with respect to four categories of interacting variables: subject variables, task variables, process variables, and instruction variables. An overview of representative research and current trends followed. The purpose of this section was to discuss those efforts that typify problem-solving investigations in recent years and that point out the directions in which the research is moving. The third section presented seven issues for the future.

The common belief that problem solving is the most important activity of mathematics is supported by the vast quantity of research literature. There is an urgent need for this research to become more systematic, co-ordinated, and focused. Future efforts should be more systematic and coordinated in the sense that they should be based on solid conceptual frameworks, build on past efforts, and be disseminated widely. In line with this, replications of the best of the research are sorely needed. Future research should become more focused in the sense that more attention must be paid to the way in which the four categories of variables influence each other.

In this regard, one possible focus for the future would be to collect data on problem-solving episodes of individuals of different ages and abilities while keeping the set of problems constant. Another focus would be the reverse of the first. That is, instead of studying problem-solving behavior for a fixed set of problems across problem solvers, data would be collected on problem-solving episodes of a particular group of problem solvers for a wide variety of problems. In either event, researchers should gather extensive data, both qualitative and quantitative, about how individuals solve problems naturally, without instruction. Such information will not only add to the body of knowledge but also significantly aid in the design of research on problem-solving instruction.

Although the discussion of representative research indicates a rather chaotic state of the art, there are signs of progress toward a more orderly pursuit of knowledge. There is an ever-growing community of mathematical problem-solving researchers who are becoming increasingly influential in determining the direction of research. Evidence of this community of researchers is seen in the activities of the Task Variables Working Group (discussed earlier) and the Applied Problem Solving Working Group (Lesh, Mierkiewicz, & Kantowski, in press). In addition, a new monthly newsletter, published by the Franklin Institute Press (n.d.), is devoted exclusively to problem solving.

Another promising development is the increased sophistication among mathematical problem-solving researchers with respect to their knowledge of experimental and nonexperimental research designs, their understanding of the various psychological theories relevant to problem solving, and their sensitivity to the practical considerations involved in teaching mathematics. Indeed, we have reason to believe that despite the tremendous complexity of problem solving, significant progress will be made in the near future toward the development of sound new theories that will guide inquiry and lead ultimately to a more stable body of knowledge.

REFERENCES

Balow, I. H. Reading and computation ability as determinants of problem solving. *Arithmetic Teacher*, 1964, *11*, 18–22.

Bana, J., & Nelson, D. Distractors in nonverbal mathematical problems. *Journal for Research in Mathematics Education*, 1978, *9* (1), 55–61.

Barnett, J. C. Toward a theory of sequencing: Study 3–7: An investigation of the relationships of structural variables, instruction, and difficulty in verbal, arithmetic problem solving. *Dissertation Abstracts International*, 1975, *36*(1), 99A. (a)

Barnett, J. C. Untitled research proposal prepared for the Workshop in Problem Solving, University of Georgia, Athens, May, 1975. (b)

Bassler, O. C., Beers, M. I., & Richardson, L. I. Comparison of two instructional strategies for teaching the solution of verbal problems. *Journal for Research in Mathematics Education*, 1975, *6*(3), 170–177.

Blake, R. N. The effect of problem context upon the problem-solving processes used by field dependent and independent students: A clinical study. *Dissertation Abstracts International*, 1977, *37*, 4191A–4192A.

Bourne, L. E., & Dominowski, R. L. Thinking. *Annual Review of Psychology*, 1972, 105–130.

Bourne, L. E., Ekstrand, B. R., & Dominowski, R. L. *The psychology of thinking*. Englewood Cliffs, N.J.: Prentice-Hall, 1971.

Brownell, W. A. Problem solving. In *The psychology of learning*. Forty-first Yearbook of the National Society for the Study of Education, Part II. Chicago: The Society, 1942, 415–443.

Caldwell, J. H. Cognitive development and difficulty in solving word problems in mathematics (Doctoral thesis, University of Pennsylvania, 1977). *Dissertation Abstracts International*, 1978, *38*(1), 4637A.

Chase, C. I. The position of certain variables in the prediction of problem-solving in arithmetic. *Journal of Educational Research*, 1960, *54*(1), 9–14.

Covington, M. V., & Crutchfield, R. S. Facilitation of creative problem solving. *Programmed Instruction*, 1965, *4*(10), 3–5.

Crutchfield, R. S., & Covington, M. V. *Facilitation of creative thinking and problem solving in school children*. Paper presented at a symposium on learning research pertinent to educational improvement, American Association for the Advancement of Science, Cleveland, Ohio, 1963.

Dahmus, M. E. How to teach verbal problems. *School Science and Mathematics*, 1970, *70*(2), 121–138.

Davis, G. A. *Psychology of problem solving: Theory and practice*. New York: Basic Books, 1973.

Davis, G. A. Current status of research and theory in human problem solving. *Psychological Bulletin*, 1966, *66*(1), 36–54.

Days, H., Wheatley, G. H., & Kulm, G. Problem structure, cognitive level, and problem-solving performance. *Journal for Research in Mathematics Education*, 1979, *10*(2), 135–146.

Dodd, D. H., & Bourne, L. E. Thinking and problem solving. In B. B. Wolman (Ed.), *Handbook of general psychology*. Englewood Cliffs, N.J.: Prentice-Hall, 1973.

Dodson, J. W. Characteristics of successful insightful problem solvers. *NLSMA Report No. 31*. Stanford, Calif.: School Mathematics Study Group, 1972.

Duncker, K. On problem-solving. *Psychological Monographs*, 1945, *58*(5).

Fennema, E. Mathematics learning and the sexes: A review. *Journal for Research in Mathematics Education*, 1974, *5*(3), 126–139.

Fennema, E., & Sherman, J. Sex-related differences in mathematics achievement and related factors: A further study. *Journal for Research in Mathematics Education*, 1978, *9*(3), 189–203.

Franklin Institute Press. *Problem solving: A newsletter*. Monthly publication. Philadelphia: The Press, n.d.

Goldberg, D. J. The effects of training in heuristic methods in the ability to write proofs in number theory. Unpublished doctoral dissertation, Teacher's College, Columbia University, 1974.

Goldin, G. A., & Luger, G. F. *State-space representations of problem structure and problem solving behavior*. University of Pennsylvania Technical Report, 1974.

Goldin, G. A., & Luger, G. F. *Problem structure and problem solving behavior*. Proceedings of the Fourth International Joint Conference on Artificial Intelligence, Tbilisi, USSR, and Cambridge, Mass.: MIT-AI Press, 1975.

Goldin, G. A., McClintock, C. E., & Webb, N. Task variables in problem solving research. Panel presentation at the Annual Meeting of the National Council of Teachers of Mathematics, Cincinnati, Ohio, April 1977.

Goldin, G. A., & McClintock, C. E. *Task variables in mathematical problem solving*. Columbus, Ohio: ERIC/SMEAC, in press.

Gorman, C. J. A critical analysis of research on written problems in elementary school mathematics. *Dissertation Abstracts*, 1968, *28*(12), 4818A–4819A.

Green, B. F. Introduction: Current trends in problem-solving. In B. Kleinmuntz (Ed.), *Problem solving: Research, methods and theory*. New York: Wiley, 1966.

Haecker, V., & Ziehen, T. Beitrag zur lehre von der bererbung und analyse der zeichnerischen und mathematischen begabung, insbesondere mit bezug auf die korrelation zur musikalischen begabung. *Zeitschrift fur Psychologie*, 1931, 120–121.

Hatfield, L. L. Heuristical emphases in the instruction of mathematical problem solving: Rationales and research. In L. L. Hatfield & D. A. Bradbard (Eds.), *Mathematical problem solving: Papers from a research workshop.* Columbus, Ohio: ERIC/SMEAC, 1978.

Hatfield, L. L. *The problem solving project of the Georgia Center for the Study of Learning and Teaching Mathematics.* Paper presented at the Third International Congress on Mathematical Education, Karlsruhe, Federal Republic of Germany, 1976.

Hatfield, L. L., & Bradbard, D. A. *Mathematical problem solving: Papers from a research workshop.* Columbus, Ohio: ERIC/SMEAC, 1978.

Henderson, K. B., & Pingry, R. E. Problem-solving in mathematics. In *The learning of mathematics: Its theory and practice.* Twenty-first Yearbook of the National Council of Teachers of Mathematics. Washington, D.C.: The Council, 1953.

Hollander, S. K. Strategies of selected sixth graders reading and working verbal arithmetic problems (Doctoral dissertation, Hofstra University, 1973). *Dissertation Abstracts International,* 1974, *34*(10), 6258A.

Inhelder, B., & Piaget, J. *The growth of logical thinking from childhood to adolescence.* New York: Basic Books, 1958.

Ingle, J. A. Prediction of word problem difficulty on the basis of problem characteristics. *Dissertation Abstracts International,* 1975, *36,* 2157A.

Jerman, M. E. Problem solving in arithmetic as a transfer from a Productive Thinking Program. Unpublished doctoral dissertation, Stanford University, 1971.

Jerman, M. E. Problem length as a structural variable in verbal arithmetic problems. *Educational Studies in Mathematics,* 1974, *5,* 109–123.

Jerman, M. E. Individualized instruction in problem solving in elementary school mathematics. *Journal for Research in Mathematics Education,* 1973, *4*(1), 6–19.

Jerman, M. E., & Rees, R. Predicting the relative difficulty of verbal arithmetic problems. *Educational Studies in Mathematics,* 1972, *4,* 306–323.

Kantowski, E. L. Processes involved in mathematical problem solving. Unpublished doctoral dissertation, University of Georgia, 1974.

Kantowski, M. G. The teaching experiment and Soviet studies of problem solving. In L. L. Hatfield & D. A. Bradbard (Eds.), *Mathematical problem solving: Papers from a research workshop.* Columbus, Ohio: ERIC/SMEAC, 1978.

Kantowski, M. G. Processes involved in mathematical problem solving. *Journal for Research in Mathematics Education,* 1977, *8*(3), 163–180.

Kantowski, M. G., Branca, N., Goldberg, D., Kellogg, H., Lucas, J., Miller, S., Rachlin, S., & Smith, P. Use of heuristics in problem solving: An exploratory study. Research reporting session, Annual Meeting of the National Council of Teachers of Mathematics, San Diego, April, 1978.

Kilpatrick, J. Variables and methodologies in research on problem solving. In L. L. Hatfield & D. A. Bradbard (Eds.), *Mathematical problem solving: Papers from a research workshop.* Columbus, Ohio: ERIC/SMEAC, 1978.

Kilpatrick, J. Problem-solving and creative behavior in mathematics. In J. W. Wilson & L. R. Carry (Eds.), *Reviews of recent research in mathematics education.* Studies in Mathematics Series, Vol. 19, pp. 153–187. Stanford, Calif.: School Mathematics Study Group, 1969.

Kilpatrick, J. Analyzing the solution of word problems in mathematics: An exploratory study (Doctoral dissertation, Stanford University, 1967). *Dissertation Abstracts,* 1968, *28*(11), 4380A.

Kilpatrick, J., & Wirszup, I. (Eds.). *Soviet studies in the psychology of learning and teaching mathematics* (14 vols.). Stanford, Calif.: School Mathematics Study Group, 1969–75.

Kinsella, J. J. Problem solving. In *The teaching of secondary school mathematics.* Thirty-third Yearbook of the National Council of Teachers of Mathematics. Washington, D.C.: The Council, 1970.

Knifong, J. D., & Holtan, B. An analysis of children's written solutions to word problems. *Journal for Research in Mathematics Education,* 1976, *7*(2), 106–112.

Krutetskii, V. A. *The psychology of mathematical abilities in schoolchildren.* Chicago: University of Chicago Press, 1976.

Krutetskii, V. A. An analysis of the individual structure of mathematical abilities in schoolchildren. In J. Kilpatrick & I. Wirszup (Eds.), *Soviet studies in the psychology of learning and teaching mathematics* (Vol. 2). Stanford, Calif.: School Mathematics Study Group, 1969.

Krutetskii, V. A. Some characteristics of the thinking of pupils with little capacity for mathematics. In B. Simon & J. Simon (Eds.), *Educational psychology in the USSR.* Stanford, Calif.: Stanford University Press, 1963.

LeBlanc, J. F., & Kerr, D. R. The Mathematical Problem Solving Project: Problem solving strategies and applications of mathematics in the elementary school. Final Report. Bloomington, Ind.: Mathematics Education Development Center, 1977.

Lesh, R. *Applied problem solving in early mathematics learning.* Unpublished manuscript, 1979. (Available from the author, Northwestern University, School of Education.)

Lesh, R., Mierkiewicz, D., & Kantowski, M. G. *Applied mathematical problem solving.* Columbus, Ohio: ERIC/SMEAC, in press.

Lester, F. K. Developmental aspects of children's ability to understand mathematical proof. *Journal for Research in Mathematics Education,* 1975, 6(1), 14–25.

Lester, F. K. Mathematical problem solving in the elementary school: Some educational and psychological considerations. In L. L. Hatfield & D. A. Bradbard (Eds.), *Mathematical problem solving: Papers from a research workshop.* Columbus, Ohio: ERIC/SMEAC, 1978.

Linville, W. J. The effects of syntax and vocabulary upon the difficulty of verbal arithmetic problems with fourth grade students. *Dissertation Abstracts International,* 1970, 30, 4310A.

Lucas, J. F. The teaching of heuristic problem-solving strategies in elementary calculus. *Journal for Research in Mathematics Education,* 1974, 5(1), 36–46.

Luger, G. F. The use of "artificial intelligence" techniques for the study of problem solving behavior. *Dissertation Abstracts International,* 1974, 34(8), 4571A.

Martin, M. D. Reading comprehension, abstract verbal reasoning, and computation as factors in arithmetic problem solving. *Dissertation Abstracts,* 1964, 24, 4547–4548.

Meyer, R. A. Mathematical problem-solving performance and intellectual abilities of fourth-grade children. *Journal for Research in Mathematics Education,* 1978, 9(5), 334–348.

Moses, B. E. The nature of spatial ability and its relationship to mathematical problem solving. Unpublished doctoral dissertation, Indiana University, 1977.

Neimark, E. D., & Lewis, N. The development of logical problem-solving strategies. *Child Development,* 1967, 38(1–2), 107–117.

Nesher, P. Three determinants of difficulty in verbal arithmetic problems. *Educational Studies in Mathematics,* 1976, 7, 369–388.

Newell, A., & Simon, H. A. *Human problem solving.* Englewood Cliffs, N.J.: Prentice-Hall, 1972.

Nilsson, N. *Problem solving methods in artificial intelligence.* New York: McGraw-Hill, 1971.

Olton, R. M., Wardrop, J. L., Covington, M. V., Goodwin, W. L., Crutchfield, R. S., Klausmeier, H. J., & Ronda, T. *The development of productive thinking skills in fifth grade children* (Tech. Rep. No. 34). Madison: University of Wisconsin, Center for Cognitive Learning, 1967.

Polya, G. *How to solve it* (2nd ed.). New York: Doubleday, 1957.

Polya, G. *Mathematical discovery: On understanding, learning and teaching problem solving* (Vol. 1). New York: Wiley, 1962.

Polya, G. *Mathematical discovery: On understanding, learning and teaching problem solving* (Vol. 2). New York: Wiley, 1965.

Post, T. R. The effects of the presentation of a structure of the problem-solving process upon problem solving ability in seventh grade mathematics. Unpublished doctoral dissertation, Indiana University, 1967.

Post, T. R., & Brennan, M. L. An experimental study of the effectiveness of a formal versus an informal presentation of a general heuristic process on problem solving in tenth-grade geometry. *Journal for Research in Mathematics Education,* 1976, 7(1), 59-64.

Proudfit, L. *The development of a process evaluation instrument* (Tech. Rep. V). Mathematical Problem Solving Project. Bloomington, Ind.: Mathematics Education Development Center, 1977.

Putt, I. J. An exploratory investigation of two methods of instruction in mathematical problem solving at the fifth grade level. Unpublished doctoral dissertation, Indiana University, 1978.

Resnick, L. B., & Glaser, R. Problem solving and intelligence. In L. B. Resnick (Ed.), *The nature of intelligence.* Hillsdale, N.J.: Erlbaum, 1976.

Robinson, M. L. An investigation of problem solving behavior and cognitive and affective characteristics of good and poor problem solvers in sixth grade mathematics. *Dissertation Abstracts International,* 1973, *33,* 5620A.

Sanders, V. A. Arithmetic problem-solving strategies of fourth grade children. *Dissertation Abstracts International,* 1973, *33*(11), 5983A-5984A.

Scandura, J. M. *Problem solving: A structural/process approach with instructional implications.* New York: Academic Press, 1977.

Schoenfeld, A. H. *Problem solving strategies in college level mathematics.* Unpublished manuscript, 1978. (Available from the author, Hamilton College.)

Schonberger, A. K. The interrelationship of sex, visual spatial abilities, and mathematical problem solving ability in grade seven. *Dissertation Abstracts International,* 1976, *37,* 3536A.

Shulman, L. S. Reconstruction of educational research. *Review of Educational Research,* 1970, *40*(3), 371-396.

Shulman, L. S., & Elstein, A. S. Studies of problem solving, judgment, and decision making: Implications for educational research. In F. N. Kerlinger (Ed.), *Review of research in education* (Vol. 3, pp. 3-42). Itasca, Ill.: F. E. Peacock Publishers, 1975.

Silver, E. A. Student perceptions of relatedness among mathematical verbal problems. *Journal for Research in Mathematics Education,* 1979, *10*(3), 195-210.

Smith, J. P. The effect of general versus specific heuristics in mathematical problem-solving tasks. Unpublished doctoral dissertation, Columbia University, 1973.

Smith, P., Branca, N., Goldberg, D., Kellogg, H., & Lucas, J. Research in problem solving processes. Research reporting session, Annual Meeting of the National Council of Teachers of Mathematics, Cincinnati, April 1977.

Stengel, A., LeBlanc, J., Jacobson, M., & Lester, F. *Learning to solve problems by solving problems* (Tech. Rep. 2. D). Mathematical Problem Solving Project. Bloomington, Ind.: Mathematics Education Development Center, 1977.

Stevenson, H. W. Learning and cognition. In J. N. Payne (Ed.), *Mathematics learning in early childhood.* Thirty-seventh Yearbook of the National Council of Teachers of Mathematics. Reston, Va.: The Council, 1975.

Suydam, M. N. Research related to the mathematics learning process. In *Forschung zum Prozess des Mathematiklernens: Materialen und Studien.* Bielefeld, Germany: Institut für Didaktik der Mathematik, Universität Bielefeld, 1976.

Treffinger, D. J. The effects of programmed instruction in productive thinking on verbal creativity and problem solving among pupils in grades four, five, six, and seven (Doctoral dissertation, Cornell University, 1969). *Dissertation Abstracts International,* 1969, *30,* 1031A.

Trimmer, R. G. A review of the research relating problem solving and mathematics achievement to psychological variables and relating these variables to methods involving or compatible with self-correcting manipulative mathematics materials. Unpublished manuscript, 1974. (ERIC Document Reproduction Service No. ED-092-402)

Vos, K. The effects of three instructional strategies on problem-solving behaviors in secondary school mathematics. *Journal for Research in Mathematics Education,* 1976, 7(5), 264-275.

Webb, N. L. *An exploration of mathematical problem-solving processes.* Paper presented at the Annual Meeting of the American Education Research Association, Washington, D.C., 1975.

Webb, N. L. *A review of the literature related to problem-solving tasks and problem-solving strategies used by students in grades 4, 5, and 6* (Tech. Rep. 1.A). Mathematical Problem Solving Project. Bloomington, Ind.: Mathematics Education Development Center, 1977.

Webb, N. L., & Charles, R. I. *Module development and formative evaluation* (Tech. Rep. 3). Mathematical Problem Solving Project. Bloomington, Ind.: Mathematics Education Development Center, 1977.

Webb, N. L., Moses, B. E., & Kerr, D. R. *Developmental activities related to summative evaluation (1975-76)* (Tech. Rep. 4). Mathematical Problem Solving Project. Bloomington, Ind.: Mathematics Education Development Center, 1977.

Weir, M. W. Developmental changes in problem solving strategies. *Psychological Review,* 1964, *71*(6), 473–490.

Wheatley, G. H., Mitchell, R., Frankland, R. L., & Kraft, R. Hemispheric specialization and cognitive development: Implications for mathematics education. *Journal for Research in Mathematics Education,* 1978, *9*(1), 20–32.

Wickelgren, W. A. *How to solve problems: Elements of a theory of problems and problem solving.* San Francisco: Freeman, 1974.

Wilson, James W. Patterns of mathematics achievement in grade 11: Z-population. *NLSMA Report No. 17.* Stanford, Calif.: School Mathematics Study Group, 1972.

Wilson, James W. Generality of heuristics as an instructional variable. Unpublished doctoral dissertation, Stanford University, 1967.

Wilson, James W., & Begle, E. G. (Eds.). Intercorrelations of mathematical and psychological variables. *NLSMA Report No. 33.* Sanford, Calif.: School Mathematics Study Group, 1972.

Wilson, John W. The role of structure in verbal problem solving in arithmetic: An analytical and experimental comparison of three problem-solving programs. Unpublished doctoral dissertation, Syracuse University, 1964.

11

Individual Differences and the Learning of Mathematics

Elizabeth Fennema
University of Wisconsin—Madison
Merlyn J. Behr
Northern Illinois University

A LTHOUGH developmental psychologists and some other scholars claim that human beings are alike in more ways than they are different, most people believe that humans differ in important and significant ways on many variables that are of vital importance to the teaching-learning process. Over a period of decades such variables have formed the bases of much research focused on the learning of mathematics as well as the bases for the organization of many instructional programs. It is widely accepted in scholarly inquiry about educational processes that individuals differ on numerous cognitive and affective variables. Therefore, it is important to examine the current state of knowledge and inquiry about individual differences.

This chapter (a) reports the status of the knowledge about individual differences in variables related to mathematics learning and instruction, (b) discusses and evaluates new trends in examining individual differences, and (c) identifies some areas where research concerned with individual differences and the organization of the curriculum might significantly improve the learning of mathematics.

THE STATUS OF KNOWLEDGE ABOUT INDIVIDUAL DIFFERENCES

Since early in the 20th century, there have been two distinct facets of inquiry dealing with individual differences: one dealing with the identification of important characteristics on which individuals differ and the other dealing with the organization of instruction so that individuals who differ might learn. The titles of two early books on the subject illustrate these facets clearly: Thorndike's monograph entitled *Individuality* (Thorndike, 1911) and the NSSE Yearbook entitled *Adapting the Schools to Individual Differences* (Whipple, 1925). Since these have been pervasive themes for at least five decades, it is interesting as well as important to know how far our knowledge has progressed in these two important areas.

The Identification of Important Individual Differences

Within the mathematics education literature there has been agreement on individual differences that has not changed much over at least a 20-year period. In 1954 Weaver summarized what was known about individual differences:

> Children in a given class or grade show a wide range of ability in each phase of instruction. Furthermore, these variations generally increase from the lower to the upper elementary grades.
> Children exhibit considerable variation in their profiles or patterns of ability in the various phases of arithmetic instruction. (p. 300)

In 1976 Romberg and Montgomery stated that four things were known about individual differences that were important to instruction:

1. Students achieve at different rates.
2. Differences in achievement increase as students advance through school.
3. Achievement is often marked by spurts and plateaus which differ in appearance and length among individuals.
4. Intra-individual differences may be as great as inter-individual differences. (p. 11)

An inspection of these summary statements, made over 20 years apart, clearly points to a lack of progress in the understanding of individual differences in mathematics learning.

This lack of progress in the understanding of individual differences is not unique to mathematics education but permeates research on learning in general. Gagné (1967) stated that "it seems fair to say that we know considerably more about learning, its varieties and conditions, than we did ten years ago ... [but] we do not know much more about individual differences in learning than we did thirty years ago. We are still in the position of not being able to make definitive statements about differences in human learning abilities" (pp. xi–xii). Yet many traits on which humans differ have been identified and can be measured. In fact, Tyler (1974) says that "the measurement of individual differences in traits of some importance to society can be considered a major achievement of twentieth-century psychology" (p. 9). (For thorough reviews of the psychological literature, see Horn, 1976; Kagan & Kogan, 1970; Tyler, 1972, 1974.) For mathematics education, traits that have been of interest can be categorized within the cognitive (intellective) domain or the affective (nonintellective) domain. (For thorough reviews, see Aiken, 1970b, 1971; Meyer, 1976). Many studies have been conducted using these traits as variables. From these studies we know that individuals vary on such cognitive abilities as general intelligence, verbal ability, and spatial visualization. Individuals also vary on measures of affective traits. In addition, factor analyses produce different factor patterns for different populations depending on tests given and the sample studied.

The Organization of the Schools for Individual Instruction

Considerable interest has been shown in the question of how knowledge about individual differences should be used to affect instructional procedures. Weaver in 1954 said, "Effective provisions for individual differences is dependent in large measure upon appropriate differentiated instruction" (p. 300). That statement, and many that followed, accepted almost without question the premise that the way to handle individual differences is to provide programs of individualized instruction. As a consequence, individualizing instruction has become a major topic in American education.

Growing out of the two major strands of philosophy that have influenced 20th-century educational beliefs—humanism and behaviorism—two major and antithetical goals of individualized instruction have emerged (DeVault & Fox, 1977). One philosophical theme, detailed in *Individualizing Instruction*, the ASCD 1964 Yearbook, can be summarized as follows: Individuals differ not only in abilities but in potentialities. The purpose of education is to provide for the "release of potential in the individual learners" (Doll, 1964, p. 13). This can be done by identifying ways in which individuals differ not only in aptitudes or traits but in ways in which they wish (either subconsciously or consciously) to develop. In order to achieve individual potential, individuals must be permitted to make choices about what to learn, how to learn, and even whether to learn. If the goals of such a program are achieved, learners become increasingly different from one another. Schools currently attempting to implement this point of view are often identified as being "alternative" or "open" schools. Unfortunately, although volumes have been written concerning the importance of this position, most of it is in a philosophical framework and little is known empirically about attaining the goal of individual development.

The other philosophical position, illustrated in the NSSE Yearbook, *Individualizing Instruction* (Henry, 1962), is that schools exist to enable all people to learn approximately the same things: their cultural heritage, specific knowledge, or vocational skills, for example. Learners within such a program should become increasingly alike, at least in the knowledge they possess. Schools espousing this point of view often employ the systems approach, behavioral objectives, and instructional management. Within this philosophical framework, Glaser identifies a selective and an adaptive educational mode. "A selective mode is characterized by minimal variation in the conditions under which individuals are expected to learn" (1972, p. 6). In other words, learners must fit themselves to the educational environment. The adaptive mode is characterized by alternative means of learning, which "are adapted to and are in some way attached to knowledge about each individual—his background, talents, interests and the nature of his past performance" (p. 6). In this adaptive mode, even though the goals of instruction remain the same, the methods of achieving these goals are adapted to individual differences. In order to do this, individual differences in a variety of traits must be described and measured and instruction adapted to these differences so that all people attain the common goals.

Many mathematical programs have been developed within this adaptive mode: *Developing Mathematical Processes* (Romberg, Harvey, Moser, & Montgomery, 1974, 1975, 1976), *Individually Prescribed Instruction* (Research for Better Schools, 1972), and Science Research Associates' *Mathematics Learning System* (DeVault, Greenberg, Frehmeyer, & Bezuszka, 1974). Fey (1977) suggests, however, in a thoughtful summary of these and other programs, that we have little knowledge about their effectiveness:

> The accumulated experimental research does not provide convincing evidence in favor of those who urge implementation of an individualized instruction system or those who decline such an innovation. There appear to be some situations in which particular types of individualized instruction are more effective than conventional methods; and there are other conditions in which certain individual instruction systems are less effective. (p. 16)

Within these two broad philosophies of education, research that seeks to increase the understanding of the relationship between individual differences and instructional procedures must be structured.

TRENDS IN STUDYING INDIVIDUAL DIFFERENCES

Relatively little study of individual differences has taken place in the last decade. However, the study of individual differences appears to be gaining vitality, changing direction and emphasis. Four trends can be identified and will be discussed in this section:

1. Specific traits to be studied are being redefined.
2. A qualitative change in the focus of study is emerging.
3. The use of differing aptitudes as bases for instruction is being examined.
4. Some different variables are being studied as explanatory.

The Set of Individual Differences to Study

It is assumed without question that only those individual differences related to the learning of mathematics are important for study by mathematics educators, but defining the elements of this set of individual differences is difficult, if not impossible. In fact, the elements have no common name. At different times they have been called traits, abilities, aptitudes, factors, or attributes. A single term is helpful, and for this chapter the term *aptitude* has been selected. It is used here as defined by Cronbach and Snow (1977)—any characteristic of an individual that increases (or impairs) the probability of success in learning. Aptitude thus refers to variables within both the cognitive and the affective domains. The aptitudes within each domain that appear to have saliency for the learning of mathematics will be discussed in some detail.

The Cognitive Domain

Few scholars believe that many new aptitudes in the cognitive domain will be identified (Snow, 1976b; Tyler, 1972). Certainly general intelligence and various verbal aptitudes continue to be of interest. In addition, certain mathematical aptitudes, such as numerical ability, mathematical reasoning, and inductive/deductive ability, are receiving some attention. (For a review of cognitive variables related to mathematics, see Aiken, 1971.) It appears that the understanding of these aptitudes will deepen and change and new combinations may appear. Spatial visualization is receiving increased emphasis, and one major set of writers is strongly suggesting that the idea of cognitive style must be considered. These latter two will be discussed in depth.

Spatial visualization. Spatial visualization is an aptitude that has to do with the mental manipulation of rigid figures. The aptitude emerges as a component of mathematics ability in most factor analytic studies (Schonberger, 1976), and it shows about the same magnitude of correlation with mathematics achievement as verbal ability does (Fennema & Sherman, 1977). The role of spatial visualization in mathematics learning is unclear. Questions being investigated include the following:

1. Is spatial visualization more important to learning at certain levels of mathematics instruction than at others? On the one hand Smith (1964) hypothesized that as students move into advanced mathematics courses such as calculus, spatial visualization assumes increasing importance. Fennema (1975), on the other hand, hypothesized that spatial visualization is highly important to the learning of mathematics in the primary grades because of increased emphasis on concrete and pictorial representations, all of which have spatial attributes.

2. Does different mathematical content rely differently on spatial visualization skills? Even though the relationship between geometry and spatial visualization is logically evident, does the learning of geometry rely more heavily on this aptitude than the learning of algebra?

3. What is the role of spatial visualization skills in the problem-solving process? Are some people more apt to rely predominantly on spatial skills to solve problems and others on verbal skills? Are these differences related to specific problem types that can be identified?

4. How is spatial visualization aptitude developed? Would an elementary mathematics program with emphasis on manipulatives facilitate the development of children's spatial skills more adequately than a program emphasizing symbols?

5. In what way should learning environments be structured in response to spatial visualization aptitude? This question has been addressed in aptitude-treatment interaction research, where the hypothesis has been that if one has a high level of spatial visualization, then one should learn better with an instructional methodology that uses pictures and graphical representations. Results of these studies have indicated that contrary to the hypothesis, students high in spatial visualization ability do not learn better from a spatial treatment than from a verbal treatment, and students high in verbal ability do not learn better in a verbal treatment than in a spatial treatment. After carefully reviewing these studies, Cronbach and Snow (1977) conclude that maybe the original hypothesis was wrong:

> A spatial treatment may be designed so as to demand considerable spatial reasoning or it may be so brilliantly executed that the program serves as a prosthesis for the student who has poor spatial ability. That is to say, the program can do the spatial reasoning for him. (p. 282)

Cognitive style. Many researchers believe that exploring the dimensions of cognitive style holds great promise for understanding behavior. The following statement demonstrates this clearly:

> While relatively little research has been done, compared to what is possible and needed, it is already clear that cognitive style is a potent variable affecting

> a number of areas: the student's academic choices and vocational preferences, the student's continuing academic development, how students learn and teachers teach, and how students and teachers interact in the classroom. (Witkin, 1976, pp. 38–39)

Although any experienced researcher or educator reacts to such a strong statement with skepticism, the construct of cognitive style does need to be understood and evaluated.

A cognitive style is a "characteristic mode of functioning that [is revealed] throughout our perceptual and intellectual activities in a highly consistent and pervasive way" (Witkin, 1976, p. 39). Cognitive styles "represent consistencies in the manner or form of cognition, as distinct from the content of cognition or the level of skill displayed in the cognitive performance" (Messick, 1976, p. 5).

According to Messick, the construct of cognitive style differs from the construct of traditional abilities in a variety of ways:

1. The dimension of each cognitive style is a continuum stretching from one manner of cognitive functioning to another. An ability, however, varies from a low level to a high level with increasing levels implying more of a given ability. High spatial ability, for example, suggests that a person will be able to complete successfully a relatively larger number of spatial items than a person with lower spatial ability.

2. Although performing nearer one end of a cognitive style continuum has different implications for cognitive functioning, theoretically no value is attached to the type of cognitive style one exhibits or where one performs on the continuum. In contrast, having more of a traditional ability has a value connotation as reflected by the belief that a high score on a spatial visualization test, for example, represents a good spatial visualizer.

3. On the one hand, a cognitive style permeates the totality of behavior including cognitive, affective, and intersocial aspects. Cognitive styles permeate all of an individual's behavior. They are theorized to serve as heuristics of a high level that organize lower-level strategies, operations, and inclinations, often including abilities in complex cognitive processes such as problem solving and learning. Abilities, on the other hand, are more domain specific.

4. Investigations of cognitive style have more to do with how, or the manner in which, behavior occurs rather than with what kind of information or content is being processed or exhibited.

Messick's book (1976) is an excellent first reference about cognitive style. Its excellent glossary of cognitive styles includes the following: field independence/field dependence, field articulation, conceptualizing styles, breadth of categorization, conceptual differentiation, compartmentalization, conceptual articulation, cognitive complexity/simplicity, leveling/

sharpening, scanning, reflection/impulsivity, risk taking/cautiousness, tolerance for unrealistic experiences, constructed/flexible control, strong/ weak automatization, conceptual/perceptual-motor dominance, sensory modality preferences, converging/diverging.

Any one of the styles might have implications for research into mathematics learning. The two that have the most apparent implications for the learning of mathematics—field dependence/field independence and reflection/impulsivity—will be discussed.

Field independence/field dependence is the style that has the largest research base and that is generating the most interest and controversy. It also appears to be the most interesting to researchers in mathematics education. Herman Witkin and his associates have made major contributions to understanding this cognitive style (see Witkin, 1976, for a discussion of their work). Briefly, the theory goes as follows. At the field dependence end of the continuum, activities and perceptions are global, that is, subjects focus on the total environment. At the field independence end of the continuum, activities and perceptions are analytical, that is, subjects perceive the environment in its component parts. At the one extreme of the performance range, perception and mental activities are dominated by the prevailing field; at the other extreme they are relatively independent of the surrounding field.

This cognitive style is usually measured by specific tests (Rod and Frame Test—RFT—and Embedded Figures Test—EFT) in which subjects are asked to "disembed" something. In the RFT, subjects in a darkened room are required to move a bar to a vertical position with respect to a tilted frame. This involves being able to mentally disembed the bar from the frame. In the EFT, subjects find a simple plane figure, such as a triangle, in a more complicated set of lines. Witkin (1976) says that the common denominator underlying individual differences in performance in both of these tasks is "the extent to which a person is able to deal with a part of a field separately from the field as a whole" (p. 41) or to disembed an item from its context. From such tests it is inferred that people have either a field dependent or a field independent cognitive style.

Witkin cites evidence which he believes is a clear indication that "field independence/dependence is a manifestation in the perceptual sphere of a broad dimension of personal functioning that extends into the sphere of social behavior and into the sphere of personality" (p. 44).

In general, Witkin says that field dependent persons—

1. tend to use the prevailing social frame of reference to define their attitudes, beliefs, feelings, and self-view from moment to moment;

2. are prone to be guided by the positions attributed to an authority figure or peer group when forming their attitudes on an issue;

3. are particularly sensitive and attuned to the social environment;

4. prefer work areas that feature interpersonal relations, work that requires involvement with people, and tend not to choose more advanced optional mathematics and science courses in high school. (1976, p. 44)

He further states that students can ordinarily be expected to do better in subject matter areas in which cognitive demands fit their cognitive styles. For example, field dependent students are less likely to succeed in mathematics and science than field independent students.

Witkin believes that a field independent cognitive style appears in good problem-solving behavior or mathematical reasoning, particularly in those problems that require disembedding a critical portion and restructuring the problem materials so that the disembedded portion is used in a different way. Indeed, if this theory is valid, a significant area of individual differences with potentially great impact on mathematics education research has been identified.

However, many are raising important questions about the conclusions drawn by Witkin (Horn, 1976; Kagan & Kogan, 1970). One important assumption on which Witkin's theory of field dependence/independence rests is that the RFT and EFT are indicators of the same aptitude. Horn questions this assumption. The EFT appears to involve spatial visualization ability, whereas the RFT tasks seem to involve a more general function. The relation of field independence/field dependence to general intelligence is another questionable dimension. Horn states that when general intelligence is taken into account, "results do not support Witkin's claims that field independence represents a pervasive influence throughout cognitive behavior" (1976, p. 499). Threadgill (1976) disagrees with Horn. She concludes, after citing studies that support both sides of the question, that although intelligence and field independence/field dependence are related, the amount of shared variance is low enough to indicate that two different facets of individual differences are being measured.

These appear to be the major questions about Witkin's work, but several others are relevant. Does disembedding on a perceptual task require the same ability as that required in mathematical problem solving? Is the analytical thinking talked about by mathematicians similar in process to disembedding? Although Horn's position (1976, p. 449) that it is wise to drop the theory of field independence/dependence is probably an overreaction to some of its negative aspects, research must take into consideration that the assumptions underlying it are being severely questioned.

The other cognitive style relevant to mathematics learning is called reflection/impulsivity. This cognitive style involves an individual's consistency in the speed and accuracy with which alternative hypotheses are formulated and information processed. Since a desirable behavior in mathematics is to formulate, reflect on, and reformulate hypotheses, this construct warrants study in the context of mathematical learning. Individuals who score toward the impulsive end on this continuum tend to offer the first answer that occurs to them, even though it is frequently incorrect. Reflective individuals tend to ponder various possibilities before deciding. Messick (1976) says that "this dimension is thus mainly concerned with the degree to which an individual reflects on the validity of his hypothesis for solution in problems that contain response uncertainty" (p. 19).

Hypotheses about the relationship between this cognitive style and various problem-solving heuristics seem plausible. For example, are reflective learners more likely than impulsive learners to employ the problem-solving heuristic called identification of a simpler problem? Are reflective learners more likely than impulsive learners to take the time to employ the heuristic of understanding the problem by identifying the unknown?

In the area of both of these cognitive styles, as well as the others listed, a formulation of hypotheses for mathematics learning is largely nonexistent, although Witkin has recently hypothesized direct implications for instruction (Witkin, Moore, Goodenough, & Cox, 1977). Whether or not the effect of various cognitive styles on mathematics learning emerges as an important research area will depend on more adequate validation of cognitive style as a construct and on the development and testing of creative hypotheses by researchers in mathematics education.

The Affective Domain

Aptitudes within the affective domain are not as well defined as those within the cognitive domain; nevertheless, increased emphasis is being placed on attitudinal variables. (For reviews, see Aiken, 1970a, 1976; Callahan & Glennon, 1975; Suydam & Weaver, 1975). There are a number of problems with the work in this area, the most serious being the definitions of the construct "attitude." One problem is the lack of precision in the definition. For example, Callahan and Glennon define an attitude as children's liking or disliking of mathematics. Aiken offered a definition in one place (1970a) that was basically in agreement with Callahan and Glennon; in another (1970b) he defined attitudes as "variables which are not explicitly measured by tests of ability" (p. 28). What is the actual dimension that has been measured in studies dealing with attitudes? Does it include euphoria, depression, confidence in one's ability to perform the task, a belief that mathematics is useful, the recognition of success from peers, anxiety, or a sense of failure? These dimensions are quite often included in a single scale purporting to measure "attitude."

Another serious flaw in many studies of attitude is the global definition of mathematics that is used. Mathematics is a complex discipline involving many kinds of related but diverse content and skills. To assume that a person feels the same toward different parts of mathematics is not reasonable. For example, computing the answers to 50 three-digit by three-digit multiplication problems could easily arouse feelings in a person entirely different from those aroused when solving a mathematical puzzle.

When these definitional problems are taken into consideration, the literature suggests several tentative conclusions (Fennema, 1977):

1. There is a positive relationship between attitude and mathematics achievement which seems to increase as learners progress in school.

2. Attitudes toward mathematics are fairly stable—particularly above the sixth grade, although one longitudinal study showed a marked decrease from sixth grade to twelfth grade.

3. Grades 6–8 seem to be critical in the development of attitudes.

4. Extremely positive or negative attitudes appear to be better predictors of achievement than more neutral feelings.

5. There are sex-related differences in attitudes toward mathematics. (p. 104)

Confidence/anxiety. Work within the confidence/anxiety attitudinal dimension is producing some interesting results. Although confidence and anxiety have been defined as separate traits, it appears that they are very similar in relation to mathematical learning (Fennema & Sherman, 1977). Although it may be possible to talk about the two independently, it may be more profitable to recognize confidence and anxiety as two poles of one dimension. The relationship of confidence/anxiety and mathematics learning has been explored by a variety of methodologies. Also, instruments have been employed that purport to measure debilitative or facilitative anxiety in general or specifically to mathematics. Callahan and Glennon (1975) concluded that "anxiety and mathematics are related. In general high anxiety is associated with lower achievement in mathematics" (p. 82). Reports from the National Longitudinal Study of Mathematical Abilities (NLSMA) indicate that across Grades 4–10, decreases in facilitating anxiety appeared, with females' scores decreasing more than males' scores. Debilitating anxiety increased for females during these grade levels (Crosswhite, 1972).

The literature strongly suggests that there are sex-related differences in the confidence/anxiety dimension (Fennema & Sherman, 1978). It appears reasonable to believe that less confidence or greater anxiety on the part of females is an important variable that helps explain the difference in the number of males and females entering mathematics-related fields of study and employment. Crandall, Katkovsky, and Preston (1962) concluded that girls underestimate their own ability to solve mathematical problems. Others have concluded that females feel inadequate when faced with a variety of intellective problem-solving activities (Kagan, 1964). Maccoby and Jacklin (1973) reported that "girls tend to underestimate their own intellectual abilities more than boys do" (p. 41).

Fennema and Sherman (1978) found boys at each grade level 6–12 to be significantly more confident about their ability to deal with mathematics than were girls. Moreover, this was found when there were no significant sex-related differences in mathematics achievement. In addition, confidence in learning mathematics and achievement were more highly correlated than any other affective variable and achievement ($r \cong .40$). Confidence was almost as highly related to achievement as the cognitive variables of verbal ability and spatial visualization.

In addition to being important in explaining sex-related differences, the confidence/anxiety dimension is being used as an aptitude in aptitude-treatment interaction research. Summarizing the results of many studies from a variety of content areas, Snow (1976a) reports that high-anxiety students appear to perform better in a highly structured instructional treatment, whereas low-anxiety students perform better in a less structured instructional treatment.

Achievement motivation. Within the psychological literature, achievement motivation is being widely discussed and appears to have saliency for the learning of mathematics. There is consensus on the basic definition and the central concepts of achievement motivation because its study has been of a single school of scholars working under the somewhat indirect leadership of D. C. McClelland:

> The achievement motive is a pattern of planning, of actions, and of feelings connected with striving to achieve some internalized standard of excellence.... Achievement motivation is not necessarily the same thing as the search for observable accomplishments, such as obtaining high test scores, socially approved positions, or a high salary. Though it involves planning and striving for excellence, it is the attitude toward achievement that is important, rather than the accomplishments per se. (Vidler, 1977, p. 67)

The most widely used method of assessing achievement motivation has been the Thematic Apperception Test (TAT). The subject is shown a picture and asked to write a story that tells what is happening in the picture, what happened previously, and what is going to happen. The resulting story is then analyzed for content that indicates achievement motivation (see Atkinson, 1958, for a complete discussion). Unfortunately, this scoring is complex and time-consuming, and serious questions have been raised about its validity and reliability. However, some evidence has accumulated over the years indicating that this construct does have consistency and usefulness in helping educators understand some human behavior (Vidler, 1977).

Several personality correlates of persons with high achievement motivation have been identified (Alschuler, 1973). Among these are an interest in excellence for its own sake, a desire to work in areas where personal responsibility can be taken for actions, and self-reliance in decision-making areas. Up until a few years ago, it was accepted that there were strong sex-related differences in achievement motivation, with males consistently scoring higher. However, as research techniques have become more precise and less biased (Tittle, McCarthy, & Steckler, 1974), different conclusions are being reached. Some researchers are beginning to offer evidence that motivational patterns are essentially the same for both sexes and that the differences observed in these patterns relate to the domain of the activities. Females express achievement motivation in areas defined as feminine, and males express achievement motivation in areas defined as masculine (Stein & Bailey, 1973).

One aspect of achievement motivation that may have important implications for mathematics education is related to those motivating characteristics of individuals that lead them to select tasks of varying degrees of difficulty (Atkinson, 1966; Atkinson & Litwen, 1966). An individual is classified as being either motivated to achieve success or motivated to avoid failure. Individuals motivated to achieve success tend to select tasks of moderate difficulty and to avoid difficult tasks (because of the low probability of success) and also easy tasks (because no recognition for success would be received). An individual motivated to avoid failure tends to choose tasks that are either very easy or very hard. Easy tasks are selected because failure is unlikely, and hard tasks are selected because, since failure is expected, no stigma is attached. Also of interest is the behavior of individuals after they have failed a task. The theory predicts that the individual who is oriented toward success achievement will next choose a task of lesser difficulty or experience an increase in facilitative anxiety about failure, which increases task persistence. These behaviors are seen as desirable. The individual oriented toward avoiding failure tends to withdraw after failure. Thus, the motive to avoid failure is seen as inhibiting.

In recent years another aspect of achievement motivation has been developed and supported by the work of Horner (1968). She hypothesizes— and offers evidence to substantiate the hypothesis—that some individuals have a motive to avoid success. In particular, this motive has been shown to exist in high-achieving females who are afraid of success in male-dominated areas because such women fear rejection from their male peers. Although Horner's work has not been replicated (Horner, 1975), this addition to the theory is an important consideration.

As with many psychological constructs, achievement motivation has been investigated mainly outside of school settings, and the work that has been done in educational environments has resulted in equivocal findings. Small but positive correlations appear to exist between achievement motivation and achievement in school (Vidler, 1977). Training studies that attempt to increase students' orientation toward achieving success do not seem to improve their grades in school but do seem to result in more purposeful planning and action outside of school. However, the scarcity of research on the question of how the motivation to achieve is related to school achievement suggests that much remains to be learned.

Some obvious questions arise from this theory of achievement motivation for research and practice in mathematics education: Does presenting a learner a learning task with an empirically determined difficulty index affect the selection of tasks as predicted by the achievement motivation theory? What are characteristics of instructional treatments that interact with varying levels of achievement motivation? What are the implications of stereotyping mathematics as a male domain (Fennema & Sherman, 1978; Stein & Bailey, 1975) on females' achievement motivation in mathematics?

Performance to Process: A Qualitative Change

The shift from studying performance to studying process is a major redefinition of the study of individual differences. Instead of using overt responses as indicators of aptitudes, researchers are increasingly turning to the study of internal mental processes. In psychological literature, scholars are attempting to describe intelligent behavior instead of measuring intelligence. In mathematics education research, the qualitative change is clearly seen in the study of problem solving. Rather than inferring that a student has a certain amount of problem-solving aptitude from the production of correct solutions, researchers are asking students to solve problems and then observing the solving of these problems in a variety of ways.

For a thorough discussion of this qualitative change in emphasis, readers should see the book edited by Resnick (1976). Resnick examines cognitive and adaptive processes involved in intelligent behavior and asks how these processes might be related to tested intelligence (p. 4). Many researchers believe that the study of products of thinking or performance testing, as it has been, has run its course. As Tyler (1976) says,

> We have gone as far as we are going to be able to go, I believe, with psychometric procedures designed for precise quantitative evaluation of an individual's place in a norm group. . . . But to understand intelligence as a mental process and the ways individuals differ in their endowments, we must launch out in new directions. (p. 25)

Related to this qualitative change from product to cognitive process is the concern expressed by many researchers (e.g., Carroll, 1976; Glaser, 1972; Hunt & Lansman, 1975) about the long-standing separation between the psychometric tradition and cognitive psychology. The emphasis of the psychometricians has been the identification, measurement, and finally the classification of basic ways in which individual performances differ. Cognitive psychologists, who believe that such a classification is an inadequate final goal (Hunt & Lansman), believe that what is needed instead is a theory that describes cognitive processes and how people differ in these processes.

Psychologists working with cognitive processes are theorizing about them with ideas and words used to describe and analyze computer systems: *hardware, system architecture, programs,* and *control systems,* for instance. The architecture in the domain of cognitive psychology is considered fixed but usable in different ways. Although the physical principles of information processing are assumed to be the same for all humans, there are individual differences in the quality of different components. One example of this information-processing theory is provided by Atkinson and Shiffrin (1968), who propose a model of memory in which the following events are hypothesized to occur when information is presented:

1. The information is entered into short-term memory with probability α.

2. When an item is entered into short-term memory, another may or may not drop out depending on the strategy the subject uses for item rehearsal and on the number of items in short-term memory.

3. Information that is in short-term memory is transferred to long-term memory at a rate θ.

4. Information in long-term memory decays (i.e., becomes unavailable) by a negative exponential function with decay parameter τ.

This model has been given some validity by Hunt, Frost, and Lunneborg (1973), who found that individual parameter estimates for a group of college students did not vary as a function of verbal ability. However, they did find statistically significant differences associated with quantitative ability.

Atkinson and Shiffrin are also concerned with problem solving, which they hypothesized as a sequence of transformations in the memory system. This sequence is under the control of transformation rules, which in effect constitute the memory of how to solve problems. Hunt and Lansman (1975) discuss this model and observe that "the minimal statement that can be made about work connected with this theory is that students with varying psychometrically defined qualitative abilities differ in the use of their memory systems." They go on to say that "the parameter estimation approach alone has taken us beyond the simple statement that some people have better memories than others and has given us qualitative insight into differences in the way certain subjects use their memory systems" (p. 89).

Glaser (1972) is another researcher who advocates that cognitive-processing variables should form the bases of research. Research, he claims, gives ample evidence that in school learning a variety of cognitive processes are involved that can be identified and influenced. For example, consider *mental elaboration*. This refers to the elaborating of content to accomplish a recoding or transformation: Given the words *girl* and *pony* to remember, a child might elaborate this content to "the girl rides the pony." As children grow older, they develop their own forms of mental elaboration, but young children profit from being encouraged to engage in the elaboration process.

In accord with the qualitative change, Carroll (1976) has suggested modifying the traditional research methodology of factor analysis, proposing that instead of starting from the results of factor analysis one should start with a model of cognitive processes derived from theory and experimental findings and to interpret factors identified from a factor analysis according to this model. What is badly needed, says Carroll, is "a general methodology and theory for interpreting psychometric tests as cognitive processes, and for characterizing (but not necessarily classifying) factor-analytic factors according to the model of cognitive processes" (p. 31).

The cognitive process model Carroll has chosen is a theory proposed by Hunt (1971). This model includes short-, intermediate-, and long-term memories; sensory mechanisms through which information enters; and a "program" or "production system," assumed to be stored in memory, which controls the flow of information. Individuals differ in their production systems depending on their characteristics and past experience. Production systems probably differ with respect to particular strategies and the kinds of data available in the memory systems. The essential result of Carroll's work is the identification of cognitive processes as being characteristics of each of 24 chosen factor-analytic factors. The identified processes are diverse with respect to type, memory store involved, temporal parameters, and other details. Furthermore, most of the factor-analytic factors differ markedly from one another according to this coding.

Currently, research in cognitive processing—such as that of Carroll—has little to say for instruction in mathematical learning. However, such work does suggest models that can be points of departure for the analysis of cognitive processes involved in mathematical learning. Work by Carroll and Glaser makes one optimistic that identifying individual differences in cognitive processing might be the key for unlocking many mysteries about the learning of mathematics.

Cognitive processing variables involved in problem solving are receiving specific attention in mathematics education. Kilpatrick (1975) defines these as variables "based on the solution path the subject takes; they are derived from either the subject's verbal report of his thinking or the manipulation he makes with an apparatus. Process variables relate to such things as the subject's strategy (as inferred from the sequence of steps he takes), the heuristics he uses, the algorithms he uses, the extent of his perseveration in blind alleys, the nature and number of the errors he makes, and his response to hints'' (p. 7). Kilpatrick goes on to emphasize that ''any respectable study of problem solving in mathematics should include measurements of process variables'' (p. 7). The importance of this area is clearly recognized, but the scope of individual differences in problem solving is still unknown. Whether each person develops unique problem-solving processes or whether there are commonalities of problem-solving behavior is a fertile field for research.

Krutetskii (1976) has related problem-solving processes to information processing by postulating three stages in solving mathematical problems: gathering, processing, and retaining information about the problem and its solution. Within each stage, one or more mathematical abilities are identified and can be outlined thus:

1. Obtaining mathematical information

   A. The ability for formalized perception of mathematical material, for grasping the formal structure of a problem.

2. Processing mathematical information

   A. The ability for *logical* thought in the sphere of quantitative and spatial relationships, number and letter symbols, (the ability to think in mathematical symbols).

   B. The ability for rapid and broad generalization of mathematical objects, relations, and operations.

   C. The ability to curtail the process of mathematical reasoning and the system of corresponding operations, (the ability to think in curtailed structures).

   D. Flexibility of mental process in mathematical activity.

   E. Striving for clarity, simplicity, economy, and rationality of solutions.

   F. The ability for rapid and free reconstruction of the directions of a mental process, switching from a direct to a reverse train of thought (reversibility of the mental process in mathematical reasoning).

3. Retaining mathematical information

   A. Mathematical memory (generalized memory for mathematical relationships, type characteristics, schemes of arguments and proofs, methods of problem-solving, and principles of approach).

4. General synthetic component

   A. Mathematical cast of mind

These components are closely interrelated, including one another and forming in their aggregate a single integral system, a distinctive syndrome of mathematical giftedness, the mathematical cast of mind. (pp. 350–351)

In the context of Krutetskii's work, Kilpatrick (1977) makes suggestions for the study of teaching mathematics to elementary school children. Some teachers should be chosen that are known to be highly effective in teaching mathematics.

> Data on the thoughts and behavior of these teachers as they plan, conduct, and evaluate mathematics lessons could be gathered by such means as interviews with the teachers, videotape recordings of the teachers' activities, and interviews with the teachers as they view recordings. Analyses of these data might be directed toward the identification of pupils perceived and treated differently during the lessons. . . . Krutetskii's outline, coupled with an analysis of the information-processing demands of instructional tasks, provides a framework for studying how teachers adapt their teaching to differences in pupils' mathematical abilities. (pp. 11, 12).

The Use of Different Aptitudes as the Bases for Organizing Instruction

How to organize instruction for individuals is studied by a methodology with the distinctive name of Aptitude-Treatment Interaction (ATI). ATI's main investigators are L. J. Cronbach and R. E. Snow (1977), who define aptitude as it has been used in this chapter and treatment as "any variation in the pace or style of instruction." The philosophical framework of ATI can be stated briefly. Since people differ on important aptitudes that affect learning, these aptitudes should be major factors considered in structuring instructional environments.

The early conceptualization of ATI research (Cronbach, 1957) was extended by Salomon (1972) to include three models for ATI research. One reflected the early conceptualization by Cronbach, which Salomon calls the capitalization model. According to this model the instructional treatment should be designed to take advantage of the learner's unique ability by matching, as nearly as possible, the strongest aptitudes of the learner. A second conceptualization for ATI research is called the compensatory model. According to this model an instructional treatment should be designed to compensate for a learner's low level of aptitude on a given variable—to do for the learners what they are unable to do for themselves. A third conceptualization is called a remediation model. As the name suggests, this model calls for the design of an instructional treatment that remediates or provides experiences that will raise the learner's aptitude on a given variable.

The theory of Aptitude-Treatment Interaction and its three models is intellectually pleasing and permeates much of the writing about individualized instruction. Snow emphasizes that "all attempts at individualizing instruction rest explicitly or implicitly on hypothesized aptitude-treatment interaction'' (1976b, p. 5). The purpose of the research dealing with ATI has been to identify aptitudes and treatments that, when coexisting, result in better learning. If learners with certain aptitudes can be shown to learn better with a certain instructional methodology, then a qualitative differentiation of methodology in instruction can be planned for individual learners.

To understand more clearly the traditional ATI paradigm based on the capitalization model, consider the study reported by Behr (1970). The study took as its point of departure a general hypothesis suggested by Robert Gagné (1960) that if a theory of intelligence and the accompanying means of measurement have merit, then it should be possible to show experimentally that persons who demonstrate high figural, semantic, or symbolic abilities should be able to learn better if the content is presented in one of these respective forms. More specifically, the study sought information about whether subjects who demonstrated high figural or verbal aptitude learned specific content better when it was presented in these respective modes. Aptitudes for potential interactions with treatments were chosen from the "structure of intellect" model and its accompanying theory as developed by Guilford (1967). After being tested on the battery of mental factor tests, subjects were randomly assigned to one of two treatment groups. Two instructional treatments on the topic of modulus seven arithmetic were written to reflect figural and verbal teaching modes. Following treatment, subjects were given tests on learning, retention, and transfer. Investigation for ATIs was accomplished by regressing the learning, retention, and transfer scores on the several aptitude variables and then testing to determine whether or not regression equations for each of the two groups for a given criterion variable had equal slopes. Significant interactions were found between selected figural semantic aptitudes and methods of instruction.

A fairly substantial body of ATI research has emerged dealing with broad instructional areas as well as specifically with mathematics instruction (see Berliner & Cahen, 1973; Cronbach, 1975; Cronbach & Snow, 1977; Snow, 1976a, 1976b; Tobias, 1976). Cronbach and Snow concluded that the existence of the phenomena of ATI is clearly established. However, according to Snow (1976b), "while some ATI findings are plausible and some are replicable, few are well understood and none are yet applicable to instructional practice" (p. 1). In the area of mathematics the results of these studies have been mixed, and there are few replicated interactions that permit prescriptions of instructional treatment to individual learners. Some interesting findings and some worthwhile clues about the organization of instruction have emerged (Tobias, 1976).

However, more important than specific findings is the recognition that ATI, as originally conceived, is too simplistic (Cronbach, 1975). Both the aptitudes and the treatments, as well as their interactions, need reexamination. Different aptitudes are being hypothesized as having importance. Originally, aptitudes for study were specialized aptitudes selected from, or related to, Guilford's theory about the factorial structure of the intellect. Cronbach (1975) reports that a typical ATI hypothesis went like this: "High spatial ability makes for success when the instruction uses diagrams as much as possible, and minimizes words" (p. 119). In other words, the instructional treatment should reflect as precisely as possible the aptitude in which the learner excelled, an example of the capitalization model. Studies employing the compensatory and remediation models also used specialized aptitudes as bases for instructional treatments. However, the results of studies that used such aptitudes to plan instructional treatments have produced enough mixed results to bring into question the use of specialized aptitudes (Cronbach, 1975; Cronbach & Snow, 1969; Eastman & Behr, 1977). Tobias (1976) expands on the problem caused by using specialized aptitudes and raises two questions: (a) Can instructional methods be designed to rely predominantly on one aptitude? and (b) What is the temporal consistency of aptitudes required by the learning task? Do the aptitudes needed to achieve the learning task change as the student works through the task? If so, the instructional strategies designed to teach the task would also have to change.

Some of the difficulties with using specialized abilities as aptitudes in ATI research might be reduced if the interaction between prior achievement and instructional treatment is measured. In a number of ATI studies conducted by Tobias (1976) using such aptitudes as associative novelty or anxiety and preferences, few consistent interactions between individual differences and instruction emerged. A consistent finding in these ATI studies was that the treatment interacted, not with the aptitudes, but with the students' prior achievement in the subject matter. A general hypothesis based on these studies has emerged: The higher the level of prior achievement, the lower the instructional support required to accomplish instructional objectives. Conversely, as the level of prior achievement decreases, the amount of instructional support required increases.

An emerging emphasis in ATI study is a more careful examination of instructional treatments. Instructional treatments vary dramatically in the information-processing burdens they place on, or remove from, the learner (Snow, 1976b). It appears that the higher the intelligence, the greater one's capabilities to figure things out, to organize one's own study, and to build one's own comprehension. Therefore, in an ATI study using intelligence as the aptitude, any treatment that varies in the organizational demands placed on students results in significant interactions.

An important broadening of ATI research has been to select an affective variable as the aptitude under consideration. The use of anxiety, for example, as an aptitude has produced significant ATIs when combined with the amount of structure or instructional support as treatment, particularly in college students (Snow, 1976a). Significant ATIs have resulted when low anxiety is matched with minimal instructional support and vice versa.

Another important restructuring of the ATI paradigm is the recognition of the need to focus on more complex aptitudes as well as more complex instructional treatments. To hypothesize that a simple interaction exists between one specialized aptitude and one dimension of instruction is concise but not realistic. No person employs only one aptitude (either cognitive or affective), and to attempt to isolate one dimension of a treatment is to ignore the complexity of the instructional process. In Cronbach's words, "The trait measure has negligible power to forecast what the high scorer is likely to do in any one situation. The contention that behavior is determined by the situation alone is equally wrong" (1975, p. 120).

The complexity of ATI research is further highlighted by Cronbach's argument (1975) that serious attention must be given to higher-order interactions. He says that his own inability to generalize from ATI studies reported in the literature results from inconsistencies, rising especially from higher-order interactions. This position is stronger than that taken in 1957 when he argued that it is inappropriate to generalize about the main effect of an aptitude when an ATI is present. He now holds that the same argument must be applied to the ATI as well. An aptitude-by-treatment interaction can be considered to be a general effect only if the interaction is not further moderated by interactions with additional variables. "However far we carry our analysis—to third order or fifth order or any other—untested interactions of a still higher order can be envisioned" (Cronbach, 1975, p. 119).

Cronbach and Snow's beliefs (1977) about how ATI research should develop reflect the qualitative change from product to process discussed earlier. They state:

> We need more sophisticated hypotheses, based on a careful analysis of the information processing required in the course of learning, and a corresponding analysis of tests to identify the processes that account for high scores. . . . To date, no major study has framed hypotheses in terms of the acts the learner must perform. (pp. 282, 292–293)

A new variable has been hypothesized to be important and should be added to the ATI paradigm. Walberg (1976) states: "It seems ironic that in educational research enormous efforts have gone into the measurement of aptitude that cannot be manipulated very effectively after school age (except in the sense of selecting students for instruction), while few studies have been made of environment that can be manipulated" (p. 17). In particular, Walberg believes that since a series of studies have demonstrated that student perceptions of the classroom learning environment can be reliably measured and that these environmental variables are valid predictors of cognitive, affective, and behavioral measures of learning, then environmental variables must also be employed as one studies the makeup of optimum learning situations. In this context, studies would address questions such as these: (a) Which instruction (content, media, method) individualized in what way is best for a student with a given aptitude? (b) Which environment, individualized for students with given characteristics, is best for a given method of instruction? The relative importance of these variables—aptitudes, environment, and instruction—is suggested by Walberg's summary, which indicates that of the variance in learning variables, 40 to 60% is accounted for by environmental variables and 16 to 20% by aptitude variables, leaving only 20 to 44% for instruction and error.

In summary, it seems clear that ATI is still with us but that changing its direction in several ways would increase its benefit:

1. Since most ATI studies have been conducted in the laboratory for short instructional times, there is a necessity for large-scale, real-school studies of long duration.
2. A variety of aptitudes in combination need investigation.
3. Instructional treatments need to be broadened.
4. Environmental variables should be considered.
5. The research methodology should be modified to include clinical techniques.

Since Cronbach's initiation, ATI studies have been conducted in the rigid modes of experimental psychology. In particular, the measurement of the aptitude and criterion variables has been determined basically by the psychometric tradition. Little attempt has been made to examine cognitive processes, and interactions have been observed by statistical tests only. Any research that has as its ultimate goal the individualization of instruction must direct its attention to the clinical observation of interactions between aptitudes and instruction. We agree with Cronbach's remark (1975) and wish to emphasize and extend it:

> The experimenter or the correlational researcher should look within his data for local effects arising from uncontrolled conditions and intermediate responses ... [which he can do] only if he collected adequate protocol data from the start. ... An *observer* [emphasis ours] collecting data in one place and particular situation is in a position to appraise a practice or proposition in that setting, observing effects in context. In trying to describe and account for what happened he will give attention to whatever variables were controlled, but he will give equally careful attention to uncontrolled conditions. (p. 124)

It is important to observe that one who enters the research area of adapting instruction in specific content to individuals has, in fact, knowingly or unknowingly, willingly or unwillingly, for better or for worse, entered the area of ATI study. To adapt instruction in specific content to individuals necessarily asks the question of what instructional treatment is uniquely best to enable an individual to achieve specified goals within a given educational environment.

Within ATI research, different kinds of hypotheses need to be generated. Snow (1976a) states that

> the list of results appears to be a patchwork, without showing much evidence of coherent or sustained attacks on well formulated ATI hypotheses, because, frankly, that is the present state of the art. Past research has been a hodgepodge of oversimplified hypotheses investigated with research methods poorly designed for the purpose; hence progress has been slow, and significant findings are still quite scattered. (p. 274)

The generating of nontrivial and viable hypotheses is crucial. In particular, hypotheses dealing with affective variables and process variables as traditionally studied aptitudes would appear to be salient. Observational data should be incorporated in selecting both aptitudes and treatments. More complex interactions should be sought, and the learning environment should be incorporated as a variable.

Explanatory Variables

Researchers are always interested in explaining why individual differences exist, and recently there have been major attempts to use the idea of environmental variables to explain individual differences in achievement. Educational sociologists have attempted to explain differential achievement, not on the basis of what schools do or what abilities learners have, but on the basis of environmental variables of the learner's school, home, neighborhood, and community. This has taken place outside the mathematics education area for the most part, and the need exists for translating these important ideas into mathematics education literature.

The model of learning espoused by Wiley and Harnischfeger (1974) is a sociological line of inquiry that appears to have direct relevance to the learning of mathematics. This model deals with the time students spend in school on specified tasks and the type and quality of their activities during the time on task. The very obvious idea that the more time one spends learning, the more one learns is the basis for the model. According to Wiley and Harnischfeger, their data indicate that over a period of a year "in schools where students receive 24% more schooling [than in comparison schools] they will increase . . . gains in mathematics and verbal skills by more than one-third" (p. 9). This research raises interesting questions. Do pupils indeed vary a great deal in the amount of time actually spent learning mathematics? Do school requirements of time spent on mathematics differ? In classes of equal length, do the learners actually spend the same amount of time learning mathematics? It would appear that counting just the time allocated to mathematics is insufficient. If one believes as Wittrock (1974) does that learning occurs only when the learner is actively engaged in generating relationships between new information and previous experience, then one must ascertain how much learners differ in the amount of time actively involved in mathematics.

The nature/nurture argument appears to have reared its nonproductive head again as an explanatory variable. After many years of quiescence, authors are addressing the issue of inherited abilities—and addressing it as it relates to sex and race. In relation to sex, Stafford (1972) hypothesized that quantitative ability and spatial visualization ability are sex- or X-linked and carried as recessive characteristics on the X chromosome. If this is true, females would inherit a high potential for quantitative and spatial visualization skills less often than males would. Such hypotheses about sex-linked differences are usually studied in one of three ways: by matching curves of obtained data distributions with theoretical ones, by studying performances of twins, or by inspecting intrafamilial correlations. At best this is strongly inferential research, which always leaves many questions unanswered. Stafford believes his analyses confirm the hypotheses, whereas Sherman (1977) concludes that "there is no acceptable, scientific evidence of X-linked inheritance of mathematical problem solving," and that the "accumulation of negative findings disconfirms the X-linked hypothesis of the inheritance of spatial skills" (pp. 24–25).

The use of race-related differences caused by genetic influences was brought back to life by the Jensen (1969) article in the *Harvard Educational Review,* and the controversy that article caused has flourished since then (see Horn, 1976, for a complete review). Jensen believes the evidence indicates that mean differences in measures of intellectual achievement are indicative of innate ability differences between blacks and whites. Much of the work published since the Jensen article involves reanalyses of extant data and seems "to be rather hastily done or by amateurs" (Horn, 1976, p. 473). Much controversy, shoddy writing, innuendos, and direct statements concerning the type of training that people of various intelligence should receive have emerged since the Jensen article. The original data on which Jensen based his argument has been attacked as seriously inaccurate and falsified (Kamin, 1974). Certainly, all the evidence is equivocal and unconvincing as a genetic basis for differences in intelligence between races.

The study of inherited abilities is essentially nonproductive for educators. In the past it has not generated knowledge that is useful for planning instruction and probably will not do so in the future. However, the study of sex-related and race-related variations, probably based on cultural causes, is profitable, although whether or not such a discussion belongs in this chapter could be debated. Certainly, as one talks about a sex-related difference or a race-related difference, one is talking, not about individual differences, but group differences. However, because the studies of sex-related and race-related differences are increasing in number, the implications of such study need examination.

Because of its applied nature, educational research should address in some manner the implications of its significant as well as its nonsignificant findings. These implications should result in eliminating false beliefs in the case of nonsignificant findings, in further research to understand more adequately the significant differences found, or in direct educational change. Such has not been true with either sex- or race-related research.

Consider the sex-related research and its implications. Although strongly questioned (Fennema, 1974; Fennema & Sherman, 1977), the belief has been held for years that research indicates that males learn mathematics better than females (Aiken, 1971; Callahan & Glennon, 1975). Most research reporting in the area has ignored nonsignificant findings and reported significant findings. The implications of such significant findings for educational change have seldom been explored. Similarly, neither the issues raised by saying that 50% of the population performs less well in mathematics than the other 50% nor the nongenetic reasons for such differences have been adequately investigated. The innuendo that frequently emerges is that these differences are large and cannot be changed. If one believes that educational research should address the implications of its findings, then this belief about females' less adequate performance in mathematics should have been reflected in further educational research about these differences or in direct educational change. Such is not the case. The only apparent effect of this body of research knowledge has been to solidify the belief that mathematics is—and should be—a male domain (Fennema & Sherman, 1977). Research concerned with sex-related differences in mathematics learning has had a deleterious influence on females' learning of mathematics. It has somehow assisted in perpetuating the myth that females are inherently less capable than males of learning mathematics even when an overall examination of the literature does not support this. (For a thorough review of sex-related differences in mathematics, see Fennema, 1975; Fennema & Sherman, 1977.)

The examination of race-related differences has been discussed at length in the area of general intelligence (see Horn, 1976). The same problems exist with this literature that existed in the sex-related literature, including the problem of the falsification of data (Gillie, 1977; Horn, 1976). There is little in the literature about race-related issues in the learning of mathematics, and such study would be profitable if the long-term effect would be an increased equality of mathematics learning for all races.

DIRECTIONS FOR RESEARCH ON INDIVIDUAL DIFFERENCES

Research on characteristics of individuals and how they affect the learning of mathematics is a profitable area of investigation. Although many suggestions for future research have already been made, a few specific suggestions follow, and several topics profitable to future research will be discussed: (a) research methodology, (b) the identification and study of characteristics on which people differ, and (c) individualized instruction.

Research Methodology

The identification of meaningful hypotheses for study can occur when researchers employ two dimensions of the acquisition of knowledge simultaneously: reported literature of a multidisciplinary nature and observation in the real world of learners and teachers. Because of the complexity of the educational process, the researcher must be thoroughly acquainted with psychological, sociological, and educational literature. In addition, in order to identify viable hypotheses, the researcher should be closely involved in the teaching-learning process as an observer-participant in what is frequently referred to as a clinical investigation. For too long, research in individual differences has drawn its hypotheses from too narrow a literature and has ignored the observations of learners and teachers for the generating of viable hypotheses. The clinical approach is particularly necessary as one considers the process dimension of problem solving. Consider Kilpatrick's (1975) remarks:

> Given the present state of the art the most promising methodologies for research are those involving intensive study of the same set of subjects over an extended period of time. The subjects must solve a large number of problems of diverse types in order to permit confident generalizations about the processes they use. Numerous measures of trait variables should be obtained, and control should be exercised over instructional history variables. Case studies of subjects selected because of notable giftedness in mathematics or notable difficulty with mathematics may be particularly useful. Cross age studies of developmental trends in problem solving may help to suggest process variables that should be studied further, but longitudinal studies are obviously to be preferred. (p. 11)

To explore adequately both the multidisciplinary approach and the clinical method as a way of generating hypotheses is beyond this chapter's scope—but both must be a concern of researchers investigating individual differences.

Characteristics on Which People Differ

It must be emphasized that the mere identification of traits on which individuals differ is not a particularly profitable area for research. It will become so only as the relation of these traits to the learning of mathematics is ascertained and the implications for instruction are delineated. In addition to interindividual differences, intraindividual differences should be explored. Tyler (1974) speaks to the issue of the pluralistic approach to individuality that should be investigated. This should be done because each person is several potential individuals. Each has the potential to respond in a variety of ways, and whatever response is made depends on a complex matrix of environmental and individual variables. This repertoire of possible responses is worthy of study. For example, do individuals possess a variety of problem-solving heuristics? Is the successful problem solver one who is able to apply different techniques depending on the problem being solved?

Certain intraindividual differences over time should also be investigated as the developmental ideas of Piaget differ from more traditional individual difference variables. Piagetian constructs suggest a qualitative difference of cognitive behavior over time, whereas the more traditional constructs suggest that the difference is in the amount of a particular aptitude or knowledge accumulated. How instructional and environmental factors interact with intraindividual differences that change over time has scarcely been investigated. Questions of adapting instruction to be compatible with these qualitative differences or to facilitate the transition from a given qualitative level to another need investigators' attention.

Individualized Instruction

The need for investigating the individualized instruction programs currently being offered by schools is so overwhelming that it is impossible to list specific areas of study. One set of studies that would at least help define the field are status studies that aid in the definition of variables to be considered. The Descriptor for Individualized Instruction (Golladay & Skuldt, 1974) is one instrument developed to empirically analyze procedural variables in individualized instruction programs. The Descriptor does describe and differentiate between programs, and as a paradigm it is a means of communicating the various strategies being employed for individualizing different instructional programs. Further such work may facilitate the identification of teacher, instructional, and environmental variables for research relating to the adaptation of instructional environments.

CONCLUDING REMARKS

We have reported briefly the status of knowledge about individual differences in variables related to mathematics learning and instruction, discussed and evaluated new trends in the study of individual differences, and identified some areas where research concerned with individual differences might improve mathematics learning. We have pointed out that the way schools are organized to account for individual differences depends on one of two philosophical frameworks—humanistic or behavioristic. Furthermore, research on individual differences, insofar as it relates to education, has been presented in two major areas of concern: (a) the identifying, measuring, and characterizing of differences among individuals and (b) the adapting of instructional treatments and environments to individuals.

Probably as much progress as possible has been made in the identification and psychometric measurement of individual differences. What remains is to understand in greater depth these differences and what they mean to organizing instruction. This chapter has identified numerous individual differences that, according to the literature, are relevant to the learning of mathematics. In addition, an indication of the depth of understanding about some of these variables has been included, and the paucity of knowledge about what these differences mean in the educational enterprise has been indicated. The need is great for translating research on individual differences into knowledge about educational practice as well as for the generating and study of more viable hypotheses within the educational framework. It is hoped that new study will provide such translation and hypotheses.

The most important direction that research in individual differences can take is to unify research on (a) identifying the differences and (b) organizing instruction to provide for them. As the first step in this process, researchers must clearly identify the philosophical framework and goals of instruction from which they (or the schools) are operating and then design studies to reflect those goals. Those who believe that individuals should become increasingly different will use means of evaluating learning that are different from those who believe that all learners should learn the same content.

REFERENCES

Aiken, L. R., Jr. Attitudes toward mathematics. *Review of Educational Research*, 1970, *40*, 551–596. (a)

Aiken, L. R., Jr. Nonintellective variables and mathematics achievement: Directions for research. *Journal of School Psychology*, 1970, *8*, 28–36. (b)

Aiken, L. R., Jr. Intellective variables and mathematics achievement: Directions for research. *Journal of School Psychology*, 1971, *9*, 201–212.

Aiken, L. R., Jr. Update on attitudes and other affective variables in learning mathematics. *Review of Educational Research*, 1976, *46*, 293–311.

Alschuler, A. S. *Developing achievement motivation in adolescents*. Englewood Cliffs, N.J.: Educational Technology Publications, 1973.

Atkinson, J. W. (Ed.). *Motives in fantasy, action, and society*. Toronto: Van Nostrand, 1958.

Atkinson, J. W. Motivational determinants of risk-taking behavior. In J. W. Atkinson & N. T. Feather (Eds.), *A theory of achievement motivation*. New York: Wiley, 1966.

Atkinson, J. W., & Litwin, G. H. Achievement motive and test anxiety conceived as motive to approach success and motive to avoid failure. In J. W. Atkinson & N. T. Feather (Eds.), *A theory of achievement motivation*. New York: Wiley, 1966.

Atkinson, R. C., & Shiffrin, R. M. Human memory: A proposed system and its control processes. In K. Spence & J. Spence (Eds.), *The psychology of learning and motivation* (Vol. 2). New York: Academic Press, 1968.

Behr, M. J. Interactions between "structure-of-intellect" factors and two methods of presenting concepts of modular arithmetic—A summary paper. *Journal for Research in Mathematics Education*, 1970, *1*, 29–42.

Berliner, D. C., & Cahen, L. S. Trait-treatment interaction and learning. *Review of Research in Education*, 1973, *1*, 58–94.

Callahan, L. G., & Glennon, V. J. *Elementary school mathematics: A guide to current research* (4th ed.). Washington, D.C.: Association for Supervision and Curriculum Development, 1975.

Carroll, J. B. Psychometric tests as cognitive tasks: A new structure of intellect. In L. B. Resnick (Ed.), *The nature of intelligence*. Hillsdale, N.J.: Lawrence Erlbaum Associates, 1976.

Crandall, V. C., Katkovsky, W., & Preston, A. Motivational and ability determinants of young children's intellectual achievement behaviors. *Child Development*, 1962, *33*, 643–661.

Cronbach, L. J. The two disciplines of scientific psychology. *American Psychologist*, 1957, *12*, 671–684.

Cronbach, L. J. Beyond the two disciplines of scientific psychology. *American Psychologist*, 1975, *30*, 116–127.

Cronbach, L. J., & Snow, R. E. *Individual differences in learning ability as a function of instructional variables* (Final Report No. USOE DEC 4-6-061269-1217). Stanford, Calif.: Stanford University, 1969.

Cronbach, L. J., & Snow, R. E. *Aptitudes and instructional methods*. New York: Irvington Publishers, 1977.

Crosswhite, F. J. *Correlates of attitudes toward mathematics* (National Longitudinal Study of Mathematical Abilities, Report No. 20). Palo Alto, Calif.: Stanford University Press, 1972.

DeVault, M. V., & Fox, G. T., Jr. *Historical perspectives on individualized instruction*. Unpublished manuscript, 1977. (Available from M. Vere DeVault, Department of Curriculum and Instruction, University of Wisconsin, Madison, Wis.)

DeVault, M. V., Greenberg, H. J., Frehmeyer, H., & Bezuszka, S. J. *SRA mathematics learning system*. Chicago: Science Research Associates, 1974.

Doll, R. (Ed.). *Individualizing instruction: ASCD 1964 yearbook*. Washington, D.C.: Association for Supervision and Curriculum Development, 1964.

Eastman, P. M., & Behr, M. J. Interaction between structure of intellect factors and two methods of presenting concepts of logic. *Journal for Research in Mathematics Education*, 1977, *8*, 379–381.

Fennema, E. Sex differences in mathematics achievement: A review. *Journal for Research in Mathematics Education*, 1974, *5*, 126–139.

Fennema, E. Mathematics, spatial ability and the sexes. In E. Fennema (Ed.), *Mathematics learning: What research says about sex differences.* Columbus, Ohio: ERIC Center for Science, Mathematics, and Environmental Education, 1975.

Fennema, E. Influences of selected cognitive, affective and educational variables on sex-related differences in mathematics learning and studying. In L. H. Fox, E. Fennema, & J. Sherman (Eds.), *Women and mathematics: Research perspectives for change.* Washington, D.C.: National Institute of Education, 1977.

Fennema, E., & Sherman, J. Sex-related differences in mathematics achievement, spatial visualization and affective factors. *American Educational Research Journal,* 1977, *14,* 51–71.

Fennema, E., & Sherman, J. Sex-related differences in mathematics achievement and related factors: A further study. *Journal for Research in Mathematics Education,* 1978, *9,* 189–203.

Fey, J. T. *Individualized mathematics instruction: The next steps.* Unpublished manuscript, 1977. (Available from James Fey, University of Maryland, College Park, Md.)

Gagné, R. M. Implications of some doctrines of mathematics teaching for research in human learning. In *Research problems in mathematics education* (Cooperative Research Monograph No. 3, OE-12008). Washington, D.C.: U.S. Government Printing Office, 1960.

Gagné, R. M. (Ed.). *Learning and individual differences.* Columbus, Ohio: Charles E. Merrill, 1967.

Gillie, O. Did Sir Cyril Burt fake his research on hereditability of intelligence? Part I. *Phi Delta Kappan,* 1977, *58,* 469–471.

Glaser, R. Individuals and learning: The new aptitudes. *Educational Researcher,* 1972, *1,* 5–13.

Golladay, M. A., DeVault, M. V., Fox, G. T., Jr., & Skuldt, K. Problems in empirical research on individualized mathematics programs. *Journal for Research in Mathematics Education,* 1975, *5,* 159–169.

Guilford, J. P. *The nature of human intelligence.* New York: McGraw-Hill, 1967.

Henry, N. B. (Ed.). *Individualizing instruction: The sixty-first yearbook of the National Society for the Study of Education, part I.* Chicago: University of Chicago Press, 1962.

Horn, J. L. Human abilities: A review of research and theory in the early 1970's. *Annual Review of Psychology,* 1976, *27,* 437–485.

Horner, M. *Sex differences in achievement motivation and performance in competive and non-competitive situations.* Unpublished doctoral dissertation, University of Michigan, 1968.

Horner, M. Toward an understanding of achievement related conflicts in women. In M. T. S. Mednick, S. S. Tangri, & L. W. Hoffman (Eds.), *Women and achievement: Social and motivational analyses,* pp. 206–220. Washington, D.C.: Hemisphere, 1975.

Hunt, E. What kind of computer is man? *Cognitive Psychology,* 1971, *2,* 57–98.

Hunt, E., Frost, N., & Lunneborg, C. Individual differences in cognition: A new approach to intelligence. In C. Bower (Ed.), *Advances in learning and motivation* (Vol. 7). New York: Academic Press, 1973.

Hunt, E., & Lansman, M. Cognitive theory applied to individual differences. In W. K. Estes (Ed.), *Handbook of learning and cognitive processes.* Hillsdale, N.J.: Lawrence Erlbaum Associates, 1975.

Jensen, A. R. How much can we boost IQ and scholastic achievement? *Harvard Educational Review,* 1969, *39,* 1–123.

Kagan, J. Acquisition and significance of sex typing and sex role identity. In M. L. Hoffman & L. Hoffman (Eds.), *Review of child development research.* New York: Russell Sage Foundation, 1964.

Kagan, J., & Kogan, N. Individual variation in cognitive processes. In P. H. Mussen (Ed.), *Carmichael's manual of child psychology* (Vol. 1). New York: Wiley, 1970.

Kamin, L. J. *The science and politics of IQ.* New York: Wiley, 1974.

Kilpatrick, J. *Variables and methodologies in research on problem solving.* Paper presented at Research Workshop of Problem Solving in Mathematics Education, Athens, Georgia, May 1975. (Available from J. Kilpatrick, University of Georgia, Athens, Ga.)

Kilpatrick, J. *Research on teaching mathematics to the elementary school pupil.* Paper presented at the conference on Research on Teaching Mathematics sponsored by the Institute for Research on Teaching, Michigan State University, May 2–3, 1977. (Available from J. Kilpatrick, University of Georgia, Athens, Ga.)

Krutetskii, V. A. [*The psychology of mathematical abilities in schoolchildren*] (J. Kilpatrick & I. Wirszup, Eds., and J. Teller, trans.). Chicago: University of Chicago Press, 1976. (Originally published 1968.)

Maccoby, E. E., & Jacklin, C. N. Sex differences in intellectual functioning. In *Assessment in a pluralistic society: Proceedings of the 1972 Invitational Conference on Testing Problems.* Princeton, N.J.: Educational Testing Service, 1973.

Messick, S. Personality consistencies in cognition and creativity. In S. Messick & Associates (Eds.), *Individuality in learning.* San Francisco: Jossey-Bass, 1976.

Meyer, R. A. *A study of the relationship of mathematical problem solving performance and intellectual abilities of fourth-grade boys and girls.* Unpublished doctoral dissertation, University of Wisconsin, 1976.

Research for Better Schools. *Individually prescribed instruction* (IPI mathematics). New York: New Century Education, 1972.

Resnick, L. B. (Ed.). *The nature of intelligence.* Hillsdale, N.J.: Lawrence Erlbaum Associates, 1976.

Romberg, T. A., Harvey, J. G., Moser, J. M., & Montgomery, M. E. *Developing mathematical processes (DMP).* Chicago: Rand McNally, 1974, 1975, 1976.

Romberg, T. A., & Montgomery, M. E. Introduction to individually guided mathematics instruction. In T. A. Romberg (Ed.), *Individually guided mathematics.* Reading, Mass.: Addison-Wesley, 1976.

Salomon, G. Heuristic models for the generation of aptitude-treatment-interaction hypotheses. *Review of Educational Research,* 1972, *42*, 327–343.

Schonberger, A. K. *The interrelationship of sex, visual spatial abilities, and mathematical problem solving ability in grade seven.* Unpublished doctoral dissertation, University of Wisconsin, 1976.

Sherman, J. Effects of biological factors on sex-related differences in mathematics achievement. In L. H. Fox, E. Fennema, & J. Sherman (Eds.), *Women and mathematics: Research perspectives for change.* Washington, D.C.: National Institute of Education, 1977.

Smith, I. M. *Spatial ability.* San Diego: Knapp, 1964.

Snow, R. E. Aptitude-treatment interactions and individualized alternatives in higher education. In S. Messick & Associates (Eds.), *Individuality in learning.* San Francisco: Jossey-Bass, 1976. (a)

Snow, R. E. *Research on aptitude for learning: A progress report.* Unpublished manuscript, 1976. (Available from Richard E. Snow, School of Education, Stanford University.) (b)

Stafford, R. E. Hereditary and environmental components of quantitative reasoning. *Review of Educational Research,* 1972, *42*, 183–201.

Stein, A. H., & Bailey, M. M. The socialization of achievement orientation in females. *Psychological Bulletin,* 1973, *80*, 345–366.

Suydam, M. N., & Weaver, J. F. *Using research: A key to elementary school mathematics.* Columbus, Ohio: ERIC Center for Science, Mathematics, and Environmental Education, 1975.

Thorndike, E. L. *Individuality.* Boston: Houghton Mifflin, 1911.

Threadgill, J. A. M. *The relationship of analytic-global cognitive style and two methods of instruction in mathematical concept learning.* Unpublished doctoral dissertation, University of Oregon, 1976.

Tittle, C. K., McCarthy, K., & Steckler, J. F. *Women and educational testing.* Princeton, N.J.: Educational Testing Service, 1974.

Tobias, S. Achievement treatment interaction. *Review of Educational Research,* 1976, *46,* 61–74.

Tyler, L. E. Human abilities. *Annual Review of Psychology,* 1972, *23,* 177–206.

Tyler, L. E. *Individual differences: Abilities and motivational directions.* Englewood Cliffs, N.J.: Prentice-Hall, 1974.

Tyler, L. E. The intelligence we test—An evolving concept. In L. B. Resnick (Ed.), *The nature of intelligence.* Hillsdale, N.J.: Lawrence Erlbaum Associates, 1976.

Vidler, C. Achievement motivation. In S. Ball (Ed.), *Motivation in education.* New York: Academic Press, 1977.

Walberg, H. J. Models for optimizing and individualizing school learning. *Interchange,* 1976, *2* (3), 15–27.

Weaver, J. F. Differentiated instruction in arithmetic: An overview and promising trend. *Education,* 1954, *74,* 300–305.

Whipple, G. M. (Ed.). *Adapting the schools to individual differences: The twenty-fourth yearbook of the National Society for the Study of Education, part II.* Bloomington, Ill.: Public School Publishing Co., 1925.

Wiley, D. E., & Harnischfeger, A. Explosion of a myth: Quantity of schooling and exposure to instruction, major educational vehicles. *Educational Researcher,* 1974, *3* (4), 7–12.

Witkin, H. A. Cognitive style in academic performance and in teacher-student relations. In S. Messick & Associates (Eds.), *Individuality in learning.* San Francisco: Jossey-Bass, 1976.

Witkin, H. A., Moore, C. A., Goodenough, D. R., & Cox, P. W. Field-dependent and field-independent cognitive styles and their educational implications. *Review of Educational Research,* 1977, *47,* 1–64.

Wittrock, M. C. A generative model of mathematics learning. *Journal for Research in Mathematics Education,* 1974, *5,* 181–196.

12

Research on Mathematics Attitude

Gerald Kulm
Purdue University

DEFINITION OF ATTITUDE

THE first task in exploring the research done on attitude is to define what is meant by *attitude*. Although many definitions have been proposed by psychologists, the most recent trend has been to avoid explicit definition and to settle for operational definitions implied by items of instruments measuring attitude. Nevertheless, it may be useful to provide several definitions, many of which arise from work on attitudes and their measurement in social psychology. One of the influential early definitions of attitude was Allport's (1935):

> An attitude is a mental and neural state of readiness, organized through experience, exerting a directive or dynamic influence upon the individual's response to all objects and situations with which it is related. (p. 810)

The major characteristics of this early definition have not changed much, as evidenced by a more recent definition (Rokeach, 1972):

> Attitude is an organization of several beliefs focused on a specific object or situation predisposing one to respond in some preferential manner. (p. 159)

One of the most influential characterizations of noncognitive behaviors has been Krathwohl, Bloom, and Masia's taxonomy of the affective domain (1964). This taxonomy was developed to help educators develop and measure affective objectives. The authors view affective behaviors as a hierarchical continuum. At the lowest level *(receiving)*, students are merely aware of the phenomenon. Next they have some feeling about it *(responding)*, and then they go out of their way to interact with it *(valuing)*. At the next level, they conceptualize their behavior and feelings *(organization)*, and then finally they develop a consistent philosophy *(characterization)*.

356

If "attitude" is viewed in this way, it takes on a variety of meanings ranging from responding behavior, in which some feeling may be expressed, to
characterization, in which students are able to state clearly their attitude
toward mathematics, for example, and relate this attitude to other aspects
of their life (Bloom, Hastings, & Madaus, 1971).

A slightly different conceptualization of attitude is based on probabilistic
notions and represents an information-processing approach. An example
of this type of definition is that of Wyer (1974):

> An attitude is a subjective probability associated with (a) membership of a
> stimulus in a given category or (b) the relationship between members of differ-
> ent categories.

This definition differs from many probabilistic conceptualizations in that
no description or prediction of behavior is included. Instead, the subjective
nature of probability indicates the requirement that situational variables
be identified. For example, one might compare these probabilities:

P (A):   Mathematics is a liked school subject.
P (B):   An elective mathematics course has been taken.

Furthermore, the probabilities $P(A|B)$ and $P(B|A)$ could also be studied.

Although attitude toward mathematics is usually either undefined or
defined by the instruments used in the study (Husén, 1967), at least two
definitions of attitude in general have been used by mathematics educators
who have been prominent in attitude research. In their report of the development of NLSMA tests, Romberg and Wilson (1969) described attitudes
as follows:

> If an individual has a set of predispositions toward an object in the environ-
> ment (e.g., mathematics, self, school, teacher, etc.), it is reasonable to expect
> that such predispositions would interact with the perception of the object in
> such a way as to affect the individual's response to that object. (p. 151)

In one of his reviews of attitudes, Aiken (1972) stated that

> the term *attitude* as used in the studies referred to here means approximately
> the same thing as *enjoyment, interest,* and to some extent, *level of anxiety.*
> (p. 229)

It seems apparent from these last two definitions that researchers in
mathematics education do not believe that attitudes toward mathematics
differ in their underlying constructs from the kinds of attitudes that social
psychologists have attempted to define. In attitudes toward mathematics,
for example, the object or situation in Allport's definition might be "mathematics" or "solving word problems." In Wyer's definition, mathematics
attitude might be determined by finding the probability that students place
mathematics in the category of "school subjects liked."

The component of preferential responding included in Allport's and Rokeach's definitions would include such behaviors as attending mathematics class, doing mathematics homework, or taking more mathematics courses. Wyer's more cautious approach in avoiding behavior prediction would imply that these behaviors should be included in calculating conditional subjective probabilities.

The causal relationship between attitudes and behavior is far from clear. Although there is evidence that attitudes influence behavior, there is also evidence that behavior influences attitudes (Calder & Ross, 1973). This controversy becomes even more complex with attitudes toward school subjects, in which behavior is related to academic achievement. Either direction of causation can again be supported, with evidence that school behaviors influence achievement and vice versa. For example, disliking mathematics (attitude) might contribute to inattentiveness in class (behavior) whereas (in the other direction) getting an A on a test (behavior) might influence how one feels about mathematics (attitude). It would seem to be imperative that this complex attitude-behavior-achievement relationship be carefully considered by researchers who undertake studies intended to explore or change one or more of the three.

It is probably not possible to offer a definition of attitude toward mathematics that would be suitable for all situations, and even if one were agreed on, it would probably be too general to be useful. However, it should be not only possible but required that a researcher explain as clearly as possible the attitude that a given instrument purports to measure. In addition, the inferred causal effect or directive influence that the attitude is expected to produce or be related to should also be explained. Attempts at these kinds of explications may help to define what is meant by "mathematics attitude," "mathephobia," "mathematics anxiety," or other labels intended to convey similar constructs (Brush, 1978b; Gough, 1954).

What Attitudes Are Measured

Before an exploration of the research on mathematics attitude is begun, it might be useful to delineate further the objects and situations on which attention is focused for mathematics attitudes. The researcher is usually interested in attitudes toward some object or situation X, by some population Y. The motivations for this interest vary widely, including the use of attitude as a dependent, independent, or mediating variable. The domains for X and Y also vary widely but may be categorized in a general way as shown in Figure 1.

Clearly, the categories listed in the matrix do not exhaust the possibilities for misinterpretation when a researcher reports results on a "math attitude test." Most of the attitude-object categories are themselves general and are capable of including a large number of subcategories. In order to explore

Attitude	Populations		
Objects or Situations	Students	Teachers	Others
Mathematics content			
Mathematics characteristics			
Teaching practices			
Mathematics classroom activities			
Mathematics teacher			

Figure 1. Categories of mathematics attitudes.

these categories and to explicate the kinds of attitudes relevant to mathematics education, it is worthwhile to focus on several of the rows in the Figure 1 matrix.

Mathematics content. Specific topics or processes, such as geometry, fractions, word problems, or factoring, are included as objects for attitudes in this category. It is interesting that very few attitude scales or items focus on mathematics content. Rather, they focus on the characteristics of mathematics. Perhaps the "purest" type of measure of attitude in this category would be an observation of the subject while doing a particular mathematics task, such as adding fractions. A response to a statement such as "I like fractions" may also be a good direct measure. Less likely to be valid are items such as "I avoid doing fractions whenever I can" or "Fractions are easy." A fairly unadulterated measure of this category is a response to a specific problem, such as that proposed by Dunlap (1976) in a scale for primary children. For example, children respond to $\Box + 2 = 5$ by choosing a smiling, neutral, or sad face. The NLSMA tests (Romberg & Wilson, 1969) used items such as "I like the problem $28 + 6 - 14$ (more, less) than the problem, If Joe is twice as old as Mary and she is 9, how old is Joe?" It is possible to think of similar items appropriate for other topics, not only with written but also with oral responses to specific content topics.

Mathematics characteristics. Most instruments and items actually measure attitudes toward characteristics of mathematics. Although some authors (e.g., Aiken, 1974) label scales with such headings as Enjoyment of Mathematics, the usual practice is to report results on scales having labels such as "Attitude toward Problem Solving" but to use items such as "There are many ways to solve a problem" or "It makes me nervous to think about doing a math problem." These items do not represent the student's reaction to problem solving but rather the opinions about the characteristics of problem solving. It is not clear that a response to one of these items indicates that an inference can be made about a student's attitude toward problem solving. Other subject characteristics that concern mathematics educators are usefulness, importance, relevance, elegance, difficulty, and interest.

The semantic differential technique has been used to assess subject characteristics. This method generates data on characteristics that are sometimes difficult to interpret. For example, mathematics has often been described using bipolar scales (hard-soft, bad-good, alive-dull, fast-slow, or large-small [McCallon & Brown, 1971]). Again, it seems difficult to infer that a response to such items can be interpreted directly in terms of mathematics attitude. The characteristic "fast," for example, may be positive for some students and negative for others.

Teaching practices. Attitudes in this category are most often sought from teachers, primarily to assess effects of teacher training. When students respond with attitudes toward teaching practices, the results are often interpreted in relation to course or teacher evaluation. Examples of items in this category are "The teacher should always work sample problems before making an assignment" or "Children should be encouraged to invent their own symbolism" (Collier, 1972). Not all these items are appropriate to every subject population, although it would be interesting, for example, to obtain student responses to an item such as the one about symbolism.

It is interesting that very few studies employing innovative teaching strategies or curricular treatments have used attitude items that ask students to respond to teaching practices. It would seem that more direct items of this type would yield far more information about the impact on students than items related to a general enjoyment of mathematics. Furthermore, items related to teaching practices might reveal why student attitudes to mathematics were or were not changed by the treatment.

Classroom activities. Although some of the processes under mathematics content could be classified as activities (e.g., doing problems, solving equations), this category is intended to include more general learning tasks, such as doing homework, taking tests, answering the teacher's questions, or simply attending class. Often, the focus of items is again on the characteristics rather than the activities themselves, and the category is a popular one for inclusion on scales of "Enjoyment of Math." Example items are "I am happy in math class" and "I feel nervous when taking a math test." It is again useful to note that contrary to common interpretation, these items measure attitudes toward various activities, not necessarily toward the subject itself.

Mathematics teachers. Teachers are included in the list of attitude objects, although it may not always be clear whether the attitudes measured are toward teachers in general or mathematics teachers in particular. The fact that the attitudes of mathematics students toward their teacher are measured is often used to infer that their attitudes are specific to mathematics teachers. The difficulty may be partially overcome by including in the statement of an item the description of the attitude object. For example, an item such as "My algebra teacher explains ideas well" seems to make more clear the attitude object than "This teacher explains subject matter well." Many items in this category are like those found on teacher-evaluation forms.

In the following pages, attitude research in mathematics will be discussed, producing a clarification of the status of research and the issues to which the researcher must attend. The important issue of attitude measurement will be explored, including a survey of current techniques for measuring attitude. Finally, some trends and suggested directions for research into mathematics attitude will be identified.

THE MEASUREMENT OF ATTITUDE

Because they are easy to construct, administer, and score, written self-report scales are undoubtedly the most common ways to measure attitude. They are, however, only one example of several categories of attitude-measurement approaches. Five categories for attitude assessment are given by Kiesler, Collins, and Miller (1969):

1. Self-reports
2. Observation of behavior in a natural setting
3. Reaction to partially structured stimuli
4. Performance on "objective" tasks
5. Physiological reactions

Since extensive discussions of these procedures and the statistical properties of these measures are readily available, only a brief summary will be given here to point out specific examples and implications for the use of these approaches in measuring mathematics attitudes.

Self-Report Scales

A number of self-report scales for mathematics attitudes have been developed and used in research studies. Although the number of scales is far too great to attempt a complete list and many reports that have used or developed attitude scales do not include a copy of the scale itself, a brief list of reports represents some of the more important or widely used scales (Aiken, 1974; Collier, 1972; Dutton & Blum, 1968; Fennema & Sherman, 1977; Husén, 1967; Romberg & Wilson, 1969; Sandman, 1974; Suinn, Edie, Nicoletti & Spinelli, 1972). The development of self-report scales was begun by Thurstone, who used a set of items that represented points along an interval from extremely negative to extremely positive attitudes toward a topic. Subjects are asked to check those items with which they agree, producing a measure of the proportion of subjects having attitudes represented by each of the statements. The most widely used self-report procedure has been Likert's summed-rating approach. Subjects are asked to respond to items by choosing the extent of their agreement on a five-point scale. Numerical values assigned to the responses are added, resulting in a score that indicates the attitude toward the topic represented by a "total" of all the statements. The most recently developed self-report scale is the semantic differential. The subject is asked to respond to a concept represented by a list of bipolar adjectives at opposite ends of a continuum separated by a fixed number of points. The mean score along the continuum for each adjective is used as a measure of that attitude component. The sum of the ratings is used as a "total" attitude toward the concept. For a more complete treatment of scale construction and its use in attitude measurement, see Shaw and Wright (1967).

Because these scales produce numbers that can be analyzed statistically, they have been used in favor of other self-report procedures. A wide variety of alternative self-report approaches are possible, many of which have the potential for furnishing more valid data on attitude than is possible with scales. One of the simplest and most effective approaches is to ask subjects to respond to open-ended questions such as these: What topics do you like best (least) in mathematics? Why are you taking this mathematics course? Why do you like (dislike) mathematics? What makes mathematics easy (difficult) to learn? More information might be obtained from young children or for subjects who have difficulty in written expression by using these kinds of questions in a semistructured interview. Less direct self-report questions may help to make inferences about the effects of instructional approaches or other factors on future behavior. Questions such as the following can provide useful insights into the formation of attitude, change in attitude, and the prediction of behavior: Do you plan to take more mathematics and why? Who helps you with math at home? Would you recommend this course to others?

There is little question that self-reports are an extremely valuable approach to assessing attitude. What better way is there to determine a subject's attitude toward math than to ask a direct question? Unfortunately, self-report has often come to mean "self-report scale." Some researchers have constructed scales without proper validation or used previously constructed scales that are not appropriate. A second problem is that disparate items are often combined to produce a single score. Although this procedure of reducing responses to a single numerical value may produce statistics that are manageable, it can also lead to overlooking data that are more closely related to the actual attitudes held by subjects.

Well-constructed self-report scales should continue to be developed and used. The advantages of administrative ease and objective scoring are important. More attention should be given to the external validation of scales by using the observation of students' behavior and to using responses to open-ended questions to construct stems for items. It is possible that items developed only through a construct-validity approach would not accurately tap a particular population's attitudes toward mathematics.

Observation of Behavior

It is common for teachers in their daily routines to make judgments about attitudes based on their observation of students as they participate (or do not participate) in mathematics class.

The observation and recording of classroom verbal and nonverbal behavior has become an accepted research tool for assessing classroom environment and learning factors. Simple checklists could be used in studies of mathematics attitudes to determine the existence and extent of behaviors such as smiling, voluntary responding, doing classwork, helping other students, or doing outside work. Less overt behaviors, such as sitting in the back row, being tardy or absent, or being attentive, could also be used to make inferences about attitudes. It would seem that observing students and recording behaviors has great usefulness in providing firsthand and valid attitude data—second only to asking a direct question. For younger students who do not verbalize well, this approach may be more valid than self-reports. The disadvantage might be that the researcher may have more difficulty in establishing a sound argument that the observed behaviors are indeed attitude related than if a self-report format is used.

Reaction to Structured Stimuli

The use of structured stimuli in the form of photographs, drawings, role-played scenarios, and other controlled situations has long been practiced by social psychologists to determine attitudes and attitude-related behavior in relation to prejudice-laden factors. In a sense, mathematics attitudes can be thought to be similar to prejudices in that opinions are often formed emotionally and sometimes without basis in fact. It may be useful to explore the nature of these belief systems through the controlled experimentation offered by structured situations. Examples of stimuli might be pictures of classrooms or exposure to "real life" classrooms in which a single factor is varied, such as small-group work versus lecture. The subject can be questioned or observed to determine the response to viewing or participating in the structured situation. This procedure allows careful examination of specific attitude factors in a way that is not possible in the intact classroom in which complex and varied stimuli make attitudes toward specific factors difficult to assess.

Performance on Tasks

Closely related to observation in a natural classroom setting and reaction to structured stimuli, the subject's performance on an "objective" task can provide considerable information about attitudes. Through requesting the subject to do a computation, solve a problem, or draw a figure, it may be possible to infer the nature of the subject's attitudes. If a mathematical task is completed and is done carefully, if a student asks for more work, or if the student works industriously, interestedly, or attentively, then it would seem that a great deal could be concluded about attitude. Tasks could be varied from individual to individual, making it possible to determine variations in attitudes toward different types of mathematical content or activity.

Physiological Reactions

Although the traditional physiological reactions used in measuring emotional or attitudinal responses are galvanic skin response, heart rate, blood pressure, and breathing depth, a number of physically evident responses are known to indicate the degree of stress or enjoyment. These less refined responses would seem to be useful and sufficiently accurate indications of attitude for use in classroom research. Is a subject physically agitated or calm in mathematics class? Are there unusual speech behaviors that are not present in other settings? Is the subject aggressive? Does the subject try to avoid certain tasks or exhibit certain behaviors in approaching a task? The observation of physiological responses such as these, along with a record of the types of situations in which they occur, might be useful in assessing the effects of instructional approaches or programs.

Summary

At the present time, the measurement of attitude in mathematics is done almost exclusively through the use of self-report scales. Although the increased use of well-developed scales by several researchers offers a common basis for comparing results, the lack of other approaches to measurement represents an area in obvious need of development. The use of scales that claim to measure a concept as broad as "mathematics attitude" or "enjoyment of mathematics" runs the risk of overlooking important attributes of mathematics attitude. Many of these difficulties stem from misinterpretations of what measurement means. Gardner (1975) has done an excellent job of using a physical measurement analogy to point out the common errors in attitude measurement. When we measure a physical object such as a table, we actually measure some clearly defined characteristic of it, such as its length. In measuring mathematics attitude, the researcher must identify and define clearly the characteristics to be measured. In many studies using attitude as a variable, the assumption seems to be that attitude is defined to be the total of whatever items were used on an attitude scale. Little regard is given to explicating a theoretical construct that might provide justification for choosing a particular item or set of items that are related to clearly stated attitude characteristics.

Gardner also points out that measurements can be useful or useless and meaningful or meaningless and that various combinations of these are possible. Once a characteristic of an object has been defined and measured, it should be required to be both meaningful and useful. For example, the sum of the scores on items measuring "fun in math class" and "feeling nervous taking a math test" may not be meaningful and, therefore, may be useless. The measurement of mathematics attitude must be carried out with attention to the characteristics of the attitude being measured and with caution in combining in meaningless ways characteristics that ought to be considered separately.

The alternative approaches in attitude measurement might be characterized with two attributes. First, the researcher should consider more commonsense, realistic views of assessing attitude. Teachers use these methods every day and adjust their teaching accordingly in order to attain better response, more interest, or any number of other aspects of attitude. Second, the researcher should consider direct observation of individuals rather than groups. One consequence of observing individuals is that a host of independent variables become important almost immediately. A group does not have difficulties with a mother, a father, or reading, but an individual may have all these and many other characteristics that influence attitudes. Out of an apparent concern for expressing relationships concisely and numerically and the desire to perform statistical tests on means and variances, the most potentially fruitful approaches to individual attitude measurement may have been overlooked. The measurement of mathematics attitudes in the future should make use of many approaches, and researchers should not believe that scales with proper names attached to them are the only acceptable way to measure attitudes.

PRESENT RESEARCH ON ATTITUDE

Research on attitudes in mathematics was a popular enterprise during the early 1970s. Aiken (1976) noted in his review that more research pertaining to the topic of mathematics attitudes had appeared in the preceding five years than in the ten years covered by an earlier review in

1970. Although a great variety of different aspects of attitude have been studied, it is possible to identify several categories that have received attention. In addition to research in developing measures of attitude, the areas investigated include (a) relationships between attitude and achievement, (b) factors related to attitudes, (c) relationships between parent, teacher, and student attitudes, and (d) approaches to improving attitude. Finally, a great many studies have dealt with the various aspects of the attitudes of preservice teachers, especially elementary school teachers.

The reviews by Aiken (1970, 1976) and Fennema (1974) provide an excellent summary of the results of investigations in these areas. A slightly different perspective of this research can be gained, however, by examining the kinds of questions and hypotheses posed by these studies. With the advantage of hindsight, it is also possible to explore the reasons for the success or failure of the investigations in providing answers to the questions posed. This exploration may clarify the issues and trends in attitude research and point the way for proposing research questions and hypotheses for future investigations.

In the following pages, a great many results or possible trends from research on mathematics attitude are discussed. Although it is not the purpose of this discussion to provide a comprehensive review of research, some references are given to provide the reader with specific examples of studies that may be consulted. Usually the reference given is simply a representative of several studies that have investigated the factor. The reader who wishes to pursue the question should explore the literature more completely.

Attitude and Achievement

The general question asked by current researchers is "What is the strength of relationship between attitudes and achievement?" Although the answer to the question appears to indicate a low positive correlation (Crosswhite, 1972), researchers continue to ask the question. Apparently, the commonsense feeling that achievement ought to depend heavily on attitudes stimulates the search for a clear, simple relationship between these variables. Often, the hypothesis is that the relationship is causal, so that attitudes are investigated as predictors of achievement.

A few studies have looked at the long-term aspects of the general attitude-achievement relationship (Beattie, Deichmann, & Lewis, 1973; Crosswhite, 1972). In this case, some important questions can be asked: What changes in the attitude-achievement relationship occur over a period of time? Is the relationship stable? Are the influences of other factors on the relationship constant over time? Although the call for longitudinal studies has become a repeated theme, the field of attitude research is one in which such studies are necessary in order to answer these important questions. It can be argued that these long-term relationships must be understood before it makes sense to investigate in detail the procedures for enhancing attitudes. For example, if attitudes are found to be completely formed and stable by eighth grade, how does one attempt to change attitudes at the high school, college, or adult level?

Mathematics attitude and achievement have been investigated in relation to other population variables as well as to variables in learning environments. Studies of this kind are designed to determine whether attitude and achievement are affected by a given treatment. Examples of such questions are these: Do achievement and attitude differ for tutored and nontutored subjects (Carman, 1975)? Are achievement and attitude affected for students in CAI programs (Pavlic, 1975)? In laboratory instructional settings (Cohen, 1971)? Most often, these questions on learning environment are aimed at using attitude and achievement as dependent variables in comparing instructional settings. Achievement is compared for different instructional approaches, as attitude is, but their relationship is not. The present research practice of comparing the effectiveness of an innovational instructional approach with a traditional approach does not provide comparisons of results stated in terms of relationships between variables. Instead of reporting only that experimental groups did or did not differ with respect to achievement or attitude, it would be useful to compare attitudes for various achievement levels within treatments or vice versa. This approach would shed light on the relationships between attitude and achievement across instructional approaches. It may be that certain attitude-achievement patterns would become evident on reviewing a number of studies reporting such results. Future "methods studies" could add to the knowledge of the nature of attitudes by making this fairly simple idea a component of their reports.

The attitude-achievement relationship for special groups is a rich area for producing further knowledge. The recent interest in sex differences provides an example of the usefulness in studying carefully a factor that may have many complex influences on both attitudes and achievement. Once again, it would appear to be most helpful to study the relationship between mathematics attitudes and achievement for different groups in addition to simply comparing group attitude and achievement means.

It seems paradoxical that research findings indicate that the attitude-achievement relationship is not as strong as common sense might expect, at least when a correlation measure is used. When confronted with the paradox in research, classroom teachers are usually quick to point out that most attitude tests measure attitude toward mathematics itself rather than toward the class or the teacher. It is perfectly reasonable for a subject to have a poor attitude toward mathmatics but to enjoy the class because the teacher is good or the class is interesting or any number of other reasons.

Unless this state of affairs is repeated year after year, it is unlikely that the subject's attitude will change. However, in that particular class the subject's achievement may be much higher than might be predicted by his or her general mathematics attitude, producing a low correlation between attitude and achievement. One implication of this interpretation of the attitude-achievement relationship is that researchers should measure attitude as it relates to the specific classroom situation rather than expecting a more general measure to mirror the effects of a specific treatment or environmental setting.

Attitude-related Factors

The structure of attitudes toward mathematics is unquestionably complex, and although achievement appears to be a major factor, there are other factors that may mediate the way that attitudes form or change. The research questions and hypotheses of studies in this area are generally of this form: Do subjects who are classified according to factor X differ in mathematics attitude and achievement? Or is there a significant correlation between mathematics attitude and factor X? One factor of current interest, for example, is sex differences. There is evidence not only that male and female attitudes toward mathematics are different but that the changes in their attitudes over the grades differ in some ways (Crosswhite, 1972; Fennema, 1974; Hilton & Berglund, 1974).

The list of factors that researchers have considered is long, since it seems possible to provide a somewhat reasonable rationale for almost any personality or environmental factor that impinges on a learning situation. Some of the more popular factors have included grade level, achievement motivation, socioeconomic status, race, anxiety, learning style, and vocational preference. As long as correlational relationships or isolated comparisons of means are the focus, it is likely that for a given population sample any of these factors can be significantly related to mathematics attitude. However, in the absence of a large number of studies on a particular variable, such as those done on sex differences, it is unlikely that meaningful generalizations can be made about the variable. The implication for future research would appear to be that a few potentially important attitude-related factors be chosen for intensive study. An alternative is to design a more sophisticated or longer-range study of the variable in question. For example, a longitudinal or cross-lagged study may clarify the nature of attitude formation or change with respect to a given variable. Above all, it seems reasonable to advise researchers to select attitude-related factors with solid evidence of their potential as important and generalizable variables in the formation or change of mathematics attitudes. The approach of casting about for as many variables as possible to intercorrelate is not only inefficient but may add confusion rather than clarity to the relationships among attitudes and related variables.

Parent, Teacher, Student Attitude Relationships

The attitudes of parents would appear to be an extremely important factor in determining children's attitudes and achievement. The preschool aspirations and the influence of parental expectations and interest are potentially greater factors in guiding student success or failure than any single factor, with the possible exception of intellectual ability. On the one hand, parental attitudes can mitigate the effects of the most positive or negative of teacher effects. On the other hand, teachers also have important roles in forming attitudes, since they play a major role in students' achievement as well as having the potential to transfer their own attitudes toward mathematics to their students.

The possibilities for causal relationships outlined in the previous paragraph provide the basis for the questions and hypotheses of studies of parent or teacher attitudes as they relate to student attitudes. Some common questions of interest are these: Are the attitudes of students and their teachers the same? Do teacher behaviors influence student achievement and attitudes? Are parent and student attitudes the same? Do parents and teachers differ in their attitudes toward mathematics? Relatively few answers to these interesting questions are available, indicating a need for further research. A few general patterns seem to emerge, however, and suggest areas for focus. Students have good attitudes when they perceive mathematics as useful and interesting and when they have had good teachers (Callahan, 1971). Students develop poor attitudes when they do not do well or find mathematics uninteresting (Selkirk, 1975).

These reasons for liking or not liking mathematics suggest differences in patterns of attitude formation and illustrate areas in which the logic of attitude change is complex. For example, good teachers produce good attitudes in their students (Phillips, 1973); however, it is not clear what aspects of teaching are perceived by students and result in good attitudes. Perhaps the same teacher who presents mathematics as a challenge and devotes little time to slower students is "good" for some students but produces low achievement and poor attitudes in others. It seems quite obvious that a great deal of research is needed in developing clear understandings of the variables that define the parent-student-teacher relationship. This understanding is not likely to result from gross comparisons of group means on general attitude scales. Instead, attention must be paid to measuring a specific attitude aimed, perhaps, at specific triads of students, teachers, and parents.

Attitude Improvement

A great many studies having the word *attitude* in their titles are in the category of "methods studies," in which an innovative instructional approach or a new curriculum is investigated or, most often, compared with something traditional. Except for isolated instances, these studies are aimed at improving or comparing mathematics achievement and attitudes (in that order) rather than being specifically designed to improve attitudes. The inclusion of an attitude test in studies of this type seems to have become mandatory in the opinion of many researchers.

Although there is no question that data on attitude can be extremely useful in evaluating the effects of instructional or curriculum innovations, the design of the attitude portion often appears to be an afterthought. Few of these studies attend to theoretical rationale, the problems of design, and the measurement of attitudes in the same way they attend to achievement. Usually, questions and hypotheses parallel to those for achievement are stated, taking the form "What is the effect of treatment X on attitudes?" An attitude scale is selected, sometimes without regard for the question of whether the attitudes measured by the scale are those that might be expected to be affected by the treatment. For example, a brief review of research revealed that the same popular scale for mathematics attitude was used to measure the effects of group testing, a parent workshop, films, contracts, computer-assisted instruction, a probability unit, and a transformational approach to geometry. Subjects for these studies ranged from seventh graders to adults.

As with many areas of research, the results of attempts to improve mathematics attitudes are mixed, even for those studies aimed specifically at improving attitude. Even more disturbing is the fact that some studies designed to improve attitudes result in even less positive attitudes. There may be some clues to these results in the design of many experiments. Because a change in attitude is of central interest, many studies employ attitude pretests and posttests. Completing a pretest may affect the subject in a number of ways that might be overlooked by many researchers. First, any attitude test has a sensitizing effect. It has been observed that subjects don't know what they think about an object or situation until someone asks. The act of taking an attitude pretest may cause subjects to examine their opinions and to respond differently a second time, regardless of the intervening treatment.

A second important factor may be the subjects' general attitudes at the beginning and end of an instructional period. Often, students feel optimistic and eager at the beginning of a semester, which is when many pretests are administered. As time goes along, this initial enthusiasm may moderate, and if posttesting is done at a stressful time, perhaps nearly concurrent with a comprehensive examination, the general attitude may be lower. It is even possible that the attitude posttest might be viewed as a waste of valuable class time, producing further negative effects.

Most of these difficulties can be overcome with attention to research designs that include appropriate control groups and careful attention to the timing of tests. It should be realized that subjects' responses and motivations with respect to attitude and achievement tests are quite different, making it necessary to consider the consequences of administering attitude tests at the same times in the experiment as achievement tests. Finally, the need to select the appropriate technique for measuring attitude to fit the desired effects of a treatment should be reiterated. A general mathematics-attitude scale is less likely to measure the specific effects of learner contracts, for example, than a few well-chosen items that get at what the subjects have actually experienced.

A need exists for research designed specifically to explore the nature of attitude improvement or change, including the investigation of the effects of such factors as pretesting, the time of testing, and the age of the subject. The last variable is a particularly crucial one, since there appears to be evidence that mathematics attitudes are formed primarily in Grades 4 through 8 (Callahan, 1971; Malcolm, 1971). Is it worth trying to change attitudes before or after that? What are the most potent agents for change at different age levels? These are just samples of many questions that are yet unanswered.

Attitudes of Preservice Teachers

There are at least two reasons that research on the attitudes of preservice elementary school teachers is of interest and fairly abundant. First, these teachers have the potential of greatly influencing their future students' attitudes. It seems reasonable that a knowledge of these teachers' attitudes might help researchers understand the formation of student attitudes. A second, more practical reason for the abundance of research is that prospective elementary teachers are a readily available population. As a consequence, some studies appear to have very general objectives, such as determining the effect of a course on teaching methods or simply an exploration of the factors that are related to teachers' mathematics attitudes. There are substantial data providing evidence that prospective elementary teachers' attitudes improve over the various stages of their preparation, especially during the methods course (Collier, 1972; Hilton, 1970; Hunkler & Quast, 1972). Although this improvement usually represents only a change from negative to neutral or slightly positive attitudes, it does indicate that subjects who have a positive motivation to a situation (becoming a teacher) can change their attitudes toward aspects of it. This result may provide a clue to the area of attitude improvement; that is, perhaps the subjects' intentions as well as their attitudes are important variables to consider in predicting behavior. A model proposed by Fishbein takes these variables into account. This theory suggests that beliefs about an object or situation, for example, studying or teaching mathematics, determine attitudes toward it. Attitudes, in turn, influence a person's intentions with respect to the object. It is these intentions that predict a person's behaviors toward the object. Attitude is viewed as a general predisposition leading to a set of intentions to behave in a certain fashion (Fishbein & Ajzen, 1975).

Among the factors related to teacher attitude, the relationship of grade-level preference and mathematics ability to attitude toward teaching mathematics has interesting implications. Generally, teachers who prefer to teach primary grades have less favorable attitudes toward teaching mathematics than teachers who prefer upper-elementary grades (Early, 1970; Raines, 1971). Of course, this pattern is clearly evident in that high school mathematics teachers are usually the most able in mathematics, choosing to teach it exclusively in preference to other subjects. Apparently, the result is that teachers who can influence student attitudes and achievement in their formative stages may be those who have the poorest attitudes themselves. Little research seems to have been done to determine what effect primary teachers with positive attitudes and high mathematics ability have on student attitudes.

ISSUES IN ATTITUDE RESEARCH

The discussion in the two previous sections has suggested a number of both general and specific issues in research on attitude. In this section, a few of the more important general issues will be discussed. These issues exist primarily because theoretical constructs in many areas of attitude research have not been clarified. Few studies on attitude take the form of hypothesis testing, usually because the theoretical background necessary for making hypotheses is not available. In methods comparison studies that hypothesize improvements in attitude, a theoretical argument leading to the hypothesis is seldom presented. The implication to be drawn from this state of research is that theory development studies are necessary. This conclusion is especially relevant now when a great many fundamental changes appear to be taking place in mathematics-related attitudes. For example, attitudes seem to be changing relative to such topics as the place of calculators and computers, the learning of basic computational facts, the role of the teacher in a learning environment, and the use of instructional materials. These factors have a direct bearing on the development of attitudes toward mathematics and suggest that research on attitude will continue to be an important and active field of study.

Measurement of Attitude

If future research on attitude is to be effective in assessing and explaining the impact of current educational changes, it will be important to use techniques of measurement that provide valid representations of these changes. One important issue, then, is the question of how attitudes ought to be measured. Although it is an oversimplification, this issue centers on the use of carefully normed, objective, reliable, easy-to-administer scales on the one hand or less structured, designed-for-the-situation, subjective, open-ended techniques on the other. The same arguments that make the former methods attractive for purposes of theory testing make them less useful in theory development. The nature of current questions and issues on attitude seem to imply the need for methods of assessment that are sensitive to nuances and inferences from beliefs, opinions, and behaviors. Furthermore, in order to make effective use of these methods, the researchers must be capable of drawing important patterns from subjective data.

At the present time few researchers seem to be aware of the issue of techniques for measuring attitude. Perhaps, in the sense that there are no active contestants on either side, it is not a true current issue. However, if any of the "real" issues are to be settled, the measurement question must be considered. As stated earlier, most issues in research actually represent areas in which theory is not developed, theory is unclear, or contradictory theories exist. In the latter instances, carefully designed studies using objective, sophisticated measures can be used to clarify the issue. Where adequate theory is not available, an issue can be settled only by first developing a theory. In the following pages, some issues illustrating areas needing theory development will be discussed.

The Importance of Attitudes

If there is a true issue in research on attitude, as evidenced by published, contested points of view (Aiken, 1970; Neale, 1969), it is this most basic of issues: Are mathematics attitudes important? The generally low correlation between attitude and achievement is the most often cited evidence that attitudes may not matter too much in explaining achievement. There are high achievers in mathematics who do not have high scores on mathematics attitude tests.

The arguments that attitudes are important are centered on the risks of drawing conclusions from studies using measurement techniques of questionable validity. The problem of measurement also arises in that attitudes typically measured are not necessarily valid assessments of more specific attitudes that may be important and more highly correlated with achievement. Finally, perhaps attitudes are related to factors more important than achievement, such as staying in school or selecting a career.

There is reason to believe that attitudes may become increasingly important in mathematics learning. In the past, students studied mathematics

and other school subjects with little question, assuming that higher education was a requirement for success. Even if postsecondary education was not
the goal, competence in computation was accepted as a necessity for functioning in society. Both of these reasons for mathematics education have
begun to erode recently. The need for a traditional college education has
been questioned, and the alternatives, such as vocational or trade schools,
have not established the same mathematics prerequisites that colleges have
in the past. Automated banking, tax-preparation services, shoppers' guides,
and other services designed to minimize the necessity for computational
work, coupled with the availability of inexpensive calculators, will continue to argue against the necessity for training in advanced mathematics
for the majority of students.

Some significant implications appear to arise for mathematics-attitude
theory. For example, these kinds of attitude-formation variables seem to
be more closely related to such factors as the importance, value, or utility
of mathematics than to an interest in, or enjoyment of, the subject. Whatever the factors are, a need exists for careful theoretical development before the issue of the importance of attitudes can be explored. What does
"important" mean for different populations? How is the concept of importance developed? How do attitudes related to the value of mathematics
vary? These questions represent the significant areas to be answered by
research.

Attitudes and Achievement

The relationship between attitude and achievement (or apparent lack of
it) has already been discussed. The nature of the strength of the relationship probably lies in the field of precise measurement. A valid and reliable
assessment of attitude in relation to specific achievement is capable of
putting this issue to rest. However, the direction of causation is a more
fundamental issue that requires careful study and theory development. The
complexity of the formation of attitude and the myriad factors that affect
achievement are reasons to believe that this issue will remain for some
time to come. There are, however, aspects of the issue that should be investigated. One of the most important of these is the causal relationship in
early childhood. For example, it is interesting that very young children are
not deterred in their attitudes or efforts by "failure." The child learning
to walk falls down again and again without apparent decrement in attitude.
Yet a child can easily learn that something is "bad" through a parent's
behavior toward it. How is early attitude toward mathematics affected by
parents' (or others') behavior and by the child's behavior (achievement)?
Related to this question is the frequent observation that the great majority
of children in early grades have generally favorable attitudes toward mathematics. Is the later decline caused by teachers' (or others') behavior or by

the child's achievement? If either of these is a cause, what factors are different from the situations in which the child "failed" in learning to walk and talk? Although these questions indicate that the causal relationship for young children may be in either direction, it seems difficult to justify any but the attitude-causes-achievement direction for very young children who have had very little experience with achievement or failure in mathematics.

The argument above raises the issue of whether the direction of causation changes as the child grows older or whether one simply reinforces the other. If the latter is true, the issue of how the chain is to be broken arises. Should effort be focused on changing attitudes, thereby improving achievement, or is it possible to provide enough success to reverse the cycle? As noted in the section on present research, it does not appear to be productive to continue isolated attempts at special programs designed to use one of the approaches. Instead, careful exploration is necessary to develop theoretical bases for predicting that a particular type of program will be successful for a certain population. Parenthetically, it should be clear that studies seeking causal directions and factors related to them should employ a variety of measurement and statistical approaches. In this type of exploration, traditional predictive statistics such as multiple regression would seem to be overly restrictive and may eliminate potentially important variables.

The issue of attitude-achievement causation has an important relation to the issue of the importance of mathematics attitudes. If such factors as college entrance requirements and a decreased need for computation tend to influence attitudes toward mathematics, making attitudes a more important factor, then the nature of attitude-achievement causation takes on an increased significance. It may become extremely important to be able to identify approaches that encourage positive attitudes and increased achievement.

Change of Attitude

The ineffectiveness of most experimental treatments in producing a significant improvement in mathematics attitude raises the issue of how to change mathematics attitudes. Of course, this issue involves a number of specific related questions such as the direction and magnitude of change, the type of subjects, or the permanence of the change. The concept of changing attitudes implies that attitudes have been formed and are, to some extent, stable. Alternatively, it can be argued that attitudes are in a continuous state of formation and change, making meaningless the question of how to change them. In this case some of the questions surrounding the issue are different and involve such things as when attitudes begin forming, what factors are most influential, and whether these factors are different at various stages in the formation of attitudes.

Whether the issue involves the change or the formation of attitudes, it is important to keep in mind that these attitudes exist in individuals rather than groups. If a researcher reports that a given treatment has produced no significant improvement in attitude, it is usually overlooked that for some subjects significant changes, both positive and negative, did take place. The fact that responses to five-point scales tend to be near the middle and that total mean scores tend to mask variations in individual items and subjects contributes to the possibility of missing important results in studies of attitude. The implication for the measurement of attitude appears to be twofold. First, it may be useful, even in a homogeneous one-dimensional scale, to examine and report scores on single items or small clusters of items that elicit varied responses or responses indicating a change in attitude from a previous time. Second, valuable information may be gained by examining individual subjects' scores, especially subjects who appear to have been affected in a particular way by a treatment. These data, together with information about subject-related variables, may provide clues to how a treatment works. A more careful analysis of a change of attitude in individual subjects would be possible through the case-study approach in observing and reporting factors affecting a change in attitude.

In the assessment of any long-term process such as the formation or change of attitude, it seems obvious that longitudinal or developmental designs are indicated. The most worn and repeated phrases in research reports are those that justify the lack of improvement in attitude by citing the short experimental treatment, although it is possible to give examples in which opinions and attitudes have been changed significantly in a very short time through an especially convincing or impressive experience. The problem might be to identify those attitudes that are resistant to quick change and those that are not. Is this factor related to the rate at which attitudes form? That is, if an attitude forms gradually, is it more resistant to change than one that is formed quickly? Since school-related attitudes appear to be among those that form gradually, answers to these questions would be valuable in suggesting the type of research designs that might be most effective.

In summary, it appears that the issue of attitude change is another area in which theoretical bases are still to be developed. Until some of the questions raised in this section are answered through exploratory studies, it is questionable whether hypotheses related to attitude improvement can be tested in studies of instructional methods.

The Nature of Mathematics Attitudes

The existence of a major area of research dealing with attitudes in mathematics is strong evidence that it is of great concern to many educators. This concern evidently is sparked by an agreement that a significant number of students have poor attitudes toward mathematics. Given this agreement, it would seem that there is no issue concerning whether mathematics attitudes are poor. However, it may be the most important unresolved issue of all. First, there is some evidence in studies asking children to react to their school subjects that mathematics is among their top choices, especially in early grades (Saxe, 1971). Also, in many studies the scores on mathematics-attitude scales reflect neutral rather than negative attitudes.

Perhaps the concern over attitudes and the intensity of research has the effect of magnifying the problem. After all, few educators seem to be interested in measuring attitude toward spelling or history or French. If one did measure these attitudes, there is a good possibility of discovering that some students have poor attitudes toward those subjects. There appears to be a great deal of acceptance, even among many mathematics teachers, that mathematics is disliked. This opinion is probably self-fulfilling in that students are told things like "You won't like word problems but we have to study them" or "Fractions aren't interesting but we'll be finished with them soon."

Some children seem to learn quite early that it is more acceptable socially not to like mathematics than to like it (Brush, 1978a). It may be possible that this situation is also self-fulfilling in that it produces negative attitudes.

An important variable related to the issue of poor attitudes in mathematics is the stability of attitudes. There is an intuitive feeling that children's attitudes change from day to day, depending on what happened in class, how much homework was assigned, how they did on a quiz, or any number of other factors. It is possible that the usual procedures for measuring attitude do not reflect this situation. Attitude scales may be too general to reveal these specific variations, since students cannot respond to an item such as "I enjoy mathematics" by answering "Only when I get a good grade" or "Except when the teacher doesn't explain things clearly." Also, attitudes are usually measured only at the beginning or end of some fairly lengthy time period. Often, the underlying assumption is that the test represents a cumulative assessment of attitude formation and factors influencing it over the time preceding the test. Although this assumption may be correct, it is also possible that an attitude test given on any particular day measures nothing more than the subjects' attitudes on that day, which may be determined largely by a few specific, recent experiences. The result of measuring attitudes immediately after a final examination, for example, supports the latter possibility.

It is, of course, impractical and inadvisable to administer an attitude scale every day or every few days to determine the stability of mathematics attitudes and the factors affecting this stability. But it is possible—

and it would be extremely useful—to use more informal continuous-assessment approaches. For example, the response each day after class to a stem such as "Today math was _____" could be used, along with a brief log of what happened in class, to discover patterns in day-to-day attitudes for individual students as well as patterns in the kinds of classroom activities and mathematics content that influence attitudes for different types of students.

In summary, the nature of attitudes in mathematics appears to be an open and real issue. An a priori decision or assumption on the part of a researcher about the nature of these attitudes would have unfortunate implications for the design and interpretation of experimental studies. The discovery of what people really mean when they say they dislike mathematics represents a fruitful area for research.

FUTURE DIRECTIONS OF RESEARCH

A great many questions and issues surrounding mathematics attitudes have been raised or discussed in the preceding pages, most of which could be developed and stated as testable hypotheses. In this section, a few of these hypotheses will be presented as having importance in the next several years in that they are timely and represent promising areas for obtaining significant and useful results. In the previous section, it was mentioned that in many areas of study on mathematics attitude, sufficient theory has not been developed to provide the rationale for hypothesis-testing experiments. In the following section, a model is proposed that illustrates the relationship between attitudes and behavior. This model will be used to develop a set of hypotheses for research on attitude.

A Model for the Relationship between Attitudes and Behavior

Many of the potential implications to be drawn from the results of research on attitude involve the assumption that some students have "good" attitudes and others have "poor" attitudes toward mathematics. Furthermore, it is often implicit that these attitudes are somewhat stable over fairly long periods of time. Even if these assumptions are supported, a fundamental problem is the effect of mathematics attitudes on behavior —specifically on behavior related to mathematics learning. This problem seems to be especially relevant at this time in view of the freedom students often have in modern instructional settings to select, or influence the nature of, their learning experience.

The theoretical bases for predicting behavior from atttitude include the idea that attitude produces a variety of responses rather than a single response to a stimulus (Doob, 1947). For example, consider the stimulus of a mathematics homework assignment for a student who has the attitude of "disliking math." In the absence of the attitude, the response would probably be the completion of the assignment within an amount of time and at a level of mastery predicted by the student's ability and the instructional variables. However, different students having the same attitude ("disliking math") may react with careless work, a late assignment, absence from the next class, or nothing unusual at all, other variables being similar. The explanation for the variety of responses would seem to come from the variety of reasons for disliking mathematics, coupled with opposing mediating variables, such as the importance of the assignment, attitude toward the teacher, parental influence, difficulty of the assignment, and so on. The combination of these opposing variables that produces the final response may explain the weak relationship between mathematics attitude and achievement.

Before hypotheses are suggested, it may be helpful to present a model of the possible relationships among attitude-related factors and their implications for behavior (see Figure 2). In the model, the simplest case of a dichotomy of categories (positive-negative) is represented. As measures become more precise, hypotheses based on the model could be refined, but the most direct procedure for applying the model at the present time would be to interview subjects on their attitudes and reasons for behavior according to the simple dichotomous model.

A specific example based on the model might be as follows. A subject feels that mathematics is useless (−A) but likes the mathematics teacher (+B). When given an easy homework assignment (+C), the subject completes the work on time at the expected level of mastery (+ Behavioral

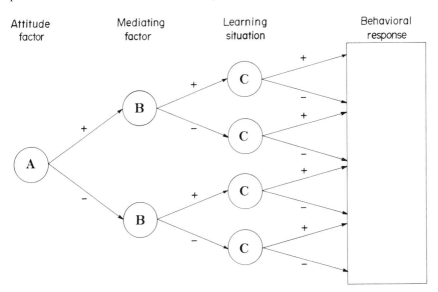

Figure 2. Model for attitude-behavior relationships.

response). In this example, it can be inferred that attitude toward the teacher is the stronger factor if the learning situation is not demanding. A number of interesting questions arise, providing hypotheses to be tested. Are some attitude factors strong enough (positively or negatively) to overcome all mediating factors and learning situations? Repeat the question with the three types of factors interchanged. Are mediating factors or learning situations more important for negative attitude factors than for positive ones? What kinds of mediating factors overcome what kinds of attitude factors?

The questions suggested by the model give rise to many specific hypotheses, all of the same general form:

> *Hypothesis:* Given attitude factor A(+ or –), mediating factor B(+ or –), and learning situation C(+ or –), the subject's response will be (positive or negative).

A specific form of the hypothesis might go as follows:

> *Hypothesis:* Given attitude factor A(+), the subject's response will be positive for any B and any C.

An even more specific form might go like this:

> *Hypothesis:* Given the attitude "enjoys mathematics," the subject will complete difficult homework assignments in the presence of a negative attitude toward the teacher and insufficient instructional time.

In order to satisfy the requirement that hypotheses of this type are timely, important, and testable, it is necessary to identify the domains for A, B, and C. That is, what are the attitudes, mediating factors, and learning situations that are most relevant to current concerns in mathematics learning? The following sections outline some possibilities.

Attitude Factors

In the past, measures of attitude have been primarily concerned with the enjoyment factor. The failure of this factor to predict achievement may indicate that many students' learning behavior depends more heavily on their views of the usefulness of mathematics than on how much they like the subject. Since there are certainly some students for whom the enjoyment of mathematics is the most important factor in their learning, one must not discount enjoyment. However, the view that enjoyment is the most important factor may influence teachers' choices of learning situational factors in such a way as to make mathematics interesting only to students who enjoy mathematics anyway. Aiken (1974) has provided evidence for a value-of-mathematics factor, and Bowling (1976) developed a nature-of-mathematics scale. In a review of open-response attitude scales in which students indicated their reasons for liking or disliking mathematics, Brush (1978a) identified Difficulty and Success, Nature, Usefulness, and Emotional Reactions as the main categories for issues mentioned by students.

The Difficulty and Success and Emotional Reactions factors contained responses related to anxiety or self-concept, which appear to be mediating factors rather than attitude factors. In view of its potential importance in determining students' choices of mathematics-related fields for further study, the factor of perceived value or usefulness would appear to be of primary interest in the future. If the value of mathematics is found to be an important attitude factor, it may influence the selection of learning situations that can help many students overcome their dislike of mathematics. Further research may also reveal the relationships between students' perceptions of the nature of mathematics and their behaviors, making it possible for them to overcome the effects of a negative view of mathematics.

Although it may be possible to identify and validate further important factors of mathematics attitude, the primary focus should be on exploring the relationships among the Enjoyment, Value, and Nature factors and on determining cause-and-effect relationships between these factors and behavior through their interaction with mediating factors and learning situations. It may be possible through the use of open-ended self-report measures to refine the present measures of these factors so that they represent clearly different aspects of mathematics attitude. However, continued work in exploring factors of attitude must be done through the use of a variety of measurement approaches.

Mediating Factors

A great many factors in the learning environment have the potential to overshadow, either temporarily or permanently, the effect of a given attitude toward mathematics. Of these factors, the teacher is probably the most obvious one, though there appears to be evidence against the immediate effect of the teacher (Phillips, 1973; Van de Walle, 1973; Wess, 1970). In particular, it is difficult to explain the steady decrease in positive attitudes from elementary through high school in light of the increase in the mathematical competence and training of teachers from elementary to high school. Although many factors of learning environment, such as instructional strategy and materials, are under the control of the teacher, research appears to show that these factors often do not have important effects (for example, see Cohen, 1971; Demars, 1972; Miller, 1975; Pavlick, 1975).

Other mediating factors that bear investigation are those variables that impinge on the judged utility or enjoyment of mathematics, especially for subgroups such as females, minorities, the non–college bound, and the gifted. Many of these variables actually operate outside the classroom, although they have important implications both in the classroom as well as for whether students enter a mathematics classroom. Among these factors are (a) employment opportunities in mathematics-related fields, (b) societal pressures for mathematics achievement, (c) parental expectations for educational achievement, and (d) utility of higher education for social and economic advancement.

This view of the kinds of mediating factors that are important for mathematics learning represents a significant departure from the directions of previous research in mathmetics attitudes. Perhaps past concerns have been somewhat narrowly focused in considering classroom factors. It seems possible that more permanent and important effects of attitude come about through factors that influence students through the home and other social settings that are central to developing adolescents' value systems. The effect of home, classroom, and other social factors probably is complex, and the strength of each one changes as the child matures. Research related to the effects of parental influence (Fennema & Sherman, 1977) provides an indication that these factors are specifically related to mathematics learning. In the early grades, home and classroom variables probably play an important role. During junior and senior high school, classroom instructional variables may become less important, whereas those related to social interaction gain in influence, as do societal and utility variables. At the college level, classroom variables may be less important than those related to utility and employment opportunities. The influence of home-related variables in these later years is probably quite varied but has an important role throughout. Of course, the attitudes developed as a consequence of the most crucial variables at each stage also play an important part in the formation of attitudes and behavior at any given point.

Little research has been done on the developmental aspects of attitudes toward mathematics. In order to understand the effect of mediating factors on behavior, a precise description of the relationships outlined in the previous paragraph is necessary. It seems clear that mediating factors, as used in this discussion, have impact both on immediate behavior and on the continuing formation of attitudes toward mathematics.

Factors Related to the Learning Situation

The final behavioral outcome in terms of mathematics achievement is most closely linked to factors related to the learning task. All the attitude and mediating factors are brought to bear on the specific task or type of task that students confront. As with mediating factors, it is important not to take too narrow a view of the types of learning factors. For example, if the class attendance for subjects having poor attitudes toward mathematics is being predicted, learning tasks such as a final examination or a class discussion might well produce different results. This example illustrates that it might be more fundamentally important to characterize learning tasks according to the levels of anxiety or stress that they produce. The problem then becomes one of determining the relative importance of attitude in predicting behavior, depending on the level of stress in the learning situation. Many of the important learning factors are not new, but when they are considered in the context of their relationship to attitudes, they represent possible directions for testing a hypothesis.

Some of the fundamental factors that bear investigation are (a) the difficulty of the learning task, (b) the importance of the learning task, (c) the relevance or usefulness of the task (as judged by the student), and (d) the length of time required for the task. It is possible that these factors are sufficiently powerful in their classroom application to relegate attitude to a lower level of importance.

The learning factors that have received the most attention in past research have been those related to curriculum and methodology. Although the general patterns may not be entirely clear due to the variety of studies conducted, it is clear that specific curricular and instructional innovations have had important impact on learners' attitudes and behaviors in specific settings and for specific populations.

The application of curricular and methodological factors in the proposed model represents a fruitful and important area for attitude-achievement research. Because a great many studies employing these factors have used attitude measures as dependent variables, it should be possible to make specific hypotheses about their relationship to attitude and behavior. This area of research would be aided by a careful review of research that relates curricular and methodological variables to attitudes.

Hypotheses for Future Research

An issue raised in an earlier section concerned the stability of mathematics attitudes. One of the first objectives of research should be to determine the variation of attitude over time periods of several months. Although this objective does not fit the hypothesis-generating model proposed in the previous section, tests of this important null hypothesis should be made at different grade levels under many learning conditions:

> *Hypothesis:* Mathematics attitudes are stable from day to day over a period of several months.

Further hypotheses may be stated by considering some of the important factors related to the proposed model. Although many hypotheses are possible, only a few samples will be given here to illustrate some of the directions that might be taken.

Hypotheses about attitude factors

Hypothesis: Students who have the attitude that mathematics is needed to get a job will spend more time on task, regardless of mediating factors and learning situations, than students who do not have this attitude.

Hypothesis: Students who have the attitude that mathematics is not useful to them will have lower achievement scores, regardless of mediating factors and learning situations, than students who do not have this attitude.

Hypotheses about mediating factors

Hypothesis: College students who believe there are more employment opportunities in mathematics-related fields will spend more time on mathematics homework, regardless of mathematics attitudes and learning situations, than students who do not have this belief.

Hypothesis: Students who believe their parents do not expect them to get high grades in mathematics will not think mathematics is as important to learn, regardless of other mathematical attitudes and learning situations, as students who do not have this belief.

Hypotheses about learning situations

Hypothesis: Students who do not enjoy mathematics and who are working on an important assignment will show more persistence, regardless of mediating factors and other mathematics attitudes, than students who are working on a less important task.

Hypothesis: Students who are given sufficient time to complete a mathematics problem-solving task will believe mathematics is more enjoyable, regardless of the mediating factors, than students who are not given sufficient time.

In these sample hypotheses, attitudes are important both as independent variables in determining their effect on behaviors and as dependent variables in determining the effects of other factors on attitudes. Although it is not the purpose of this chapter to discuss research design, it might be helpful to point out some basic problems in conducting studies to test hypotheses such as these. Theoretically, controlled experimental designs are implied by the hypotheses. However, owing to the ethical and common-sense considerations related to manipulating attitudes, especially to test negative effects, many compromises will be necessary.

One approach is to use correlational, especially partial correlational, data with existing attitudes and other variables. Although it is not as controlled, this approach can yield useful information. The second approach is to use the attitude, mediating, or learning-situation factors as blocking variables in factorial studies. Again, since some assumptions of randomness cannot be met, the result is less generalizability and weaker support of hypotheses than in more controlled studies. However, the use of replication and study over longer periods of time can lead to stronger conclusions. Other approaches, such as using interview techniques on case studies, can be used with individuals or small groups of subjects who have acute problems of attitude to investigate negative factors. The accumulation of evidence relating attitudes to other variables can proceed through the use of designs that will not violate established standards for research using human subjects.

In summary, the hypotheses for future research in mathematics attitudes require a careful consideration of the mechanisms by which attitudes have impact on learning behavior. The ability to state hypotheses in the form "Attitude A in the presence of variable B has a (positive, negative, neutral) effect on behavior C in relation to learning factor D" requires that the researcher understand the various relationships rather than simply state an attitude-related hypothesis as an afterthought. Although this focus on hypothesis development does not guarantee future success in research on attitude, it provides a setting for making systematic progress in determining the results related to the factors that have been suggested as important to mathematics attitudes.

REFERENCES

Aiken, L. R. Attitudes toward mathematics. *Review of Educational Research*, 1970, *40*, 551–596.

Aiken, L. R. Research on attitudes toward mathematics. *Arithmetic Teacher*, 1972, *19*, 229–234.

Aiken, L. R. Two scales of attitude toward mathematics. *Journal for Research in Mathematics Education*, 1974, *5*, 67–71.

Aiken, L. R. Update on attitudes and other affective variables in learning mathematics. *Review of Educational Research*, 1976, *46*, 293–311.

Allport, G. W. Attitudes. In C. Murchison (Ed.), *A handbook of social psychology*. Worcester, Mass.: Clark University Press, 1935.

Beattie, I. D., Deichmann, J., & Lewis, E. *The relationship of achievement and attitudes towards mathematics in the elementary school: A longitudinal study*. Paper presented at the annual meeting of the American Educational Research Association, New Orleans, 1973. (ED 076 424)

Bloom, B. S., Hastings, J. T., & Madaus, G. F. *Handbook on formative and summative evaluation of student learning*. New York: McGraw-Hill, 1971.

Bowling, J. M. *Three scales of attitude toward mathematics*. Unpublished doctoral dissertation, Ohio State University, 1976.

Brush, L. R. *Analyzing students' attitudes toward mathematics: An item by item review of scale content*. Unpublished manuscript, 1978. (a)

Brush, L. R. A validation study of the mathematics anxiety rating scale (MARS). *Educational and Psychological Measurement*, 1978, *38*, 485–490. (b)

Calder, B. J., & Ross, M. *Attitudes and behavior.* Morristown, N.J.: General Learning Press, 1973.

Callahan, W. J. Adolescent attitudes toward mathematics. *Mathematics Teacher,* 1971, *64,* 751–755.

Carman, R. A. The effects of tutoring in developmental mathematics on the academic performance, attrition and attitudes of community college students. *Dissertation Abstracts International,* 1975, *36,* 623A–624A.

Cohen, M. S. A comparison of effects of laboratory and conventional mathematics teaching upon underachieving middle school boys. *Dissertation Abstracts International,* 1971, *31,* 5026A–5027A.

Collier, C. P. Prospective elementary teachers' intensity and ambivalence of beliefs about mathematics and mathematics instruction. *Journal for Research in Mathematics Education,* 1972, *3,* 155–163.

Crosswhite, F. J. *Correlates of attitudes toward mathematics.* NLSMA Report No. 20. Pasadena, Calif.: A. C. Vroman, 1972.

Demars, R. J. A comparative study of seventh grade low achievers' attitudes and achievement in mathematics under two approaches, UICSM and traditional. *Dissertation Abstracts International,* 1972, *32,* 4832A–4853A.

Doob, L. W. The behavior of attitudes. *Psychological Review,* 1947, *3,* 155–163.

Dunlap, W. P. An attitudinal device for primary children. *Arithmetic Teacher,* 1976, *23,* 29–31.

Dutton, W. H., & Blum, M. P. The measurement of attitudes toward arithmetic with a Likert-type test. *Elementary School Journal,* 1968, *68,* 259–264.

Early, J. C. A study of the grade level teaching preferences of prospective elementary teachers with respect to their attitudes toward arithmetic and achievement in mathematics. *Dissertation Abstracts International,* 1970, *30,* 3345A–3346A.

Fennema, E. Mathematics learning and the sexes: A review. *Journal for Research in Mathematics Education,* 1974, *5,* 126–139.

Fennema, E., & Sherman, J. Sex-related differences in mathematics achievement, spatial-visualization and affective factors. *American Educational Research Journal,* 1977, *14,* 51–71.

Fishbein, M., & Ajzen, I. *Belief, attitude, intention and behavior: An introduction to theory and research.* Reading, Mass.: Addison-Wesley, 1975.

Gardner, P. L. Attitude measurement, a critique of some recent research. *Education Research,* 1975, *7,* 101–109.

Gough, M. F. Mathephobia: Causes and treatments. *Clearing House,* 1954, *28,* 290–292.

Hilton, A. S. The understandings of mathematics and the attitudes toward mathematics expressed by prospective elementary teachers. *Dissertation Abstracts International,* 1970, *31,* 266A.

Hilton, T. L., & Berglund, G. W. Sex differences in mathematics achievement—A longitudinal study. *Journal of Educational Research,* 1974, *67,* 231–237.

Hunkler, R., & Quast, W. G. Improving the mathematics attitudes of prospective elementary school teachers. *School Science and Mathematics,* 1972, *72,* 709–714.

Husén, T. (Ed.). *International study of achievement.* Vol. 1. New York: Wiley, 1967.

Kiesler, C. A., Collins, B. E., & Miller, N. *Attitude change.* New York: Wiley, 1969.

Krathwohl, D. R., Bloom, B. S., & Masia, B. B. *Taxonomy of educational objectives: The classification of educational goals. Handbook 2: Affective domain.* New York: McKay, 1964.

McCallon, E. L., & Brown, J. D. A semantic differential instrument for measuring attitude toward mathematics. *Journal of Experimental Education,* 1971, *39,* 69–72.

Malcolm, S. V. A longitudinal study of attitudes toward arithmetic in grades four, six, and seven. *Dissertation Abstracts International,* 1971, *32,* 1194A.

Miller, W. L. A study of the relations between contract/traditional teaching methods and attitude/achievement in community college mathematics instruction. *Dissertation Abstracts International*, 1975, *35*, 4053A.

Neale, D. C. The role of attitudes in learning mathematics. *Arithmetic Teacher*, 1969, *16*, 631–640.

Pavlic, F. M. The attitudinal effect of using the computer in an elementary statistics course. *International Journal for Mathematical Education in Science and Technology*, 1975, *16*, 353–360.

Phillips, R. B. Teacher attitude as related to student attitude and achievement in elementary school mathematics. *School Science and Mathematics*, 1973, *73*, 501–507.

Raines, B. G. Personal, situational, and behavioral predisposition factors related to the elementary teachers' attitude toward teaching mathematics. *Dissertation Abstracts International*, 1971, *31*, 4631A.

Rokeach, M. *Beliefs, attitudes and values*. San Francisco: Jossey-Bass, 1972.

Romberg, T. A., & Wilson, J. W. *The development of tests*. NLSMA Report No. 7. Pasadena, Calif.: A. C. Vroman, 1969.

Sandman, R. S. The development, validation, and application of a multidimensional mathematics attitude instrument. *Dissertation Abstracts International*, 1974, *34*, 7054A–7055A.

Saxe, R. W. What's a school for? *Elementary School Journal*, 1971, *72*, 7–11.

Selkirk, J. An enquiry into adverse attitudes toward advanced level mathematics. *International Journal of Mathematical Education in Science and Technology*, 1975, *6*, 181–186.

Shaw, M. E., & Wright, J. M. *Scales for the measurement of attitudes*. New York: McGraw-Hill, 1967.

Suinn, R. M., Edie, C. A., Nicoletti, J., & Spinelli, P. R. The MARS, a measure of mathematics anxiety: Psychometric data. *Journal of Clinical Psychology*, 1972, *28*, 373–375.

Van de Walle, J. A. Attitudes and perceptions of elementary mathematics possessed by third and sixth grade teachers as related to student attitude and achievement in mathematics. *Dissertation Abstracts International*, 1973, *33*, 4254A–4255A.

Wess, R. G. An analysis of the relationship of teachers' attitudes as compared to pupils' attitudes and achievement in mathematics. *Dissertation Abstracts International*, 1970, *30*, 3844A–3845A.

Wyer, R. S. *Cognitive organization and change: An information processing approach*. Potomac, Md.: Lawrence Erlbaum Associates, 1974.

13

Mathematics Education Research on Curriculum and Instruction

James T. Fey
University of Maryland

THE immediately preceding chapters of this volume have addressed specific aspects of mathematics education, such as concept formation, skill development, and problem solving. Each topic has been the subject of a reasonably long history of careful experimental research that suggests guidelines for classroom practice. In fact, Suydam and Riedesel (1972) composed a list of 52 recommendations based on an exhaustive review of pre-1970 research, a list they "believe to be clearly substantiated by the research on elementary school mathematics" (p. 44). However, if one studies any large sample of mathematics classes in action, instructional materials, and teacher education programs or if one talks to the teachers, textbook authors, and teacher educators, it becomes clear that results from research play a very limited direct role in the actual business of school mathematics. Instead, when authors plan and construct instructional materials or when teachers plan and execute classroom learning activities, they seem to rely more heavily on personal experience, intuition, and a kind of cumulative wisdom of the profession, although research probably affects these judgments in some indirect ways.

Many plausible explanations can be given for this failure to apply the findings or methods of educational research to the design of curricula and instructional procedures. Much of the experimental research on aspects of mathematics education has taken place in laboratories or very special classroom environments, yielding results that curriculum developers then perceive as irrelevant to the situations they face. Also, classroom teachers can quite reasonably claim that the daily pressure of meeting five or six classes of 150–200 students does not permit them the luxury of lessons carefully conceived to reflect the refinements suggested by research.

In the balance of this chapter we shall examine four fundamental questions facing those interested in research to improve school mathematics curricula and instruction.

1. What are the proper goals of curricular and instructional research in mathematics?
2. What is the current status of research knowledge and methodology?
3. What are the most important problems and the most promising hypotheses?
4. What are the most appropriate and promising strategies for future research?

Good curricular and instructional research is difficult. As Begle (1968) has pointed out:

> For one thing, the number of variables that should be taken into account is very large. . . . In order to isolate and compare two different curriculum treatments, for example, it is necessary to take all these variables into account so that the effects due to these variables will not be confounded with those due to the curriculum treatments. To do this generally requires either a large experiment or a large number of carefully correlated small ones. (p. 44)

Furthermore, the track record of those attempting to apply rigorous research methods to curricular or instructional design is, to date, less than impressive. In fact, one of the developers of Individually Prescribed Instruction (IPI) recently reflected on that experience with dismay (Lipson, 1976):

> When an instructional program has been developed on the basis of advanced concepts of learning psychology and with impressive support from the federal government, and intelligent and well-intentioned people have worked on the project, how do you explain why the average achievement levels of conventional classes are about as good as those in the innovative program when measured by standardized achievement tests? What is happening in the conventional classroom that enables it to succeed as well as an innovative, carefully planned program? (p. 11)

The magnitude of effort required and the discouraging pattern of results in research on curriculum and instruction have led many researchers to focus on more manageable special topics. But for most practitioners, curriculum and instruction are the center of the action, posing fascinating questions for research and emphasizing vital needs for improved school mathematics programs.

GOALS OF RESEARCH ON CURRICULUM AND INSTRUCTION

The most natural first step in an analysis of the knowledge, methods, and problems of research would be to formulate precise definitions of the central terms *curriculum* and *instruction*. These two words are used freely and with apparent clarity of meaning in everyday educational discussions. Yet every effort to establish rigorous, widely accepted definitions reveals an immense range of interpretations triggered by these very familiar terms. For some, a curriculum is simply a list of mathematical concepts and skills; for others, it is a scope-and-sequence outline, a set of instructional materials, or a hierarchy of performance objectives for students. Recently many developers have come to think of the curriculum as a total system of content topics, student objectives, learning experiences, evaluation procedures, and a management scheme to coordinate the different component activities.

Even if one accepts the broadest possible definition of curriculum and instruction, there remains the difficult task of specifying the range of curriculum and instruction activities that might appropriately be considered research. Among designers of new curriculum materials or instructional procedures, there is strong tradition to base their efforts on personal creativity, informal field tests, and intuitive judgments. However, there is an equally strong tradition that denies the label of "research" for these nonexperimental development projects.

Several recent developments in curriculum and instruction promise a productive blend of the best methods from development and research traditions. A number of investigators have assembled conceptual models of instructional programs in an effort to encourage systematic and comprehensive approaches to the broad range of significant variables in curricular and instructional design.

For instance, drawing on their experiences with the TICCIT system of computer-controlled instructional television, Merrill and Wood (1974) suggest that instruction be thought of as consisting of four facets: (a) student aptitudes, (b) subject matter content and sequence, (c) instructional strategies consisting of various types and sequences of "displays," and (d) delivery systems. They argue that each display can be described by the specification of eight characteristics: content type (identity, concept, or rule), response conditions (recall, classification, rule using, rule finding), content mode (generality or instance), response mode (expository or inquisitory), content representation (enactive, iconic, symbolic), response representation (enactive, . . .), mathemagenic prompting (mnemonic, attribute isolation, algorithm, heuristic), and mathemagenic feedback (knowledge of results, correct answer, mnemonic, . . .). By identifying what they see to be the central components or variables in the design of curricula and instruction, Merrill and Wood set an agenda for research—trying to understand the combinations of content, sequence, strategy, and delivery system most effective for various student-aptitude profiles.

A somewhat different model of the components in an instructional program has been proposed by DeVault and his associates at the University of Wisconsin (Golladay, DeVault, Fox, & Skuldt, 1975). Typical curricular or instructional research compares the effectiveness of two or more treatments by controlling many important variables and systematically manipulating one or more other variables. When one of the treatments is an individualized program, that treatment itself offers a great variety of educational opportunities and experiences. Thus, attributing observed criterion results to an individualized program does not contribute much to an understanding of how the results are being produced. To help describe more accurately the nature of instructional programs, Golladay et al. developed a Descriptor for Individualized Instruction that aims to conceptualize the critical components of an instructional system. The Descriptor has three main components:

1. Aims, including

   - objectives (concepts, skills, attitudes, etc.)
   - assessment procedures (tests, conferences, etc.)

2. Instruction, including

   - sequence (linear, branched, network, etc.)
   - rate
   - program pattern (typical sequence of learner activity)
   - grouping (self, with instructor, without instructor, etc.)
   - media (reading, audiovisual, manipulative, etc.)

3. Management System, including
   - record of information
   - use of information

The Descriptor sets an agenda for research similar to that proposed by Merrill and Wood.

The theoretical models of curriculum and instruction described above offer promise of organizing research in the complex field by focusing on crucial variables. However, they also suggest a misleading orderliness in both the development and the evaluation of curricular programs. The actual working procedure of curriculum projects such as SMSG or SSMCIS was typically a cycle of syllabus-planning conferences, summer text writing, informally monitored field trials, and text revision based on teacher feedback and the professional judgment of consultants. In an attempt to apply scientific procedures and standards to this developmental process, several recent projects have employed a systems approach in planning, constructing, and evaluating new instructional programs. The techniques of needs assessment, task analysis, formative evaluation, and summative evaluation have been explored and promoted as important steps in bringing effective, objective methodology to instructional design.

Despite the widely heralded introduction of theoretical models and systematic, objective development procedures, any reasonable assessment of current mathematics curricula and instructional programs must credit important contributions to individuals and groups who work in the older, more informal tradition. Thus, the subsequent analysis of the knowledge and needs of research is organized around the tasks involved in mathematics program design, with insight from a broad range of sources and investigatory styles applied to these tasks. Our definition of research on curriculum and instruction is simply this: a disciplined inquiry intended to understand or improve (a) the *selection and structure of mathematical ideas,* (b) the *presentation of those ideas to students,* and (c) the *evaluation of program effectiveness and student achievement.* Such a broad definition of appropriate research might seem to encompass all the concerns of preceding chapters! The intent is to examine the synthesis of those separate pieces of knowledge from research into school mathematics and to encourage the application of research approaches that are not confined to narrow statistical models of experimental tradition.

CURRENT KNOWLEDGE AND STRATEGIES OF RESEARCH

To what extent can the design of curricula or instruction be confidently based on results of past research? Until very recently, research directed at better understanding the issues in curriculum or instruction has typically sought quite general guidelines to the *best* content and sequence, the *most effective* method of teaching, and the *most effective* medium of instruction, all determined by one test. Past research is unimpressive as evidence of progress toward these goals. In fact, many program developers have examined the research that offers some promise of guidance for different phases of instructional design and have concluded that the accumulated studies offer such inconclusive, contradictory, or limited information as to be of no help at all. Others have examined much the same evidence from research and felt justified in formulating some principles of curriculum and instruction in mathematics.

The following state-of-the-art review should not be read as an exhaustive analysis of all research that might be used to plan curricula or instruction in mathematics. Instead, it attempts to identify and critically analyze the variables, hypotheses, and methods of research that have been most prominent in previous research. The description of major findings and problems in the research will be augmented by an examination of individual studies that are particularly representative of promise in results or methods.

Selection of Mathematical Content

Traditionally, the construction of a school mathematics curriculum has primarily involved selecting content topics to be covered and arranging the topics in a suggested grade level or teaching sequence. Even with the more detailed and comprehensive systems approach that is popular today, judgments about proper subject matter content and sequence are critical tasks in curricular and instructional design. The ultimate choice of the mathematics content in a curriculum usually reflects a composite judgment of what *should be learned* and what *can be learned*.

It seems logical to determine what should be learned by assessing (a) the values, problems, and demands of society, (b) the needs and interests of individual students, and (c) the structure of disciplines or organized subject matter (Johnson, 1967, p. 132). These issues seem amenable to different kinds of survey and analytic research, but there is surprisingly little evidence of such investigation.

1. *What mathematical competence is demanded and valued by society?* Choosing mathematical content that will be valuable far in the future to individuals and society as a whole is, perhaps, the most important and most difficult problem to be investigated by objective research. In 1937 Wilson and Dalrymple reported the results of a survey of business and social uses of fractions. After tabulating the occurrence of fractions in the work of people in different occupations, they concluded that "needed mastery in fractions for common usage is limited to halves, thirds, fourths, eighths, and twelfths... subtraction of fractions seldom occurs... [and] division of a fraction by a fraction almost never occurs" (p. 347). They suggested that necessary instruction in fractions could be accomplished quickly in school with any further work left to be learned on the job! Some similar studies of approximately the same vintage indicated the importance of facility in arithmetic with problems involving time and money; these studies confirmed the suggestion that division is not often used by young people.

The obvious criticism, that observing current uses of mathematics yields a shortsighted measure of curricular priorities, has discouraged such investigations in the recent past. There is continuing public pressure for a school mathematics program that guarantees minimal mathematical competence for survival—both in daily life and in postschooling occupation in business or skilled trades. Unfortunately, the current school syllabi that respond to such concern reflect only the most casual and immediate-focus assessment of needs. Curricular priorities are being established by asking panels of citizens and professionals such questions as "What mathematical skills are essential for survival or effective consumer behavior?" The curricular impact of these studies is unclear. Curricular emphases also reflect a response to increasing accountability and competence testing. We really need a greater understanding of this change process, too.

2. *What mathematics is of most interest to various types of students?* Concern for student interests as a factor in the selection of topics for school mathematics curricula varies with changes in broad educational philosophy. When student interests are considered, they tend to be assessed by experience-based generalizations such as "low-ability students like practical problems" or "bright students like puzzle problems." Undoubtedly the situation is much more complex than the "common wisdom" suggests. A recent study by Hogan (1977) illustrates one type of investigation that might prove fruitful. After surveying attitudes toward specific mathematics topics among 13 000 students in Grade 1–8, Hogan found several broad trends in the responses: positive attitudes toward computation, negative attitudes toward geometry, attitudes becoming less positive from primary to elementary grades, and less positive feelings toward "hard" topics. However, the most striking result was the diversity of student preferences and the unexplained causes of those attitudes. One is tempted to conjecture that teacher preference and curricular emphasis or the style of presentation play a crucial role in shaping student preferences; some teachers and texts do particularly good jobs of selling particular topics.

3. *What mathematics is required for success in other school courses?* The most influential factors in any teacher's selection of the mathematics content for instruction are the expectations of teachers in other subject areas and, predominantly, in succeeding mathematics courses.

The correlation of the mathematics and science curricula, particularly at the secondary school level, has been a much debated but little studied problem. Comparing the mathematics and science programs of British secondary schools, Malpas (1973) found that the mathematical ideas most important in science included ratios; rates; proportion; straight-line graphs; formulas; measurement and statistical treatment of data, including descriptive statistics and probability; the calculation of averages; approximations; and uses of standard form in handling very large and very small numbers. Some aspects of geometry and trigonometry were essential in physics. He commented further:

> One is struck ... how little use is made in the science courses of the many other mathematical ideas which go to make up a modern course. . . .
>
> There are some mathematical topics about which, notwithstanding the fact that they are treated consonantly in both mathematics and science courses, there are persistent reports from teachers of students' difficulties. One such topic is proportionality, linear relationships and variation. (pp. 239–240)

Earlier analyses by Thorndike (1924) and Bell (1970) offer similar support for the conjecture that mathematics curricula correlate with, or are determined by, demands of science courses only by accident, if at all.

Thus, one is led to the conclusion that the selection of school mathematics topics is, to a very great extent, determined by the internal structure of the discipline and that these decisions are guided largely by tradition, informal expressions and measures of public concern, the recommendations of prestigious advisory boards, and the commercial textbook and testing industry—all, in practice, filtered through the very diverse and little understood screen of classroom teachers' experiences and judgments. We don't know how research has affected this process, if at all, and we have little research that explains the dynamics of the system that transforms a collage of needs, interests, and values into an operating school curriculum. This situation is particularly serious when one considers that the only curricular and instructional variable consistently related to student achievement is the content of the student text (Begle, 1973). Research analyzed later in this chapter explores nearly every other conceivable curricular variable with inconclusive results; the only factor that appears to make a predictable difference, the mathematics content, is usually planned without benefit of the knowledge or methods of research.

Structuring Mathematical Content

Prior to 1960 the content and sequence of school mathematics had remained basically unchanged for a long period of time, except for a gradual shift downward of topics previously viewed appropriate for higher-level study. According to long-standing tradition, this implied the progression from the arithmetic of whole numbers, fractions, and decimals to algebra, geometry, trigonometry, and, ultimately, calculus. But the theorists and developers of the "new math" era stimulated a searching reexamination of the curricular possibilities that arise from alternative ways of structuring the ideas in school mathematics. Earlier, Washburne (1931) had reported results of his extensive studies on measuring what students were actually learning under then current approaches, and his results were widely interpreted as guidelines to what could be taught. But the challenge of the 1960s and 1970s was to find better ways to represent and sequence concepts and skills in order to accelerate the traditional pace.

1. *What are the most effective ways to represent mathematical ideas for various types of students?* Mathematical ideas are primarily useful as efficient abstractions of real-life problem situations. Typically, the development of student understanding and skill begins with a problem setting that is familiar to students while embodying the mathematical ideas of interest. For most mathematical ideas there are many possible introductory models, and so the choice of an effective way to represent concepts and processes becomes an important challenge to curriculum developers. They are concerned, for instance, with questions such as the following:

- What are the relative merits of different manipulative models of mathematical concepts, such as Cuisenaire, Dienes, or Stern blocks?
- What is the proper blend of formal and informal or concrete and symbolic presentations in the mathematics curriculum at different levels?
- What physical models or analogies are effective aids to the learning of higher-level mathematical skills, such as solving equations or ratio, proportion, and percent problems?
- What are the benefits of ordered pairs, arrow diagrams, Cartesian graphs, or input-output machines in developing elementary concepts of function?
- Is the limit concept of calculus more accessible when approached through sequences, epsilon-delta neighborhoods, or some other formulation?

These and other similar questions have provoked extensive debate and the development of curricula to compare the alternatives. There has also been considerable formal research of the type that compares the effectiveness of two or more approaches to a particular topic or to an entire course. Although much of this research has strong ties to more specific fields such as concept formation or development of learning abilities, there are definite issues of curriculum practice that generate and are influenced by the studies described below.

By far the most extensive and coherent program of research on the effects of content-representation modes has been the nearly 100 studies reported since 1960 on the effects of various manipulative-material models for arithmetic concepts and skills. The typical study compared two or more of the well-known materials. Although many of those studies were of small scale and compared a manipulative-material program with some vaguely defined "conventional" method of teaching, several strong studies stand out. Brownell (1968) compared the relative effectiveness of Cuisenaire models, Dienes models, and conventional teaching approaches in third-grade classes in Scotland and England. In the common ambiguous pattern for such comparative-method research, significant differences favored the Cuisenaire group in Scotland and the conventional group in England. Biggs (1965) reported a longitudinal study, conducted in England and Wales, that compared uni- and multi-model approaches with manipulative material. In a pattern of results that suggests both the type of hypotheses and methods of analysis most likely to be fruitful in future research, Biggs found that (a) traditional methods produced good computational facility but high number anxiety, (b) the uni-model approach produced better understanding and attitude among high IQ boys than a nonmanipulative environment did, and (c) the multi-model environment was superior to the other methods overall.

The general theoretical issue underlying the investigation of different manipulative aids to learning is the question of optimal use of concrete and abstract modes of presentation. It is highly unlikely that any simple answer will emerge from research. For instance, Fennema (1972) investigated the relative effectiveness of concrete and symbolic approaches to multiplication concepts in the second grade. She found no significant difference between the two groups on achievement. Results of a transfer test favored the symbolic group, suggesting the interpretation that students in the treatment group had sufficient previous concrete experience with the relevant concepts to make manipulative materials unnecessary. Furthermore, in a review of over 50 Canadian studies with Cuisenaire materials, Nelson (1964) found that the initial advantage of manipulative materials in promoting computational skills faded over time and that there were indications of a negative influence on problem solving and transfer tasks. Summarizing the much studied but as yet unclear situation, Kieren (1971) suggested that instead of studying the simple question "Is activity learning better than something else?" we should follow Cronbach's advice to study a fivefold interaction among subject matter, instructional type, timing, type of pupil, and desired outcomes.

Those studying the effectiveness of different modes for representing mathematical knowledge at the elementary school level have focused on comparing concrete and abstract approaches. However, for older students with richer background experience in mathematics, the naive dichotomy between concrete and abstract representation breaks down. The presentation that is apparently abstract to one learner might seem comfortably concrete to another. The range of alternative modes for representing ideas thus expands to include alternative derivations of new mathematics from previously acquired concepts and skills.

Typical of a large body of such studies is the Bauer (1975) comparison of three approaches to decimal computation—the common-fraction equivalent, expanded notation, and point-on-a-number-line models. All three methods were shown to be equally effective. The effectiveness of each alternative is probably linked to the previous learning experiences of individual students and the particular skills of individual teachers. The Brownell (1968) study mentioned above suggested that the approach most apt to be effective was whichever a teacher felt most comfortable with and most able to sell to his or her students.

Among alternative approaches to high school Euclidean geometry, the most prominent are those in which the familiar properties of plane and space figures are organized through a study of transformations of size and position. Usiskin (1972) compared the effectiveness of such a presentation to that of more conventional geometry curricula. The results from a traditional geometry achievement test indicated that the transformation approach was less effective than the others. But Kort (1971) found that in a succeeding course, which emphasized functions and graphs, the students with experience in transformation methods were more successful than their counterparts who had the more conventional background. Thus, once again there is strong support for those who look at more complex interactions of curricular input and output variables.

The Bauer, Usiskin, and Kort studies, like many others conducted under the typical time and financial constraints of doctoral students, can be criticized for using a small sample size (assuming that the class is the appropriate unit of statistical analysis) and for attempting to prove one method or the other best for all students and teachers. One quite reasonable response to these problems of doctoral research in curricular representation modes would be to discourage all investigators except those few who are able to garner the resources to do massive longitudinal studies. Yet the results from several of the studies suggest that there is substantial room for small-scale studies in which the principal investigator does extensive exploratory clinical investigation in search of differential effects of treatments.

2. *What alterations of traditional curriculum sequence would lead to improved student learning?* Many mathematics educators have asked this question, beginning in about 1960 and continuing through the period of intense interest in individualization during the 1970s. Alternative sequencing of topics is one option in the representation of mathematical ideas. Recent motivation to experiment with topic sequence in school mathematics has come from three main sources: Mathematicians have suggested organizing new and traditional topics within a unifying structure of fundamental concepts, much in the pattern of contemporary higher mathematics; cognitive psychologists have conjectured that such curricula, emphasizing the broad structures and processes of the discipline, would lead to a productive transfer of learning; and behavioral psychologists have proposed the analysis of learning objectives in carefully sequenced hierarchies of subordinate objectives.

The major curriculum-structure hypotheses of mathematicians and cognitive psychologists were persuasively argued in *The Process of Education*, Jerome Bruner's (1960) analysis of a Woods Hole conference of mathematicians and scientists with an interest in curriculum reform. Bruner argued for—

- rewriting the basic subjects and their teaching materials in such a way that the pervading and powerful ideas and attitudes relating to them are given a central role;
- matching the levels of these materials to the capacities of students of different abilities at different grades in school;

- developing an attitude toward learning and inquiry among students by presenting the fundamental structures of a discipline in such a way as to preserve some of the exciting sequences that lead students to discover for themselves. (pp. 18–20)

He introduced this substantial agenda for research with the startling proposal that "we begin with the hypothesis that any subject can be taught effectively in some intellectually honest form to any child at any stage of development" (p. 33).

Although many curriculum developers of the 1960s claimed, and may have intended, to explore Bruner's ideas about curriculum structure, the experience of the past 20 years hardly suggests definitive support for any of the broad proposals. New curricula, such as those of SMSG, tried to weave together the techniques of arithmetic and algebra by placing conscious emphasis on the structural patterns that mature mathematicians see in those subjects. Elementary school students began seeing the form and language of commutative, associative, and distributive properties; high school algebra students began justifying the algorithms for solving equations using those same algebraic properties and others such as the addition property of equality. Curriculum evaluations did not reveal any noteworthy influence of such understanding of structure on general ability in mathematics. Whereas NLSMA results suggest that elementary school students of the more structured SMSG curriculum became better problem solvers than their counterparts in more traditional curricula (Begle, 1973), there is precious little other evidence that an emphasis on structure enhances achievement or retention of traditional mathematical skills and understanding.

If one views the commercial textbook marketplace as a measure of extensive informal research on classroom teaching, current trends away from a structural emphasis in texts at all grade levels must be interpreted as a sign that the structural approach in curriculum organization has been largely unsuccessful. Many critics of the school programs generated by "new math" efforts make just such an interpretation of current curricular trends. However, it seems more accurate to say that the first efforts at presenting school mathematics in a way that emphasized the fundamental structural ideas were less effective than the wildly enthusiastic had hoped. Unfortunately, some very promising second-round attempts at using structural ideas in curricula are being largely swept aside by a general tide of disenchantment with student performance.

Bruner's suggestion that young students could learn mathematical ideas at much earlier ages than had traditionally been supposed was based in part on the experience of gifted teachers like David Page, who said:

> In teaching from kindergarten to graduate school, I have been amazed at the

intellectual similarity of human beings at all ages. . . . As far as I am concerned, young children learn almost anything faster than adults do if it can
be given to them in terms they understand. (Bruner, 1960, pp. 39–40)

And Bärbel Inhelder, an associate of Piaget, argued that in the mathematics curriculum

> often the sequence of psychological development follows more closely the
> axiomatic order of a subject matter than it does the historical order of develop-
> ment of concepts within the field. . . . These examples lead us to think that it
> is possible to draw up methods of teaching the basic ideas in science and
> mathematics to children considerably younger than the traditional age.
> (Bruner, 1960, pp. 43–44)

Whereas teachers have become disenchanted with a structural emphasis
in school curricula, they have become even more skeptical about curriculum
sequences that call for early introduction of ideas previously believed
appropriate only in advanced years of school. Begle claimed as recently as
1973 that the experience of SMSG showed "that the location of specific
topics in the curriculum should be based not on the age of the student but
rather on the overall structure of mathematics" (Begle, 1973, p. 210). But
there is a chorus of voices in mathematics education echoing Bell's (1974)
contention that future improvements in school programs will depend on
better consideration of important psychological factors. There is only
limited evidence from research that helps one find a reasoned way through
these issues in the sequence of mathematics instruction.

First, several studies have explored the ability of elementary school
children to learn and use algebraic concepts such as commutativity, identities, inverses, associativity, and distributivity. The studies, taken as a
whole, suggest that a meaningful grasp of these ideas develops fairly slowly
in the elementary grades. Weaver (1972) pointed out that the study of a
property such as distributivity is often characterized by meaningless and
inconsistent "symbol pushing." Crawford (1964) investigated the age-grade
trends in understanding field axioms and found a generally linear increase
in performance from Grade 4 to Grade 12. He also identified an index of
difficulty for the different properties. Sorting out the effects of each
child's school experience from natural maturation factors is, of course, an
unavoidable problem in attempting to trace development of such concepts
over a wide range of ages.

One of the research reports that most encouraged the optimistic curricular experimentation of the 1960s was a study by Suppes and Binford
(1965) suggesting that talented fifth and sixth graders could learn concepts
of elementary logic to a level nearly 90% of that attained by university
students. However, subsequent studies by O'Brien and Shapiro (1968) and
others have suggested some limitations to the hopes raised by the Suppes

study; the general conclusion seems to be that formal logical reasoning ability develops quite slowly in children.

Geometry has been a topic of less research investigating the interaction of curriculum and inherent limitations of student abilities. Several studies have demonstrated that a variety of geometry topics can be taught in an "intellectually honest form" to elementary school students, but most people still consider geometry only as enrichment in the grade school curriculum.

Few investigations have explored the implications of developmental factors for junior and senior high school curricula. The best-known studies are those of Lovell (1971) and Karplus, Karplus, and Wollman (1974) concerning the concepts of ratio and proportion. Both studies found that deep and useful understanding of proportional thinking develops much slower than the structure of ordinary school curricula presumes.

The curriculum development and research activity that explores the influence of student cognitive development on curriculum sequence possibilities has frequently been described as an attempt to determine the implications for instruction of Piagetian psychology. However, despite extensive replication of Piaget's research methods and topics, the transformation of that psychological position into a prescription for curricular and instructional procedure is unclear. According to Callahan and Glennon (1975),

> The arguments for an isomorphism of mental processes between [Piaget's] genetic developmental theory and the systematic learning of conceptual mathematics by children in schools get their primary strength from *a priori* claims rather than empirical evidence. (p. 30)

If implications of human cognitive development for curricular organization are unclear, several of the other "new math" hypotheses about sequence have gone completely unexamined. There has been no substantial research on the effects of the spiral style versus the mastery style of curricular sequence. Also, the efforts to develop curriculum materials that preserve significant amounts of student discovery have been modest. Most so-called discovery research has focused on the sequence of instructional presentation within a specific classroom lesson and thus has not affected the overall sequence or pace of course organization. The instructional implications of such discovery research are examined later.

Whereas Bruner's proposals for curriculum organization evolved from a cognitive-developmental approach in explaining human learning, the behaviorist view of learning, largely provoked by the work of Robert Gagné, was also being applied to questions of curriculum sequence. For those inclined to a behaviorist approach in curriculum and instruction, content is defined as observable performance by students. The structure of content consists of the relations of dependency among different performance abilities. Gagné (1967) set the agenda for research in sequence theory as follows:

1. Any human task may be analyzed into a set of component tasks which are quite distinct from each other.

2. These task components are mediators of the final task performance; that is, their presence insures positive transfer and their absence reduces such transfer to near-zero.

3. The basic principles of training design consist of
   (a) identifying the component tasks of a final performance;
   (b) insuring that each of these component tasks is fully achieved;
   (c) arranging the total learning situation in a sequence which will insure optimal mediational effects from one component to another. (p. 177)

Thus, for Gagné the process of curriculum design consists of constructing terminal and subordinate performance objectives and organizing these objectives into a hierarchy in which each objective is supported by necessary and sufficient subordinates.

The most obvious impact of Gagné's point of view on mathematics curricula in schools is the growing tendency for goals to be expressed in terms of specific student behaviors. The hierarchy hypothesis has had much less impact on instructional practice in most classrooms, but it has received substantial attention in research (cf. King, 1970). The original investigations by Gagné sought to validate the hypothesis that "an individual will not be able to learn a particular topic if he has failed to achieve any of the subordinate topics that support it" (Gagné, 1963, p. 624). Three of his studies seemed to support the contention, but another by Merrill (1965) offered contrary evidence. Attempts to reconcile these contradictory findings produced an argument that has stymied further efforts to determine whether Gagné's hierarchical analysis is the correct explanation of how learning must occur. Simply put, the critics of Merrill's study contend that he failed to confirm the Gagné hypothesis because the hierarchy he investigated was not a valid analysis of the terminal behavior. But this criticism can clearly be leveled at any other study in which the achievement of subordinate behaviors does not appear essential for higher-level behaviors.

Another collection of studies initiated by Roe has also confused the connection between the apparent logical dependencies of performance abilities, as embodied in a hierarchy, and the sequence in which instructional stimuli are presented in order to teach the desired behaviors. Roe, Case, and Roe (1962) found little difference in the final performance of students who studied a logically sequenced programmed unit on probability and other students who studied the same programmed frames in scrambled order. A number of other studies have found similar results, including one (Niedermayer, Brown, & Sulzen 1969) in which two students studied the steps of a program in reverse order and yet achieved perfect scores on the posttest!

The naive interpretation of the research by Roe et al. might be that curriculum sequence seems to make no difference whatsoever. Although the findings certainly do seem to caution against an inflexible application of some presumed logical order of topics, a study by H. R. Miller probably explains the situation more accurately. Miller (1969) investigated different patterns of scrambling instructional sequence, both on a microlevel (frames related to a single-performance objective) and on a macrolevel (frames relating to several major performance objectives). Miller concluded,

> Students apparently were able to overcome any difficulties caused by the disruption of micro-order through some means of mental reorganization of the information. . . . Logical sequence still appears to be the best in terms of overall effectiveness and efficiency. On the other hand, these results do question the necessity for laboring over program construction, using rigorous methods of content sequencing. (pp. 73–74)

The research on scrambling instructional stimuli, although full of implications for the construction of curriculum materials, also raises questions that many mathematics educators would describe as problems of instruction; these questions are discussed in that context later in the chapter. We turn now to questions of curriculum and instructional pace.

3. *What improvements in student learning can be accomplished by accelerating or retarding the pace of mathematics instruction?* Whereas most recent curricular developments have sought to improve the learning of mathematics by emphasizing fundamental structures or by devising more effective learning hierarchies, the traditional approach has simply been to compress the syllabus. Algebra and geometry have been moved down gradually from college-level study to high school and often to junior high school with no fundamental change in the structure of the courses. Attempts to accelerate standard curricula for able junior high school students have yielded a fairly consistent collection of promising results (see Begle, 1976). The Advanced Placement Calculus Program has allowed many students to speed their entry into advanced college-level study (Lefkowitz, 1971). And the Johns Hopkins Study of Mathematically Precocious Youth (SMPY) has demonstrated that grade skipping and early college entrance are feasible for talented students with a drive to move quickly through fast-paced versions of standard secondary school courses (Keating, 1975). The latest SMPY exploration is a special one-day trip through first-year algebra for students who have acquired much of that knowledge through incidental learning in earlier courses.

One of the activities that evolved from the curriculum development of SMSG was the investigation of whether less able students could essentially reach, if the pace of instruction was radically slowed, the same levels of understanding and skill as the students for whom the courses were designed. In one study (Begle, 1973), seventh and ninth graders who ranked between the 25th and 50th percentile in previous mathematics achievement were given two years to cover the same subject matter that more capable students cover in one year. The below-average seventh graders did almost as well on a final test as an above-average control group; the below-average ninth-grade students actually outperformed the above-average group. Such studies may have encouraged the currently popular two-part first-year algebra course, even though the teachability of such a course does not justify the content.

As a general observation, it seems safe to say that previous research on curricular representation, sequence, and questions of pace has greatly increased ouw awareness of factors to be considered and has suggested promising methods for the investigation of those factors. However, we have only begun to untangle the complex interactions of content structure and learner aptitudes.

Instructional Presentation of Mathematical Content

In considering the curriculum problems of content selection, representation, sequence, and pace, we can see how each decision about mathematical content raises an associated question of instructional presentation—the design of the instructional activities through which learners interact with mathematical ideas and make those ideas and skills part of their own repertoire of understanding and ability. In this section we shall examine research knowledge that contributes to instructional design. The diverse studies that seem appropriate for consideration fit into three broad categories—methods, media, and management systems for instruction.

1. *What are the most effective methods of presenting mathematical ideas to students of different ages and abilities?* Until about 1965, the most common type of research in mathematics education was a comparison of the relative effectiveness of two brand-name methods of instruction: the lecture method versus the discovery method; the inductive method versus the deductive method; the theory method versus the applied method; and so on. Although one might be tempted to draw insight from an aggregation of these studies, the typical investigation has such crucial flaws that one would be equally justified in dismissing all such studies.

One large group of studies comparing instructional methods consists of doctoral dissertation research in which the principal investigator taught one class by an experimental method and another by the "traditional," or "conventional," method. The repeated flaws in most of these studies read like a litany of pitfalls in experimental research: lack of random assignment to treatments; attempts to correct for initial differences by analysis of covariance; small sample size; short duration of time for treatments; imprecise defintion of experimental treatments; and bias of the experimenter, usually in favor of the experimental treatment.

Although many of these weaknesses of methods research are clearly endemic to the limited resources of doctoral students, the most critical in appraising results or in planning useful investigations of the effectiveness of methods is the problem of accurately defining the instructional procedures assumed to constitute the treatments. For example, prompted by Bruner's musings on the importance of discovery experience in learning, many studies have purported to compare discovery teaching with conventional teaching. Yet for some, the essential difference between discovery and expository instruction is the amount of guidance by the teacher; for others, it is a difference between inductive and deductive presentation of mathematical principles (rule/example vs. example/rule); and for still others, discovery implies an active rather than a passive involvement in the learning situation. With such a diversity of interpretations, it is not surprising that the discovery research does not yield consistent findings. But even more damaging to the cause of discovery research is the failure of most investigators to measure the extent to which their prescribed instructional treatments were accurately carried out by the experimental teachers. Studies on methods turned, for a time, to written self-instructional material in an effort to avoid this crucial problem, but this experimental approach differs so markedly from normal classroom settings that acceptance of the research results has been limited.

One outstanding example of an investigation comparing the effects of instructional methods is Worthen's (1967) study of discovery and expository sequencing in elementary mathematics. Admitting that discovery has many meanings in mathematics teaching, Worthen proposed only to compare "two methods which may be somewhat typical of the characteristics that normally serve to differentiate discovery techniques from expository techniques" (p. 46). He made the distinction clear by prescribing that the discovery method is one in which the verbalization of each concept or generalization is delayed until the end of the instructional sequence by which the concept or generalization is to be taught. The expository method is one in which the verbalization of each concept or generalization is the initial step in the instructional sequence. Eight fifth- and sixth-grade teachers were given extensive training in the use of each instructional procedure. The lessons taught by these teachers were observed live, recorded on audiotape, and rated by their students to get three measures of the extent to which the prescribed instructional methods were used. Both discovery and expository classes were given common mathematical experiences prior to the experiment, and extensive efforts were made to ensure that the two treatment groups were of comparable ability and attitude prior to the experiment. The effectiveness of the two methods was measured by a battery of ten instruments covering acquisition, retention, and transfer of mathematical ideas and heuristics.

Worthen's data showed that teachers of the experimental classes were able to model the two distinctly different teaching procedures successfully. The test results give guarded encouragement to several intuitively generated hypotheses about discovery and expository instruction: The students of expository-method classes outperformed their discovery-method counterparts on the test of immediate recall; the discovery-class students performed better on tests of retention and transfer. But neither result was significant when conservative statistical analysis was used.

Despite the admirable technical quality and intriguing results of Worthen's study, the past 10 years have seen very little progress in that type of general research on methods. In 1973 Olander and Robertson reported an investigation that confirmed the basic pattern of Worthen's results. However, by analyzing the interaction of instructional style and student ability, they suggested that the matter is probably much more complex than any broad characterization of methods will reveal. Olander and Robertson found, for instance, that students who scored low on an arithmetic computation pretest fared better under the expository teaching method, whereas students scoring high on the pretest fared better under the discovery method. Their strongest conclusion from the study was that "instruction should be individualized. What is appropriate for one pupil may be inappropriate for another" (Olander & Robertson, 1973, p. 44).

The general disillusion with research investigating broad or vaguely characterized methods has recently led investigators to focus on more specific aspects of instructional presentation. The most talked-about approaches have been aptitude-treatment interaction (ATI) studies, generated by ideas of Cronbach (Cronbach & Snow, 1977), and advance-organizer or postorganizer studies that explore the hypotheses of Ausubel (1963).

Aptitude-treatment interaction research has sought to identify ways in which the effectiveness of mathematical instruction can be optimized by matching the style of instructional presentation to the personality and cognitive styles of individual students. For instance, in 1968 Carry hypothesized that ability in spatial visualization would predict success in a graphic treatment of quadratic inequalities, whereas general reasoning ability would predict success in an analytical treatment of the same mathematical material. Studies by Carry (1968) and Webb (1975) failed to confirm this hypothesis, but in 1975 Eastman and Carry found that those cognitive factors were predictive of effective learning in inductive-graphical and deductive-analytic treatments, respectively.

Numerous other ATI studies have failed to produce a clear or simple picture of the ways that instructional treatments can be effectively matched to student aptitudes. Furthermore, the fact that most such studies have used programmed instruction and very short instructional periods has earned them perhaps undeserved scorn from a mathematics education community seeking practical help in teaching problems. A more fundamental challenge to the direction of the ATI investigation is the concern that students who are relatively weak in some aptitude area should perhaps receive instructional treatments that strengthen their aptitudes rather than avoid their use.

The investigation of advance organizers or postorganizers starts from the reasoning that meaningful verbal learning can occur only when more inclusive relevant concepts exist and are readily available in the cognitive structure of the learner. This reasoning suggests that effective instruction should include the presentation of an advance-organizing concept prior to a verbal learning task. A kind of converse to this proposition suggests that discovery learning could be enhanced if overt postorganizers were presented near the end of instruction. A number of tests of the advance-organizer hypothesis in mathematics instruction have failed to yield firm support for the efficacy of providing such preinstructional aids for learners. And a study of postorganizers by Romberg and Wilson (1973) suggests that formal postinstructional organization might have a negative effect on student learning.

Although Ausubel cannot be described as a behaviorist in his view of human learning, there is an obvious connection between research on the advance organizer and that of behaviorists investigating the value of telling students, in advance of instruction, the performance objectives for their subsequent activity. However, studies of telling students the objectives have not produced a clear guide to instructional design. It appears that when students know enough to understand what the objective is really saying, the statement of that objective helps focus their subsequent study.

Reflecting on the inconclusive results of research on advance organizers, though not directly on that concerned with telling behavioral obectives, Lesh (1976) has made a penetrating critical analysis of the advance-organizer hypotheses. Returning essentially to questions of curriculum sequence discussed earlier in this chapter, Lesh points out that the use of advance organizers attempts to impose one structure on the mathematical ideas and skills about to be presented. He argues, however, that

> the point is that an important distinction frequently exists between the logical development of an idea and the way students come to understand it. At least three types of structures occur in mathematics education: (a) mathematical structures ... (b) instructional structures ... and (c) cognitive structures. ... Furthermore, unless special care is taken to ensure that these three types of structures are compatible, they frequently can be in conflict. In particular, the

distinction between cognitive structures and mathematical structures can be especially crucial in mathematics education. (p. 71)

Lesh goes on to reject the hierarchical point of view about learning, suggesting that concepts are never fully formed, but are only in a process of continuing evolution and abstraction.

> Through intuitive use, an entire system of ideas can be gradually coordinated until individual ideas within the system cease to be considered one at a time in isolation and begin to take on new significance by being treated as part of a whole system of ideas. So, neither the "parts" nor the "whole" must be mastered first (in an absolute sense); rather, both can be organized simultaneously into a system through use at a more intuitive level. (Lesh, 1976, p. 73)

In summary, research on the effectiveness of instructional methods has recently turned away from a naive approach that led doctoral students in search of that one style of presentation that would be best for all students and all subject matter. But to date investigators have made little headway in sorting out the maze of more specific variables proposed to have important roles in effecting learning.

2. *What are the most effective uses of different media for mathematics instruction?* Throughout the 20th century, each major breakthrough in the technological capability of communication media has promised immense payoff for education. Yet today the predominant media in mathematics classes remain chalkboard and printed textbooks. In 1974, Jamison, Suppes, and Wells reviewed research knowledge about instructional radio (IR), instructional television (ITV), programmed instruction (PI), and computer-assisted instruction (CAI) in all school disciplines, with many of the major studies focusing on mathematics. Their general conclusion was that students appear to learn effectively from all these media. Few studies indicated a significant difference in the use of one medium over another. However, they cautioned that an adequately deep assessment of the strengths and weaknesses of the technological alternatives to traditional instruction will require many years of study.

Instructional radio has been little studied in major developed countries, although experience in several developing countries indicates that it can be as effective as traditional instruction in mathematics. Instructional television has received considerably more attention in both development and research. Here, also, the evidence suggests that ITV is as effective as traditional instruction in mathematics. There is a tendency for ITV to be less popular with older students than with elementary school students. However, as Jamison et al. point out, in most research comparing the effectiveness of ITV with traditional instruction, the television presentation is designed to emulate that of a "live" instructor, not to exploit the unique capabilities of the medium. Furthermore, the tendency has been to look at

ITV as a potential substitute for traditional instruction rather than as an adjunct to enhance the quality or productivity of traditional methods. Careful appraisal of Britain's Open University program or the "Infinity Factory" series of public television in the United States should give a better measure of the potential of ITV.

After a burst of enthusiasm for programmed instruction during the 1950s and early 1960s, the use of this instructional medium in mathematics has faded to a minor role. A major factor in the decline of interest in PI was doubtless the monotonous regularity of research results showing PI no more effective than traditional instruction, with indications that both interest and achievement in PI declined as treatment time lengthened. Zoll's (1969) review of 35 PI studies involving mathematics undoubtedly encouraged critics with its overall finding of no significant difference between the highly touted alternative and traditional instruction. However, Zoll pointed out that research had barely scratched the surface in investigating effects of PI on the maturation of individual students, on the development of higher-level thinking capabilities, and in offering learning rates that matched the capacities of individual students. Since Zoll's review, PI has become a part of many individualized instruction programs; but, as the later discussion of individualization reveals, several of these fundamental questions remain unanswered. Research in programmed instruction has generally focused on improving program quality and interest to students and on identifying situations where PI is particularly effective. The continually unsuccessful attempts to prove PI the single best method of instruction have been, sensibly, abandoned.

Although a variety of influential uses of computers have been found in education, the predominant and most natural instructional application has been in mathematics. The first and still most common use of computers in mathematics classes is as an aid in student problem-solving activities. Several early studies in the Minnesota Computer-Assisted Mathematics Project (CAMP) tried to identify material in the existing school mathematics program that might be more effectively studied through the design of computer programs. Hatfield and Kieren (1972) compared the impact of an instructional approach in which students programmed problem-solution procedures for many concepts in their course with conventional instruction that involved no programming. Although the computer seemed to offer little advantage in achievement, there were indications that programming was helpful in learning complex tasks that require the organization of data or infinite processes. Since those early CAMP studies, the use of computers as a problem-solving adjunct to instruction has spread rapidly. Although many doctoral theses have compared traditional and computer-augmented calculus instruction, this does not seem an important area for future research. Computer access will increasingly be a fact of life, and students will learn how to use the power as one problem-solving tool.

The use of computers as a medium of mathematics instruction (CAI) has emerged more slowly, since work is restricted to research facilities that have the resources to support the required development of hardware and "courseware." The most widely tested CAI effort has been Stanford University's drill-and-practice system. Through its use in augmenting regular arithmetic instruction, the Stanford system has recorded several startling successes and some less impressive results (Jamison et al., 1974). The PLATO and TICCIT approaches to CAI have produced some fascinating display tools for enhancing the capability of computers to generate instruction that goes beyond drill and practice. But for both systems, the efforts to date have concentrated on exploring the potential of the medium without much careful evaluative research. If CAI is to make a greater impact on normal instructional practice, it will be necessary to produce a clearer picture of the cost-benefit prospects.

The cost-benefit challenge facing CAI is magnified by the emergence of low-cost microcomputers and the variety of hand-held calculating devices now becoming common equipment in mathematics classes. Though the potential impact of calculators on school mathematics has been extensively debated in public and professional discussions of educational policy, there has been little research to indicate the actual results that will or can derive from their appropriate use. The most common research has been a simple comparison of classes allowed to use calculators with classes not allowed to use calculators. The criterion variables most often used are growth in arithmetic skills, problem-solving ability, or attitudes. The results of these generally small-scale studies have been mixed. Furthermore, the capabilities of available calculators are changing so rapidly that it seems fair to say that any aspect of their use for instruction is open to further investigation.

The range of instructional media useful in mathematics instruction is not limited to those covered by the Jamison et al. review. Many schools are experimenting with videotape, audiotape, motion-picture cassette, and slide-tape equipment and instructional packages. It seems safe to say, however, that current research says little about the cost effectiveness of any such augmentation of instruction. The common pattern in previous research has been to compare a media-enriched instructional presentation or an alternative medium presentation with that vaguely defined traditional instruction. And, particularly in mathematics education research, that quest is usually doomed from the outset.

Considering the continuing dominance of textbooks as the medium of instruction, there has been surprisingly little study of learning from the mathematical text. Hater and Kane (1975) have developed a variation of the classical Cloze procedure that reliably predicts the relative difficulty of passages from mathematics texts. Although this work gives the developers of mathematics curricula a tool for measuring the readability of their material, it still leaves open the question of what factors in the written text are the underlying causes of reading difficulty and how the problems might be avoided.

The heavy allocation of resources for media research to the exploration of potential in television and computers rather than an improvement of the still predominant written text clearly reflects hopes for some major instructional breakthrough aided by those electronic media. But at the present time there is only modest evidence that such promise will be soon fulfilled.

3. *What are the relative merits of different patterns of organizing instruction?* One of the most widely held beliefs in education is that teaching is an art, not a science. Adherence to this view leads curriculum developers to concentrate on the selection and sequence of mathematics topics, leaving to individual teachers the task of devising an effective presentation of the ideas to students. Recently, however, educators have often followed the model of business, industry, and government in applying a systems approach to curricular and instructional design. The result has been the production of several instructional systems that include content outline, prescriptions of presentation style, and evaluation procedures.

Those applying the systems approach to the design of mathematics instruction have most often been inspired by a desire to offer individualized programs—that is, a presentation of content that matches instructional style and pace to the personal needs and learning traits of individual students. This commitment to individualization has led to the development of a wide range of school mathematics programs at all grade levels from elementary school through college. But most programs of individualized instruction share the following broad characteristics:

- Content goals expressed as student performance objectives and organized into scope-and-sequence strands or hierarchies
- Instructional material packages to guide independent student learning of individual objectives or groups of related objectives
- Criterion-referenced tests to assess student mastery of objectives and to guide the prescription of appropriate learning activities
- Substantial freedom for students to choose their own pace, if not content sequence, of learning
- Teacher role defined primarily by managerial tasks—record keeping, testing, prescribing student learning activities, and tutoring individual students or small groups with similar problems

The most striking feature of programs in individualized instruction is the change in roles of students and teachers from traditional instructional patterns. Students are expected to assume a major responsibility for their learning; teachers do very little expository instruction and substantially more managerial and tutorial work. Each promise of new benefits for students is accompanied by certain risks and implicit or explicit threats to the established methods and skills of many teachers. Thus, the major innovative features of individualized instruction have been subjected to intense critical scrutiny in the journals and the meetings of mathematics teachers; there have also been at least 100 recent research investigations comparing the effects of individualized instruction and more conventional approaches to instruction.

R. L. Miller (1976) reviewed the research on individualized instruction (I. I.) prior to 1976 and concluded that the programs tested appeared to yield slightly higher achievement and slightly better attitudes than conventional programs. Measures of retention, transfer, student personality variables, sex differences, and student study skills, although sketchy, showed no advantage attributable to I. I. programs. And surprisingly, the average student rate of progress through an I. I. program does not appear to be markedly faster than in conventional class-paced instruction. Schoen (1976a, 1976b) reviewed many of the same studies, and by attributing greater weight to better-designed and larger-scale research, he reached the conclusion that compared to conventional programs, current individualized programs are more expensive, are not likely to increase student achievement or attitudes, and make more work for teachers.

Numerous critical analyses of the existing individualized programs have charged that objectives overemphasize low-level mathematical skills and that the modularization of objectives, instruction, and assessment leads students to a misleading and ultimately unproductive view of mathematical ideas and methods. Erlwanger's (1973) clinical interview studies of IPI students raise serious concerns about the meaning of mastery in current self-paced progress systems; his studies cite devastating instances of gross misunderstanding among students apparently successful in the IPI system.

Any curriculum developers and teachers contemplating a move to individualization can probably find research evidence to support a decision for or against such innovation. The research can be criticized for comparing an innovative method with the vague "conventional" instruction and often failing to assess the impact of alternative modes across a wide range of desirable student outcomes and instructional situations. Failure to demonstrate the superiority of the innovative method can be explained by saying that we've not yet determined the best way to individualize instruction. Inspection of the major I. I. programs in use today suggests that they are only very crude approximations of the lofty goals set by their proponents.

In colleges and universities the thrust toward individualized programs has been led by proponents of the Keller plan, or Personalized System of Instruction (PSI). Sharing many of the features of I. I. programs in elementary and secondary schools, PSI emphasizes self-pacing, mastery learning, and independent study by the student. However, the PSI approach generally involves the development of materials only in preparing study guides and unit tests for use with a conventional college-level textbook. Dozens of college-level studies during the past five years have compared the effectiveness of PSI courses with conventional methods. In general, these studies show the PSI method to be superior to conventional instruction when measured by conventional achievement and attitude criteria. However, most studies are small-scale efforts involving an investigator committed to the PSI method, and students frequently appear in PSI sections by personal choice, not random assignment. The verdict is still out on where PSI is most effective as an alternative to the conventional teacher-directed, lecture-discussion instruction.

Although PSI stands for Personalized System of Instruction, many of its critics have claimed that the entire range of individualized programs actually depersonalize and dehumanize instruction by shunting students to lonely self-study settings. Arguing that an important aspect of mathematics learning is the ability to communicate one's ideas, they urge instructional methods that increase student interaction centered on mathematical problem solving. Several high school mathematics texts have been written especially for use in a small-group, problem-solving instructional style, but the most intense interest and systematic research in small-group organization for mathematics instruction has been concentrated at the college level. Beginning with Davidson's (1971) doctoral thesis, which developed guidelines for small-group discovery curricula and instructional procedures, a series of investigations has demonstrated the efficacy of small-group methods and explored refinements of the Davidson procedures. In general these studies have shown small-group discovery to be an extremely popular method of instruction that produces satisfactory learning in courses ranging from elementary calculus through abstract algebra.

Most individualized systems of instruction, including PSI, are derived from basically behavioristic views of learning. The devotees of small-group instruction have been influenced by the group dynamics work of social psychologists. And the cognitive-developmental theories of Piaget have been largely responsible for a growth of interest in the mathematics-laboratory type of organization of mathematics instruction in elementary schools, and to some extent in secondary schools and higher education.

Whereas mathematics laboratories are many things to many people, the essence of the concept has been expressed well by Fitzgerald (1972):

> Primarily, a mathematics laboratory is a state of mind. It is characterized by a questioning atmosphere and a continuous involvement with problem solving situations. Emphasis is placed upon discovery resulting from student experimentation. A teacher acts as a catalyst in the activity between students and knowledge.
> Secondarily, a math lab is a physical plant equipped with material objects. . . . Since a student learns by doing, the lab is designed to give him the objects with which he can do and learn. (pp. 12–13)

Because of the extremely diverse ways that laboratory methods can be used to replace or augment conventional modes of instruction, it is difficult to summarize quickly the state of research knowledge. However, in 1974 R. L. Miller examined recent studies on mathematics laboratories in which results of student attitude or achievement were compared to those of students in control classes. In only 1 of 23 studies was conventional instruction significantly more effective in producing student achievement; in 11, the laboratory method was superior. In 5 of 16 studies the laboratory method produced better student attitudes; in none was the conventional method superior. Although these studies cover a wide range of content, grade, and ability levels, the reasonable interpretation is that many investigators have found effective situations and procedures for employing the methods used in mathematics laboratories. The studies generally do very little to measure the influence of laboratory methods on variables other than composite achievement and general attitudes. Thus, although encouraging the expansion of laboratory methods at different levels, they leave an incomplete picture of the likely effects from laboratory experiences.

In summary, the various recent explorations of alternative organizational approaches for mathematics instruction have not demonstrated a clearly superior substitute for the conventional methods of teacher-directed chalk and talk. However, the proposed alternatives have focused attention on several fundamental questions, such as the nature and nurture of individual differences in the style and rate of mathematics learning, the role of student-teacher and student-student interaction in learning, the effects of different combinations of manipulative-play-abstract experiences in learning, and the relative roles of the teacher, curriculum, and individual student in structuring ideas that become mathematical knowledge and skills. Research will undoubtedly continue trying to address the question of which method of teaching is best in mathematics. But one can only hope that the consistently inconclusive results of such investigations and the growing awarenesss of the complexity in teaching and learning situations will lead to more focused research that aims at finding the virtues in each alternative or combination of alternatives.

The State of the Art in Curricular and Instructional Research

At the outset of this chapter we noted that among available definitions of *curriculum* and *instruction* one could find nearly every aspect of education; therefore, research in mathematics curriculum and instruction addresses or uses information about nearly every question considered in the more specific research domains of this volume. But the central concerns of curriculum designers are the selection, sequence, and presentation of mathematical ideas—finding the concepts and skills most interesting and useful to students with different aptitudes and goals and identifying the instructional strategies that most effectively convey that knowledge and ability.

The extensive review shows that central curricular variables have been the subject of a considerable amount of research. However, it is also clear that fundamental open questions exist in each aspect of curriculum and instruction. The long-standing pattern of searching for the single best method of instruction has been almost uniformly unproductive in identifying appropriate instructional procedures, sequencing strategies, or forms of presentation. Research has recently turned to a more microscopic analysis of curriculum processes that searches for a picture of the effects to be expected from particular approaches in particular situations. In the next section of this chapter we shall single out what appear to be the most important questions for such investigations and what characteristics of research strategy are likely to yield useful information.

IMPORTANT QUESTIONS AND STRATEGIES FOR FUTURE RESEARCH

The preceding review of research on mathematics curricula and instruction was organized to identify the major challenges in designing instructional activities and materials and to describe the research-based knowledge that could contribute to improved school mathematics programs. Even the most generous appraisal of the research cited leaves many perennial questions about curricula unanswered and other contemporary issues completely unexamined by objective research. In this section we shall ask how students of mathematics curriculum and instruction might refocus their attention and revise their research strategies so that future instructional programs can profit from the findings of careful investigation.

There is no shortage of recent attempts to suggest an agenda and strategies for mathematics education research (e.g., Begle, 1968, 1973;

Bruner, 1966; Davis, 1971–72; Esty, 1975; Esty & Payne, 1977; Fehr, 1966; Golladay et al., 1975; Heimer, 1969; Kersh, 1967; Merrill & Wood, 1974; NACOME, 1975; Romberg & DeVault, 1967). The proposals for research on curriculum and instruction from these prestigious individuals and conferences fall into two quite different categories. The first, and most ambitious, includes those proposals that outline theoretical models relating major curricular and instructional variables. They call for research that will generate broadly applicable principles for optimal structure, sequence, pace, and presentation of mathematical ideas; they seek a theory of instruction. Research proposals of the second kind deal with questions of more specific and immediate educational importance. For instance:

- What minimal mathematical competencies are required for effective citizenship or postschool employment in business, industry, or government?
- How can calculators best aid mathematics teaching? How should calculator availability influence the sequence and emphasis of traditional curricula?
- How can conventional curricula be revised and their materials rewritten to give students a more realistic and impressive view of the applications of mathematics?

Whereas the folklore and periodic fashions of mathematics education have long embodied general maxims for curriculum and instruction, the extensive research efforts of the past 20 years have failed to provide scientific support for any such ingredients of a "theory of instruction." Instead, they have revealed the subtle complexity of matching specific learner aptitudes, instructional style, and structured mathematical ideas. Furthermore, the optimal pattern among these variables should probably reflect current educational and societal conditions that influence the interests and efforts of students and teachers.

One common reaction to the complexity of the problems in curricular and instructional research is to claim that promise lies either in large-scale, longitudinal studies by interdisciplinary research teams (Romberg & DeVault, 1967) or in a large number of correlated small studies (Begle, 1968). The research suggestions that follow represent an opinion that is neither optimistic about the potential of large-scale studies searching for general principles of instructional design nor pessimistic about the potential contribution to curriculum of suitable small-scale efforts by doctoral students.

Selection of Content

Decisions on the proper mathematical substance of school curricula will inevitably reflect the value judgments of professionals and the public constituency of education. But there are several ways that research could improve the product and the process of this crucial decision-making activity.

One of the most striking findings of the National Advisory Committee on Mathematical Education (NACOME, 1975) was that those who would criticize or change school curricula must work from a very sketchy and unreliable knowledge of the program now in operation and of how that program can be changed effectively. For instance, NACOME conjectured that despite formal changes in the school syllabi and classroom texts of the "new math" era, the actual mathematics experience of elementary school students during the 1960s reflected few of the reformers' intentions. As an essential background for informed efforts at future change, NACOME called for extensive descriptive studies of the curricula and instructional activities of representative classes in action: How much class time is devoted to different mathematics topics? What is the relative emphasis on different levels of cognitive activity—factual recall, comprehension, or problem solving and critical thinking? What are the emphases in classroom and standardized tests? How do school systems and individual teachers make the curricular and instructional decisions that lead to the operational classroom programs? Is it true, as many suggest, that the textbook dictates the curriculum? What is the influence of external examinations? Who is involved in the curriculum-planning process, and what are the value orientations that they bring to the task of preparing course outlines and selecting textbooks and tests?

The effectiveness of future efforts to improve school mathematics programs depends on a comprehensive picture of where we are and how public and professional influences act to shape school curricula.

The standard methodological approach to these influences is some sort of survey by questionnaire. But despite the comfortable simplicity of such procedures of data collection, there is a good reason to question the validity of teacher-reported profiles of classroom activity. Brown (1974) and Conant (1973) went directly to the classroom to observe the way teaching time is used; their work suggests a fruitful direction for sharper methodology in studies of the survey variety. The resources required to support such observational procedures would commonly suggest a major national project if a reasonably accurate overview of mathematics instruction is to be obtained. But at the present time more limited or localized investigations can contribute valuable insight. Furthermore, case studies of curricular innovation in particular situations could provide useful raw material from which a broad understanding of the process could be pieced together.

Studies of "the way teaching is" are often criticized because they provide only temporal knowledge and not the general principles and theories that constitute knowledge in such scientific domains as physics or chemistry. But education functions in a situation where fundamental factors are always changing in a way that is seldom predictable. Thus, regular replications of the descriptive-analytic studies outlined above are probably essential and certainly useful.

The content of school mathematics reflects at any one time a blend of topics judged as best meeting student interests and needs, both immediate and long range. Very often the judgment is based on a mixture of tradition and very sketchy or shortsighted estimates of the world in which students will spend their productive lives. Without denigrating the intrinsic value of mathematical study, it seems reasonable to suspect the following:

Curricular decision making could be improved by regular survey and thoughtful projection *of the mathematics required by society, skilled trades, business, government, science, and the study of other school subjects.*

The preceding recommendations call for regular survey-analytic research providing general background information for decisions about content selection. Several important specific issues face curriculum developers as they select the mathematics content for current programs:

- How should curricula be revised to reflect emerging computer and calculator technology?
- What is the appropriate blend of theory and application in different courses?
- What mathematical study is appropriate for gifted students?
- What approach to geometry is appropriate in high school?

The conventional research mentality has usually suggested investigating each of these questions with a "find the *best* way" approach: Do students learn better with or without access to calculators? Is it better to start with problems or theory? Is acceleration or enrichment best for gifted students? Is coordinate or synthetic geometry more effective? Of course, to compare fairly two different treatments, it is essential to measure achievement on the intersection of treatment objectives and to compare the means of treatment groups. But is this the only approach to be recommended?

It seems likely that future research will be much more helpful in curricular decision making if it adopts different goals and different procedures. It should aim to explore and analyze the full range of possible responses to a curricular problem and to determine the specific effects of each. Then, those charged with the selection of curriculum content can design programs matched to their particular goals and teaching conditions.

For instance, research on computer-assisted calculus instruction has tended to show no significant difference between experimental and control groups. Yet it is certainly reasonable to expect that there are specific aspects of skill, understanding, and attitude on which the treatment groups differ. Furthermore, future capabilities of computer technology continually suggest new ways that calculus instruction might be affected. A research report that displays and analyzes the options and describes in detail the outcomes that might be expected from alternative approaches should be very useful to anyone reassessing a calculus program.

Recent research on calculators has tried to show that access to calculators improves student attitudes and general mathematics achievement. Debate about applications suggests that one must choose between a pure or an applied course on the basis of a composite achievement test. But wouldn't a more profitable investigation explore all the possible ways to use calculators or applications in teaching, noting in some detail the ways that they do or do not effectively enhance the learning of concepts, skills, and problem solving for different types of students? Couldn't similar studies provide insight into decisions about the geometry curriculum or programs for talented students?

Several recent reports have outlined an agenda of research questions involving computers (NACOME, 1975), calculators (Esty & Payne, 1977), applications (NACOME, 1975), geometry (Gearhart, 1975), and curricula for gifted students (Davis, 1976). Research will provide useful information on these and other issues of current interest if it abandons the simplistic search for a single best approach and aims for the measurement of differential effects among the options.

Structure of Content

As we noted in the review of research on modes of content representation, it is not very likely that further investigations will yield any simple or broadly applicable guidelines such as "progression from concrete to abstract is always best" or "multiple models are best for able students and single models for the less able." Similarly, in the secondary school different approaches to geometry or functions or trigonometry are likely to have different virtues and limitations, with none clearly superior for all desired outcomes. A line of research that seems potentially productive is an analysis of the different possible ways of representing each mathematical concept of interest and the preparation of curriculum materials that embody each. Teachers can then draw on the different possible approaches as their students demonstrate a need for different explanations or an ability to grasp different manifestations of a concept.

There has been a beginning of this kind of work at several levels. Most analysis research on specific manipulative materials at the elementary school level has led to precisely the suggestion of looking at the interaction of material, student, teacher, and situational attribute (Kieren, 1971).

J. W. Wilson (1976) devised a comprehensive, multidimensional taxonomy of conceptual and representational modes in elementary mathematics. The next step in this research agenda is working on teaching approaches that embody each combination of attributes of representation modes. In Usiskin's (1976) course on first-year algebra through applications there is a conscious attempt to present different modes of representing operations on numbers and to use those representations throughout the balance of the algebra course. The natural research question suggested by such analysis is whether one representation or another leads more effectively to skill in computation or problem solving. But again, it is probably true that each representation has particular advantages and particular disadvantages. For instance, the repeated-addition model of multiplication is probably easiest for elementary students to learn quickly, but that model is much less effective than an area model when work with fractions begins.

If one were forced to formulate broad hypotheses about the use of different modes for representing mathematical ideas, the most likely candidates would be (a) that teachers who know, and can use in the classroom, several different representational schemes for any given mathematical concept will be more effective than teachers with limited flexibility; and (b) that students who have learned several different models for any given mathematical idea will be more effective problem solvers and will be able to transfer their conceptual knowledge to new situations more easily than their counterparts. To support research on these hypotheses, we also need creative development activity that explores the full potential of different curricular approaches.

In many ways the most puzzling problem facing curriculum research is finding principles that might guide the sequence and pace of presenting mathematical ideas. The logical structure of mathematics would seem to permit a natural analysis of the subject into hierarchies of conceptual dependence. Knowledge about the development of cognitive abilities would seem to yield guidelines for the pace of instruction through that hierarchy. In practice, however, the situation is not at all simple. Mathematicians have shown that there are many possible ways to weave the familiar facts of mathematics into logically sequenced hierarchies; there is no such thing as *the* structure of the discipline. Furthermore, the processes by which students internalize mathematical ideas do not, except perhaps for the most primitive concepts, follow any immutable chain of psychological dependence. The research on scrambled instructional sequences is striking evidence that students skillfully absorb, and restructure in their own ways, ideas that have been laid out for them in the supposed logical order.

Given this perplexing situation, what research holds promise of ultimate help in devising effective instructional sequences for school mathematics? The easiest projection is that for U.S. schools the combination of the adoption of the metric system and the calculator will require complete rethinking of the sequence for presenting topics in arithmetic. Decimals might well come early—before common fractions—and negative integers will naturally occur early. Such possibilities should command development and research on new curricular sequences.

In search of more general principles of sequence, the incredible diversity of ways that mathematical topics can be structured—in the mind of the instructor and the mind of the learner—suggests that a single line of march through a fixed sequence of topics is unlikely to yield learning that produces maximum meaning, retention, and transfer for all students. Instead, the following principle seems likely:

A spiral style of sequence in which students return several times to each topic, meeting it each time at a higher level of abstraction and complexity and from a different point of view, will be more effective than a mastery sequence in which students are expected to demonstrate thorough comprehension and skill in a single topic before they move on to another.

Despite extensive discussion of the spiral-sequence hypothesis by Bruner (1960) and the Cambridge Conference on School Mathematics (1963), it really has not been given a careful evaluation through research.

Adequate investigation of the spiral-mastery options for curriculum sequence will not be a simple experiment comparing two clearly defined and obviously different treatments. Anyone trying to embody the spiral philosophy in a school program has several choices to explore: How tight should the spirals be? What level of competence should be sought in each pass through a topic? What different approaches to a single topic should be used at each stage of the spiral? How can the treatments of different topics along the spiral be related effectively to each other? As in any curriculum or instruction research, any results that show Method A superior to Method B face the ultimate uncertainty that perhaps the treatments embodying the two approaches were simply not of equal quality. Of course, this again argues for curriculum research that assesses the broad range of effects of any program and for a collection of approaches to each issue—not one attempt at a definitive study.

Sharing certain similarities with the spiral-sequence proposals are the integrated (or unified) mathematics curricula that have gained substantial acceptance in Europe but have made almost no inroad in the standard American sequence of topically distinct courses. The goal of unified syllabi is to capitalize on mathematical and conceptual similarities in the structures of topics that have traditionally been treated independently, with the expectation that such interrelated knowledge will be retained, generalized, and applied more readily than less interconnected abilities. The main research question that has been directed at these unified courses is whether they produce acceptable performance on conventional tests. What seems more useful is an in-depth analysis of the ways that students of unified curricula perceive mathematics, approach problem-solving tasks, or learn new mathematical ideas. What is the range of ways that 16-year-old School Mathematics Project (SMP) students differ from comparable students who have studied the standard U.S. sequence of algebra-geometry-algebra?

The foregoing research proposals might be interpreted to suggest a curriculum without structure—a mathematical smorgasbord placed before naive students. No such lack of structure is implicit in a spiral or unified sequence, and the intuition of most teachers suggests a need for some carefully considered sequence of presenting topics in arithmetic, algebra, or geometry. But one of the aspects of a truly individualized program is an element of student choice in the scope and sequence of his or her learning. In practice, very few current individualized mathematics programs offer much freedom of choice except in the pace of learning. It is precisely the freedom of pace that has raised serious questions about the underlying philosophy of individualized programs. Most research has shown very little advantage from a pace matched to students' natural learning rates. In fact, many critics have conjectured that a student's optimal rate of learning is a function of the instructional mode and that self-paced, independent study is certainly not best for all students.

Many mathematics educators hold out hope that research in human cognitive development will reveal guiding principles for matching the sequence and pace of mathematics curricula to evolving student abilities and aptitudes. In view of the impressive acceleration of instruction that has been a regular process in school mathematics and the potential for developing new and better ways to approach apparently difficult topics, such hopes seem unfounded.

Instructional Presentation

Many of the variables that are central to macroscale research in curriculum content structure have analogous impact on microscale decisions about instructional presentation. It is hard to be optimistic about prospects that results from future research will reveal the superiority of simple, well-defined instructional procedures. However, the obvious weaknesses in the design and procedures of past research on instruction do offer some encouragement for new efforts.

As Bruner (1966) has observed, a theory of instruction should prescribe procedures for arranging environments to optimize learning according to various criteria. A theory of learning describes conditions under which learning takes place. Thus it is natural to look toward learning theory for ingredients in a theory of instruction and for suggestions on how to arrange environments. At the present time there is very little hard psychological knowledge about the conditions that favor the learning of complicated, abstract concepts and skills such as those of mathematics. Even where some extrapolation of learning to mathematical topics is plausible, as in elementary concept formation, there is an additional difficulty when the complexity of classroom settings is faced. Nevertheless, several propositions from psychology have suggested parallel hypotheses about instruction that seem worthy of continued research in mathematics education.

First, for a great many psychologists in the cognitive-developmental tradition, one essential feature of effective learning environments is active, rather than passive, involvement of the learner as he or she restructures and internalizes knowledge. Much of the past research on methods seems to have centered on testing, in various forms, the application of this proposition to instruction: discovery versus exposition, inductive versus deductive, or small group versus lecture. The few well-done studies in this area (Orlander & Robertson, 1973; Worthen, 1967) suggest areas in which future investigation might pay off. Although it is not essential that each study compare exactly the same active and passive methods, it is crucial that whatever methods are used be clearly defined and that part of the research procedure involve checking that the treatments are administered as defined. Furthermore, the results to date suggest that the effects of active and passive student experiences will not fit some simple, predictive rule. The active learning mode might be slower and less effective for highly anxious students or less effective for short-term achievement. Conversely, active learning methods might be best for high-ability students and long-term retention or transfer of knowledge. Thus, any measurement of the effects of methods must consider the range, not just the means, of a variety of input and output variables. Given these goals, a series of variegated, but coordinated and well-executed, small-scale studies might be as productive as any effort expended to mount a single investigation with sufficient statistical power to "settle the question."

Aptitude-treatment interaction (ATI) instructional research also draws its inspiration and central variables from psychological propositions about individual differences. The effects of efforts to match instruction to learner aptitude have not been impressive so far. And the likelihood of uncovering any principles suitably general to be useful in planning instruction seems low. Similarly, the basic advance-organizer and postorganizer hypotheses derived from Ausubel's (1963) ideas about meaningful verbal learning have not yet found clear confirmation in research on mathematics education. However, the mixture of results in this area suggest a general area of research on the ways that instructional materials and activities aid or interfere with student strategies for structuring mathematical ideas. It seems entirely possible that the study of the effects of verbal organizers moved too quickly to experimental research with narrow conceptions of treatment variations and with shallow measurement of treatment effects. These studies seem to run roughshod over potentially significant variation in student learning styles. What holds promise is a series of exploratory teaching studies that try *different* strategies for helping students acquire structured knowledge. These exploratory studies should be monitored by the observation of classroom interaction and an assessment of student perceptions by interviews and written instruments. Cooney and Henderson (1972) have outlined the beginnings of a scheme to study instructional activity; Geeslin and Shavelson (1975) have pioneered similar techniques for measuring the ways students perceive structure.

The fourth prominent psychological source of hypotheses for a theory of instruction is the work of Gagné (1963), who states, "The design of an instructional situation is basically a matter of designing a *sequence of topics*" (p. 626). Thus, the impact of task analysis is a factor in curriculum structure as well as instructional design. Although it may be true that the hierarchies of task analysis describe patterns of dependence governing the order in which performance skills are acquired, it has never been clearly established that an instructional presentation must inexorably follow the steps up the hierarchical ladder. This kind of ordered presentation seems particularly questionable when a small number of very specific and closely related objectives are involved. Different research results suggest presenting students with more open-ended instructional situations, giving them the freedom to fit the pieces together in their own way.

The preceding suggestions for research on methods of instruction offer no bright new ideas about potentially important variables influencing the effectiveness of instruction. Instead, the main thrust of the proposals is to direct attention away from an inevitably inconclusive search for a single method that is best for all situations. There is a risk that research attempting to determine more detailed effects of different methods in specific situations will yield a potpourri of studies with no external validity or general credibility—exactly the criticism leveled at the current research in this area. However, it seems quite possible that a carefully planned series of investigations might ultimately yield some useful knowledge.

Those who hope for a dramatic breakthrough toward more effective instruction have looked, quite understandably, toward novel media or management approaches as ways to accomplish the matching of instructional style to specific learner attributes. In retrospect it is not hard to understand the expansive hopes of those who first explored television or computer mediation and management for individualized school mathematics instruction. But the initial naive belief that technology and systems-analysis approaches to instruction would yield a broad and marked improvement of student achievement has not been supported by research.

Nearly all recent curricular and instructional research involving alternative media—ITV, PI, or CAI—has been concerned with the evaluation of different experimental programs. At the present time it is hard to imagine any exciting new results coming forth from research on televised or programmed instruction. The PLATO approach to computer-assisted instruction has generated some very striking ways of teaching mathematics, but at this time it is hard to identify research activities that would lead to broad media principles in a theory of mathematics instruction. The most appropriate current effort is creative development that explores the situations in which alternative media might be most effective.

Recent serious concern for innovative systems of instructional presentation has been stimulated by renewed attention to a disarmingly simple proposition:

Students of all ages come to mathematics class with widely varying needs, interests, background knowledge, and learning aptitudes. Thus the only sensible instructional program is one that addresses those learners as individuals, a program that provides content chosen after assessment of learner needs and presented with instructional style and pace that are optimally matched to the personal traits of individual students.

Of course, no one disagrees with this assertion; the problem is delivering such promised instruction. Many individualized, small-group, personalized, and laboratory approaches to mathematics instruction have been conceived to make the management of such a learning situation feasible. Despite the failure of research to show any such scheme more effective than traditional methods, enthusiasm for the alternatives continues.

The most obvious recommendation for future research on organizational schemes for mathematics instruction is to redirect efforts away from the winner-take-all type of methods comparison and toward the determination of the advantages offered by each method in different situations. But the alternatives for individualized instruction have suggested deeper research questions about their presentation and management.

Recent individualized mathematics programs have demonstrated the most notable effects in learning rates. Given freedom to learn at their self-chosen pace, students at nearly every grade level do indeed learn at dramatically different speeds. Yet this observation in itself is hardly convincing support for existing individualized programs, since research shows that the average rate is comparable to that in conventional programs— some students go faster than group pace, others go slower. This pattern has suggested to critics of complete individualization that learning rate is a complex function of subject matter, student abilities, and social setting for learning, with no simple way to optimize the learning pace.

Thorough investigation of the factors that influence learning rate will be essential to further development of individualized programs, since the desire to let students progress at individual rates seems to be the aspect of individualized instruction that leads to the most disruption of traditional student-teacher interaction styles.

The entire area of interaction between students' abilities and the mode of presentation for instruction is a fascinating topic for basic research in learning theory, and it is fundamental to many assumptions of individualized programs. In the future it will not be enough simply to repeat the sales pitch that "students who have trouble learning in one style will be able to turn to another presentation."

We need a deeper understanding of how the different instructional media affect different students and, quite simply, whether the current array of options are cost-effective.

Many proponents of individualization argue that their methods reduce the stigma of slow learning and enhance student self-concepts and attitudes toward mathematics. This attractive hypothesis has not been confirmed by research, but the few studies investigating affective outcomes of individualization should certainly be extended to give a better understanding of these important variables.

One of the sharpest and most telling criticisms of existing individualized mathematics programs is that they replace nearly all student-teacher dialogue about mathematics with an instructional regimen of self-study by the student through written seatwork. Teachers are forced to devote most of their time and energy simply to organizing the paperwork of the system. There has been some largely inconclusive research on aspects of the role that verbalization plays in mathematics learning, but we need much greater understanding about the impact of different patterns of social interaction in the classroom.

It is likely that for some types of students and some instructional objectives in mathematics a solitary learning mode will be most effective; and for some it will be most efficacious to have a reasonably large group of students interacting with a highly directive teacher. There are probably some learning situations in which knowledgeable peers or student aides are the most effective teachers.

In assessing the impact of different approaches to organizing mathematics instruction, it is particularly important that judgments not be based on superficial or short-term goals for teaching. For instance, it seems very likely that some of the educational outcomes that develop most slowly and are most difficult to measure—outcomes such as attitudes, critical thinking, or problem-solving ability—are precisely those most apt to develop in group-interaction settings. In fact, the selling of small-group and laboratory styles of instructional organization is usually based on such contentions; these methods face skeptical reception because short-term general achievement evaluations demonstrate little clear advantage for the innovative methods over traditional instructional styles.

There is a clear need to evaluate small-group and laboratory approaches to mathematics instruction using more varied, sensitive, and long-range assessment procedures. Furthermore, there is promise in research that shows how these instructional styles can be woven into the fabric of courses organized according to traditional or individualized procedures.

There are several other important specific questions concerning small-group instruction in mathematics. Whereas much previous research has been done at the college level, devotees of the small-group approach urge that the technique be applied at the junior and senior high school levels also. The instincts of many junior high school teachers caution against the apparent lack of structure in extended group work, but others suggest that small-group or laboratory activity will generate a lively and inviting class-room atmosphere that ultimately decreases problems of class management. The cooperative nature of most small-group and laboratory tasks also contrasts sharply with the conventional emphasis on competition among individual students. It raises intriguing questions about the motivational and instructive effects of cooperation versus competition.

The strongest arguments for the use of laboratory activities as an essential component of mathematics instruction emphasize the premises that (a) students who frequently operate in exploratory or open-ended problem-solving situations will develop general heuristic skills and creative approaches to new situations, and (b) students whose learning progresses naturally from concrete to abstract understanding of concepts will possess deeper and more readily applicable comprehension of different mathematical ideas. The learning outcomes promised here are neither quick to develop nor easy to assess. Past research on mathematics laboratories has not come close to testing the hypotheses, although even short-term assessment on simple achievement criteria supports optimism for payoff in skillfully coordinated mathematics-laboratory instruction. However, a fair test of any broad pattern for organizing instruction demands resources and experimental controls that are not easy to assemble. The best hope lies in a consortium approach with coordinated smaller studies.

CONCLUSIONS AND PROSPECTS

The determination of school mathematics curricular goals, the translation of goals into instructional materials or presentations, and the assessment of the effects of those efforts commonly occur in situations characterized by a complexity that defies easy or rigorous experimental research. Not surprisingly, past research efforts have not been successful in finding clear principles of curricular and instructional design and, consequently, in affecting the modus operandi of school mathematics. If there has been an unmistakable theme running throughout this chapter, it has been the urging that mathematics educators should expect less, or certainly different, insight from research than the simple assessment of which curriculum or instructional style is most effective.

The clearest promise in curricular and instructional research lies in measuring the effects of varied curriculum content, sequence, pace, mode of presentation, and instructional organization as those alternatives are applied in different school situations. Valuable knowledge is likely to arise from thoughtful analyses of informal teaching investigations as well as from carefully monitored experimental research. But the crucial factor will be better coordination of the traditionally diffuse individual studies that have dominated research in mathematics education.

If such programs of coordinated research are planned and executed, the most promising and important topics seem to be the following:

1. To what extent do actual curricular and instructional practices match those goals recommended by mathematics education specialists or reported in the self-perceptions of teachers? What strategies for educational change operate effectively for improving mathematics programs in school?

2. What are the effects of different strategies for sequencing mathematical learning—for instance, spiral, mastery, student selection, and so on? How do the options influence the rate, retention, and structure of learning?

3. In what ways do students internally structure and make meaningful the variety of skills and concepts in mathematics curricula? What are the contributions of logical, psychological, and instructional variables in assisting student acquisition of not only specific pieces of knowledge but also large collections of variously interrelated ideas?

At this point it is difficult to conjecture what specific statements of curricular and instructional theory might emerge from investigations of these questions. Yet the issues do seem of central concern, and different approaches seem likely to have quite different effects. At the very least, the investigation of alternative curricular and instructional practices will enrich the repertoire of developers and teachers as they approach the complex task of putting it all together in workable school programs.

REFERENCES

Ausubel, D. P. *The psychology of meaningful verbal learning.* New York: Grune & Stratton, 1963.

Bauer, J. L. The effect of three instructional bases for decimals on computational skills of seventh grade students (Doctoral dissertation, Ohio State University, 1974). *Dissertation Abstracts International,* 1975, *35,* 7024A.

Begle, E. G. Curriculum research in mathematics. *Journal of Experimental Education,* 1968, *37,* 44–48.

Begle, E. G. Some lessons learned by SMSG. *Mathematics Teacher,* 1973, *66,* 207–214.

Begle, E. G. *Acceleration for students talented in mathematics* (Working Paper No. 19). Stanford, Calif.: Stanford University Mathematics Education Study Group, 1976.

Bell, M. S. Studies with respect to the uses of mathematics in secondary school curricula (Doctoral dissertation, University of Michigan, 1969). *Dissertation Abstracts International,* 1970, *30,* 3813A–3814A.

Bell, M. S. What does "everyman" really need from school mathematics? *Mathematics Teacher,* 1974, *67,* 196–202.

Biggs, J. Towards a psychology of educative learning. *International Review of Education,* 1965, *11,* 77–92.

Brown, J. K. Textbook use by teachers and students of geometry and second-year algebra (Doctoral dissertation, University of Illinois, 1973). *Dissertation Abstracts International,* 1974, *34,* 5795A–5796A.

Brownell, W. A. Conceptual maturity in arithmetic under differing systems of instruction. *Elementary School Journal,* 1968, *68,* 151–163.

Bruner, J. *The process of education.* New York: Vintage Books, 1960.

Bruner, J. *Toward a theory of instruction.* Cambridge, Mass.: Harvard University Press, 1966.

Callahan, L. G., & Glennon, V. J. *Elementary school mathematics: A guide to current research* (4th ed.). Washington, D.C.: Association for Supervision and Curriculum Development, 1975.

Cambridge Conference on School Mathematics. *Goals for school mathematics.* Boston: Houghton Mifflin, 1963.

Carry, L. R. Interaction of visualization and general reasoning abilities with instructional treatment in algebra (Doctoral dissertation, Stanford University, 1968). *Dissertation Abstracts International,* 1968, *29,* 475A–476A.

Cronbach, L. J., & Snow, R. E. *Aptitudes and instructional methods.* New York: Irvington Publishers, 1977.

Conant, E. H. *Teacher and paraprofessional work productivity, a public school cost-effectiveness study.* Lexington, Mass.: D. C. Heath, 1973.

Cooney, T., & Henderson, K. B. Ways mathematics teachers help students organize knowledge. *Journal for Research in Mathematics Education,* 1972, *3,* 21–32.

Crawford, D. *An investigation of age-grade trends in understanding the field axioms.* Unpublished doctoral dissertation, Syracuse University, 1964.

Davidson, N. A. The small group discovery method: 1967–1977. In J. Harvey & T. Romberg (Eds.), *Problem solving in mathematics.* Madison: Wisconsin Research and Development Center for Individualized Schooling, 1979.

Davis, R. B. Observing children's mathematical behavior as a foundation for curriculum planning. *Journal of Children's Mathematical Behavior,* 1971–72, *1* (1), 7–59.

Davis, R. B. Mathematics for gifted children. *Journal of Children's Mathematical Behavior,* 1976, supplement no. 1, 176–216.

Eastman, P. M., & Carry, L. R. Interaction of spatial visualization and general reasoning abilities with instructional treatment in quadratic inequalities: A further investigation. *Journal for Research in Mathematics Education*, 1975, *6*, 142–149.

Erlwanger, S. Benny's conception of rules and answers in IPI mathematics. *Journal of Children's Mathematical Behavior*, 1973, *1* (2), 7–26.

Esty, E. (Ed.). *Conference on basic mathematical skills and learning*. Washington, D.C.: National Institute of Education, 1975.

Esty, E., & Payne, J. (Eds.). *Report of the conference on needed research and development on hand-held calculators in school mathematics*. Washington, D.C.: National Institute of Education, National Science Foundation, 1977.

Fehr, H. F. (Ed.). *Needed research in mathematics education*. New York: Teachers College Press, 1966.

Fennema, E. H. The relative effectiveness of a symbolic and a concrete model in learning a selected mathematical principle. *Journal for Research in Mathematics Education*, 1972, *3*, 233–238.

Fitzgerald, W. M. *About mathematics laboratories*. East Lansing, Mich.: Michigan State University, 1972.

Gagné, R. M. Learning and proficiency in mathematics. *Mathematics Teacher*, 1963, *56*, 620–626.

Gagné, R. M. Training and principles of learning. In E. A. Fleishman (Ed.), *Studies in personnel and industrial psychology*. Homewood, Ill.: Dorsey Press, 1967.

Gearhart, G. What do teachers think of the high school geometry controversy? *Mathematics Teacher*, 1975, *68*, 486–493.

Geeslin, W. E., & Shavelson, R. J. Comparison of content structure and cognitive structure in high school students' learning of probability. *Journal for Research in Mathematics Education*, 1975, *6*, 109–120.

Golladay, M. A., DeVault, M. V., Fox, G. T., Jr., & Skuldt, K. Problems in empirical research on individualized instruction. *Journal for Research in Mathematics Education*, 1975, *6*, 159–169.

Hater, M. A., & Kane, R. B. The Cloze procedure as a measure of mathematical English. *Journal for Research in Mathematics Education*, 1975, *6*, 121–127.

Hatfield, L. L., & Kieren, T. E. Computer-assisted problem solving in school mathematics. *Journal for Research in Mathematics Education*, 1972, *3*, 99–112.

Heimer, R. Conditions of learning in mathematics: Sequence theory development. *Review of Educational Research*, 1969, *39*, 509–522.

Hogan, P. Students' interest in particular mathematics topics. *Journal for Research in Mathematics Education*, 1977, *8*, 115–122.

Jamison, D., Suppes, P., & Wells, S. The effectiveness of alternative instructional media: A survey. *Review of Educational Research*, 1974, *44*, 1–67.

Johnson, M. Definitions and models in curriculum theory. *Educational Theory*, 1967, *17*, 127–140.

Karplus, E. F., Karplus, R., & Wollman, W. Intellectual development beyond elementary school IV: Ratio, the influence of cognitive style. *School Science and Mathematics*, 1974, *74*, 476–482.

Keating, D. P. (Ed.). *Intellectual talent: Research and development*. Baltimore: Johns Hopkins University Press, 1975.

Kersh, B. Y. Engineering instructional sequences for the mathematics classroom. In J. M. Scandura (Ed.), *Research in mathematics education*. Washington, D.C.: National Council of Teachers of Mathematics, 1967.

Kieren, T. E. Manipulative activity in mathematics learning. *Journal for Research in Mathematics Education*, 1971, *2*, 228–234.

King, B. W. On scrambling instructional stimuli. *Journal for Research in Mathematics Education*, 1970, *1*, 233–240.

Kort, A. P. Transformation vs. non-transformation tenth grade geometry: Effects on retention of geometry and on transfer in eleventh grade mathematics (Doctoral dissertation, Northwestern University, 1971). *Dissertation Abstracts International*, 1971, *32*, 3157A.

Lefkowitz, R. S. The first nine years—A study of the advanced placement program in mathematics. *Journal for Research in Mathematics Education*, 1971, *2*, 23–25.

Lesh, R. An interpretation of advanced organizers. *Journal for Research in Mathematics Education*, 1976, *7*, 69–74.

Lipson, J. I. Hidden strengths of conventional instruction. *Arithmetic Teacher*, 1976, *23*, 11–15.

Lovell, K. *Intellectual growth and understanding mathematics*. Columbus, Ohio: ERIC Information Analysis Center for Science and Mathematics Education, 1971.

Malpas, A. J. Mathematics and science in secondary school. In A. G. Howson (Ed.), *Development in mathematics education*. London: Cambridge University Press, 1973.

Merrill, M. D. Correction and review on successive parts in learning a hierarchical task. *Journal of Educational Psychology*, 1965, *56*, 225–234.

Merrill, M. D., & Wood, N. D. *Instructional strategies: A preliminary taxonomy*. Columbus, Ohio: ERIC Information Analysis Center for Science, Mathematics, and Environmental Education, 1974.

Miller, H. R. Sequencing and prior information in linear programmed instruction. *AV Communication Review*, 1969, *17*, 63–76.

Miller, R. L. *Mathematics laboratories: A review of research to determine effectiveness*. Unpublished manuscript, University of Maryland at College Park, 1974.

Miller, R. L. Individualized instruction in mathematics: A review of research. *Mathematics Teacher*, 1976, *69*, 345–351.

National Advisory Committee on Mathematical Education (NACOME). *Overview and analysis of school mathematics, K–12*. Washington, D.C.: Conference Board of the Mathematical Sciences, 1975. (Available from the National Council of Teachers of Mathematics, 1906 Association Drive, Reston, VA 22091.)

Nelson, L. D. Analysis of Canadian research on the effectiveness of Cuisenaire materials. In *Canadian experience with Cuisenaire method*. Ottawa: Canadian Council for Research in Education, 1964.

Niedermayer, F. C., Brown, J., & Sulzen, R. Learning and varying sequences of ninth grade mathematics materials. *Journal of Experimental Education*, 1969, *37*, 61–66.

O'Brien, T., & Shapiro, B. The development of logical thinking in children. *American Educational Research Journal*, 1968, *5*, 531–541.

Olander, H. T., & Robertson, H. C. The effectiveness of discovery and expository methods in the teaching of fourth-grade mathematics. *Journal for Research in Mathematics Education*, 1973, *4*, 33–44.

Roe, A., Case, H. W., & Row, A. Scrambled versus ordered sequence in autoinstructional programs. *Journal of Education Psychology*, 1962, *53*, 101–104.

Romberg, T., & DeVault, M. V. Mathematics curriculum: Needed research. *Journal of Research and Development in Education*, 1967, *1*, 95–112.

Romberg, T., & Wilson, J. W. The effect of an advanced organizer, cognitive set, and post organizer on the learning and retention of written materials. *Journal for Research in Mathematics Education*, 1973, *4*, 68–75.

Schoen, H. L. Self-paced mathematics instruction: How effective has it been? *Arithmetic Teacher*, 1976, *23*, 90–96. (a)

Schoen, H. L. Self-paced mathematics instruction: How effective has it been in secondary and postsecondary schools? *Mathematics Teacher*, 1976, *69*, 352–357. (b)

Suppes, P., & Binford, F. Experimental teaching of mathematical logic in elementary school. *Arithmetic Teacher*, 1965, *12*, 187–195.

Suydam, M., & Riedesel, C. *Research on elementary mathematics* (PREP Report No. 11). Washington, D.C.: U.S. Department of Health, Education, and Welfare, 1972.

Thorndike, E. L. Mental discipline in high school studies. *Journal of Educational Psychology*, 1924, *15*, 1–22; 83–98.

Usiskin, Z. P. The effects of teaching Euclidean geometry via transformations on student achievement and attitudes in tenth-grade geometry. *Journal for Research in Mathematics Education*, 1972, *3*, 249–259.

Usiskin, Z. *Algebra through applications.* Chicago: University of Chicago, 1976. (Available from the National Council of Teachers of Mathematics, 1906 Association Drive, Reston, VA 22091.)

Washburne, C. Mental age and the arithmetic curriculum: A summary of the Committee of Seven grade placement investigations to date. *Journal of Educational Research*, 1931, *23*, 210–231.

Weaver, J. F. Some concerns about the application of Piaget's theory and research to mathematical learning and instruction. *Arithmetic Teacher*, 1972, *19*, 263–270.

Webb, L. F., & Carry, L. R. Interaction of spatial visualization and general reasoning abilities with instructional treatment in quadratic inequalities: A follow-up study. *Journal for Research in Mathematics Education*, 1975, *6*, 132–140.

Wilson, G., & Dalrymple, C. O. Useful fractions. *Journal of Educational Research*, 1937, *30*, 341–347.

Wilson, J. W. *Diagnosis and treatment in arithmetic: Beliefs, guiding models, and procedures.* College Park, Md.: Arithmetic Center, University of Maryland, 1976.

Worthen, B. R. A comparison of discovery and expository sequencing in elementary mathematics instruction. In J. M. Scandura (Ed.), *Research in mathematics education.* Washington, D.C.: National Council of Teachers of Mathematics, 1967.

Zoll, E. Research in programmed instruction in mathematics. *Mathematics Teacher*, 1969, *62*, 103–110.

14

Research on Teaching
and Teacher Education

Thomas J. Cooney
University of Georgia

MATHEMATICS is learned in situations or settings in which a learner's interaction with stimuli gives rise to various behaviors. A teaching agent need not be present to arrange the stimuli or foster the interaction for learning to occur: Observe two children dividing candy. However, we cannot rely solely on unplanned, unsupervised interactions as the basis for mathematics learning. Without the ministrations of a teaching agent and left to the chance juxtaposition of suitable stimuli and a motivated learner, the learning of a systematic body of knowledge like mathematics would rarely occur. The role of the teaching agent is to engage in behavior (actions) that gives rise to setting-learner interactions that cause the student to learn. This behavior is called teaching.

Previous chapters on cognitive development and individual differences deal with variables and constructs associated with the learner. Other chapters on skill learning, concepts and principles, and problem solving concentrate on research into aspects of subject matter in mathematics. The focus of this chapter is primarily on the actions of a teaching agent. The emphasis differs from that of the chapter on curriculum and instruction, since that chapter focuses on research involving broader concerns of the instructional process.

Henderson (1963) conceived of teaching as a ternary relation denoted by $T(x, y, z)$. He argued that it would be more profitable to consider the domain x as sequences of actions, either verbal or nonverbal, of teachers rather than as teachers themselves. He considered z to be the behaviors of those taught and y the subject matter to be taught. Such a classification provides a means by which variables related to teaching can be categorized. But there is one exception—perhaps one should say extension. The manifestation of $T(x, y, z)$ occurs in some sort of setting. Further, the setting itself is often a determining factor of a teacher's behavior, the content selected, and the student's behavior. Setting variables include the socioeconomic status of a community, the community's attitude toward education, physical facilities, the environment of the classroom, and the like. Hence, Henderson's triadic relation will be extended to include a fourth domain, namely, setting variables denoted by w. Setting variables and their potential impact on the teaching-learning process are becoming increasingly important to researchers, as evidenced by the increase in ethnographic studies in educational research.

The four indicated domains will serve as the basis for viewing research on teaching and teacher education, although the domain of x will constitute the chapter's primary focus. The chart in Figure 1 depicts how these domains can be considered with respect to research on teaching and teacher education.

	x Teaching Behavior	y Subject Matter	z Learning Behavior	w Setting

Teaching	Emoting
	Exploring
	Demonstrating
	Providing drill
	  activities
	Providing exploratory
	  activities
		Mathematical
		concepts
		generali-
		zations
		prescriptions
			Computational skill
			Concept learning
			Principle learning
			Problem solving
				Classroom
				  environment
				Socioeconomic
				  status
				Community
				  attitudes
				Grade levels

Teacher Education	Demonstration
	  teaching
	Providing oppor-
	  tunities to
	  analyze instruc-
	  tions
	Providing
	  microteaching
	  activities
		Pedagogical
		concepts
		generali-
		zations
		prescriptions
			Explaining
			Demonstrating
			Asking questions
			(much the same as
			  x in teaching)
				Preservice
				In-service
				College class-
				  room settings
				Field-based
				  settings

Figure 1. Domains of variables in research on teaching and teacher education with examples.

This classification is similar to others developed by researchers. For example, Merrill and Wood (1974) conceptualized instruction as consisting of four relatively independent facets: (a) learner aptitudes, (b) subject matter context, (c) instructional strategies, and (d) instructional delivery systems. Their categories of subject matter content and instructional strategies match domains y and x, respectively. The category *instructional delivery systems* refers to the various means of presenting an instructional strategy; it includes teachers, computer-assisted instruction, and the like. The term *teaching agent* is used here to refer to such delivery systems.

Merrill and Wood categorize learner aptitudes as *traits*—that is, pervasive characteristics that are relatively stable—or as *states*—aptitudes that change from moment to moment. This category differs from domain z in that trait and state aptitudes characterize the learner; domain z refers to learner behaviors, not to the learners themselves.

Similarly, Turner (1976) identified five domains of variables to be considered by the researcher: subject matter, student attributes, teaching strategies, student learning outcomes, and setting variables. It is clear that Turner's classification scheme matches the proposed one with one exception: the domain of student attributes, which was discussed in the previous paragraph. I am not arguing that student attributes are unimportant. They are essential for describing a learner and in providing a context for interpreting the learner's behavior.

The primary focus of this chapter is on research related to a teaching agent. This research can be subdivided into research on teaching and research on teacher education. Research on teaching includes studies that investigate variables and constructs that explain and provide an understanding of the relationships among actions of teaching agents on student achievement. Research on teacher education involves studies that investigate variables that influence the repertoire of the teaching agent's actions, which in turn influence achievement. Research on teaching will be considered first.

RESEARCH ON TEACHING

Within the last decade and a half, at least three extensive reviews of research on teaching mathematics have been conducted. Fey (1969) provided a comprehensive review of research on teaching mathematics which focused on characteristics of effective teachers, their classroom activities, and their education. From Fey's review, it is safe to conclude that no definitive statements are warranted regarding the relationship between teachers' characteristics and students' achievement. In reference to the Minnesota National Laboratory Study, Fey noted that the "effectiveness of teachers' using the SMSG materials is not significantly correlated with teachers' experience, collegiate courses and grades, or participation in professional activities" (p. 55). Fey also noted that "the Minnesota study confirms earlier indications that the search for predictors of effective teaching must move beyond the gross measures of ability and formally identifiable qualification" (p. 55). The author's review of other research on teacher characteristics indicated that few studies reveal significant findings. This circumstance gives credence to Henderson's position (1963) that the domain x should be teacher behavior, not teachers or their characteristics.

In reviewing research on teaching elementary school mathematics, Riedesel and Burns (1973) emphasized research on teaching by discovery and the laboratory method. Their review seemed to indicate that discovery or laboratory approaches promote better retention and problem-solving skills. Expository teaching seemed to be more efficient and appeared to result in better short-term effects—for example, computational skills. Dessart and Frandsen (1973) also discussed research on teaching by discovery. Their review suggested that there is no obvious advantage in favor of teaching by discovery over expository methods of teaching. It is probably fair to say that neither of these reviews reveal much that could constitute a theoretical framework for teaching. The single most reviewed approach to instruction was teaching by discovery, and those results were largely equivocal.

The fact that the reviews by Riedesel and Burns and by Dessart and Frandsen yielded basically equivocal results can be attributed to at least two factors. First, the concepts of expository and discovery teaching are not always well defined. Hence, many different types of teaching strategies are inconsistently billed under the rubrics of expository or discovery teaching. Second, the constructs of expository and discovery teaching are not monolithic. There are good and bad discovery strategies and good and bad expository strategies. Research on teaching behavior is not likely to be productive as long as the variables investigated are so globally defined as expository or discovery. These factors suggest that a more careful analysis of variables in teaching behavior is needed.

VARIABLES IN TEACHING BEHAVIOR

There is no shortage of lists of what teachers (or teaching agents in general) do in the classroom. How the various activities are classified or grouped depends on the nature of the filter used to analyze the behavior. Three categories of variables, each representing a particular aspect of teaching, will be considered. The categories are *affective, cognitive,* and *managerial.* Further, the variables that exemplify these categories are subdivided into high-inference variables and low-inference variables (Rosenshine & Furst, 1971). This leads to the 3 X 2 matrix of variables illustrated in Figure 2.

	High-Inference Variables	Low-Inference Variables
Affective	Conviviality, enthusiasm	Praise in form of saying "OK"
Cognitive	Clarity, variability	Use of examples, nonexamples
Managerial	Businesslike approach, directness	Wait time for students' responses

Figure 2. Classification of teaching variables with examples.

A definition of the variables follows and then a discussion of the research related to those variables.

Affective, Cognitive, and Managerial Variables

A plethora of variables can be included under the heading of affective variables. Affective variables will refer to the more emotive aspects of teaching, such as a teacher's conviviality, anxiety, use of sarcasm, attitudes, and enthusiasm. Thus, if the teaching agent is computer-assisted instruction, the affective variables are fairly controlled. However, if the teaching agent is human, then affective variables must play some role in affecting student achievement.

The term *cognitive variables* refers to the manipulation of the content being taught, such as the use of examples and nonexamples, the mathematical correctness of a lesson, the variability with which a theorem is explained or an algorithm is demonstrated, and the use of heuristics in teaching problem solving.

Because the third category, managerial variables, is difficult to define, there is a temptation to define it residually. Clearly teachers do things that seem to be neither emotive nor cognitive—for example, asking students to go to the chalkboard, giving directions on how to do homework, and providing time for supervised study. But in a sense these are organizational variables. Yet Kounin's (1970) variables of "withitness" (the extent to which a teacher is monitoring students) seem more related to managing the classroom than organizing it (if one will allow such a distinction), and yet withitness seems separate from affective and cognitive considerations. Hence, the term *managerial variables* was selected to account for organizational considerations, including the role of time as a variable and the various means a teacher might use to promote students' being on task.

This classification scheme is appealing for at least two reasons. First, it seems to reflect intuitively what actually transpires in the classroom. Sometimes teachers try to bolster the confidence of students by praising them, other times they ask students to solve problems, and still other times they ask students to work at their seats. Second, much of the existing research can be classified according to the scheme above.

Lest one should feel unduly comfortable with this classification, a categorical problem should be identified. To illustrate, consider this locution:

Henry, give me an example of a prime number.

In the absence of a context, this statement appears to belong to the cognitive category. But teaching is necessarily contextual. Hence, a teacher who is overtly asking for a cognitive outcome may, in fact, be using the question to help Henry feel good about newly acquired knowledge. If so, the locution would be better classified as affective. If the teacher is trying to gain Henry's attention, the locution could be classified as managerial.

Given the indicated problem, does the scheme still seem viable? In terms of reviewing past research, the answer is yes. It seems reasonable to assume that it can also serve as an organizer for future studies, but that remains to be seen.

High-Inference and Low-Inference Variables

When a variable is inferred from observed behavior or conditions, it is called an *inferential variable*. For example, an investigator might observe a teacher and on the basis of impressionistic data decide whether or not the teacher exhibited warmth. The construct of warmth is inferred from the observed behavior. Some inferential variables require greater inferential "leaps" than others—hence, the categories *high-inference variables* and *low-inference variables*. High-inference variables—for instance, clarity, variability, warmth, and enthusiasm—are more intuitive. Low-inference variables, which are more specific, can sometimes be determined by counting the occurrences of a behavior. Examples of low-inference variables include moves for teaching concepts, generalizations, and skills (Cooney, Davis, & Henderson, 1975), the acceptance of students' ideas, and the occurrence of low-level or high-level questions. Classifying variables as *high inference* or *low inference* does involve a certain degree of arbitrariness and the epistemological question of whether or not knowledge is an inferred entity. Despite these concerns, however, I feel that the proposed categories are useful in conceptualizing research on teaching.

Generally, high-inference variables are more stable than low-inference variables for a particular teacher in a given setting. Many of the studies on teaching behavior are process-product studies, in which various quantifications of a variable across teachers (process) is correlated with measures of student achievement (product). In such studies, the stability of a variable is of no small consequence in interpreting outcomes. Hence process-product studies that have focused on high-inference variables have generally been more productive. Because considerable research involving high-inference variables has been conducted, a few remarks concerning that research are in order.

Dunkin and Biddle (1974) and Rosenshine and Furst (1971) have provided extensive syntheses of research on teaching. In both reviews high-inference variables seem to offer promise for future investigations. Dunkin and Biddle suggest that process variables are the heartland of theories on teaching. Four types of models for explaining classroom events are suggested: trait, interaction, social system, and the curriculum model. In particular, the trait model can be used as a means of characterizing teachers as exhibiting or not exhibiting certain traits and then used to explain classroom achievement in terms of the presence or absence of a given trait or collection of traits. Examples of traits are praise, acceptance, lecturing, vagueness, and criticism. Although the traits could consist of high- or low-inference variables, the research to date has generally favored high-inference variables.

In relation to research on traits, Rosenshine and Furst's synthesis of the literature identified 11 of the strongest variables present in process-product studies: clarity, variability, enthusiasm, task-oriented or businesslike behavior, opportunity to learn, the use of student ideas and general indirectness, criticism, the use of structuring comments, types of questions, probing, and the level of difficulty of instruction. Of these 11, the first five have strong support from correlational studies. The last six have less support but deserve further consideration, according to Rosenshine and Furst. Again, these were process-product studies in which the potent variables were generally the high-inference type.

Although research on high-inference variables has served as something of a beacon of light in an otherwise dark and murky area, such research is not without challenge. For example, Heath and Nielsen (1974) took issue with Rosenshine and Furst's review. Even though their criticisms were not directed toward the investigation of high-inference variables per se, many of their concerns reflect, by implication, on the research of such variables.

Heath and Nielsen's criticism was based on two primary positions. First, extensive problems of design were noted. Second, the authors maintained that the operational definitions of teacher behavior were rather sterile and often did not correspond to the variables cited by Rosenshine and Furst. The second criticism is particularly noteworthy for those involved in research on high-inference variables.

The "definitional" problem of high-inference variables surfaces in at least three ways. First, there is the problem of generalizing across studies, a major criticism by Heath and Nielsen. Second, if a variable is identified as a strong correlate to achievement, it is difficult to treat that variable experimentally if its precise definition is lacking. Third, the variable might not lend itself to being included in a teacher education program unless it can be readily defined, observed, and taught. The possibility that correlates of student learning can be identified but are not teachable would not put either the researcher or the teacher educator in a very enviable position.

At least two questions should be considered with respect to high-inference variables. First, do certain high-inference variables appear to be more appropriate in analyzing mathematics teaching behavior than in analyzing teaching behavior in general? The answer may be no for variables associated with the affective domain. Enthusiasm and conviviality are probably similar in any classroom. But more cognitively related variables, such as variability and clarity, might be definable in ways more specific to teaching mathematics. Second, is it possible to define high-inference variables in teaching mathematics in terms of more specific behaviors? Smith (1977) conducted a study on the teaching of mathematics in which the construct of vagueness was defined in terms of the frequency of such words as *somewhere, almost, a bunch, may, chances are, sometimes, frequently*, and *often*. Smith found a significant ($p < .10$) *negative* correlation between the frequency of the vagueness terms and mathematical achievement. Smith's work represents an attempt marked by a promising outcome to define a high-inference construct in terms of specific and quantifiable behaviors. When high-inference variables can justifiably be defined in terms of specific behaviors, the incorporation of research findings into teacher education programs is much simpler. Of course, one cannot assume that variables identified through correlational studies will result in causal relationships affecting achievement.

There are several ways one could go about defining high-inference variables in terms of specific behaviors. One approach consists of identifying more effective and less effective teachers and then analyzing their behaviors relative to the teaching of particular types of teachable objects— for example, concepts or principles—or relative to a specific construct, such as clarity of teaching. Another approach would be to determine by some sort of consensus those teachers who consistently exhibit a certain general behavior and those who do not. Then more specific aspects of the teaching behaviors of the respective groups could be analyzed in an effort to identify defining components of the more general behaviors.

Besides the attempt to determine low-inference variables that could be considered defining characteristics of high-inference variables and yet be relatively stable, it might be fruitful to examine the contexts under which teacher behavior does change. Instability in characteristics of teaching behavior may be desirable even though it confounds statistical investigations. If so, then the contexts that seem to precipitate change ought to be identified. Medley (1973) reflected on this point when he wrote the following:

> Medical research does not concern itself with whether the best doctors use penicillin more often than, say cortisone; it concerns itself with what penicillin is good for, and what parameters or conditions determine its effects, as well as with what cortisone is good for and what parameters determine its effects. (p. 44)

A major contribution to the field would be to determine the contexts in which both high-inference and low-inference variables contribute most to learning and to analyze those situations, preferably in terms of mathematical considerations.

Research on Affective Variables

This section and its companion sections on cognitive and managerial variables will be divided into three parts: high-inference variables, low-inference variables, and questions and concerns.

High-inference variables. Tikunoff, Berliner, and Rist (1975) conducted an investigation in whch an extensive number of affective variables were related to achievement. The study was ethnographic in nature. The sample consisted of 20 second-grade teachers and 20 fifth-grade teachers. Two units were taught for each grade level, one in mathematics and one in reading. At each grade level, 10 teachers were defined as more effective and 10 as less effective on the basis of student achievement. The teaching behavior was analyzed by trained ethnographers who observed each teacher continuously for one week. Sixty-one dimensions of teacher behavior were eventually identified. Of these, 21 were found to be significantly ($p < .05$) related to student achievement at both grade levels and in both subjects. Those positively related to achievement included accepting, adult involvement, optimism, pacing, promoting self-sufficiency, spontaneity, and structuring. Those negatively related to student achievement cluded abruptness, belittling, defiance, filling time, and recognition seeking.

The following variables were found to be significantly related (some positively, some negatively) to mathematics at both grade levels but not to reading: being liked (–), excluding (–), open questioning (+), personalizing (+), politeness (+), sarcasm (–), and shaming (–). The significant variables seem to relate to "those familial interactions in the home which have been attributed traditionally to the successful rearing of children" (p. 22). One gets the feeling from this study that warm, supportive teachers who have rapport with elementary school children are essential for effective teaching.

Further support for the "warm" teacher can be found in Rosenshine and Furst's review (1971). Their review indicated moderately negative correlations between criticism and student achievement. Their review also revealed a fairly strong relationship between teacher enthusiasm and student achievement. It should be kept in mind, however, that many of the studies reviewed by Rosenshine and Furst did not involve the teaching of mathematics.

Low-inference variables. Dunkin and Biddle (1974) reviewed over 100 studies involving the variable *indirectness* (praise, acceptance, and questioning). (It is assumed here that lower-inference variables were used, since the author stated that rating scales were not used for coding the variables.) In general, their review is rather pessimistic. They state that "where 'indirectness' does have an influence upon pupil achievement, it is quite small" (p. 119). The authors note that the variable is conceptually confused, that studies both confirm and deny its importance to effective teaching, that students of "indirect" teachers tend to initiate, and that teachers can be trained to be more "indirect." Although it may be misleading to summarize such an extensive review of one variable in a single sentence, the bottom line seems to be that "the case for 'indirectness' is not demonstrated" (p. 132).

Despite the extensiveness of their review, Dunkin and Biddle's conclusion can be challenged, at least in the opinion of Gage (1976b). He argues that a count of studies that "confirm" or "deny" the importance of a variable is not a viable means of evaluating research. Using the variable "indirectness," he makes the following points:

1. Any single variable is likely to have a low correlation ($\pm.1$ to $\pm.4$) with achievement.

2. Most studies involving "indirectness" employ a small number of teachers; hence, it is difficult to achieve a statistically significant result.

3. It is possible, through a rather complex statistical procedure, to determine the significance of the combined effects of a number of separate investigations—assuming certain conditions are satisfied. In particular, by combining data from single studies, Gage found that indirectness significantly correlated ($p < .001$) with achievement.

Dunkin and Biddle also reviewed research related to a teacher's "warmth." Although warmth is generally construed to be a high-inference variable, it is not clear how it would be classified by these authors. Given that rating scales were not used to determine warmth, one might assume that warmth was defined in terms of low-inference behaviors. In any event, Dunkin and Biddle use the same "counting technique" to conclude that "the case for warmth is also not yet demonstrated" (p. 132). The argument posited by Gage above would apply equally to this conclusion.

Questions and concerns. Many questions stem from research on affective variables. One relates to how the variables should be defined. Clearly there are definitional problems that inhibit generalizing across studies. Part of this problem is identifying the psychological basis for defining the variables. Should the variables be defined from a behavioral-modification viewpoint, from a sociological basis, or from some other perspective? How the variables are conceived could say a great deal about interpreting the results or relating the findings to other research or theoretical positions. If Gage's statistical technique of combining data from single studies stands the test of time and criticism, then the definitional problem is even more basic to productive research.

Another question to be considered is whether the findings on affective variables are highly contextual in nature. Brophy and Evertson (1976) found that in classrooms of children of high socioeconomic status (SES), praise was negatively related to gains in student learning. They conjectured that this might occur because the less capable student continually sought verbal praise. However, criticism (albeit infrequent) of students for poor work (not misbehavior) was positively related to learning gains. Symbolic rewards (stars, etc.) were effective motivators. In schools of lower SES, students prospered in warm, supportive classroom atmospheres. In general, teachers in schools of higher SES were effective by being demanding and sometimes critical. Future research on affective variables should take relevant variables of setting into consideration. There are several such variables one might consider. The age of the student, the difficulty of the mathematics (consider dividing fractions versus multiplying whole numbers), and whether or not a mathematics course is elective could all influence the impact that affective variables might have on achievement.

An age-old question is how generic affective variables are. Are there aspects of affective considerations that are unique to the teaching of mathematics? This is a difficult question to answer, particularly since so many of the studies reviewed above did not involve mathematics and were not conducted by mathematics educators. This in no way impugns the findings, but it does leave the mathematics educator in a quandary as to what can be assumed to be true about the relationship of affective variables to mathematics achievement. It would be a bit more reassuring to mathematics educators to have research on affective variables conducted by those familiar with, and sensitive to, mathematical considerations.

One facet of research in this area might be a study of the relationship between teachers' views of teaching mathematics and the various affective variables. For example, how does a like or dislike of mathematics translate into a teacher's interactions with students? How does a teacher's view of what mathematics is translate into various affective interactions? The investigation of these questions would be more central to the interests of most mathematics educators.

Research on Cognitive Variables

Cognitive variables involve the manipulation of content. In considering educational research on such variables, we find that it is appropriate and perhaps productive to ask, "Do these variables have particular promise with respect to research on teaching mathematics?" Some of the research cited below either did not involve mathematics or simply used mathematics as a convenient subject for the investigation. Again, research on teaching mathematics as an area of research per se has not matured to the point where a synthesis can be developed relative to specific variables.

High-inference variables. One of the high-inference variables that has captured the interest of a number of educational researchers is clarity. Clarity was one of the most potent variables identified in Rosenshine and

Furst's review as being correlated with student achievement. Besides having empirical support, clarity has some intuitive appeal where the teaching of mathematics is concerned.

Seven investigations on the clarity of a teacher's presentation were cited by Rosenshine and Furst. Clarity was generally described in terms of whether the teacher's points were clear and easy to understand, whether the teacher had facility with the subject and could react to students in an intelligent way, and whether the cognitive level of the teacher's lessons was generally regarded to be appropriate for the students. In general, clarity accounted for a significant part of the variance of student achievement. The authors noted that "in those studies for which simple correlations were available, the significant correlations ranged from .37 to .71" (p. 44). Rosenshine and Furst identified other studies in which the variables investigated were related to clarity and were significantly related to student achievement. Some of the variables were coherence of presentation, organization, and vagueness (negatively related to achievement). It is difficult, however, to ascertain what specific behaviors characterize clarity or related variables even though ratings of clarity were relatively stable across occasions for a particular teacher and class.

Bush, Kennedy, and Cruickshank (1977) grappled with the problem of defining the construct of clarity in terms of specific behaviors. They concluded that a high-inference variable such as clarity could be defined in terms of the observable, specific behaviors that are distinguishable. The specific behaviors they related to clarity were these:

1. Takes time when explaining
2. Stresses difficult points
3. Explains new words
4. Demonstrates how to do something
5. Works difficult problems on the board
6. Gives students an example and lets them try to do it

Cruickshank, Kennedy, Myers, and Bush (1976) used students' perceptions in trying to define a teacher's clarity. Junior high school students were asked to identify their most clear and unclear teachers. The students then identified low-inference behaviors that characterized clear and unclear teachers. Ten low-inference behaviors were identified by students as performed frequently by their most clear teachers but infrequently by their least clear teachers. These behaviors included giving students individual help, explaining something and then allowing students to think about it, explaining the work and showing how to do it, repeating questions and explanations if students don't understand, asking the students before they start work if they know what to do and how to do it, giving explanations that students understand, teaching at a pace appropriate to the topic and the students, taking time when explaining, answering students' questions, and stressing difficult points.

Despite the obvious difficulties with such an approach, it presents an alternative to other research efforts to identify low-inference variables. One of the problems, however, is to identify those behaviors that can be associated with the specific variable *clarity* and not just with "good teaching" in general. Could students identify "clear" teachers who were not necessarily their "best" teacher or, to students, are clear teachers and best teachers one and the same?

Thornton (1977), in a study concerned with the training of preservice elementary mathematics teachers, found clarity to be a strong correlate of student achievement. She defined clarity in terms of the following six rating scales:

1. Mathematical objectives of the lesson are identifiable.
2. Lesson is well planned and executed.
3. Instruction builds on previous learning and experiences.
4. Models and illustrations are effectively used.
5. Flow of ideas—from instructor to pupils—is understood.
6. Evaluation is ongoing, to check that ideas are clearly grasped. (p. 19)

Thornton's definition of clarity provides a basis for defining clarity in more specific mathematical terms. Consider her third rating scale: This scale could be defined in terms of how a teacher attends to developmental factors in teaching basic processes or in terms of the explicit attention by teachers to concepts prerequisite to the learning of a principle.

Given the analytic nature of mathematical knowledge, clarity may be a particularly potent variable with respect to research on teaching mathematics. Smith's research (1977) on vagueness terms provides some support for this position, as does Thornton's study (1977). However, additional work needs to be done in defining clarity and drawing a distinction between clarity of presentation and other characteristics of good teaching that do not necessarily lend clarity to the lesson. Further, can clarity be defined in ways more specific to mathematics? For example, to what extent (a) is the clarity of a lesson related to the mathematical correctness of a lesson, (b) are relationships among mathematical concepts and principles emphasized, or (c) is the lesson presentation free from irrelevant knowledge? To be more specific, perhaps clarity could be better defined in terms of the simplicity of inference patterns, the absence of terms (concepts) that have not been previously defined (taught), the use of examples and instances where they are appropriate, or the high ratio of simple sentences to complex sentences (Henderson, 1978).

Another variable identified in the Rosenshine and Furst review that shows promise is *variability*. Variability was defined in a number of ways, including the variety of materials used, the cognitive level of questions asked, the variety of student activities provided, and a general rating of a teacher's flexibility in reacting to classroom events. The authors' review on variability was not confined to high-inference variables but included some low-inference ones as well.

It appears that variability has considerable promise for research on teaching mathematics. An index of teachers' variability could be constructed by considering several factors. One might be the extent to which a teacher introduces mathematical applications or problem-solving situations into the classroom. Another might focus on a teacher's ability to provide alternative explanations when students fail to comprehend a given topic. Still another might be the variety of moves (as defined by Cooney, Davis, & Henderson, 1975) in teaching concepts or principles. In the teaching of younger children, variability could be defined in terms of the way a teacher adjusts the content to accommodate a child's development.

Of the high-inference cognitive variables reviewed, it appeared that clarity and variability had the most potential for research in mathematics education. Both of these variables have been found to be associated with achievement. Further, they are amenable to being defined in terms of mathematical considerations, even though their empirical support is not generated by studies in mathematics education.

Low-inference variables. The research initiated by Smith and Meux (1967) and continued by Henderson (1967, 1969, 1970), which focused on the more logical nature of classroom discourse, involved low-inference variables. In a series of dissertations, various pedagogical concepts were explicated by considering an interaction of logical considerations and analyses of classroom behavior. The dissertations included ways mathematics teachers justify principles (Wolfe, 1969), organize knowledge (Cooney, 1969), teach concepts (Pavelka, 1975), teach skills (Todd, 1973), and teach generalizations (Semilla, 1972). These descriptive studies formed a basis for a series of empirical investigations, most of which have focused on the role of a "move" in teaching a mathematical concept.

Programmed instruction was used to determine the efficacy of various sequences of moves in teaching concepts. The sequences chosen were based on those occurring naturally in mathematics classrooms or from various theoretical positions in psychology. Dossey (1976) provides the following summary of this research:

1. Different logical forms of concepts may affect the relative efficacy of concept teaching strategies.

2. Strategies that explicitly illustrate characteristics of examples of

concepts (rather than strategies relying primarily on just examples and nonexamples) seem to be quite effective in promoting student achievement of conjunctive concepts, at least at the knowledge and comprehension levels of understanding.

3. Differences exist in students' ability to handle algebraic and geometric disjunctive concepts, as well as in their ability to deal with inclusive and exclusive disjunctive concepts.

4. Strategies and various uses of examples and nonexamples differ in their abilities to handle algebraic and inclusive disjunctive concepts.

Swank (1976) took a more global approach in comparing various strategies. Swank contrasted the variables—high number of moves (high amount of content information) with low number of moves and high student participation with low student participation. Teaching the concept of function to 80 eighth-grade students for two weeks, Swank formed four treatment groups (H,H), (H,L), (L,H), (L,L), the first component indicating the variable of concept moves and the second reflecting student participation. Swank found that students receiving a high-frequency concept move strategy achieved significantly more than students receiving a low-frequency concept move strategy. The students receiving the high interaction treatment also scored significantly higher.

Kolb (1977) has provided a model for predicting the effect of various strategies. Kolb's approach is concerned with the question "What outcomes are produced by a specific strategy?" Kolb's model essentially predicts that exemplification moves (E-moves) produce more learning than characterization moves (C-moves) for students with little prerequisite knowledge, although there is a "law of diminishing returns" with the E-moves. The difference in meaningful verbal learning between an E-move strategy and a C-move strategy becomes greater when the number of moves in each strategy is increased for students with little prerequisite knowledge; the difference becomes less for students with a high degree of prerequisite knowledge. To be sure, this statement is an oversimplification of a rather complex and intricate model. But what Kolb has provided is a means by which future research on moves and strategies can be viewed from a theoretical perspective. (See Sowder's chapter "Concept and Principle Learning" for additional discussions of Kolb's model.)

Generally the measures of outcome in the research reviewed by Dossey as well as other research on moves and strategies are categorized by some psychometric criteria. As a result, the strategies are not related to various types of "horizontal" outcomes; that is, perhaps an E-move strategy has qualitatively different outcomes from a C-move strategy. For example, Gregory and Osborne (1975) found that a teacher's use of the language of conditional logic was positively correlated with students' ability to

RESEARCH IN MATHEMATICS EDUCATION

answer questions on conditional logic successfully. A particular type of teacher behavior was linked with a particular type of student behavior. Associating a certain type of teacher behavior with a specific outcome has merit. Frequently, learning is defined by the use of some sort of learning hierarchy. But existing hierarchies do not account for qualitatively different outcomes (e.g., using conditional logic versus producing an example of a concept with certain restrictions). Gregory and Osborne's study suggests that certain types of teaching behavior can be linked to certain types of student performance. Perhaps this emphasis should be a focus of investigations for those involved in research on moves.

Questions and concerns. Dunkin and Biddle (1974) argued that one of the most important outcomes of educational research is the development of concepts for viewing the instructional process. A related question is the extent to which concepts are generic or specific to subject matter. Much of the research on cognitive variables on teaching is not specific to mathematics. Hence, one is left in the position of either disregarding the research or, as was done here, considering that research and seeing how it might apply to the teaching of mathematics. Another question concerns the extent to which one believes that effective teaching behaviors are specific to grade level. At either extreme a problem exists. On the one hand, a theory of teaching can be envisioned that consists of teaching principles across a two-dimensional matrix, content by age level. On the other hand, a theory of teaching could consist of deterministic statements that cut across all ages and all content. In the extreme, both positions seem preposterous.

Another concern involves possible confounding factors between high-inference variables and low-inference variables. Much of the research reviewed by Dossey (1976) involved programmed instruction. Such an approach allows a high degree of precision in defining and investigating various independent variables. But care must be taken not to compromise internally the strategies being investigated. That is, in comparing the relative efficacy of CEC, EC, CE, and ECE strategies, one must take care to ensure that the permutation of *moves* is not confounded by variance in clarity or information provided by a *move.* For example, if one finds that a CEC strategy is more effective than an ECE strategy, can the differential effects be explained in terms of the different ordering of moves (low inference) or can it be explained in terms of the clarity of the moves (high inference) in the information provided by the moves? That is, clarity and the information provided must be held constant, for surely there are "good" ECE strategies and "poor" CEC strategies, which could negate any general statement about the efficacy of the two strategies.

An analogous situation arises when one considers classroom research. Consider teaching by discovery. It was mentioned earlier that Riedesel and

Burns's review (1973) suggested that discovery teaching promotes better short-term effects. Dessart and Frandsen's review (1973) indicated no basic differences between the two approaches. The differences might be attributed to the fact that Riedesel and Burns reviewed research in elementary school mathematics, whereas Dessart and Frandsen reviewed research at the secondary school level. It is also possible that many confounding factors compromised the studies reviewed. The analogy suggests that any investigations on the efficacy of various treatments must hold constant any extraneous factors that could potentially compromise the effects of the independent variables—for example, clarity, student involvement, or, in general, "richness of a presentation."

Research on Managerial Variables

Managerial variables consist of organizational considerations, including managerial techniques to promote keeping students on task. Under the subheading of high-inference managerial variables, two general classes of variables will be considered: techniques for maintaining effective classroom control and the "directness" of the teacher. The primary low-inference variable discussed will be *time*, which will be considered in a variety of ways.

High-inference variables. First, variables associated with techniques of classroom management will be considered. Are such variables of interest to mathematics educators? It is difficult to convince oneself that they are specific to the teaching of mathematics. Research investigating managerial variables need not be conducted by mathematics educators. Still, two of the problems associated with helping students learn mathematics are "behavior problems" and "keeping students on task." Hence, a brief review of this research will be given.

One of the most highly regarded pieces of research in this field has been conducted by Kounin (1970). Kounin, who focused primarily on teachers' behaviors in managing groups of students, investigated the following variables and their relationship to achievement:

1. *Withitness* and *overlapping.* These dimensions deal with a teacher communicating that she knows what is going on regarding children's behavior and with her attending to two issues simultaneously when two different issues are present.
2. *Smoothness* and *momentum.* These parameters measure how the teacher manages movement during recitations and at transition periods.
3. *Group alerting* and *accountability.* These aspects of a teacher's technique deal with the extent to which she maintains a group focus during recitations in contrast to becoming immersed in a single child.
4. *Valence* and *challenge arousal.*
5. *Seatwork variety* and *challenge.* (Kounin, 1970, pp. 143–144)

Withitness was found to be the strongest correlate of student achievement. In reviewing Kounin's research, Dunkin and Biddle observed that it held "considerable promise for the eventual improvement of classroom teaching." (See Dunkin and Biddle's critique for an extensive analysis of Kounin's work.)

Brophy and Evertson (1976) conducted a two-year observational study of teachers who had been consistently effective. Their findings contained considerable support for Kounin's findings. The more successful teachers were more "withit," used less criticism to correct misbehavior problems, and correspondingly spent more time teaching substantive knowledge. Further, Brophy and Evertson noted the same "ripple effect" that Kounin did— namely, teachers designated as less "withit" tended not to cope with misbehavior involving one or two students, and consequently the behavior problems spread to other students. "Withit" teachers tended not to have this problem. The more successful teachers also had "smoother" transitional periods for changing classroom activities. This, too, was consistent with Kounin's findings. The more successful teachers tended to have classroom rules that were more general. Less successful teachers tended either to have no classroom rules and to make ad hoc decisions or to have so many specific rules that the rules were generally useless.

It is questionable that variables like "withitness" will be objects of research per se in mathematics education. But it might behoove mathematics educators doing field studies to gather evidence relative to the variables above. The purpose would be to account for differences in teacher performance (apart from mathematical considerations) that might account for differences in student achievement. Further, it would be desirable to hold variables related to classroom management as constant as possible across treatments. One of the very problems with doing field studies is the confounding factors of behavior problems and other behaviors not explicitly studied.

Another facet of teaching that has received some notice is the "directness" or "businesslikeness" of the teacher. In Rosenshine and Furst's review (1971) variables categorized as "task-oriented and/or businesslike behaviors" were found to be significantly correlated with achievement. Good (1978) found from preliminary results that a fairly direct means of teaching was effective and could produce significant increases in mathematics achievement. To Good, "direct" teaching entails the setting of goals by the teacher, with a continued assessment of students' progress toward those goals. In general, such a concept of teaching is similar to what Rosenshine and Furst call "task oriented or businesslike."

Rosenshine and Furst identified a major concern with research of this type, namely, that it demonstrates only that "you get what you teach for." Another concern, particularly for mathematics educators, is that achievement is defined in terms of lower-level behaviors. The implication is that a task-oriented or direct teacher is less likely to promote higher-order outcomes than a heuristically oriented teacher. So long as an emphasis on basic skills is an important concern, there may be considerable support for research on teaching methods that are direct and are aimed at keeping students on task.

Low-inference variables. One of the low-inference variables that has attracted a great deal of attention is that of *time.* Time has been used as a metric to define a number of variables. One variable defined by time is *wait time* (Rowe, 1978). According to Rowe, there are two kinds of wait time:

1. The pause following a question by the teacher
2. The pause following a student response

A pause was usually measured in terms of seconds. Rowe's research, which involved elementary science teachers, showed that (a) teachers typically wait less than one second before commenting on an answer or before asking an additional question and (b) when the two types of wait time are increased, the length of student responses increased, the number of unsolicited but appropriate responses increased, failures to respond decreased, students' confidence increased, disciplinary problems decreased, slower students participated more, and, in general, students were more reflective in their responses.

It would be interesting to see if mathematics teachers use such rapid-fire questioning techniques as Rowe found for science teachers. The guess here is that mathematics teachers do behave similarly. If so, then one can ask whether Rowe's findings relative to increasing wait time would also apply to mathematics teachers.

Time has also been used in other ways to quantify classroom processes. In studying mathematics teachers, Berliner (1978) defined three time-related variables: *allocated time, engaged time,* and *academic learning time.* Allocated time refers to the time specified for instruction in a given content area. Allocated time is an upper bound for engaged time, which is essentially the amount of time students are on task. Engaged time is an upper bound for academic learning time (ALT), which is defined as the time a student is engaged in activities with an error rate of less than 20%. Berliner's report focused on research with four second-grade and four fifth-grade mathematics teachers. Berliner's basic position is that

the marked variability in allocated time, engaged time, and in ALT, between and within classes, is the most potent explanatory variable to account for variability in student achievement, after initial aptitude has been removed as a predictor variable. A corollary of this thesis is that interactive teaching behavior (praise, questioning, the use of organizers, feedback, etc.) can only be understood through their effects on ALT. (p. 4)

Berliner's report indicated that there was a great deal of variance in allocated time for teaching mathematical topics. For example, one class of second graders had 400 minutes of allocated time to study concepts and operations involved in linear measurement, whereas another had only 29 minutes. From these variances in allocated time, it would be expected that wide variances would also occur in engaged time. Such was true, with the average engaged time for the second-grade classes ranging from 20 minutes to 40 minutes, and a range of 17 minutes to 49 minutes for the fifth-grade classes. Berliner noted that there was considerable slippage between the assigned time for mathematics (say 10:15 A.M. to 11:00 A.M.) and the time students were actually involved in mathematical activities.

Two points should be made with respect to ALT. First, the ALT variable, in regression analysis, accounted for about 10% of the variance in student achievement. Second, there was a very low amount of ALT across the school year. Estimates of ALT ranged from 33 to 58 hours for a 150-day school year for the four second grades (a range of 13 to 23 minutes each day!) and from 18 to 53 hours for the four fifth-grade classes (a range of 7 to 21 minutes each day!). When the multitude of mathematical objectives for a given year are considered, the amount of ALT (or scarcity of it) is rather sobering.

The identification of such extreme variance for the various classes is noteworthy. Regardless of the teaching strategies used, if the engaged time is as low as suggested by Berliner, learning is likely to come in very small increments. Such variance should give pause to those engaged in studies in which the efficacy of various strategies is compared. What are the relative effects of various strategies in comparison to time variables? There are also implications for teacher education. Teacher educators would be wise to sensitize interns to increasing their engaged time (and perhaps ALT), as well as having them acquire certain skills and philosophies in teaching mathematics.

Questions and concerns. The notion of ALT as an intervening variable is an intriguing thought. To Berliner, ALT is an intervening variable between teacher behavior and student achievement—that is, one can study teacher behavior from the standpoint of how it affects ALT, which in turn affects achievement. According to this position, ALT is a product of process-product studies in which teacher behavior is a process. Such an approach to process-product studies would simplify such investigations considerably. But given the present weak link that exists between teacher behaviors and student achievement, the merit of interjecting an intervening variable is questionable.

A defining attribute of ALT is that students must be engaged in work with error rates of less than 20%. This raises a philosophical question. Should mathematics educators promote more instruction at low error rates? For many mathematics educators this would be heresy. Must ALT be defined in terms of some fixed error rate? Although it may be desirable to define ALT in terms of some sort of student production, that production could be defined in terms of many types of mathematical activity. In fact, if problem solving is a treasured outcome, then an investigator could define ALT in terms of the time a student spends solving problems. The question arises whether or not ALT and related time variables are essentially the same as "opportunity to learn" variables. Perhaps Berliner's position of viewing ALT as an intervening variable will prove productive and hence ALT *is* more than simply an "opportunity to learn" variable. At the very least, Berliner's identification of such a wide variance of engaged time across classrooms should not go unnoticed by mathematics educators.

CONTENT VARIABLES

Since content variables are a primary concern of another chapter, only a few comments will be offered here. In any investigation there is some object of instruction, referred to as a *teachable object,* such as a mathematical concept or a mathematical generalization. One of the major problems associated with research on teaching mathematics is a lack of structure that permits sampling from homogeneous classes within the set of teachable objects. Without such structure it is difficult to conduct "additive" studies, since the teaching and acquisition of one type of knowledge may be unlike that of another. Smith, Cohen, and Pearl (1969) and Henderson (1976) have argued that the nature of a teachable object is a determining factor in how the object is taught and subsequently learned.

The domain of teachable objects in mathematics can be categorized in several ways. Merrill and Wood (1974) separate the domain into sets of identities, concepts, and rules. Cooney, Davis, and Henderson (1975) discuss three types of mathematical knowledge: concepts (e.g., function), generalizations (e.g., the Pythagorean theorem), and skills (e.g., solving equations). In whatever way the domain of teachable objects is categorized, at least two characteristics should be exhibited. First, the categories should constitute a partition—that is, be nonempty and disjoint and should collectively exhaust the set of teachable objects. Second, clusters within cells should share some attribute(s) deemed important for research. Those attributes might consist of logical or psychological considerations or be based on empirical evidence relating the acquisition of knowledge to difficulty or some other criterion. With such a structure, investigators could randomly select content from the various cells or their subdivisions and have a justifiable basis for generalizing beyond the specific content selected.

In addition, communication among investigators could be enhanced by better understanding the characteristics of the knowledge being taught. It is difficult to summarize research on concept training, for example, when such diverse content as symmetry, distributivity, partitioning a set, computing in modular systems, and such a statement as "The sum of the measures of the angles of a triangle is 180" are considered to be concepts. In the absence of a sampling procedure or some consistency in the concepts that are selected, research is likely to be idiosyncratic to the specific content that is selected. The categorization of the teachable objects in mathematics into homogeneous classes would be a worthy endeavor and could promote a much needed "additivity" of research findings.

OUTCOME VARIABLES

Turner (1976) has argued for the necessity of constructing indicators of student achievement and then determining the relationship between treatments and different types of indicators. This requires the structuring of indicators prior to investigations.

Indicators can be developed from several perspectives. Indicators for student achievement are usually based on some sort of hierarchical taxonomy such as that of Bloom, Englehart, Furst, Hill, & Krathwohl, 1956. Such taxonomies encourage the construction of "vertical" indicators based on some psychometric scale, not "horizontal" ones that focus on the more logical aspects of the knowledge being tested. Cooney and Dossey (1978) have constructed a framework for developing indicators for the acquisition of concepts that account for both vertical and horizontal indicators. A simplified version of their model is depicted in Figure 3. The horizontal indicators are exemplary only, not exhaustive.

The development of indicators could also be constructed specific to a given mathematical area. This perspective is not necessarily disjoint from the Cooney and Dossey model (1978). Van Hiele's work, as presented by Wirszup (1976), identifies various indicators for geometric content. Thomas (1969) identified developmental stages for the acquisition of the concept of function. At this point, it is an open question whether general indicators, as suggested by Cooney and Dossey, should be developed or whether indicators should be developed for specific content or topic areas.

The structuring of outcome variables into homogeneous classes by whatever model or method is used could be a great asset in promoting "additivity" of research findings. As Turner (1976) pointed out, indicators could then be randomly selected from the various classes, thus enabling researchers to generalize their findings to a broader range of possible learning outcomes. The structuring of indicators is basic to developing a means of interpreting findings from one study in light of another.

Psychometric Scale	Scale Based on Nature of a Concept			
	Term→ Example of concept	Term→ Nonexample of concept	Term→ Necessary condition for concept	Term→ Sufficient condition for concept
Recall				
Comprehension				
Concept usage				

Selected cells are illustrated below. Assume the items were constructed for 11th-grade students studying functions.

term→example X concept usage:
Create an example of a function in which the elements of the domain constitute a function and the range consists of the integers

term→nonexample X recall:
Give an example of a function

term→necessary condition X comprehension:
Suppose P(X) denotes a function. Which one of the following must be true about P(X)?
1. P(X) determines a one-to-one correspondence between the elements in the range and the domain.
2. P(X) has a finite range.
3. P(X) defines a linear function.
4. P(X) is a relation.

term→sufficient condition X comprehension:
Which one of the following will ensure that the relation P(X) is a function?
1. P(X) has a single element in its range.
2. P(X) defines a quadratic relation.
3. P(X) defines a linear relation.
4. P(X) is a finite relation.

Figure 3.

IMPRESSIONS OF RESEARCH ON TEACHING

Trite as it is, the saying "Teaching is an immensely complex phenomenon" needs to be repeated here. This complexity makes it very difficult to conduct, review, and synthesize research on teaching—particularly with respect to specific variables. Further, the complexity also ensures that correlations with specific variables and student achievement will be low. Gage (1976b), however, has argued that although the effect of any one dimension of teaching behavior on student achievement is small, the effects of several different variables are additive. Gage pointed out that low correlations—say, .3—which characterize many correlations in educational research, can be extremely important in promoting action. The analogy drawn was with the correlation between cigarette smoking and lung cancer. A correlation of about .3 prompted federal legislation and altered the habits of millions of people.

Part of the complexity of teaching can be attributed to the settings in which the teaching occurs. Since teachers, schools, and students are not monolithic, settings become an important consideration in designing and interpreting investigations. For example, as we mentioned earlier, Brophy and Evertson (1976) found that in classrooms where the socioeconomic status (SES) was high, praise was negatively related to gains in student learning, whereas the more successful teacher in schools where the SES was low promoted achievement through patience and encouragement. It is the impression here that not enough attention has been paid to setting variables in designing and interpreting research.

Given the complexity of teaching and the importance of setting variables, a critical question for mathematics educators is the extent to which variables of interest, especially cognitive ones, can be defined in ways specific to mathematics education. The variables *clarity* and *variability* appear to be potent ones in research outside of mathematics education. What is important, then, is the investigation of their potency in the teaching of mathematics. Can variables such as *clarity* and *variability* be defined in ways peculiar to mathematics? Given the structure of mathematical knowledge, it seems reasonable that many of the variables discussed earlier in this chapter can be so defined. Such definitions are basic to the development of acceptable principles for teaching mathematics.

Another basic question to be considered is whether the teaching of elementary school mathematics is qualitatively different from the teaching of secondary school mathematics. A related question involves the determination of whether the variables discussed previously can provide a viable basis for investigations across grade levels. Is the teaching of mathematics to young children different enough from the teaching of secondary school mathematics to warrant the consideration of a different set of variables (teaching behaviors) for the two areas? Before a justifiable answer can be given, more information on classroom processes across grade levels is needed. One point to consider is how the content of elementary school mathematics differs from the content in the secondary school mathematics curriculum. The extent to which the nature of the mathematical content in the respective areas varies could be a determining factor in deciding whether or not variables should be specific to a given age level.

Another impression that one can glean from existing research is the apparent support for the organized, task-oriented, and direct teacher. In the research reviewed for preparing this chapter, support was found to be stronger for the direct teacher than for the more heuristically oriented teacher. In addition, Berliner suggests that academic learning time accounts for a significant amount of variance in student achievement, a finding supported by Wiley and Harnischfeger (1974). It is tempting to interpret these findings as suggesting that if you teach for low-level outcomes, then, sure enough, you get low-level outcomes. But the issue should not be so quickly dismissed. Rosenshine (1976), in discussing research on teachers asking higher-order questions, concluded that "the continual bromides that factual questions are bad and higher level questions are good, were not supported by well-defined research" (p. 61). Research might better focus on relating certain types of teacher behavior, such as directness or the use of low- (or high-) level questions, with various types of learning outcomes—for instance, computational skills or problem solving. Then one could investigate what outcomes could be expected from, say, a direct teacher and concentrate less on rather deterministic findings that specify a behavior as either good or bad.

SUGGESTIONS FOR RESEARCH ON TEACHING

An area of growing interest in research on teaching is the means by which teachers process information in making instructional decisions. This area is rich in potential and is amenable to questions specific to mathematics education.

Much of the work, sometimes referred to as "information processing," was initiated by Elstein and Shulman (1971), who investigated the thinking processes of physicians in diagnosing illness. The research often entails stimulated recall in which the subjects are shown videotapes of their behavior and then asked to reflect on their corresponding thought processes. This technique was used by MacKay and Marland (1977) as they investigated the thought processes of elementary teachers when making instructional decisions. They found that teachers are not particularly reflective of their own teaching behavior and do not consider a large range of alternatives in making decisions but do tend to adhere to recognizable self-styled principles of teaching—for example, to help compensate for the "have nots" in classes.

Shroyer (1978) also used stimulated recall to investigate the course of information processing by teachers. Shroyer was primarily interested in how teachers thought about, and reacted to, interruptions to the instructional flow (for example, a behavior problem or an unanticipated student question). Although Shroyer's analysis was not complete at this writing, she had identified three types of interruptions that teachers attend to—student insight, student difficulty, and teaching concerns—and various types of elective actions taken by the teachers.

It would seem that studying the teacher as a decision maker and as a

processor of information has considerable merit. Perhaps one of the problems with previous research efforts is that the teacher is viewed as a rather
static entity and not as one who is instrumental in affecting the instructional flow. Magoon (1977) has argued that educational research should
adapt a constructivist approach. Basic to this position is the view that the
teacher is a knowing being and operates in a purposeful manner. Research
questions consistent with a constructivist approach would focus on how
mathematics teachers develop their "professional knowledge," what
factors contribute to the acquisition of that knowledge, and how that
knowledge affects instructional decisions. To Magoon, the value derived
from such research lies in a heavy emphasis on construct validity—that is,
the meaning of events or situations to participants and in the related
hypotheses generated from such findings.

As an outgrowth of viewing the teacher as a knowing being and as a
processor of information, several basic questions are offered for consideration. First, what constructs about teaching mathematics—mathematical,
psychological, and pedagogical—do mathematics teachers bring to the
classroom? This question gives rise to others, posed below.

1. Do teachers tend to think of mathematics as a body of knowledge,
replete with logical consistencies (in a sense, a logical positivist position),
or as knowledge constructed by an individual and, hence, specific and
idiosyncratic to that individual student (that is, basically a constructivist
position)?

2. How do teachers view the importance of mathematics in terms of
societal uses, a means to develop logical thinking, and a tool for the sciences?

3. How do teachers view students as learners of mathematics?

Another question is, "What factors influence a teacher's instructional
decisions?" In part, Shroyer was asking this question. A related question
is, "What instructional alternatives can a mathematics teacher identify for
a given classroom situation?" Possible influencing factors—and alternatives
—might stem from mathematical considerations, methodological considerations, or some psychological factors—for example, developmental concerns.

To illustrate one possible context for these questions, consider the
dialogue below.

Ms. Maxwell: What do we mean, class, by linear function? How would
we define it, Jake?

Jake: I don't know, I forgot.

Ms. Maxwell: Elsie?

Elsie: Well, it has something to do with a straight line.

Ms. Maxwell: That's true. But we need more. Todd?

Todd: Things like $f(x) = 2x + 3$ and $f(x) = 4x - 10$. These are linear functions, aren't they?

Ms. Maxwell: Yes. That's good. Now let's see how we can graph some linear functions. Look at this problem.

It appeared that Ms. Maxwell was asking for the definition of linear functions, but when Todd produced two examples, she seemed satisfied. This might be an instance of a teacher being unclear about the content being taught and, hence, as Smith, Cohen, and Pearl (1969) pointed out, instruction suffered from vagueness. Or it may have been that Ms. Maxwell was willing to accept examples as evidence of understanding rather than press for a correct definition. Did she make a conscious decision to accept examples rather than a definition? If so, what factors influenced her decision? What was the likely effect on students? Did Todd and the rest of the class think a definition had been given?

This situation raises the question of the extent to which teachers are aware of instructional alternatives. Are they aware of alternative mathematical treatments of a given topic? Of various methodological approaches? In identifying alternatives, do they tend to emphasize conceptual or computational aspects of the mathematics? What cues from students seem to suggest to teachers that a different instructional approach is needed? To what extent do teachers' strategies differ from those presented in textbooks? When a teacher deviates from a textbook presentation, what factors are considered in making the decision?

All these questions are aimed at studying a teacher's decision-making processes. An open question is whether the answers to the questions are content specific. That is, must the questions and their answers always be interpreted in view of specific content, such as fractions, functions, or isometries? If we can learn more about teachers' instructional decisions and what influences them, then we shall be in a better position to define potent variables more adequately. Further, teacher education programs can be devised with increased sensitivity to the needs and problems mathematics teachers encounter.

RESEARCH ON TEACHER EDUCATION

Although various positions on teacher education are espoused with great fervor, there is usually little evidence to support the positions. The opening paragraph of the chapter on *Teacher Education* in the National Advisory Committee on Mathematics Education (NACOME) report (1975) stated:

The dominant feature of the mathematics teacher education picture is the absence of hard data concerning programs and practices, requirements, and characteristics of the products. Much of what is written, discussed in conferences, and used to justify recommended programs is based on sketchy impressionistic data, random oases of innovative activity and research, and opinion. It is impossible to even attempt a description of the "typical" graduate of a teacher education pre-service program, much less that same individual after possible exposure to a wide variety of in-service training experiences. (p. 81)

Brophy (1975) put it this way:

Teacher educators and educational researchers need to pay more attention to the accumulation of a data base that would allow truly prescriptive teacher education to emerge. Propounding ideas on the basis of commitments rather than supportive data is unscientific to say the least, and blowing with the wind by propounding the latest educational fad is even worse. (p. 15)

The concern raised in the NACOME report and by Brophy is not unique to mathematics education in North America. Otte (1976) underscored the lack of research in mathematics teacher education programs in European countries and in some Asian countries. Otte made the point that teacher education is basically reactionary to whatever school reform exists at a given point in time. Hence, teacher education is moved by forces better characterized as whimsical than as rational.

A basic issue involves the question of whether a body of pedagogical knowledge exists that is deemed important enough to warrant its inclusion in mathematics teacher education programs. This issue is not trivial. Popham (1971) investigated the performance of experienced, certified teachers with the performance of individuals who were not trained or who indicated no prior teaching experience. The subject matter consisted of content from social science, auto mechanics, and electronics. Popham concluded that "experienced teachers are not particularly skilled at bringing about prescribed behavior changes in learners" (p. 115). Although one might argue that Popham's findings do not generalize to mathematics teachers or that the instructional time was too short (four hours) or that the achievement measures were too narrowly defined, the disturbing question remains, "Do those trained in the teaching of mathematics outperform those not so trained?"

The question will not be explicitly answered here. However, a review and critique of existing research on teacher education will be provided, which should at least stimulate thought on how this and other related questions might be answered. This part of the chapter will focus on variables related to training teachers, on variables related to the content of a teacher education program, and on variables related to outcome measures of teacher education programs.

VARIABLES IN TEACHER EDUCATION BEHAVIOR

Variables in teacher education behavior will refer to those activities or techniques that teacher educators can use to train preservice or in-service teachers. The variables constitute the domain of x with respect to teacher education and are analogous to the behaviors that classroom teachers exhibit when teaching mathematics. Since research on teacher education is not as extensive as research on teaching, there will not be a classification of the variables as there was for research on teaching.

Peck and Tucker (1973) conducted an extensive review of research on teacher education (not necessarily mathematics teacher education) and identified several themes they felt reflected that research. One conclusion they reached was that a "systems" approach to teacher education substantially improves a program's effectiveness. This approach requires that (a) desired learning behaviors be precisely identified, (b) training procedures be planned to meet the objectives, and (c) attainment of the objectives be measured, followed by feedback to the teacher and a possible recycling of the entire process. The weight of the evidence is that teachers who are trained to specify objectives and then to teach to those objectives are more "effective." Apparently, the research supporting this conclusion is cut from a behavioristic cloth. This virtually assures that there will be both dissenters and accepters, depending on one's disposition toward behavioral psychology. The important question is, "Which, if any, of the desired skills in teaching mathematics can be taught through a systems approach?"

Peck and Tucker also found evidence that teachers can be taught to adopt certain teaching techniques or behaviors, at least in controlled situations, when given practice in that behavior and feedback on their progress in acquiring it. In general, teachers acquire desired behaviors or attitudes more effectively when they participate in sensitivity-training laboratories, in simulated classroom episodes, or in actual classroom teaching episodes than when they participate in remote or abstract experiences, such as lectures on instructional theory. Turner's review (1975) of research on teacher education supports Peck and Tucker's conclusion. Two studies reviewed by Turner illustrate this support. An intensive study by Borg (1972), as presented by Turner, followed the procedure of viewing films and participating in microteaching activity until 75 minutes' practice of a specific instructional skill was completed. The 48 teachers in the study were videotaped before training, immediately after training, and four months after training. In addition, 24 teachers were taped in their school settings three years after the training. The results, as described by Turner, included the following:

> Three of the skills, "refocusing," "frequency of punitive teacher responses to incorrect-pupil answers," and "pausing" were not influenced by the training

procedure. "Redirection" and "clarification" held up well over the three-year period, while "prompting" did not hold up. The negative behaviors "repeating the question," "repeating the pupil's answer" and "answering one's own questions" were distinctly reduced by the course and remained at low levels at the end of the three-year period. (p. 98)

In reviewing a study by Kocylowski (1970), Turner stated that subjects who participated in microteaching sessions outperformed those involved in role-playing activities, who outperformed those in a control group. But Turner also noted that

the resulting differences between the groups came about centrally as a result of differential losses rather than gains in skills. Teaching experience apparently has quite adverse effects on these teaching skills; nonetheless the microteaching treatments may be viewed as the better treatment in this study since the residual levels of most of the skills were greater for this group than for the others. (p. 99)

The studies reviewed by Peck and Tucker and by Turner were generally consistent in that both showed that microteaching and viewing films promoted the acquisition of desired teaching behaviors. However, the two studies reviewed by Turner suggested that it is indeed speculative to believe the acquired behaviors continue into classroom teaching situations. Similarly, Peck and Tucker found that although prospective teachers view student teaching as the most useful course in their teacher education program, the effects of that experience are not always positive. Peck and Tucker identified a large number of studies indicating that student teachers tended to become more bureaucratic, authoritarian, and less humanistic in their approach to teaching as they progress through their experience. This was particularly true with student teachers whose cooperating teachers displayed these characteristics.

In reading Peck and Tucker's and Turner's reviews, one gets the impression that preservice teachers become more businesslike in their ability to handle content but that they also become somewhat detached from the students. If the position is taken that experience helps teachers become more effective, then the finding discussed earlier that businesslike teachers tend to be more effective takes on added meaning.

At this point in the development of research on teacher education, behavior variables need to be explicitly identified. These behaviors (variables) consist, in general, of college classroom activities, laboratory activities, and field-based activities. A finer cut can be obtained by identifying different types of classroom, laboratory, and field-based activities as suggested below.

1. Classroom activities
   Lecture-discussions

   Using media materials
   Role playing
2. Laboratory activities
   Tutoring
   Microteaching
   Clinical interviews
3. Field activities
   Small-group instruction
   Large-group instruction

The list above is presented, not as a partition of possible variables, but rather as an example of what might be done. The field could profit from a more thorough identification of the variables.

A relevant question, then, is "Which of the activities above can most effectively produce desired competencies?" For example, suppose a desired competency is understanding the logic of a counterexample and recognizing when its use is appropriate. Perhaps the technique best suited to teaching this concept lies in the domain of classroom activity, whereas developing an ability to present and promote problem-solving situations would be more likely to require laboratory or field-based activities.

It should be made clear that the investigations of variables that a teacher educator might use to promote desired professional behavior should not be locked into an engineering mentality. Certainly the whole of training teachers cannot be subjected to a component analysis of teaching behavior in which each component becomes a training entity. Teaching is too complex for that, although a certain degree of component analysis might be desirable. But a rejection of the engineering mode of training teachers should not give credence to the position that teachers should be trained solely by the apprenticeship model. Total reliance on the apprenticeship model for a teacher education program is rejected here. Perhaps a goal of research on teacher education is to identify those teaching skills that are amenable to some sort of component analysis and that are too complex to be acquired through a systems approach.

VARIABLES IN TEACHER EDUCATION CONTENT

As depicted in Figure 1 at the outset of this chapter, content variables in teacher education consist of those pedagogical concepts and principles that are the objects of instruction. But determining the content is no small task. Usually the content is highly idiosyncratic to a given instructor or institution. No doubt this reflects the large divergence of views on what constitutes effective teaching.

Lester (1973) has attacked the problem of trying to lay out a domain of teaching skills in mathematics and has also identified behavior indicators to assess an intern's acquisition of a skill. The indicators were designed to include activities for the college classroom or learning lab center and microteaching, or actual classroom teaching. Cooney, Kansky, and Retzer (1975) identified various pedagogical concepts for teaching mathematics. Their work was primarily an extension of the work on moves for teaching mathematical concepts and principles initiated by Henderson (1967) and others. In addition, Retzer (1976b) has described how such content can be depicted through various media materials and be used in research in teacher education. Perhaps the most important contribution of Lester, Retzer, and Cooney et al. was providing a first approximation at attempting to lay out the domain of pedagogical content in a program for the education of mathematics teachers.

A number of variables were discussed in previous sections. Are any of those variables worthy of consideration in educating teachers? If a strong causal relationship between the variables and achievement is required, the answer is no. But some variables can provide a basis for conceptualizing aspects of teaching mathematics and, hence, can be productively incorporated. The variables might be correlated only with achievement yet provide clues to useful pedagogical concepts. Although clarity and variability are two such variables, they need to be defined in ways more specific to mathematics education. The research summarized by Dossey (1976) provides a basis for considering various strategies for teaching mathematical concepts. The descriptive study by Pavelka (1975) on teaching mathematical concepts can provide still another basis for designing instructional strategies. The time variables identified by Berliner (1978) are at least worth discussing with teachers to increase their sensitivity in using class time. Indeed, there is no shortage of constructs, identified from research, that can be profitably used in educating mathematics teachers.

I believe teachers at any level are better prepared if they have basic concepts that allow them to reflect on their teaching and if they are better prepared to identify alternative choices for making instructional decisions. This is more likely if the desired pedagogical knowledge is explicitly identified and taught. Many gifted teachers make decisions "naturally" based primarily on common sense and what Davis (1967) refers to as "practioners' maxims." Smith et al. (1969) argue that teachers who have a knowledge of their actions and a means to consciously analyze and reflect on their instruction have an added advantage in promoting achievement. Although teacher educators must take care not to foster in their trainees "paralysis by analysis," one objective of a teacher education program is to equip the trainee with a basis for understanding and analyzing instructional acts.

At the outset of this chapter the domain of y for teacher education was identified as consisting of pedagogical concepts, generalizations, and skills. Figure 4 exemplifies these types of knowledge in comparison to mathematical knowledge.

	Mathematical Content	Pedagogical Content
Concepts	Function Prime number	Clarity of a presentation, Heuristic teaching methods
Generalizations	The Pythagorean theorem The law of sines	Law of reinforcement, Various maxims for teaching by discovery
Skills	Factoring trinomials Solving equations	Diagnosing learning problems, Questioning students

Figure 4.

Although it is doubtful that pedagogical content can be as easily classified as mathematical content (and some would argue the subdivision of mathematical content is not desirable or even possible), a well-conceived classification scheme has implications for development and research. Consider a pedagogical concept such as "clarity." How could this concept be taught? It seems reasonable to assume that it could be taught in much the same way other concepts are taught—through the use of examples, nonexamples, definitions, and by pointing out its relevant and irrelevant attributes.

The differentiation between a pedagogical concept and a pedagogical skill also has implications for the teacher educator. The acquisition of a pedagogical concept might entail the identification of examples and nonexamples or of relevant and irrelevant attributes of the concept. If, in addition, an intern can present a lesson that incorporates the concept, it would indicate that a skill has been acquired. Although the concept-skill distinction is somewhat arbitrary, it is not without merit. Consider an analogy. A student cannot be skilled in factoring whole numbers into their primes until the concept of prime number has been acquired. But too often the skill of factoring is introduced without adequate attention to the underlying concept. Similarly, a pedagogical concept should be taught before an intern is expected to incorporate the concept in teaching.

Thus if one is to teach pedagogical concepts, methods of presenting a concept through lecture-discussion, analyzing transcripts, and viewing videotapes can be considered. *Using* the concept requires an instructional setting, such as peer teaching, microteaching, or classroom teaching. Hence, the type of pedagogical knowledge taught dictates to some degree the type of delivery system (behavior variables) to be used. This argues for greater attention to the identification and classification of pedagogical knowledge than has previously been necessary.

OUTCOME VARIABLES

Several types of outcome variables are appropriate goals for teacher education programs. Turner (1975) identified three classes of criterion variables for work success: student attainment, both cognitive and affective; professional judgment; and student judgment. The problem, as Turner noted, is that these three criteria do not always correlate positively with each other. In fact, Post, Ward, and Willson (1977) found that within the criteria of professional judgment, ratings from teachers, principals, and college mathematics educators were quite different. Principals and college educators differed considerably in their assessment of teaching performance, and classroom teachers agreed more with principals than with college faculty. This creates a dilemma in evaluating programs in teacher education and related research.

LeBlanc (1977) presents a number of questions for researchers to consider relative to teacher education programs. His questions focus on the following categories: point of view in teaching mathematics, knowledge related to mathematics and curriculum, instructional strategies, instructional materials, evaluation, and professional aspects. For each of these categories LeBlanc identifies questions related to what he terms *process* and *product*. Process involves the performance of teachers. Product involves the performance of their students. The notion of process and product outcomes is of some importance in considering research on teacher education.

Peck and Tucker (1973) note that many studies on teacher education end in midair. That is, dependent variables are often teacher behavior (LeBlanc's *process* variables) rather than student cognitive or affective outcomes (LeBlanc's *product* variables). A classic case of this situation is Borg's study as presented by Turner (1975). Few studies are as carefully controlled as Borg's, and few have the longitudinal component that his does; yet its Achilles heel is that no evidence exists that the behaviors acquired by the teachers related to student achievement. Similarly, in several studies reviewed by Turner only weak relationships were identified between training and student attainment.

An investigation by Gage (1976a) used student achievement as a criterion in determining the effects of training four experienced teachers to teach eight variations of a recitation strategy. The eight strategies were determined by taking high and low levels of structuring, soliciting, and reacting. The subject matter consisted of ecological facts, concepts, and principles. Gage's conclusions included the following:

1. Students learned a great deal about ecology from all the strategies.

2. The four teachers were able to vary their instructional performance in the prescribed way with great precision.

3. The variables in teaching behavior had only small effects on the students' achievement.

History seems to indicate that LeBlanc's product questions (1977), some of which are given below, are not likely to produce statistically significant results:

1. Do teachers having a greater repertoire of strategies for the models (sets, number line, etc.) produce more effective learning in children? (p. 215)

2. Can teachers trained in diagnostic and remediation procedures produce greater achievement in children? (p. 218)

3. Does school experience during the preservice training of teachers (specifically in mathematics) make a difference in the achievement of children? (p. 221)

Perhaps too much is expected in terms of trying to relate a teacher's training on a specific teaching skill to student achievement. Considering the multitude of factors that influence achievement, it is indeed optimistic to hold a single aspect of teaching, let alone training on that aspect, accountable for much variance in learning.

I believe professional judgment is a viable and desirable means of assessing outcomes of a teacher education program. Given the state of the art of both teaching and teacher education, it is unlikely that student outcomes *alone* can provide a satisfactory basis for evaluating a teacher education program. This is not to refute LeBlanc's statement (1977) that the ultimate criterion for a teacher education program is student achievement. Surely it is. But present evaluation techniques, combined with a lack of assurance as to how much potential variance in achievement can be accounted for by instruction, greatly limits the usefulness of achievement as an outcome.

Consider an analogy with the medical profession—a profession much more scientifically based than education. Medical interns are evaluated against the criterion of "the best we know at the present time." Retzer (1976a) noted that physicians are held accountable for malpractice, not malhealing. Even in education, legal suits against teachers (for not producing student achievement) are decided on the basis of whether or not the teacher was teaching in accordance with "accepted practice." The point is, then, that research on mathematics teacher education should focus on determining whether or not the gap is being closed between current practice in teaching mathematics and desired practice.

An attempt will be made to indicate how the domain of variables in teacher behavior could be laid out. Smith et al. (1969) identified three types of knowledge a teacher should have: subject matter, psychological, and pedagogical. This type of knowledge can be crossed with two phases of teaching: preactive and interactive. Preactive teaching involves activities that do not engage students, such as planning. Interactive teaching involves classroom behaviors. This leads to the matrix in Figure 5.

Types of Knowledge	Aspects of Teaching	
	Preactive Phase	Interactive Phase
Mathematical	Given a mathematical topic, can ways in which the mathematics is applied and related to other areas of mathematics be identified?	Does the teacher teach mathematics in a way that promotes applications or the interrelationships of mathematical ideas?
Psychological	Given a videotape illustrating a student's performance on various mathematical tasks, can the student's developmental level be ascertained?	Can the teacher group students within a classroom according to their development levels of understanding mathematics?
Pedagogical	Given a mathematical topic and descriptions of students, can a variety of instructional strategies be identified?	Can the teacher demonstrate a variety of instructional strategies in teaching mathematics?

Figure 5. A matrix of outcome variables with examples.

Outcomes could be measured in various ways. Preactive outcomes could be evaluated by paper-and-pencil responses or by judging an intern's responses to audiotapes or videotapes. Interactive behaviors could be evaluated on the basis of professional judgments of the teaching behavior. Judgments could be either subjective or based on explicit, predetermined criteria.

Two points should be made with respect to this position. First, it is not being maintained that successful teaching can be modularized and packaged. In all likelihood, successful teaching will always exceed the sum of its parts. But this does not argue against training teachers in certain basic techniques and concepts. To draw an analogy, a champion tennis player is more than just a person who can stroke forehands, backhands, volleys, and serves. But a player cannot be a champion without acquiring certain basic fundamentals. Why leave the acquisition of known successful teaching techniques to chance? The best of what we know should become explicit goals of instruction, and interns emerging from the program should be evaluated accordingly. Second, the ultimate goal of linking training to student achievement should not be abandoned.

SUGGESTIONS FOR RESEARCH ON TEACHER EDUCATION

Peck and Tucker's review (1973) and Turner's review (1975) suggest that teachers can be trained to incorporate certain teaching behaviors and that those behaviors will probably result in desired professional and student judgments; it has not been clearly demonstrated which of the behaviors result in student learning in either the cognitive or the affective domain. Although the research reviewed involved a broader base than the field of mathematics education, the finding above probably reflects mathematics teacher education programs as well.

Before much progress can be made with respect to research in mathematics teacher education, work needs to be done in delineating the nature of delivery systems, the nature of the content of mathematics teacher education programs, and the range of expected outcomes from the programs. Competency-based teacher education (CBTE) programs have provided some impetus for laying out the various domains, although the task does not have to be couched in a CBTE context.

Ideally, there should be a close association between research on teaching and research on teacher education. One research strategy that helps mesh the two areas of research is what Turner (1976) calls a *dyadic strategy*. A dyadic teaching strategy consists of a combination of behaviors that is determined primarily by students' responses. Hence, the strategy is to train teachers in whatever teaching behaviors are deemed important and compare their behavior and subsequent student achievement with those of "untrained" teachers. The use of dyadic strategies permits two types of variables to be studied: (a) those teaching variables that are the goals of instruction and (b) the teacher education behavior variables used to train the teachers. Differences in student achievement could be accounted for in either the teaching variables or the nature of the training or both, depending on the design of the study.

The research strategy of training teachers in instructional techniques, allowing them to use the techniques according to their own dictates, and then assessing their performance and their student outcomes has at least two advantages. First, in terms of research on teaching, it avoids the extensive problem of sampling behavior variables from an immense domain. Second, the selection of "trained" and "untrained" teachers can be made from preservice teachers, thus reducing the cost of obtaining subjects.

To illustrate, consider the following two questions:

1. Do students of teachers trained to employ heuristics for solving problems become better problem solvers than students of teachers not so trained?

2. Do students of teachers educated on various moves and strategies for teaching concepts and principles outperform students of teachers not possessing such knowledge?

The content variables (pedagogical knowledge) involve heuristics for solving problems and a knowledge of moves and strategies for the two questions respectively. The content must be explicitly defined and clearly differentiated from other pedagogical knowledge—a problem not resolved in many teacher education studies. Once the content is determined, then the problem of how that content can be presented must be addressed. The resulting teacher education behavior variables could include the use of films, the analysis of transcripts, or any of the other techniques available to teacher educators. But again the variables must be carefully defined. Process measures (outcome variables) could be determined to ascertain whether trainees had acquired the specified knowledge. Product measures could be designed to assess student performance and provide data to answer the questions posed.

Another area of research involves changes that occur in a trainee's perspective of teaching mathematics as preservice and first-year teaching experiences accumulate. Research in this area would parallel the research on teaching suggested earlier, in which the teacher is viewed from an information-processing viewpoint. The focus here would be on the relationship between teacher education activities and the way those teachers conceptualize instruction. Specifically, the following questions could be considered:

1. To what extent do interns' views of mathematics and of teaching mathematics change as they participate in field experiences? What is the qualitative nature of the changes?

2. Is there a relationship between the types of activities and the nature of the changes in perspective of the interns?

3. To what extent do changes in perspectives about teaching mathematics occur during the first year of teaching?

Answers to these questions could go a long way in providing an understanding of the dynamics of teacher education and the means by which teachers acquire various perspectives about teaching.

CONCLUSION

Research on teaching has identified a wide array of variables worthy of investigation. However, since many of the variables identified were in research that did not involve mathematics, an important question becomes, "Which of those variables have particular promise in doing research on teaching mathematics?" Another concern is the extent to which affective or cognitive variables not explicitly involving mathematics account for variance in student achievement. Research should be sensitive to such variables and not allow them to be confounding factors. For example, field studies should control those variables that are not of direct interest but are strong correlates with achievement; otherwise they can confound results. Withitness, ALT, and warmth are but a few examples of such variables.

Still another concern involves the differences that exist between the teaching of elementary school mathematics and secondary school mathematics. Berliner's findings (1978) suggest that elementary students actually study mathematics—that is, are on task—only a small amount of time. Is this true of secondary students as well? Are affective variables uniformly potent across all grade levels? Should variables such as clarity be defined differently for elementary teachers and secondary teachers? The questions are intriguing and deserve consideration.

The status of research on teaching and teacher education is eclectic, to be sure. Much needs to be done to define potentially significant variables in a lucid way. The pursuit of knowledge about teaching mathematics and educating mathematics teachers is both frustrating and exhilarating. It is frustrating because of the immense complexity of teaching; it is exhilarating because the generation of knowledge represents our finest achievement.

REFERENCES

Berliner, D. C. *Allocated time, engaged time, and academic learning time in elementary school mathematics instruction.* Paper presented at the 56th Annual Meeting of the National Council of Teachers of Mathematics, San Diego, April 1978.

Bloom, B. S., Englehart, M. D., Furst, E. J., Hill, W. H., & Krathwohl, D. R. *Taxonomy of educational objectives, handbook I: Cognitive domain.* New York: David McKay, 1956.

Borg, W. R. The minicourse as a vehicle for changing teacher behavior: A three-year follow-up. *Journal of Educational Psychology,* December 1972, *62,* 572–579.

Brophy, J. E. *Reflections on research in elementary schools.* Austin, Texas: R & D Center for Teacher Education, 1975.

Brophy, J. E., & Evertson, C. M. *Learning from teaching: A developmental perspective.* Boston: Allyn & Bacon, 1976.

Bush, A. J., Kennedy, J. J., & Cruickshank, D. R. An empirical investigation of teacher clarity. *Journal of Teacher Education,* March-April 1977, *28*(2), 53–58.

Cooney, T. J. An analysis of teachers' verbal behavior using the theory of relations (Doctoral dissertation, University of Illinois, 1969). *Dissertation Abstracts International,* 1970, *31,* 673A. (University Microfilms No. 70-13, 282)

Cooney, T. J., Davis, E. J., & Henderson, K. B. *Dynamics of teaching secondary school mathematics.* Boston: Houghton-Mifflin, 1975.

Cooney, T. J., & Dossey, J. A. *A framework for developing verbal concept acquisition indicators.* Unpublished manuscript, 1978. (Available from Thomas J. Cooney, 105 Aderhold, University of Georgia, Athens, GA 30602.)

Cooney, T., Kansky, R., & Retzer, K. *Protocol material in mathematics education: Selection of concepts.* Bloomington, Ind.: National Center for the Development of Training Materials in Teacher Education, 1975.

Cruickshank, D., Kennedy, J., Myers, B., & Bush, A. *Teacher clarity—What is it?* Paper presented at the Conference on Innovative Practices in Teacher Education, Atlanta, January 1976.

Davis, R. B. Mathematics teaching—With special reference to epistemological problems. *Journal of Research and Development in Education,* 1967, *1* (Monograph No. 1, Fall 1967).

Dessart, D. J., & Frandsen, H. Research on teaching secondary-school mathematics. In R. M. Travers (Ed.), *Second handbook of research on teaching.* Chicago: Rand McNally, 1973.

Dossey, J. A. The role of relative efficacy studies in the development of mathematical concept teaching strategies: Some findings and some directions. In T. J. Cooney & D. A. Bradbard (Eds.), *Teaching strategies: Papers from a research workshop.* Columbus, Ohio: ERIC/SMEAC, 1976.

Dunkin, M. J., & Biddle, B. J. *The study of teaching.* New York: Holt, Rinehart & Winston, 1974.

Elstein, A. S., & Shulman, L. S. *A method for the study of medical thinking and problem solving.* Paper presented at the annual meeting of the American Educational Research Association, New York, February 1971.

Fey, J. T. Classroom teaching of mathematics. In J. W. Wilson & L. R. Carry (Eds.), *Review of recent research in mathematics education* (Studies in mathematics, Vol. 19). Stanford, Calif.: School Mathematics Study Group, 1969.

Gage, N. L. A factorially designed experiment on teacher structuring, soliciting, and reacting. *Journal of Teacher Education,* Spring 1976, *27*(1), 35–38. (a)

Gage, N. L. *Four cheers for research on teaching.* Paper presented at the annual meeting of the American Educational Research Association, San Francisco, April 1976. (b)

Good, T. L. *The Missouri mathematics effectiveness project: A program of naturalistic and experimental research.* Paper presented at the annual meeting of the American Educational Research Association, Toronto, March 1978.

Gregory, J. W., & Osborne, A. R. Logical reasoning ability and teacher verbal behavior within the mathematical classroom. *Journal for Research in Mathematics Education,* January 1975, *6*(1), 26–36.

Heath, R. W., & Nielson, M. A. The research basis for performance-based teacher education. *Review of Educational Research,* Fall 1974, *44*(4), 463–484.

Henderson, K. B. Research on teaching secondary school mathematics. In N. L. Gage (Ed.), *Handbook of research on teaching.* Chicago: Rand McNally, 1963.

Henderson, K. B. A model for teaching mathematical concepts. *Mathematics Teacher,* 1967, *60,* 573–577.

Henderson, K. B. *Teaching secondary school mathematics.* Washington, D.C.: National Education Association, 1969.

Henderson, K. B. Concepts. In M. F. Rosskopf (Ed.), *The teaching of secondary school mathematics,* Thirty-third Yearbook of the National Council of Teachers of Mathematics. Washington, D.C.: The Council, 1970.

Henderson, K. B. Toward the development of pedagogical theory in mathematics. In T. J. Cooney & D. A. Bradbard (Eds.), *Teaching strategies: Papers from a research workshop.* Columbus, Ohio: ERIC/SMEAC, 1976.

Henderson, K. B. Personal communication, July 1978.

Kocylowski, M. M. *A comparison of microteaching and conventional systems of pre-service teacher education on teaching effectiveness.* Unpublished doctoral dissertation, Wayne State University, 1970.

Kolb, J. R. *A predictive model for teaching strategies research. Part I: Derivation of the model.* Athens: The Georgia Center for the Study of Learning and Teaching Mathematics, 1977.

Kounin, J. S. *Discipline and group management in classrooms.* New York: Holt, Rinehart & Winston, 1970.

LeBlanc, J. F. Teacher education in elementary mathematics: A framework for needed research. In L. Shalaway (Ed.), *Proceedings of the Research on Teaching Mathematics Conference.* East Lansing, Mich.: Institute for Research on Teaching, 1977.

Lester, F. Teaching skills in mathematics instruction. In R. Turner (Ed.), *A general catalog of teaching skills.* Bloomington: Indiana University, 1973.

MacKay, D. A., & Marland, P. W. *Thought processes of teachers.* Unpublished manuscript, 1977.

Magoon, A. J. Constructivist approaches in educational research. *Review of Educational Research,* Fall 1977, *17*(4), 651–693.

Medley, D. M. Closing the gap between research in teacher effectiveness and the teacher education curriculum. *Journal of Research and Development in Education,* 1973, *7*(1), 39–46.

Merrill, M. D., & Wood, N. D. *Instructional strategies: A preliminary taxonomy.* Columbus, Ohio: ERIC Information Analysis Center for Science, Mathematics, and Environmental Education, Ohio State University, 1974.

National Advisory Committee on Mathematical Education (NACOME). *Overview and analysis of school mathematics, grades K-12.* Washington, D.C.: Conference Board of the Mathematical Sciences, 1975.

Otte, M. *The education and professional life of mathematics teachers.* Paper presented at the Third International Congress on Mathematics Education, Karlsruhe, Germany, August 1976.

Pavelka, E. B. Moves, strategies, and models of a concept venture in secondary school mathematics (Doctoral dissertation, University of Illinois, 1974). *Dissertation Abstracts International,* 1975, *35,* 7183A. (University Microfilms No. 75-11,667)

Peck, R. F., & Tucker, J. A. Research on teacher education. In R. M. Travers (Ed.), *Second handbook of research on teaching.* Chicago: Rand McNally, 1973.

Popham, W. J. Performance tests of teaching proficiency: Rationale, development, and validation. *American Educational Research Journal,* January 1971, *8*(1), 105–117.

Post, T. R., Ward, W. H., & Willson, V. L. Teachers', principals', and university faculties' views of mathematics learning and instruction as measured by a mathematics inventory. *Journal for Research in Mathematics Education,* November 1977, *8*(5), 332–341.

Retzer, K. A. Personal communication, January 1976.(a)

Retzer, K. A. A research context for delivery systems research on strategies for teaching mathematics. In T. J. Cooney & D. A. Bradbard (Eds.), *Teaching strategies: Papers from a research workshop.* Columbus, Ohio: ERIC/SMEAC, 1976. (b)

Riedesel, C. A., & Burns, P. C. Research on the teaching of elementary school mathematics. In R. M. Travers (Ed.), *Second handbook of research on teaching.* Chicago: Rand McNally, 1973.

Rosenshine, B. Recent research on teaching behaviors and student achievement. *Journal of Teacher Education,* Spring 1976, *27*(1), 61–64.

Rosenshine, B., & Furst, N. Research in teacher performance criteria. In B. O. Smith (Ed.), *Symposium on research in teacher education.* Englewood Cliffs, N.J.: Prentice-Hall, 1971.

Rowe, M. B. Wait, wait, wait. . . . *School Science and Mathematics,* March 1978, *78*(3), 207–216.

Semilla, L. Z. Moves and strategies in a principle venture in secondary school mathematics (Doctoral dissertation, University of Illinois, 1971). *Dissertation Abstracts International,* 1972, *32,* 4495A. (University Microfilms No. 72-07054)

Shroyer, J. C. *Critical moments in the teaching of mathematics.* Paper presented at the annual meeting of the American Educational Research Association, Toronto, March 1978.

Smith, B. O., Cohen, S. B., & Pearl, A. *Teachers for the real world.* Washington, D.C.: American Association of Colleges for Teacher Education, 1969.

Smith, B. O., & Meux, M. O. *A study of the strategies of teaching.* Urbana: Bureau of Educational Research, College of Education, University of Illinois Press, 1967.

Smith, L. Aspects of teacher discourse and student achievement in mathematics. *Journal for Research in Mathematics Education,* May 1977, *8*(3), 195–204.

Swank, E. W. An empirical comparison of teaching strategies where the amount of content information and teacher-pupil interaction is varied. In T. Cooney & D. A. Bradbard (Eds.), *Teaching strategies: Papers from a research workshop.* Columbus, Ohio: ERIC/SMEAC, 1976.

Thomas, H. L. *An analysis of stages in the attainment of a concept of function.* Unpublished doctoral dissertation, Teachers College, Columbia University, 1969.

Thornton, C. D. An evaluation of the mathematics-methods program involving the study of teaching characteristics and pupil achievement in mathematics. *Journal for Research in Mathematics Education,* January 1977, *8*(1), 17–25.

Tikunoff, W. J., Berliner, D. C., & Rist, R. C. *An ethnographic study of the forty classrooms of the beginning teacher evaluation study known sample* (Tech. Rep. 75-10-5). San Francisco: Far West Laboratory, 1975.

Todd, H. W. Moves and strategies in a skill venture in secondary school mathematics (Doctoral dissertation, University of Illinois, 1972). *Dissertation Abstracts International,* 1973, *34,* 644A. (University Microfilms No. 73-17,449)

Turner, R. L. An overview of research in teacher education. In K. Ryan (Ed.), *Teacher education.* The Seventy-fourth Yearbook of the National Society for the Study of Education. Chicago: University of Chicago Press, 1975.

Turner, R. L. Design problems in research on teaching strategies in mathematics. In T. J. Cooney & D. A. Bradbard (Eds.), *Teaching strategies: Papers from a research workshop.* Columbus, Ohio: ERIC/SMEAC, 1976.

Wiley, D. E., & Harnischfeger, A. Explosion of a myth: Quantity of schooling and exposure to instruction, major educational vehicles. *Educational Researcher,* 1974, *3,* 7–12.

Wirszup, I. Breakthrough in the psychology of learning and teaching of geometry. In L. Martin & D. A. Bradbard (Eds.), *Space and geometry: Papers from a research workshop.* Columbus, Ohio: ERIC/SMEAC, 1976.

Wolfe, R. E. Strategies of justification used in the classroom by teachers of secondary school mathematics (Doctoral dissertation, University of Illinois, 1969). *Dissertation Abstracts International,* 1969, *30,* 1064A–1065A. (University Microfilms No. 69-15,422)

Index

475

McClelland, D. C., 335
McClintock, C. E., 290, 294, 302, 319
McConnell, T. R., 214, 215, 240
McCormack, R. L., 83, 95
McGinty, R. L., 267, 281
McLaughlin, J. A., 189, 205
McLellen, J. A., 163, 203
McLeod, D. B., 83, 95
McManis, D. L., 157, 203
Measurement, 41, 42, 49, 154, 163, 169, 170, 171, 172, 361 ff., 372
Mechanistic model, 146, 147, 148, 149, 155, 181, 187
Media, 408, 426
Mediating factor, 379, 381
Medley, D. M., 440, 473
Mehrens, W. A., 9, 19
Melbye, H. O., 219, 237
Memory, 181, 215
Menchinskaya, N. A., 179, 203
Merrill, M. D., 246, 256, 283, 284, 390, 391, 402, 416, 431, 434, 435, 453, 473
Messick, S., 261, 278, 283, 330, 333, 354
Meta-analysis, 25, 64
Methodologies, 35, 38, 152, 153, 154, 155, 316, 349
Meux, M. O., 473
Meyer, R. A., 296, 300, 321, 326, 354
Miel, A., 66, 95
Mierkiewicz, D., 163, 202, 290, 318, 321
Miller, C. K., 189, 205
Miller, H. R., 403, 431
Miller, N., 361, 386
Miller, P., 156, 197
Miller, R. L., 412, 414, 431
Miller, S., 305, 320
Miller, S. A., 154, 203
Miller, W. A., 267, 283
Miller, W. L., 381, 387
Minium, E. W., 52, 65
Mitchell, R., 178, 206, 298, 323
Models, 7, 23, 29, 35, 39, 72, 135, 146, 149, 150, 178, 182, 185, 230, 269, 338, 339, 342, 378, 416, 438, 454, 468
Momentum, 449
Montangero, J., 174, 203
Montgomery, M. E., 172, 192, 203, 325, 327, 354
Moore, C. A., 333, 355
Morningstar, M., 169, 205
Moser, H. E., 217, 236
Moser, J. M., 327, 354
Moses, B. E., 298, 299, 300, 321, 323
Motivation, 335 ff.
Moves, 258, 265, 270, 446, 447, 448, 469
Mpiangu, B. D., 168, 203
MPSP, 292, 295, 299, 304, 305, 309

Multidimensional scaling, 56, 60
Multiple correlation, 56, 67
Multiple regression, 55, 56, 57
Multivariate procedures, 58, 60, 61, 67
Myers, B., 444, 471

NACOME, 416, 417, 419, 431, 459, 460, 473
NAEP, 224, 225, 226
Nature/nurture, 347
NCSM, 208
NCTM, 240
Neale, D. C., 373, 387
Neisser, V., 251, 283
Nelson, L. D., 31, 38, 96, 106, 108, 109, 110, 111, 116, 118, 119, 152, 154, 211, 236, 295, 318, 397, 431
Nelson, N. Z., 223, 240
Nelson, R. J., 167, 203
Nesher, P., 294, 321
Newell, A., 287, 321
Nichols, E. J., 213, 214, 216, 240
Nicoletti, J., 362, 387
NIE, 208
Nie, N. H., 55, 57, 65
Niedermayer, F. C., 402, 431
Nielson, M. A., 439, 472
Niemark, E. D., 156, 163, 175, 176, 177, 203, 249, 283, 295, 321
Nilsson, N., 293, 321
NLSMA, 23, 24, 39, 225, 296, 334, 357, 359, 399
Noise, 54
Nonexample, 250, 256, 274
Nonparametric statistics, 69
Nonrespondents, 52
Normality, 36, 51, 57, 69, 75, 90, 91
Norman, M., 213, 214, 216, 240
Norms, 42, 155
No significant differences, 37, 51
Novillis, C. F., 220, 240, 263, 283
Nuffield Project, 192, 203
Null hypothesis, 36, 37
Number, 163, 166, 167, 168
Number skills, 165

O'Brien, T. C., 222, 240, 267, 284, 400, 431
Observational inference, 89, 90, 91
Ogilvie, E., 157, 203
Olander, H. T., 214, 241, 406, 423, 431
Olton, R. M., 307, 321
One-to-one correspondence, 152
Opper, S., 184, 200
Opportunity to learn, 439
Ordinal concepts, 165
Ordinal scale, 189, 190